University Physics

by F. C. CHAMPION, M.A., Ph.D.(Cantab.)

Professor of Physics, University of London

London · BLACKIE & SON LIMITED · Glasgow

BLACKIE & SON LIMITED
16-18 WILLIAM IV STREET
CHARING CROSS
LONDON · W.C.2
17 STANHOPE STREET
GLASGOW · C.4

BLACKIE & SON
(INDIA) LIMITED
103-5 FORT STREET
BOMBAY

BLACKIE & SON
(CANADA) LIMITED
TORONTO

First published in parts 1939
Revised one-volume edition 1960

©

F. C. Champion

PRINTED IN GREAT BRITAIN BY BLACKIE & SON LIMITED, GLASGOW

PREFACE

THIS BOOK IS PRIMARILY INTENDED FOR students taking a First Course in Physics at a University. It is designed for preparation for examinations of the standard of Part I of the Natural Sciences Tripos at Cambridge, Part I of the new B.Sc. General Degree of London, one year Ancillary Physics courses, and, by the omission of those sections marked with an asterisk, for Intermediate students who have already studied the elements of Physics at school or elsewhere.

It must be remembered that at the stage covered by this book, students will not yet have become specialists in Physics. The writer has had frequent experience of students who, during a period when they are studying two or three additional subjects, feel a great need for *one book* on Physics which contains the basic information which they must acquire. It is not suggested that this book has made others unnecessary or, more particularly, that it has rendered lectures superfluous. It remains as important as ever for students to read widely and to acquire experience of the different methods of treatment of a subject which only a diversity of Lecturers can supply.

Finally, it is becoming more and more recognized, at least as an ideal, that material usually given in formal lectures can be quite as well acquired from good text-books and that lectures will gradually develop into a tuitional tutorial system under which the time and energy of the lecturer can be devoted to the detailed elucidation of difficult points, apt illustrations and demonstrations, the discussion of essays and exercises done by the student, and the exercise of personality to engender an enthusiasm without which a subject remains " dry bones ".

F. C. CHAMPION.

PART I. GENERAL PHYSICS

PART II. HEAT

PART III. LIGHT

PART IV. WAVE MOTION AND SOUND

PART V. ELECTRICITY AND MAGNETISM

PART I

GENERAL PHYSICS

CHAPTER I

Introduction

1. The Aim of Physical Science.

The aim of physical science is the reference of natural events, which at first may seem quite disconnected, to certain general laws, the number of which should be as few as possible. For example, the vast majority of objects, when unsupported from beneath, fall to the ground with an acceleration independent of the particular object considered. This behaviour is evidence for a **general law,** in this case the law of universal gravitation. Again, bodies charged with electricity are found to exert forces on each other and experiment shows that these electrical forces are likewise governed by a general law. As further and different physical phenomena, such as light and sound, are revealed by our senses, so general laws are deduced governing each of these physical phenomena. Diligent inquiry results in the number of laws deduced in this way rapidly becoming inconveniently large for the human mind, particularly for the human memory, and attempts are therefore made to relate these different laws and reduce them all to fewer and still more basic laws. For example, light may now be explained almost entirely in terms of electricity, and sound in terms of the general mechanical laws of motion. It is broadly true to say that the aim of physical science is the reduction of all physical matter to a single primary " stuff ". A knowledge of the different forms that this " stuff " can then take, together with the mutual forces exerted by the " bits " of " stuff " would, it is hoped, account for all known phenomena. We should hasten to inform the student that we are still far short of our aim, which, indeed, must always probably remain as an ideal to future generations of physicists. It is clear, also, that before suggestions of any value can be put forward, a detailed knowledge of a great field of physical phenomena must be possessed by the natural philosopher. This book contains an account of some of the more elementary of these phenomena.

2. The Concepts of Length and Time.

The concept of **length** or **extension** arises from at least two of the basic human sensory perceptions, those of sight and touch. Visually, certain discontinuities are observed, marking off one object from another. The human eye perceives that these discontinuities are not all the same size, and so we obtain the notion of one body having greater extension than another. Confirmation of the relative sizes is provided over a limited range by touch, some objects being less than, say, the span of outstretched arms and others greater.

The concept of time originates in various ways, the strongest evidence being provided by the regular alternation of natural phenomena such as night and day and the seasons.

We defer the discussion of the choice of definite units of length and time until Chap. V, since we wish to use the results of earlier chapters in providing the student who has already passed the primary stage in Physics with more precise notions than can be gained without some quantitative background.

3. States of Matter.

The concept of **matter** arises exclusively from the sensation of touch. The student will be familiar with optical illusions in which various objects *appear* to be present as in the celebrated " Pepper's ghost " (see Part III). Whether they are " really " there depends upon whether they are " as sensible to feeling as to sight ". Common experience also informs us that there are three well-defined states of matter—solids, liquids and gases. The distinction between the three states is much clarified by the **molecular theory of matter.** The idea that matter is not continuous but consists eventually of small, separate, indivisible parts or molecules, received its first firm experimental support from chemistry, in the shape of Dalton's laws of the combining powers of the elements. Since that time a multitude of evidence has arisen, chiefly connected with the kinetic theory of matter discussed in Part II, to support the molecular hypothesis. Briefly, in the **solid state** the molecules are considered to have no translational motion, but to be capable of a certain amount of rotational, and particularly vibrational, energy. That is, they are considered mainly as vibrating within very narrow limits about fixed centres. The amplitude of these vibrations is much too small to be detected even with a microscope, and consequently a solid maintains its fixed shape over an indefinite period of time. Occasionally one of the molecules will acquire sufficient vibrational energy to break away completely from the rest of the solid. Such wandering molecules give rise to the **diffusion of solids** described on p. 129. The vapour pressure of a solid also arises in this way. In most solids it is very small; for example, gem-stones maintain their shape and weight over centuries. On the other hand, a block of solid camphor decreases in size appreciably in a few months.

In the **liquid state,** one of the chief characteristics of which is that a liquid takes up the shape of the vessel in which it is placed, the molecules have a certain amount of translational, rotational and vibrational energies. How the energy is divided between the three forms depends very much on the nature and temperature of the liquid. In general, however, the vapour pressure of liquids is much higher than that of solids and the rate of diffusion much larger, so molecules of liquids possess a considerable translational energy.

In the **gaseous state**, all the molecules possess a high translational energy although they generally possess vibrational and rotational energy as well. Their high translational energy explains the ability of a gas to " fill " any vessel into which it is placed, the existence of gas pressure, and the high rate of gaseous diffusion.

In the solid state the density is high and the molecules are comparatively tightly packed, the average distance between the centres of two adjacent molecules being about 10^{-8} cm. With gases, the density is low and the average distance between the molecules comparatively large, being about 10^{-5} cm., although it depends, of course, on the gas pressure. Liquids are in an intermediate state. When a solid is heated we imagine on the molecular picture that the molecules vibrate with larger and larger amplitude as the temperature is raised until they break away from their fixed centres. The solid body then loses its definite shape, is said to melt, and has been transformed into the liquid state. On continuing the heating process the translational energy of the molecules increases until, when the liquid boils, the molecules have sufficient energy to escape completely from the main bulk of the liquid and the liquid is being transformed into the gaseous state. In the solid and liquid states the molecules are held together by forces of **mutual attraction** which are, incidentally, electrical and not gravitational in nature. In the gaseous state, however, the molecules are sufficiently far apart to be independent of each other unless the pressure and therefore the density of the gas is high. These facts have made the development of a **kinetic theory of gases** comparatively simple, but owing to our ignorance of the precise nature of intermolecular forces in solids and liquids, these have not proved so amenable to treatment. The molecular hypothesis is of the utmost importance in obtaining an insight into physical processes and the student should always attempt to form a molecular picture of the different physical phenomena as he comes in contact with them.

It is true that in recent years the molecule and atom have been " split ", so that they can no longer be regarded as the indivisible units they were originally thought to be. For the vast majority of physical phenomena, however, matter behaves as though the molecules were the ultimate units of matter, and in the broad description of physical events a more detailed examination is unnecessary and undesirable. The simplest explanation, provided it explains all the facts, should be the aim of physical theory, not the clever elaboration of intricate hypotheses, however ingenious.

CHAPTER II

Kinematics

1. Kinematics.

Kinematics is the study of the space-time variations of bodies relative to a certain set of co-ordinates. We find it convenient to commence with the definition of **velocity.**

2. Translational Velocity.

Translational velocity is defined as the rate of change of position of a body.

Thus, if we consider the body as moving along the x-axis of our co-ordinate system, its **average** **velocity** over any short interval of time Δt is $\Delta x/\Delta t$, where Δx is the short distance traversed in the short interval Δt. Proceeding to the limit according to the principles of the differential calculus, we define the **instantaneous velocity** by dx/dt, the derivative, or differential co-efficient, of x with regard to t, which can be calculated when x is known as a function of t.

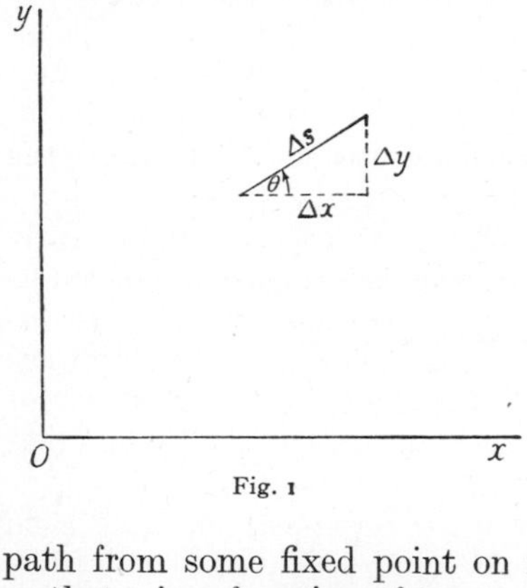

Fig. 1

In the simple example considered we have confined the motion to one particular direction. If the motion of the body was at an angle to the x-axis but was confined to the xy-plane, the actual velocity v_s at any instant would be ds/dt, where s is the distance, measured along the path from some fixed point on it up to the point reached at time t; so that s is a function of t.

Referring to fig. 1, if the short length Δs is inclined to the x-axis at an angle θ, the distance traversed in the x-direction is

$$\Delta x = \Delta s \,.\, \cos\theta.$$

Similarly, in a direction parallel to the y-axis, the distance traversed is

$$\Delta y = \Delta s \,.\, \sin\theta.$$

6

Now the velocities in these two directions are by definition $v_x = dx/dt$ and $v_y = dy/dt$; hence

$$v_x = dx/dt = (dx/ds)\,(ds/dt) = \cos\theta\,.\,ds/dt = v_s\cos\theta, \quad (2.1)$$

and $\qquad v_y = dy/dt = (dy/ds)\,(ds/dt) = \sin\theta\,.\,ds/dt = v_s\sin\theta; \quad (2.2)$

also from (2.1) and (2.2), by squaring and adding

$$v_s^2 = v_x^2 + v_y^2. \quad . \quad . \quad . \quad . \quad . \quad (2.3)$$

If the motion of the body is not confined to a plane, the short distance Δs, as shown in fig. 2, can still be resolved into two distances,

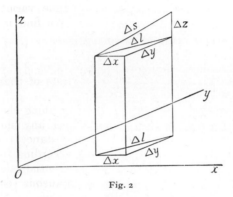

Fig. 2

one Δz parallel to the z-axis and the second, Δl, perpendicular to Δz and therefore parallel to the xy-plane. We note that Δl has itself **components** Δx and Δy, and since

$$\Delta l^2 = \Delta x^2 + \Delta y^2$$

and $\qquad \Delta s^2 = \Delta z^2 + \Delta l^2,$

therefore $\qquad \Delta s^2 = \Delta x^2 + \Delta y^2 + \Delta z^2. \quad . \quad . \quad . \quad (2.4)$

Considering equations (2.1), (2.2) and (2.3), we see that velocities, like distances, can be *resolved* in any direction. Hence, extending (2.4) to the case of velocities,

$$v_s^2 = v_x^2 + v_y^2 + v_z^2. \quad . \quad . \quad . \quad . \quad (2.5)$$

Conversely, if velocities v_x, v_y and v_z, parallel to the three axes respectively, are impressed on or possessed by a body, the latter is said to acquire or to have a **resultant velocity** v_s, given by equation (2.5), having **components** v_x, v_y and v_z.

3. Angular Velocity.

If instead of using Cartesian co-ordinates to define the position of the body, as in § 2, we use angular co-ordinates, and if we confine our discussion for simplicity to planar motion, the position of the body will be defined at any instant by the co-ordinates (r, θ) with respect to some fixed initial direction. If θ changes by an infinitely small amount $d\theta$ in an infinitely short interval dt, the **angular velocity is given by** $d\theta/dt$ and is usually represented by ω.

4. Vector and Scalar Quantities.

In § 2 we treated resultant velocity by *algebraic and trigonometrical analysis*. An alternative method is by *graphical treatment* according to the rules of *vector analysis*.

We define a scalar quantity as one possessing magnitude but not direction.

Examples of scalars are volume (cubic centimetres) and quantity of heat (calories). We may represent a scalar quantity graphically as a line, the length of which is proportional to the magnitude of the quantity involved.

There is another class of entities which possess direction as well as magnitude, and are called vectors.

Examples of vectors are velocity (cm./sec.) and magnetic field strength (oersteds). As with scalars we can again represent the magnitude by a line of certain length, but in addition we must mark the *direction* of the quantity with respect to some definite co-ordinate system.

The essential difference between scalar and vector quantities is made manifest if we wish to add two or more of these quantities. Thus the addition of 20 c.c. to 30 c.c. is (theoretically) 50 c.c. or the addition is *simply arithmetical*. On the other hand, the resultant velocity acquired by a body on which is impressed successively velocities of 10 m.p.h. and 20 m.p.h. will not be 30 m.p.h. except for the very special case where the two velocities are in the same direction.

To combine two or more velocities in the general case we may proceed as in § 2, resolving each velocity into components along a given set of co-ordinate axes, add the corresponding components algebraically, and then determine the resultant according to equation 2.5.

A graphical method, which is sometimes simpler, is however available. Represent the first velocity by a vector AB, that is, draw a line AB in the direction of the first velocity and of length proportional to its magnitude. Then from the point A draw a second vector AD to represent the second velocity. Complete the parallelogram ABCD, and the diagonal AC is the resultant velocity. This construction is known as the **Parallelogram of Velocities.** It is clearly unnecessary to complete the entire parallelogram, one half or a **Triangle of Velocities** being sufficient. Since the third side of a triangle is given by well-known trigonometrical formulæ, in practice the resultant is often *calculated*, for example, by the *cosine formula*.

Example. Velocities of 20 m.p.h. and 30 m.p.h. are impressed on a body in directions due E. and N.E. respectively. Find the resultant velocity acquired by the body.

$$v^2 = 20^2 + 30^2 + 2.20.30.\cos 45°; \quad v = 46·4 \text{ m.p.h.}$$

The direction of the resultant velocity is easily found graphically; alternatively it is found from the sine formula,

$$30/\sin \theta = 46·4/\sin 135°; \quad \theta = 27·3° \text{ N. of E.}$$

5. Acceleration.

Acceleration is defined as the rate of change of velocity.

By complete analogy with the preceding considerations on velocity, for a body moving with instantaneous velocity v along the x-axis, the **linear acceleration** will be

$$a = dv/dt = (d/dt)(dx/dt) = d^2x/dt^2, \quad . \quad . \quad . \quad (2.6)$$

since $v = dx/dt.$

For a body moving in a plane at an angle θ to the x-axis, we have by similar reasoning

$$a_x = dv_x/dt = (d/dt)(v \cos \theta) = \cos \theta . dv/dt = a \cos \theta \quad (2.7)$$

and $$a_y = dv_y/dt = (d/dt)(v \sin \theta) = \sin \theta . dv/dt = a \sin \theta, \quad (2.8)$$

where a_x and a_y are the components of the acceleration along the x- and y-axis respectively.

For a body moving in *any* direction,

$$a_s^2 = a_x^2 + a_y^2 + a_z^2, \quad . \quad . \quad . \quad . \quad (2.9)$$

where a_x, a_y and a_z are the component accelerations.

If the angular velocity of the body is changing, the angular acceleration is defined as the rate of change of angular velocity.

That is $$\alpha = d\omega/dt = d^2\theta/dt^2. \quad . \quad . \quad . \quad (2.10)$$

It is clear that, like velocity, *acceleration is a vector quantity* and will follow the rules for vector addition. **Resultant accelerations** may therefore be obtained by graphical construction, the diagram being referred to as the **Triangle** or **Parallelogram of Accelerations**.

6. Relative Motion.

If we consider two bodies A and B, moving with velocities u and v, with respect to a fixed co-ordinate system, along the common x-axis, it is of importance to inquire with what velocity either body appears to be moving to an observer situated on the other, that is, the **relative velocity** of say B to A. In this simple case, direct experiment with a stop-clock and measuring rod shows that the relative velocity is $v \pm u$. In particular, if the two velocities are in the *same* direction it is found that the negative sign gives the relative velocity.

The relative velocity of B to A is therefore obtained by reversing the velocity of A and adding this to the velocity of B.

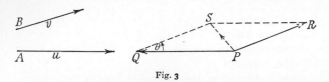

Fig. 3

If, however, the two velocities are inclined to each other we must combine the velocities according to the rules of vector addition. Graphically the construction is as follows. Draw a line PQ parallel to the velocity u and of length proportional to its magnitude; PQ is however, reversed in direction. Draw PR parallel to the velocity v and of length proportional to its magnitude. Then the relative velocity of B to A is obtained by completing the parallelogram and is given in magnitude and direction by the diagonal PS (fig. 3).

We may find the magnitude of PS analytically. Take the origin of co-ordinates at some point on the body A and the x-axis along the direction of motion of A. Then the components of the velocity of B along and perpendicular to this axis are $v \cos \theta$, $v \sin \theta$ respectively; the relative velocity of B to A will be obtained by compounding $v \sin \theta$ and $(v \cos \theta - u)$ at right angles. Hence

$$v_{\text{rel}}^2 = v^2 \sin^2 \theta + v^2 \cos^2 \theta - 2vu \cos \theta + u^2$$
$$= u^2 + v^2 - 2uv \cos \theta$$
$$= PS^2,$$

as we see from fig. 3.

7. Space-Time Relations.

The graph obtained by plotting the position of a body against the time is referred to as the **space-time curve.** The space-time curve for a body starting from rest and moving with uniform acceleration is shown in fig. 4, which is the graphical expression of equation (2.15) for the special case where

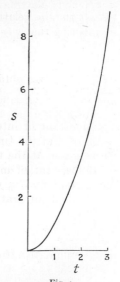

Fig. 4

$x_0 = v_0 = 0$, the space s in this case being equal to x. Since accelera-tion is defined as the derivative of velocity with respect to time, the velocity will be given by the integral of the acceleration with respect to time. Thus, since from (2.6)

$$a = dv/dt,$$

if the acceleration is constant, integration gives

$$at = v + \text{constant of integration.} \quad . \quad . \quad . \quad (2.11)$$

To determine the value of the constant of integration, we must substi-tute in (2.11) some known value of v at some known time t. Before the body commences to move, that is at time $t = 0$, $v = 0$; hence from (2.11), the constant of integration is zero and

$$v = at. \quad . \quad . \quad . \quad . \quad . \quad (2.12)$$

If, however, the body had an initial velocity of v_0 parallel to the x-axis, $v = v_0$ when $t = 0$ and substitution in (2.11) shows that the constant of integration is $(-v_0)$. Hence, generally, the relation between velocity, time and constant acceleration is

$$v = v_0 + at. \quad . \quad . \quad . \quad . \quad (2.13)$$

To obtain the relation between distance and time we use (2.13), re-membering that $v = dx/dt$; hence

$$dx = v_0 \,.\, dt + at \,.\, dt.$$

Integrating, we obtain

$$x = v_0 t + \tfrac{1}{2}at^2 + \text{constant of integration.} \quad . \quad (2.14)$$

The constant of integration is obtained as before by considering the value of x at the time $t = 0$. If the body is situated at the origin of co-ordinates at the time $t = 0$, then $x = 0$, and substitution in (2.14) gives constant of integration $= 0$. More generally, if the body is at some point $x = x_0$ when $t = 0$, substitution in (2.14) shows that the constant of integration is equal to x_0. The general form of (2.14) is therefore

$$(x - x_0) = v_0 t + \tfrac{1}{2}at^2. \quad . \quad . \quad . \quad (2.15)$$

If we eliminate t from equations (2.13) and (2.15) we get

$$v^2 = v_0{}^2 + 2a(x - x_0), \quad . \quad . \quad . \quad (2.16)$$

a useful equation connecting velocity and acceleration with the dis-tance traversed.

By similar reasoning we may deduce that the angular velocity of a body at time t is connected with its angular velocity ω_0 at time $t = 0$, and the constant angular acceleration α, by

$$\omega = \omega_0 + \alpha t. \quad \dots \dots \quad (2.17)$$

Similarly, the angular displacement θ at time t is related to θ_0, its value at time $t = 0$, by

$$(\theta - \theta_0) = \omega_0 t + \tfrac{1}{2}\alpha t^2, \quad \dots \quad (2.18)$$

by analogy with (2.15).

The preceding examples have referred to the simple case of motion with constant acceleration. In the more elementary considerations of physics there is only one important case with variable acceleration, namely, simple harmonic motion. This is discussed in detail in § 9, Chap. III.

8. Kepler's Laws of Planetary Motion.

The knowledge of physical science which is obtained by the study of kinematics is useful but very limited. One very important appli-

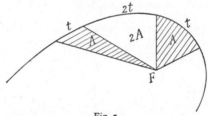

Fig. 5

cation is the description of the motion of the heavenly bodies. In particular, from the observations of Tycho Brahe, Kepler was able to formulate his three laws of planetary motion. These are:

1. *The planets describe ellipses round the sun, with the sun at one focus.*

2. *Equal focal areas are swept out in equal times* (see fig. 5).

3. *The squares of the times of revolution of the planets are proportional to the cubes of the major axes of their elliptical orbits.*

We shall refer briefly to the subject of planetary motion in § 7, Chap. VI, when discussing Newton's work on gravitation.

EXERCISES

1. Distinguish between vector and scalar quantities, giving examples from different branches of physics.

2. If the acceleration or retardation of a trolley-bus may not exceed 4 ft./sec.^{2} and its maximum allowable speed may not be greater than 30 m.p.h., find the shortest possible time for the bus to travel from rest to rest between two stations one mile apart. [131 sec.]

3. The retardation acting on a glider moving horizontally is proportional to the square of its velocity. Obtain the equations for the velocity-time and space-time curves. [$v = v_0/(kv_0t + 1)$, $ks = \log(kv_0t + 1)$.]

4. A steamer is travelling due N. at 15 knots and a vane on the mast-head points N.N.W.; the steamer turns E., whereupon the vane points N.N.E. Find the velocity and direction of the wind. [15 knots from N.W.]

5. An observer travelling due E. at a speed of 60 m.p.h. notices an object apparently moving due N. with an apparent speed of 30 m.p.h. Determine the true velocity and direction of motion of the object. [67·1 m.p.h. at $26\frac{1}{2}°$ N. of E.]

CHAPTER III

Dynamics of a Particle

In the subject of kinematics we were concerned with a simple description of *how* bodies move. Immediately we wish to discover *why* bodies move as they do, we enter the realm of **dynamics.** It was Newton who formulated the essential laws of this subject. We shall commence by stating his Three Laws of Motion, explaining later their precise significance.

1. Newton's Laws of Motion.

1. All bodies continue in their state of rest or of uniform motion in a straight line unless they are compelled to change that state by external forces.

2. Rate of change of momentum is proportional to the impressed force and takes place in the direction in which that force is acting.

3. Action and reaction are equal and opposite.

On examining the first law we see that any movement of a body from rest or any departure from uniform rectilinear motion is ascribed to an external agency—a **force.** The notion of force comes from a fundamental human sensory perception based on muscular effort. We note that it requires a definite muscular effort to stretch a spiral spring by a given amount. We observe further, by experiment, that, other things being equal, it always requires the same force to stretch the spring by the same amount.

Consider now the simple experiment in which the spring is stretched horizontally close to a large horizontal sheet of ice (frictionless plane), and suppose that two bodies A and B, lying on the ice, are successively attached to the spring. It is then found that if the spring is stretched initially by an equal amount in both cases, A and B commence to move, when released, with different horizontal accelerations. **The ratio of the accelerations acquired by two bodies when subjected to the same force is said to be inversely proportional to the masses of the bodies.** If we symbolize the force by P and the two

14

accelerations by a_1 and a_2, then, with proper choice of units, we may write

$$a_1 = \frac{P}{m_1} \Bigg\} \qquad \cdots \cdots \cdots \quad (3.1)$$
$$a_2 = \frac{P}{m_2}$$

or $\qquad\qquad P = m_1 a_1 = m_2 a_2. \quad \cdots \cdots \quad (3.2)$

Since, by (3.2), a force can be measured by the acceleration it produces in a certain mass, it follows that **force, like acceleration, is a vector magnitude.** Also, it is implied by (3.2) that the **component force in any direction is equal to the mass multiplied by the component acceleration in that direction.**

2. Mass and Weight.

Equation (3.1) may be used to define the mass of a body.

The mass of a body is defined as a quantity associated with a body which is inversely proportional to its linear acceleration when a given force is applied to it. This definition is much to be preferred to the rather vague alternative sometimes quoted: " mass is the quantity of matter in a body ".

In the above experiment with the spring we eliminated vertical forces by having the bodies moving horizontally on an almost frictionless plane. Actually, if any body situated near the surface of the earth is not supported, it is found to fall vertically with uniform acceleration, commonly denoted by g. This acceleration has a value of about 32·2 ft./sec.^{2} or 981 cm./sec.^{2} at sea-level near London. Hence, any body of mass m behaves, according to equation (3.1), as if it experienced a continual vertical force given by

$$\mathbf{P} = \boldsymbol{mg}. \quad \cdots \cdots \cdots \quad (3.3)$$

This quantity mg is termed the **weight** of the body, that is, the weight of a body is defined as its mass multiplied by the acceleration due to gravity. Since g varies over the earth's surface (see § 8, Chap. VI), the weight of a body is variable, in contrast to its mass, which is constant. If gravity could be abolished the body would cease to have weight, but its mass would still exist and could be determined by experiments with a spiral spring or some similar arrangement.

3. Momentum.

Since acceleration is defined as rate of change of velocity, (3.2) may be written

$$\mathbf{P} = \boldsymbol{ma} = m\frac{dv}{dt}, \quad \cdots \cdots \quad (3.4)$$

or, since the mass is constant,

$$\mathbf{P} = \frac{d}{dt}(mv). \qquad \qquad (3.5)$$

The product of the mass and the velocity of a body is termed its momentum. Equation (3.5) is the direct mathematical expression of Newton's Second Law of Motion; the R.H.S. is the rate of change of momentum, while the L.H.S. is the force causing this change.

If we attempt to deflect a moving body by a force applied more **or** less at right angles to the direction of motion of the body, we find that deflection is difficult if the body is moving fast or if it has a large mass. It is the **product, mass × velocity,** that is, the **momentum** of a body, which determines its power of continuing comparatively unaffected by small disturbing forces.

4. Equilibrium.

An object, say a jar, resting on a shelf, is experiencing a continual force downwards due to the action of gravity, equal in magnitude to the weight of the jar. It is clear that the jar would move downwards

under the action of this force unless there were an equal and opposite force or **reaction** acting on the jar. This reaction is provided by the shelf, which exerts a thrust upwards equal in magnitude to the weight of the jar downwards, and so **maintains the equilibrium.** While this equality of action and reaction is readily appreciated when bodies are in equilibrium, it must be studied in more detail if motion

Fig. 1

occurs. Thus if a horse pulls a cart with a force P, since action and reaction are equal and opposite the cart must be exerting, through the traces, a reaction P against the horse. Why then do both horse and cart move forward? The answer is that the forces are transmitted through the bodies concerned, and the ultimate cause of motion is the friction between the hoofs of the horse and the ground. Actually the reaction between the hoofs and the ground thrusting the horse forwards is accompanied by an equal and opposite action thrusting the earth backwards. Since the mass of the earth is so large, the effect on the earth is negligible, but the existence of such reactions is easily demonstrated by some simple experiment such as that illustrated in fig. 1.

As the man walks *forward* on the light truck the reaction of the man's feet on the truck causes the latter to move backwards, the magnitude of the movement being governed by the relative masses of the man and the truck. Another example is the revolving cage in which white mice are sometimes housed. The mouse stands in a hollow cylinder mounted on a horizontal axis; when the mouse attempts to run forward it exerts a reaction on the cylinder and the latter revolves.

Returning to the example of the jar resting on the shelf, if we exert a horizontal force on the jar, experiment shows that the jar may move horizontally or it may commence to tilt according as the force is applied to the bottom or to the top of the jar. If the jar is of very small height, no tilting is observed. Further, if the force is fairly small, and the jar is made of some material like plasticine, instead of moving as a whole, it may undergo deformation.

It has been found convenient to introduce the following abstractions;

(1) Material Particle.

For many purposes we may consider the mass of a body to be concentrated at a certain point in the body. This point is termed the **centre of gravity.** Forces applied to the body which pass through this point cause the body to behave as though its whole mass were concentrated in a **material particle** placed at this point.

(2) Rigid Body.

If forces acting on a body do not pass through the centre of gravity then rotation is produced as well as translation. Deformation of a body due to forces requires special study (see Chap. VIII on *Elasticity*), and we therefore postulate that when considering rotation and translation we may assume initially that no deformations occur. We then define the body as a **rigid body.**

In practice there is no such thing as a material particle nor a rigid body. When a given force is applied to a body, some rotation, some translation and some deformation occur simultaneously. However, if the body is hard and the force is moderate, the deformation may be neglected compared with the rotation and translation. Finally, if the resultant force passes, as far as is experimentally possible, through the centre of gravity, rotation is absent and the body moves with translational motion given by calculation based on the assumption that the body may be replaced by a material particle of the same mass situated at the centre of gravity.

We shall discuss the subjects of centre of gravity and equilibrium more fully in the chapter on *Statics*.

5. Work.

A force is said to do work when its point of application moves. and the measure of the work done is defined as the product of the force and the distance moved in the direction of the force.

If the force is denoted by P and the distance by s, the work done. W, is given by

$$W = Ps. \qquad (3.6)$$

In fig. 2. the work done when the point of application of the force moves from A to B is given by $Pl \cos\theta$. If θ is zero, the work done is Ps; on the other hand, if $\theta = 90°$, $\cos\theta = 0$, and therefore no work is done by a force when movement takes place at right angles to the force.

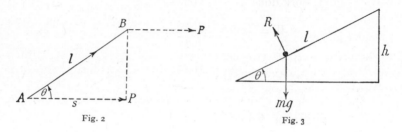

Fig. 2   Fig. 3

Since the force on a body due to gravity is equal to its weight mg, the **work done against gravity** when a weight mg is raised, or rises, a vertical distance h, is

$$W = mgh. \qquad (3.7)$$

Further, if a weight is pushed a distance l up a frictionless plane inclined at θ to the horizontal as in fig. 3, the work done is

$$W = mgl \sin\theta = mgh, \qquad (3.8)$$

where h is the vertical distance. This is because the weight mg acts vertically downwards and our definition of work done is force $\times$ component distance moved *in direction of the force*.

Equation (3.8) shows us that the weight behaves as though it had a component $mg \sin\theta$ down the plane, for the product of this effective weight $mg \sin\theta$ and the distance l moved in the direction of the component also gives us the work done. We may also note that there must be a **reaction** R, perpendicular to the plane and given by

$$R = mg \cos\theta, \qquad (3.9)$$

if there is equilibrium, for the component of the weight in a direction perpendicular to the plane is $mg \cos\theta$. This reaction R does no work when the weight is moved along the plane, since it acts at right angles to the direction of movement.

6. Energy.

The energy of a body is defined as its capacity for doing work. Consider a stone of mass m thrown vertically upwards with initial velocity v_0. It is acted upon by a uniform retarding acceleration or **retardation** g, and therefore, by (2.16), will attain a height h given by

$$0 = v_0^2 + 2(-g)h, \quad \ldots \quad (3.10)$$

since the velocity v at the highest point must be zero. From (3.10),

$$h = \frac{v_0^2}{2g}. \quad \ldots \ldots \quad (3.11)$$

Now from (3.7), work done against gravity is

$$W = mgh = \frac{mgv_0^2}{2g} = \tfrac{1}{2}mv_0^2 \quad \ldots \ldots \quad (3.12)$$

by (3.11).

The available work which may be obtained from a body of mass m possessing a velocity v_0 is therefore $\tfrac{1}{2}mv_0^2$, and this is, by definition, the energy of the body. We shall see later that energy may exist in several different forms. The form just considered is **energy possessed by the body in virtue of its motion,** and is termed **kinetic energy.**

Now at the top of its flight the velocity of the stone is zero. Its kinetic energy is therefore zero; yet it can regain that kinetic energy if it is allowed to fall back to the point from which it was projected. This hidden or *latent energy* which the stone possesses owing to its height above the earth's surface is termed **potential energy.** It is energy in virtue of the **position** of the body, and is capable of being converted into kinetic energy. This fact leads to the extremely important conclusion that the kinetic energy of the stone was *not destroyed* as its velocity fell to zero, but was merely converted into the form of potential energy, from which it could be recovered at any time in the kinetic form. We have here an illustration of the extremely important principle of the **Conservation of Energy,** which may be stated as follows:

Energy can neither be created nor destroyed, though it may be converted from one form into another.

Potential and kinetic energy are but two examples of energy in different forms. Other forms of energy are Heat, Light, Sound, Electrical, Magnetic and Chemical Energy. We shall discuss the application of the principle of the Conservation of Energy to these various forms as the occasion arises.

7. Power.

Power is defined as the rate of doing work; the average power over a given time is therefore the total energy expended divided by the time.

8. Motion in a Circle.

In the chapter on *Kinematics* we confined our attention mainly to motion in a straight line. The reason for this was that by Newton's First Law of Motion any departure from rectilinear motion must be ascribed to a force and, therefore, all non-rectilinear motion involves **Dynamics** as well as *Kinematics*. Suppose a body is moving in a circle with uniform velocity v, as shown in fig. 4. Then according to Newton's First Law of Motion there must be a force acting continually on the

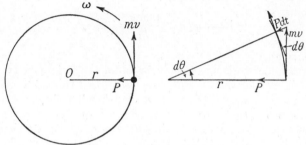

Fig. 4

body to prevent it from flying off at a tangent to the circular path. The simple experiment of whirling a stone on a piece of string held in the hand of the experimenter informs him that the force involved is a tension along the string. The force therefore acts radially. The outward radial force exerted by the body on the hand, through the string, is termed the **centrifugal force**. The force acting on the body is equal and opposite to this, and this inward force on the body is termed the **centripetal force**. To determine the value of this force, suppose the direction of motion is deflected through the small angle $d\theta$ in the short interval of time dt. This deflection is the result of the radial force P, and the momentum imparted radially to the body is, by Newton's Second Law, $P\,dt$. But the tangential momentum of the body is mv. Hence the angle $d\theta$ (fig. 4) through which the direction of motion is deflected in time dt is given by

$$d\theta = \frac{P\,dt}{mv},$$

or
$$P = mv\,\frac{d\theta}{dt} = mv\omega, \quad \ldots \ldots \ldots \quad (3.13)$$

since $\qquad d\theta/dt = \omega$, the angular velocity of rotation.

Now, in a circle of radius r, if an arc s subtends an angle θ at the centre, then $s = r\theta$, and therefore $ds/dt = r\,d\theta/dt$, that is, $v = r\omega$. Hence equation (3.13) may be written in either of the important forms

$$\mathbf{P} = m\omega^2 r, \qquad \ldots \ldots \quad (3.14)$$

$$\mathbf{P} = \frac{mv^2}{r}, \qquad \ldots \ldots \ldots \quad (3.15)$$

where r is the radius of the circle. In our deduction we have neglected the force present due to the weight of the body acting vertically downwards. Our calculation as given above therefore applies only to a body describing a horizontal circle, but the extension to a vertical circle does not involve any radical alteration and is discussed later with reference to the simple pendulum and other examples.

9. Simple Pendulum: Simple Harmonic Motion.

Consider now the motion of a particle, hanging by a light inextensible string. Normally the string hangs vertically at rest. A tension T in the string acts vertically upwards, and is equal and opposite to the weight mg of the particle acting vertically downwards. Suppose the particle is pulled to one side so that the string makes an angle θ_0 with the vertical, and that it is then released. We know by experiment that the particle moves through a circular arc in a vertical plane. Its velocity continually increases as it moves to the bottom of the arc, where it reaches a maximum. It then swings through an angle, which is nearly equal to θ_0, on the opposite side of the vertical, and comes to rest. Next, it returns to its original position, and the motion is continued as before. This apparatus is termed a **simple pendulum**. The motion is a particular case of circular motion,

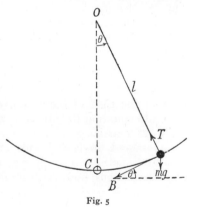

Fig. 5

but the considerations of § 8 do not apply directly since, although the path is circular, *the velocity is not constant.* If we time the vibrations with a stop clock we find that **the time required for a complete vibration is always the same.** The circular arc gradually diminishes in length, but the time required for the particle to swing from a position of rest on one side of the vertical, through the vertical to the other side and almost back to its original position, is constant. A vibration having this property is said to be **isochronous.** We shall now proceed to calculate an expression for the time of oscillation of the simple pendulum.

Referring to fig. 5, we note that the forces on the pendulum are

2

a tension T up the string, and the weight of the particle, mg, vertically downwards. Since the movement of the particle is along the arc of a circle with centre at O, the tension in the string will produce no acceleration in the direction of motion, for this force acts radially and its component along the arc is zero. The only force causing motion is therefore the component of mg down the direction of the arc. This component is $mg \sin \theta$. Hence the component acceleration down the arc is given by the equation

$$mg \sin \theta = m \times \text{acceleration} = ma$$

or
$$a = g \sin \theta. \quad . \quad . \quad . \quad . \quad . \quad . \quad (3.16)$$

If the length of the string is l, the tangential acceleration at any instant, since (p. 21) $v = l\omega$ and therefore $dv/dt = l\,d\omega/dt$, is given by the equation

$$a = l \times \text{angular acceleration.}$$

Now
$$l\,d\omega/dt = l\frac{d^2\theta}{dt^2}, \quad . \quad . \quad . \quad . \quad (3.17)$$

since ω, the angular velocity, $= d\theta/dt$.

Note that $+l\,d^2\theta/dt^2$ is the acceleration *in the direction in which θ increases.* Hence, from (3.16) and (3.17),

$$-l\frac{d^2\theta}{dt^2} = g \sin \theta. \quad . \quad . \quad . \quad . \quad (3.18)$$

To find the time of oscillation of the pendulum we clearly have to integrate equation (3.18). Now it is found experimentally that unless θ always remains small the movement of the pendulum is not isochronous and, in fact, is not of special interest. This is fortunate because equation (3.18) is not capable of simple integration. For **small oscillations,** however, we may write $\sin \theta = \theta$, and (3.18) becomes

$$l\frac{d^2\theta}{dt^2} = -g\theta. \quad . \quad . \quad . \quad . \quad (3.19)$$

This equation may be written

$$\frac{d^2\theta}{dt^2} = -p^2\theta, \quad . \quad . \quad . \quad . \quad (3.20)$$

where p^2 is written for g/l and is constant, since g and l are both constant for a pendulum of given length at a particular point on the earth's surface. *Equation (3.20) is one of the most important equations in the whole of Physics.* It states that the second derivative of a quantity (θ) is equal to a constant ($-p^2$) times the first power of the quantity. The solution of this equation is

$$\theta = \mathbf{A} \sin pt + \mathbf{B} \cos pt, \quad \ldots \ldots \quad (3.21)$$

where A and B are constants to be found in the way described later. We can prove this directly by differentiating (3.21) twice, thus

$$\frac{d\theta}{dt} = p\mathbf{A} \cos pt - p\mathbf{B} \sin pt, \quad \ldots \ldots \quad (3.22)$$

$$\frac{d^2\theta}{dt^2} = -p^2\mathbf{A} \sin pt - p^2\mathbf{B} \cos pt. \quad \ldots \quad (3.23)$$

Substitute from (3.23) and (3.21) in (3.20), and we get

$$-p^2(\mathbf{A} \sin pt + \mathbf{B} \cos pt) = -p^2(\mathbf{A} \sin pt + \mathbf{B} \cos pt),$$

which proves that our solution (3.21) is correct.

From (3.21) therefore, at any time t after the pendulum has been released, the angle at which the string is inclined to the vertical is given by

$$\theta = \mathbf{A} \sin pt + \mathbf{B} \cos pt.$$

To find A and B we must consider known values of θ and t and substitute them in (3.21). Thus, when $t = 0$, the pendulum has its initial angular displacement, θ_0. Hence (3.21) becomes

$$\theta_0 = \mathbf{B}$$

for $\sin pt = 0$ and $\cos pt = 1$ when $t = 0$. To find A we consider equation (3.22). When $t = 0$, the pendulum has no velocity and therefore $d\theta/dt = 0$: hence

$$0 = p\mathbf{A} - 0,$$

so that $\mathbf{A} = 0$.

The final solution is therefore

$$\theta = \theta_0 \cos pt = \theta_0 \cos\sqrt{\frac{g}{l}}t. \quad \ldots \ldots \quad (3.24)$$

Now if the time of a complete oscillation is τ, θ is again equal to θ_0 after a time τ. Substituting in (3.24), we get

$$\theta_0 = \theta_0 \cos p\tau,$$

or
$$\cos p\tau = 1. \quad \ldots \ldots \ldots \quad (3.25)$$

Since the cosine equals unity, when the angle is 0, 2π, 4π, etc., the first complete oscillation will end when

$$p\tau = 2\pi,$$

or
$$\tau = \frac{2\pi}{p}. \quad \ldots \ldots \ldots \quad (3 \cdot 26)$$

The period of the pendulum, that is, the time taken to make one complete oscillation, is therefore

$$\tau = 2\pi \sqrt{\frac{l}{g}}, \quad \cdots \cdots \quad (3.27)$$

for $p^2 = g/l$ by definition.

The **restoring force** acting on the body for any deflection θ is $mg \sin \theta$, which for small angles equals $mg\theta$. This force is therefore directly proportional to the angular displacement θ. Motion in a straight line governed by forces of this type is said to be simple harmonic.

Simple Harmonic Motion is defined as motion in a straight line under a force always directed towards a fixed point in the line, and of magnitude varying directly as the distance from the fixed point.

An alternative definition of simple harmonic motion is that it is *the projection of uniform motion in a circle on to a diameter of that circle.* Thus, in fig. 6, consider a body starting from A, at time $t = 0$, and moving uniformly round a circle with constant angular velocity ω. Then if at any point P of its path we drop a perpendicular on to the diameter AB we obtain the point N. Now it is clear that as P moves round the circle, N moves across the diameter and both points reach B simultaneously. Further, N returns to A by the time P has executed one complete revolution. The point N therefore moves to and fro along AB with the same period as P describes the circle. This period for P is

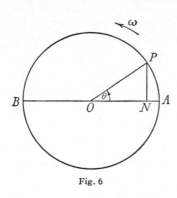

Fig. 6

$$\tau = \frac{2\pi}{\omega}. \quad \cdots \cdots \quad (3.28)$$

If $ON = x$, $OA = a$, and $\angle AOP = \theta$, then $\theta = \omega t$, and

$$x = a \cos \omega t.$$

Hence

$$\frac{dx}{dt} = -a\omega \sin \omega t,$$

and

$$\frac{d^2x}{dt^2} = -a\omega^2 \cos \omega t.$$

$$\frac{d^2x}{dt^2} = -\omega^2 x.$$

The motion of N is therefore simple harmonic, by the definition, and the acceleration for unit displacement is ω^2. Since $\tau = 2\pi/\omega$, the time of oscillation of a body undergoing simple harmonic motion is the same as that of a body executing a *uniform* circular motion with an angular velocity equal to the square root of the acceleration for unit displacement, that is

$$\tau = 2\pi \sqrt{\frac{1}{\text{acceleration for unit displacement}}}. \qquad (3.29)$$

Other examples of simple harmonic motion are the vertical oscillations of a body suspended on the end of a spiral spring, and the vertical oscillations of mercury contained in a U-tube. We shall discuss the former in detail later (see § 11 (c), p. 89); in each case it is usually the period of oscillation which is required, and this may always be determined by finding the acceleration for unit displacement and then substituting in (3.29).

10. Conservation of Momentum.

Consider the mechanical processes involved when a shell is fired from a gun. We know by experience that the gun itself recoils. The question arises as to whether the velocity of the recoil is in any definite way connected with that of the shell. Let the force acting on the shell be P at time t, and let the shell be projected with velocity v, at time T. Then if u is its velocity at any time t less than T, we have

$$P = m\frac{du}{dt},$$

so that

$$\int_0^T P\,dt = \int_0^v m\,du = mv, \quad \ldots \ldots \quad (3.30)$$

where m is the mass of the shell. Now by Newton's Third Law of Motion there must at any moment be a reaction on the gun, which at time t is also equal to P. If the gun is situated on ice so that there is negligible friction between it and the ground, and if the shell is fired horizontally, the gun will recoil with a certain velocity V; if its mass is M, exactly the same argument as above gives

$$\int_0^T P\,dt = MV. \quad \ldots \ldots \ldots \quad (3.31)$$

Now the L.H.S. of (3.30) and (3.31) are identical. Hence

$$mv = MV, \quad \ldots \ldots \ldots \quad (3.32)$$

or the momentum of the shell is equal to the momentum of the recoiling gun. Equation (3.32) may be written

$$mv - MV = 0. \quad \ldots \ldots \ldots \quad (3.33)$$

Now before the shell was fired the system was at rest and the momentum was zero. Equation (3.33) shows also that after the shell was fired the *total momentum* of the entire system is again zero. This example illustrates the principle of the **Conservation of Momentum.** In order to demonstrate this important result in the laboratory, a device known as the ballistic pendulum, shown in fig. 7, may be used. Two trays A and B are supported by strings so that the trays are in contact when they are practically horizontal. A is then pulled aside through a given amount, the displacement being observed on a circular scale. When A is released it falls and strikes B and since the edge of A has two small projecting pins and B is edged with cork,

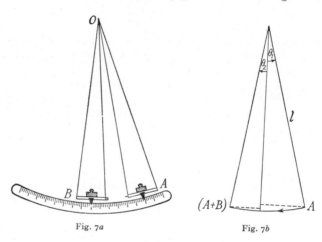

Fig. 7a   Fig. 7b

A and B adhere, and both swing an observed distance along the circular scale. Referring to fig. 7(b), if the length of the strings is l and the angles of deflection of the trays before and after collision are θ_1 and θ_2 respectively, then we note that the effective vertical height through which A falls is $l(1 - \cos\theta_1)$, whereas the height to which A and B both rise after collision is $l(1 - \cos\theta_2)$. Applying the principle of the conservation of energy to determine the velocity of A just before impact, we note that the potential energy lost by A is

$$m_A gl(1 - \cos\theta_1) = 2m_A gl \sin^2(\theta_1/2). \quad . \quad . \quad (3.34)$$

This must equal the kinetic energy possessed by A at the lowest point, that is, at the instant of impact. Denoting the velocity of A by v_A, and treating the moving masses as material particles, we therefore have

$$\tfrac{1}{2}m_A v_A{}^2 = 2m_A gl \sin^2(\theta_1/2), \quad . \quad . \quad . \quad (3.35)$$

or
$$v_A{}^2 = 4gl \sin^2(\theta_1/2). \quad . \quad . \quad . \quad (3.36)$$

Similarly, if v_{A+B} is the velocity with which A and B commence to move up after the impact

$$v_{A+B}{}^2 = 4gl \sin^2(\theta_2/2). \quad . \quad . \quad . \quad . \quad (3.37)$$

Now according to the principle of the conservation of momentum, the momentum before collision is equal to the momentum after collision, that is

$$m_A v_A = (m_A + m_B)v_{A+B}. \quad . \quad . \quad . \quad (3.38)$$

Hence, eliminating v_A and v_{A+B} from (3.37) and (3.38) we obtain

$$\frac{m_A}{m_A + m_B} = \frac{\sin(\theta_2/2)}{\sin(\theta_1/2)}. \quad . \quad . \quad . \quad . \quad (3.39)$$

The experiment is carried out with different weights in the two trays; equation (3.39) is confirmed, and hence the principle of conservation of momentum upon which the experiment rests has been verified.

It should be mentioned that we have considered only the linear momentum of the bodies. If a body is rotating it possesses angular velocity and therefore *angular momentum*. During dynamical processes, under certain conditions, angular momentum is also conserved. We shall discuss this in further detail in the next chapter.

11. Impact of Spheres. Resilience and Restitution.

In the experiment just described with the ballistic pendulum, the bouncing of the tray A from the tray B during impact was avoided by the use of cork and pins. If the same experiment were repeated with the two trays replaced, say, by two steel spheres of different sizes, a certain amount of rebound would occur on impact. By observing the heights to which each sphere rose after impact, and so evaluating the final velocity and hence final momentum of each sphere, the principle of the conservation of momentum could again be tested. It would be found that the *total* momentum after collision was always equal to that before collision, but the distribution of momentum between the two spheres was not that to be expected from their masses and initial velocities. This is explained by assuming that the *resilience* or elasticity of the material enters into consideration. If, for example, a steel sphere approaches normally to the surface of a flat steel slab with velocity u, the velocity of recoil, v, is found to be different from u. The **coefficient of resilience or restitution** for the sphere and plate is usually denoted by e and is defined by

$$e = \frac{\text{velocity of recoil}}{\text{velocity of approach}} = \frac{v}{u}. \quad . \quad . \quad (3.40)$$

An apparatus for measuring the coefficient of restitution is shown in fig. 8. A flat steel plate is mounted horizontally below a short vertical electromagnet M to which may be attached steel spheres S. On breaking the battery circuit to the electromagnet the sphere S drops and rebounds from the plate. The heights of fall and of rebound are determined with a vertical scale and a telescope as shown in the

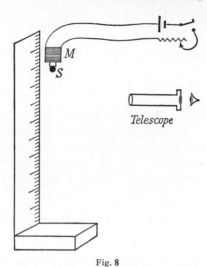

Telescope

Fig. 8

diagram. Different heights may be taken and the coefficient of restitution will be calculated from the equations

$$v_1{}^2 = 2gh_1,$$
$$v_2{}^2 = 2gh_2, \quad . \quad . \quad . \quad . \quad . \quad . \quad (3.41)$$
$$e = v_2/v_1.$$

Hence

$$e = \sqrt{\frac{h_2}{h_1}}. \quad . \quad . \quad . \quad . \quad . \quad (3.42)$$

If $e = 1$, the materials are said to be perfectly elastic; for steel e is about 0·95.

EXERCISES

1. State Newton's Laws of Motion and discuss the evidence on which they are based.

2. Define **work, energy** and **power**. In what sense can a strong man supporting a heavy weight in a fixed position be said to be doing no work?

3. What is meant by the Principle of the Conservation of Energy? Upon what evidence does it rest?

4. A spring balance hangs from the roof of a stationary lift and supports a weight of 2 Kgm. The lift starts to ascend, whereupon the balance reads 2·5 Kgm. Find the acceleration of the lift. [$\frac{1}{4}g$.]

5. A pile-driver of mass 100 lb. falls freely a distance of 10 ft. vertically on to a pile of mass 1000 lb. and drives it 1 ft. into the ground. Assuming that the pile and driver move together after the impact, find the average value of the resisting force opposing the motion of the pile into the ground. [$1190\frac{10}{11}$ lb.]

6. Determine the least velocity which an aeroplane must have at the top of a circle of radius 1000 ft. if it is to loop the loop successfully. [179 ft./sec.]

7. Show that the energy lost when two smooth spheres collide depends on the square of the coefficient of restitution.

8. A bullet of mass 50 gm. is fired horizontally into a block in which it remains embedded. The block is suspended by a fine string of unknown length to form a simple pendulum. The impact of the bullet causes the block to swing through 2°. If the time of oscillation of the block-pendulum is 10 sec. and its mass is 5 Kgm., find the initial velocity of the bullet. [5500 cm./sec.]

CHAPTER IV

Statics and Dynamics of a Rigid Body

Since a particle at rest has no component acceleration in any direction, it follows from the equation $P = ma$ (p. 15) that **a particle is in equilibrium when the algebraic sum of the component forces**

Fig. 1

acting upon it in any direction is zero. Let two forces P and Q meet in a point as in fig. 1. Since forces are vector quantities (p. 8), following the law of vector addition, like velocities and accelerations, the resultant of P and Q is obtained by representing them as the two

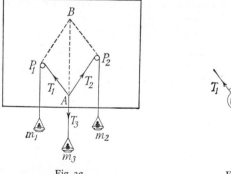

Fig. 2a   Fig. 2b

sides of a parallelogram; the diagonal R, through the point where P and Q meet, is then the resultant. That the **Parallelogram of Forces** is obeyed can be shown directly by experiment using the apparatus shown in fig. 2(a). Two pulleys P_1 and P_2 are mounted on horizontal axes and attached to a vertical board. Masses m_1 and m_2 are attached to the ends of strings, which pass over pulleys and are attached to a third mass m_3. It is found that equilibrium is attained only when the lengths P_1A, P_2A and AB are proportional to the magnitudes of m_1, m_2 and m_3 respectively; also AB must be vertical. It is clear that half the parallelogram is sufficient to represent the forces completely. The theorem is then known as the **Triangle of Forces.** Since the three sides of a triangle are proportional to the sines of the angles opposite to the sides, consideration of figs. 2(a), 2(b) shows that

$$\frac{T_1}{\sin \alpha} = \frac{T_2}{\sin \beta} = \frac{T_3}{\sin \gamma}, \quad \cdots \cdots \quad (4.1)$$

so that each force is proportional to the sine of the angle between the other two.

1. Equilibrium of a Rigid Body.

Suppose we have a rigid body of finite extent such as the uniform bar shown in fig. 3. If this bar is supported by a horizontal axis perpendicular to the plane of the paper, and passing through its centre

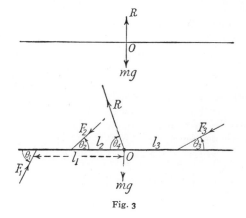

Fig. 3

at O, we should find experimentally that the bar would be in equilibrium in any position. There must clearly be a vertical reaction R exerted by the axis on the bar, to balance its weight mg acting vertically downwards. Suppose now forces F_1, F_2, F_3, *all in a vertical plane,* act as shown at points l_1, l_2 and l_3 from O in directions inclined at θ_1, θ_2 and θ_3 to the length of the bar. What are now the conditions for equilibrium? We shall first state the conditions and then explain and justify our statements:

(a) **The algebraic sum of the forces in any direction must be zero.**

(*b*) **The algebraic sum of the moments of the forces about any point in the plane containing the forces must be zero.**

(For definition of *moment of a force* see below.)

The first condition must be satisfied if there is to be no *translational* motion. The reaction R will no longer act vertically as it did before, but will be inclined at some angle θ_4 to the bar. To determine θ_4, we resolve the forces horizontally and vertically and equate the sum of each set to zero. It is usually more convenient to resolve horizontally and vertically, although any two directions mutually at right-angles will suffice. Two directions are necessary to ensure that there is no resultant force at right angles to the direction first considered. Thus we have

$$F_1 \sin \theta_1 + R \sin \theta_4 = F_2 \sin \theta_2 + F_3 \sin \theta_3 + mg, \quad (4.2)$$

and

$$F_1 \cos \theta_1 - R \cos \theta_4 = F_2 \cos \theta_2 + F_3 \cos \theta_3. \quad (4.3)$$

These equations are sufficient to determine the values of R and of θ_4.

The second condition is required to ensure that there shall be no *rotational* movement of the body.

The moment of a force about a point is defined as the product of the force and the perpendicular distance from the point to the line of the force.

The moment of a force about *an axis, to which the direction of the force is perpendicular,* is defined as the product of the force and the length of the common perpendicular to the line of the force and to the axis.

A system consisting of two equal and parallel forces in opposite directions is called a **couple.** We see at once that the sum of the moments (taken with opposite signs) of the two forces is the same about all points in their plane, being equal to the product of either force by the perpendicular distance between them. This constant algebraic sum of the moments is called the **moment of the couple,** or simply the **couple.**

Taking moments of the forces about O, or about the axis through O, in fig. 3, we have

$$F_1 l_1 \sin \theta_1 - F_2 l_2 \sin \theta_2 + F_3 l_3 \sin \theta_3 = 0, \quad (4.4)$$

for no rotational movement. Note that by taking moments about O, the contribution of R is eliminated, since for this force the perpendicular distance is zero. The same considerations apply to a body of irregular shape; we shall consider this more general case later, prior to our discussion of the compound pendulum (see Chap. VI). However, we may note here that the concept of the centre of gravity of a body arises when we consider the resultant of the forces on the body due to the weights of the innumerable small parts of which the body may be considered to consist. Thus, the irregular body shown in fig. 4 experiences an infinite number of parallel forces each equal to $\Delta m \cdot g$, due to the action of gravitational attraction. The sum total of these forces is the weight of the body, and this will act at some point termed the **Centre of Gravity.** The position of the centre of gravity is determined by the condition that a body suspended by an axis passing through this point exhibits no tendency to rotate, for since the perpendicular distance of the resultant from this point is zero, the moment about this point is zero. On the other hand, if the body is freely suspended about any other point, as shown in fig. 5, since the total weight

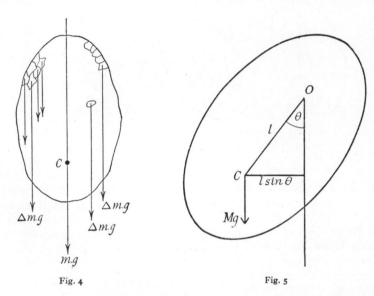

Fig. 4   Fig. 5

of the body may be considered as concentrated at the centre of gravity, there will be a turning moment about the point of suspension given by $Mgl \sin \theta$. The body will therefore turn until this turning moment is zero, that is, θ is zero. This will occur when l is vertical. Hence **the centre of gravity of a suspended body always lies in the vertical line containing the point of suspension.** This fact leads to a simple method of determining the centre of gravity of such a body as an irregularly shaped lamina; for if the latter is suspended from two points successively, the centre of gravity must be situated at the point of intersection of the two vertical lines which contained the points of suspension. We may further note that the body is in equilibrium for three positions, namely:

(*a*) with the centre of gravity vertically *below* the point of suspension. This position is said to be a position of **stable equilibrium,** since if the body is slightly displaced, the turning moment about the axis of suspension is such as to cause the body to return toward its initial (equilibrium) position;

(*b*) with the centre of gravity coinciding with the point of suspension. This is said to be a position of **neutral equilibrium**, since if the body is rotated there is no tendency for it either to return **or to** rotate further. It is in equilibrium for all orientations;

(*c*) with the centre of gravity vertically above the axis of suspension. In this position the equilibrium is said to be **unstable**, since

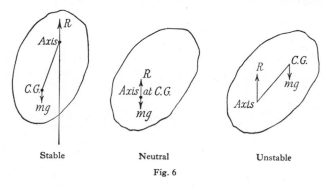

Stable   Neutral   Unstable

Fig. 6

if the body is given a slight displacement, the moment of the weight about the axis of suspension will cause the body to move farther and farther away from its initial position of unstable equilibrium until it finds its position of stable equilibrium, when its centre of gravity lies directly below the axis of suspension. These ideas are illustrated in fig. 6.

2. Machines.

We are now in a position to consider the action of a great many simple machines which are based upon the principles which we have considered.

(i) The Roman Steel-yard and the Danish Steel-yard.

These consist of uniform horizontal rods or **levers** which are used for weighing. The former has a movable counterpoise and fixed fulcrum and is calibrated by placing known masses M in the scale pan (see fig. 7) and altering the position of the counterpoise C until the moments of the two weights about the fulcrum are equal and the rod is horizontal. The value of the weight in the scale-pan is engraved on the lever at the appropriate position of the counterpoise, when balance is obtained.

With the *Danish steel-yard*, the counterpoise is fixed, consisting of a heavy sphere S, as shown in fig. 8; the fulcrum F is movable, and thus allows a balance to be obtained for various weights in the scale-

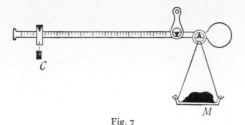

Fig. 7

pan. The appropriate weight for balance is engraved on the lever for various positions of the fulcrum.

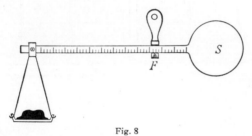

Fig. 8

(ii) The Common or Chemical Balance.

The principle of the common or chemical balance is shown in fig. 9, which shows a diagram of a modern instrument. It consists in principle of a horizontal lever balanced on a knife-edge at its centre. The lever is of compound construction, so that the centre of gravity of the system lies below the horizontal axis of suspension. In fig. 10 the balance point is at O and the centre of gravity at G. Normally, the balance arm is horizontal, in the position AB, but if unequal weights are placed in the scale-pans the arm takes up some position PQ lying at an angle θ to AB. Suppose now weights W_1 and W_2 are placed in the scale pans and the balance arm is turned through an angle θ, in which position it is in equilibrium. Then if the weight of the balance arm is W, the condition for equilibrium, as found by taking moments about O, is

$$W_1 l \cos\theta = W h \sin\theta + W_2 l \cos\theta; \quad \cdots \quad (4.5)$$

hence

$$\tan\theta = \frac{(W_1 - W_2)}{W}\frac{l}{h}, \quad \cdots \quad (4.6)$$

where l is half the length of the balance arm and h is the distance OG.

The properties of a good balance are as follows:

(a) **The balance arm should be horizontal when equal weights are placed in the two scale-pans.** This implies that the fulcrum must be exactly at the centre of the balance arm and that the mass of the

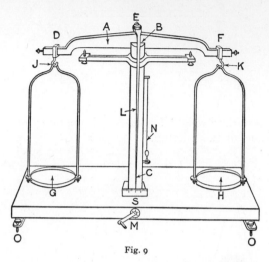

Fig. 9

latter must be distributed quite symmetrically on either side of the fulcrum. If this condition is not fulfilled, the correct mass of a body is given by $(W_1 W_2)^{\frac{1}{2}}$, where W_1 and W_2 are its apparent weights when it is weighed first in one scale-pan and then in the other. The proof of this is left to the reader as an exercise.

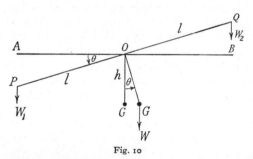

Fig. 10

(b) **The balance should have high sensitivity**; that is, it should register a large deflection for a small difference in the weights in the two scale-pans. The condition for high sensitivity is found from equation (4.6), which shows that θ is a maximum for a given value of $(W_1 - W_2)$ when l is a maximum and W and h are as small as possible. Hence for a high sensitivity the balance arm should be as long as possible but as light as possible, while the centre of gravity should be only just below the knife-edge.

(c) **The balance should be robust**; that is, it should not bend under moderate loads. This condition requires a short thick balance arm, and therefore is diametrically opposed to the conditions for maximum sensitivity. In practice a compromise must be effected, but the history of the balance shows a series of improvements with the invention of light but rigid metal alloys.

(d) **The balance should be quick in action.** This implies that the period of the oscillation which occurs when the balance is released should be as short as possible. The requirements of a short period of swing are precisely the reverse of those for high sensitivity, so again a compromise must be effected.

(e) **It should return to zero when the weights are removed**; this implies that the balance must be a system in stable equilibrium.

(f) **The sensitivity should be as far as possible independent of the load in the scale-pans.** This can only be achieved if the knife-edges which support the scale-pans and the knife-edge which constitutes the fulcrum are parallel and all lie in one horizontal plane. Otherwise, as the tilt of the beam is increased, the effective length of the arm supporting the lower pan is decreased; an additional restoring couple is therefore called into play, given by $W(l_1 - l_2)$, where W is the value of each weight in the scale-pan and l_1 and l_2 are the projected horizontal lengths of the two halves of the beam. This couple increases as W increases, and hence the sensitivity will decrease as the load in the scale-pan is increased.

(iii) Pulleys.

If we consider the simple arrangement of pulleys shown in fig. 11, we observe that the **load** or weight W is supported by the two tensions T. The latter are transmitted from the tension or **effort** applied by the operator and hence the load W is supported by an effort only half its magnitude. This ability to move weights greater than the effort applied is called the **mechanical advantage** of the machine, and is defined as the ratio of the load supported to the effort applied.

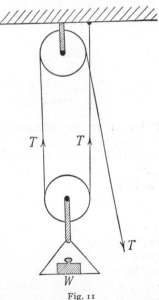

Fig. 11

We observe, however, that (not only in fig. 11, but generally) if the effort is moved through a distance a, the load will move through a distance b given by

$$Wb = Ta. \quad \cdot \ \cdot \ \cdot \ \cdot \ \cdot \ \cdot \ \cdot \quad (4.7)$$

This follows from the conservation of energy, the potential energy gained by the load equalling the work done by the effort. Since (4.7) may be written

$$\frac{a}{b} = \frac{W}{T}, \quad \cdot \ \cdot \ \cdot \ \cdot \ \cdot \ \cdot \quad (4.8)$$

we see that the distance moved by the effort is greater than that moved by the load in the ratio of load to effort. The ratio a/b in (4.8)

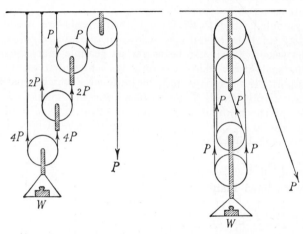

Fig. 12a Fig. 12b

is known as the **velocity ratio**; it is obviously identical with the mechanical advantage, under the conditions we have assumed. Should friction be present the equations must be modified, as the effort will have to do additional work to overcome the friction as well as raise the load.

Other systems of pulleys are shown in figs. 12(a) and 12(b), the former being known as the **Archimedean**, or **First System of Pulleys**, and the latter as the **Second** or **Common System of Pulleys**. To avoid the long length of rope required in the system last discussed, a modification termed **Weston's Differential Pulley** is used. As shown in fig. 13, this consists of a lower movable block containing an ordinary pulley and an upper fixed block containing two toothed pulleys of radii r and R respectively. A single endless chain passes round the pulleys. If the effort applied is P, then by considering the upper block

$$PR = TR - Tr, \quad \cdot \ \cdot \ \cdot \ \cdot \ \cdot \ \cdot \quad (4.9)$$

while for the lower block

$$W = 2T. \qquad \text{......} \quad (4.10)$$

Hence the **mechanical advantage is**

$$\frac{\mathbf{W}}{\mathbf{P}} = \frac{\mathbf{2R}}{\mathbf{R} - \mathbf{r}}. \qquad \text{......} \quad (4.11)$$

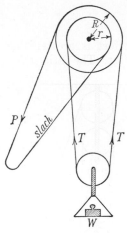

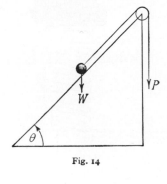

Fig. 14

Fig. 13

(iv) The Inclined Plane.

Referring to Chap. III, § 5, we note that a weight P acting parallel to a smooth plane, and given by

$$P = W \sin \theta, \qquad \text{......} \quad (4.12)$$

is sufficient to support a weight W resting on the plane. The mechanical advantage of such a system is therefore $\operatorname{cosec} \theta$. In practice the effort is applied vertically downwards and transmitted over a pulley at the top of the plane as shown in fig. 14.

(v) The Screw.

A screw may be regarded as an inclined plane which has been wrapped continuously around a vertical cylinder. In practice it is usually encountered in the form of a jack. In this machine an effort P is applied horizontally to the screw at a distance r from the axis of the screw, which is vertical (see fig. 15). The screw works upwards in a fixed nut, and the load W, which rests on the screw, is thereby raised. From the conservation of energy, the work done by the effort equals the gain in potential energy of the load, so that if the pitch of the screw is h,

$$2\pi r P = W h.$$

Hence the **mechanical advantage is**

$$\frac{\mathbf{W}}{\mathbf{P}} = \frac{2\pi r}{h};\quad \cdot \ \cdot \ \cdot \ \cdot \ \cdot \ \cdot \quad (4.11a)$$

that is, it is equal to the ratio of the circumference of the cylinder to the pitch of the screw. In practice, the friction between the nut and

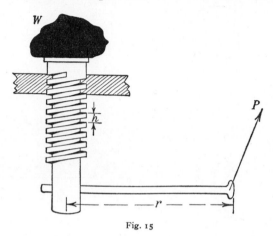

Fig. 15

the screw is often large and the mechanical advantage is then only a small fraction of that given by (4.11a).

3. Friction.

If a small body is placed on a plane inclined at a small angle θ to the horizontal, then although a force $mg \sin \theta$ acts down the plane, m being the mass of the body, the latter does not in general move down the plane. There must therefore be called into play an equal and opposite force opposing the motion. This is termed the *frictional force*; and friction may be defined as the force tending to prevent one surface moving over another. The subject was examined experimentally by Coulomb with an apparatus of the type shown in fig. 16.

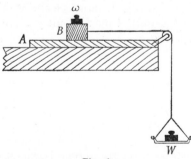

Fig. 16

The two bodies between which the friction is to be examined are made into the shape of two flat slabs A and B. One of the slabs A is clamped to a horizontal table, and the other slab B is attached by a string to a scale-pan into which various weights may be placed. The slab B is laid on A, and a horizontal tension is applied to B by the string, which passes over a pulley at the edge of the table. It is then found that if B is loaded with various weights w, certain other weights W must be placed in the scale-pan in order that sliding may just commence. In this way Coulomb was able to enunciate the **laws of static friction,** which are:

(1) **The frictional force just before motion commences, or the limiting friction, is directly proportional to the normal reaction between the two surfaces.**

(2) **The limiting friction is independent of the area of contact, provided the normal reaction remains unchanged.**

(3) **The coefficient of limiting (or static) friction,** denoted by μ. is given by

$$\mu = \frac{P}{R}, \quad \cdots \quad \cdots \quad (4.13)$$

where P is the limiting friction and R is the normal reaction.

It follows that if a small body is resting on an inclined plane, the angle of which is gradually increased, slipping will occur for some value known as the **angle of friction** or **angle of repose,** α, given by the relation

$$P = \mu R = mg \sin \alpha. \quad \cdots \quad \cdots \quad (4.14)$$

But $$R = mg \cos \alpha,$$

and therefore $$\mu = \tan \alpha. \quad \cdots \quad \cdots \quad (4.15)$$

It should be realized that the full frictional force or limiting friction is not called into play until the condition is reached when the body is about to move. When movement has started, the frictional force, which is then termed the **kinetic friction,** is found to be considerably less than the limiting static friction. For velocities which are not too large, the kinetic friction is found to be independent of the velocity and proportional to the normal reaction. We therefore have the relation

$$\nu = \frac{P}{R}, \quad \cdots \quad \cdots \quad (4.16)$$

defining ν, the coefficient of kinetic friction.

To examine kinetic friction and to determine the value of the coefficient ν, Perry's apparatus (fig. 17) may be used. This consists essentially of a vertical axle AB, to which is attached rigidly a wheel C, on the upper surface of which a circular slab of one of the materials F may be clamped. The other surface G rests on F, and is held in contact with it by a normal reaction supplied through the lever AS, the fulcrum of which is at A, by the variable effort, represented by the loaded scale-pan, at S. As the wheel is rotated, movement of G is prevented by a tangential force supplied by a string, which lies hori-

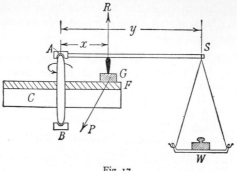

Fig. 17

zontally and passes over a pulley, and is ultimately attached to a scale-pan containing varying weights. The tension in the string then gives the value of P for equation (4.16) while the value of R is given

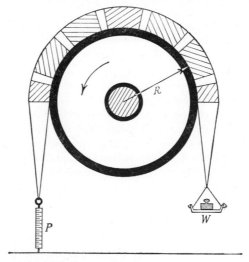

Fig. 18

by Wy/x, where x and y are the lengths indicated in fig. 17. The condition aimed at is that of floating equilibrium, in which the surface G stays approximately in one position as the surface F is revolved at at uniform speed.

In the vast majority of cases friction represents lost energy, and is therefore kept as low as possible. One important example of how friction has been turned to account is the **friction dynamometer.** This instrument is used to measure the horse-power of machines, the measure of which as obtained in this manner is sometimes referred to as the brake-output. A friction dynamometer, as shown in fig. 18, consists of a large wheel, which may be a pulley wheel or the flywheel of the machine concerned, over which passes a flexible belt attached to which are wooden brake blocks. One end of the belt is attached to a spring balance which is fixed rigidly to a beam; the other end supports a weight W. If the spring balance registers an amount P when the wheel is rotating uniformly at a rate of n revolutions per second, then **the rate at which work is being done is given by $2\pi n R(W - P)$,** where R is the radius of the wheel. The force $(W - P)$ is, of course, just balancing the frictional force which is being called into play in the condition of floating equilibrium.

4. Rotation of Rigid Bodies.

In Chap. III, § 2, we defined the mass of a body as a quantity associated with a body which is inversely proportional to linear acceleration when a given force is applied to it. Suppose now we apply a couple G (p. 32) to a rigid body which is free to rotate about a fixed axis. We shall show that there is a quantity, associated with the body and this axis, which is inversely proportional to the angular acceleration, about the axis, produced by the couple. The quantity is called the **moment of inertia** of the body about the axis. Expressing this mathematically, we have, denoting the moment of inertia by I and the angular acceleration by $d^2\theta/dt^2$,

$$G = I \frac{d^2\theta}{dt^2}. \qquad \ldots \ldots (4.17)$$

We shall now examine this formula, and at the same time find an expression for the value of I.

If we concentrate upon what is occurring to each of the small elements which make up the rigid body, we realize that each is experiencing a force urging it into rotational motion about the axis. If for any elementary particle of mass dm, situated a distance r from the axis, the force is P, and G is the *external* couple (couples due to *internal* forces cancelling out, by Newton's Third Law), then

$$G = \Sigma Pr = \Sigma(dm \, . \, \text{linear acceleration})r$$

$$= \Sigma\left(dm \, . \, r \frac{d^2\theta}{dt^2}\right)r$$

$$= \Sigma(dm \, . \, r^2)\frac{d^2\theta}{dt^2}. \qquad \ldots \ldots \ldots (4.18)$$

Comparing (4.17) and (4.18) we see that the moment of inertia I is given by the expression $\Sigma(dm \cdot r^2)$. This last expression may be written in integral form and integrated for certain special cases, but for bodies of irregular shape resort must be made to experiment, in which all the quantities may be measured except I, and hence I determined. An additional quantity of considerable use is the **radius of gyration** of a rigid body about an axis. This quantity is defined as the linear quantity k, where

$$k^2 = \frac{\Sigma(dm \cdot r^2)}{\Sigma dm}. \quad \ldots \ldots \quad (4.19)$$

It follows from (4.19) that the moment of inertia

$$I = \Sigma(dm \cdot r^2) = \Sigma dm \cdot k^2 = Mk^2$$

where M is the mass of the body. In certain circumstances it is preferable to use the form Mk^2 instead of I.

If we write (4.17) in the form

$$G = I \times \text{angular acceleration} = I \times \frac{d\omega}{dt} = \frac{d}{dt}(I\omega), \quad (4.20)$$

where ω is the angular velocity of rotation, we note that there is a formal resemblance with equation (3.5),

$$P = \frac{d}{dt}(mv).$$

By analogy with the quantity mv which is termed the linear momentum of a body, the quantity $I\omega$ is termed the **angular momentum.** The analogy is more than formal, for experiment shows that, just as for linear momentum, angular momentum is conserved in a rotating system, not subjected to external force. This also follows from (4.20), which shows that $I\omega$ is constant if $G = 0$.

Finally, in complete analogy with the expression for kinetic energy of translation $\frac{1}{2}mv^2$, we have the quantity $\frac{1}{2}I\omega^2$ which represents the **kinetic energy of rotation.** To show this more fully, let a particle of mass m be rotating about an axis at a distance r from the particle, and let the angular velocity of rotation be ω. Then the linear velocity of the particle is $v = r\omega$, so that the kinetic energy of the particle is $E = \frac{1}{2}mv^2 = \frac{1}{2}mr^2\omega^2$. If we consider a solid body as made up of a multitude of such particles, the total kinetic energy of the rotating body is $\Sigma\frac{1}{2}mr^2\omega^2 = \frac{1}{2}\omega^2\Sigma mr^2$. Now the summation term is, by definition, the moment of inertia I of the body about the axis of rotation, so the kinetic energy of rotation is $\frac{1}{2}I\omega^2$. This form of energy also obeys the general law of conservation of energy.

5. Oscillation of Rigid Bodies.

Consider the irregular rigid body shown in fig. 5 (p. 33). A horizontal axis supports the body and in the equilibrium position the centre of gravity of the body will lie directly below the axis of suspension. Let the body now be rotated slightly to one side so that the line joining the axis of suspension to the centre of gravity makes an angle θ with the vertical. Then if the body is released, the centre of gravity will describe a circular arc of radius l with the axis of suspension as centre. The problem is clearly analogous to that of the simple pendulum; and this arrangement using a rigid body is termed a **compound** or **rigid pendulum**. The couple acting about the axis of rotation is $Mg \cdot l \sin \theta$ and hence, applying (4.17), the angular acceleration with which the body moves is given by

$$ G = Mgl \sin \theta = -I \frac{d^2\theta}{dt^2}, \quad \ldots \ldots \quad (4.21) $$

where I is the moment of inertia about the axis of rotation. (For the negative sign, compare pp. 22, 24.)

For small angles, (4.21) may be written

$$ I \frac{d^2\theta}{dt^2} = -Mgl\theta, \quad \ldots \ldots \ldots \quad (4.22) $$

or

$$ \frac{d^2\theta}{dt^2} = -\frac{Mgl}{I}\theta. $$

Now equation (4.22) is precisely similar to equation (3.20) where $p^2 = Mgl/I$. Hence, by (3.26), the time of oscillation of a compound pendulum is

$$ t = 2\pi \sqrt{\frac{I}{Mgl}}. \quad \ldots \ldots \ldots \quad (4.23) $$

If we express the moment of inertia in the form Mk^2 (4.23) becomes

$$ t = 2\pi \sqrt{\frac{k^2}{gl}}. \quad \ldots \ldots \ldots \quad (4.24) $$

EXERCISES

1. State the conditions for the equilibrium of a rigid body.

A uniform ladder rests with its upper end against a smooth wall and its lower end in contact with a rough horizontal plane. If the coefficient of friction is 0·5, find the angle at which the ladder is inclined to the vertical when it is on the point of slipping. [45°.]

2. Explain carefully what is meant by the Centre of Gravity of a body.

Find the position of the C.G. of a geometrically uniform bar which increases in density at a rate proportional to its distance from one end. [$\frac{2}{3}l$.]

3. Describe the construction of a sensitive chemical balance and prove that the sensitivity is independent of the linear dimensions for geometrically similar balances of the same material.

4. Explain clearly what is meant by the moment of inertia of a rigid body about an axis.

A hoop rests in a vertical plane with its inner surface supported by a small horizontal peg. If the period of a small oscillation in a vertical plane is 3 sec., find the radius of gyration of the hoop about its centre, given that the latter is 3 ft. away from the peg. [3·6 ft.]

5. Give practical examples of the conservation of linear and of angular momentum.

If the earth suddenly contracted to half its present radius, by how much would the day be decreased? [18 hours.]

6. Explain the action of (a) Weston's Differential Pulley, (b) a car jack.

Find the effort required to lift a weight of one ton with a jack whose pitch is $\frac{1}{2}$ in. if the effort is applied 4 ft. from the axis and the efficiency is 75 per cent. [4·95 lb.]

7. Describe an experiment for measuring the coefficient of kinetic friction.

If a bobsleigh slides at constant speed down a slope inclined at 20° to the horizontal, determine the coefficient of friction which is operative, and assuming this remains constant, determine the acceleration of the bobsleigh down a slope inclined at 45°. [0·364; 0·45g.]

CHAPTER V

Units and Dimensions

1. Introduction.

We have proceeded so far on the assumption that the reader's everyday conception of what is meant by length, mass and time is sufficient to allow the general argument to be followed. We must now be more precise, introducing definite **units** and considering the **dimensions** of physical quantities.

2. Fundamental Units.

The statement that a given rod has a length of 10 feet implies that a given standard or unit of length, the foot, has been chosen and that ten of these units can be placed end to end along the length of the rod. The unit of length chosen, and indeed any unit, should have the following properties: it should be

(1) *well-defined*;
(2) *not subject to secular (time) change*;
(3) *easily compared with similar units*;
(4) *easily reproduced*.

Two systems of units which are universally recognized are termed the **British system** and the **French** or **metric system**.

The British unit of length is the **yard**, which is defined as the straight distance between the transverse lines in two gold plugs on a bronze bar kept at 62° Fahrenheit and preserved by the Board of Trade. We must emphasize that the choice of such a length was quite arbitrary. It is inconveniently large for some purposes, and is sub-divided into three equal parts, each of which is termed a **foot**. The unit of length in most other countries is the metre. This is the length of a bar, originally made to be as nearly as possible equal to one ten-millionth part of a quadrant of the earth, passing through Paris. This relation was subsequently found to be inaccurate, but the original bar was retained, and the **metre** is now defined as the quite arbitrary distance between two marks on a platinum bar kept at 0° C. and preserved in the International Bureau of Standards at Sèvres, near Paris. The metre, which is slightly more than a yard, is also inconveniently large and has been divided into 100 equal parts, each of which is called a **centimetre.** The British unit of mass is also quite arbitrary. It is termed the **pound avoirdupois,** and is the mass of a piece of platinum preserved by the Board of Trade and marked " P.S. 1844, 1 lb." It bears no simple relation to the unit of volume (the cubic foot) on the same system, and thus differs from the unit of mass in the metric system. This, the **kilogramme,** was initially made as close as possible to the weight of 1000 cubic centimetres of pure water at its temperature of maximum density. Although subsequent work has shown that the relation is not quite accurate, the original kilogramme has been retained and is now simply taken as the weight of a piece of platinum preserved at the International Bureau of Weights and Measures, Sèvres, near Paris.

The British and metric systems agree in taking for the unit of time, the **mean solar second.** This is simply the **mean solar day** divided by 86,400. In practice, the mean solar day is based on the **sidereal day.** The latter is defined as the time taken between two successive passages of the same fixed star across the meridian of the place of observation. The solar day is longer than the sidereal day, for between two successive passages over the meridian the sun moves backwards from west to east relative to the fixed stars. A year contains 366·25 sidereal days, but only 365·25 solar days, and hence the mean solar second is 366·25/365·25 of the sidereal second.

For scientific use the metre and the kilogramme are subdivided into one hundred equal parts, and the **centimetre-gram-second** or **C.G.S.** system is obtained. Unfortunately, in engineering, larger units are sometimes considered preferable and, to add to the confusion, that adopted by British countries is the **foot-pound-second** or **F.P.S.** system. The units of length, mass and time are often referred to as **fundamental units,** for reasons which we shall discuss in the next section. We should emphasize here that there is nothing fundamental about them in the sense that Nature considers them more important than other physical concepts such as velocity, electric current, &c. But the various physical quantities such as velocity, force, length, acceleration, mass, energy, and so on, are connected by definitions and physical laws, and once the units of a certain number of these quantities have been chosen as fundamental units, the units of all other quantities can be expressed in terms of them.

3. Derived Units.

Consider now the expression for the area of a surface. The unit in which the area is expressed is the area of a square whose side is the unit of length. Similarly, the unit of volume is that of a cube whose side is the unit of length. It is clear therefore that when the unit of length has been fixed, those of area and volume become fixed automatically. The latter are therefore examples of **derived units,** being derived from the arbitrarily chosen *fundamental unit* of length. Consideration of velocity takes us a stage farther. Velocity is rate of change of position, and hence will be expressed as length divided by time. Hence, velocity is expressed in derived units based on feet per sec. or cm. per sec., according as the F.P.S. or C.G.S. system is used to define the fundamental units. Again, since force may be defined by equation (3.2) of Chap. III, namely, $P = ma$, force will be expressed in lb. $\times$ ft./sec.^{2} or gm. $\times$ cm./sec.^{2}, the former being given the name **poundals** and the latter, **dynes**. Since $P = 1$ if $m = a = 1$, the **dyne is that force which will produce an acceleration of one cm. per second^2 when it acts on a mass of one gramme.** Similarly, the **poundal** may be defined as **that force which, acting on a mass of one pound, produces in it an acceleration of one foot per second.^{2}**

Other important units are given in the following Table where, for completeness, the metre-kilogram-second or M.K.S. system is also included, although this is discussed more fully on p. 697.

Quantity	Definition	C. G. S. System		British System		M. K. S. System	
		Units	Name	Units	Name	Units	Name
Kinetic Energy	$\frac{1}{2}mv^2$ or $\frac{1}{2}\frac{mv^2}{g}$	$m = 1$ gm. $v = 1$ cm./sec.	Erg	$m = 1$ lb. $v = 1$ ft./sec.	Foot-poundal	$m = 1$ kgm. $v = 1$ m./sec.	Joule
		($m = 1$ gm. $v = 1$ cm./sec. $g = 981$ cm./sec.^{2}	Gm.-cm.	$m = 1$ lb. $v = 1$ ft./sec. $g = 32$ ft./ sec.^{2}	Foot-pound	$m = 1$ kgm. $v = 1$ m./sec. $g = 9.81$ m./sec.^{2}	kgm.-m.
Potential Energy or Work	mgh	($m = 1$ gm. $h = 1$ cm. $g = 981$ cm./sec.^{2}	Erg	$m = 1$ lb. $h = 1$ ft. $g = 32$ ft./ sec.^{2}	Foot-poundal	$m = 1$ kgm. $h = 1$ m. $g = 9.81$ m./sec.^{2}	Joule
	mh	$m = 1$ gm. $h = 1$ cm.	Gm.-cm.	$m = 1$ lb. $h = 1$ ft.	Ft.-lb.	$m = 1$ kgm. $h = 1$ m.	kgm.-m.
Power	$\dfrac{mh}{t}$	($m = 1$ gm. $h = 1$ cm. $t = 1$ sec.	Gm.-cm. /sec.	$m = 1$ lb. $h = 1$ ft. $t = 1$ sec.	Ft.-lb./ sec.	$m = 1$ kgm. $h = 1$ m. $t = 1$ sec.	Watt
				One Horse-power $= 550$ ft.-lb./sec.			

The unit of force on the M.K.S. system is termed the *newton* and is the force required to produce an acceleration of 1 m./sec.^{2} in 1 kgm., it is therefore equal to 10^5 dynes.

Up to the present, all the quantities considered have been expressed in terms of either length, mass or time or of combinations of these. Such a simple and satisfactory state of affairs continues to hold while we are concerned solely with the mechanical properties of bodies. When, however, we come to consider other physical phenomena such as heat, light, electricity and magnetism, matters become more complicated. In particular it becomes necessary to introduce other fundamental units in addition to those of mass, length and time. Examples of the procedure in such cases are given as occasion arises.

4. Dimensions.

Consider equation (3.27), Chap. III, which states that the time of oscillation of a simple pendulum is given by

$$t = 2\pi\sqrt{\frac{l}{g}},$$

where l is the length of the pendulum and g is the acceleration due to gravity. Now this is an **equation,** so that not only must the numerical value of both sides of the equation be the same, but also the physical quantities expressed on the two sides must be identical. On the L.H.S. the only quantity is the time, and to denote that a measurement of this physical phenomenon is required we represent it by T. Now for equation (3.27) to be true, the R.H.S. must somehow also be expressed simply as a time measurement T. As for the individual quantities composing the expression on the R.H.S., 2 and π are simply numbers and need not be considered as far as physical measurement is concerned. On the other hand, the length of the pendulum l involves a length measurement which we shall symbolize by L, while the acceleration due to gravity involves a measurement of length and time, the nature of which is expressed by L/T^2 or LT^{-2}. These symbols L and T, which denote the type of physical measurement which has to be made, are termed the **dimensions** of the quantities involved, and the compound expressions such as LT^{-2} and MLT^{-2} for acceleration and force respectively are referred to as the **dimensional formulæ** of acceleration and force. Again, acceleration and force are said to have dimensions of 1 in L, -2 in T; and 1 in M, 1 in L and -2 in T respectively. Substituting the dimensional formulæ of length and acceleration on the R.H.S. of equation (3.27), we obtain $\sqrt{\dfrac{L}{LT^{-2}}}$, or T, which shows that the R.H.S. of the equation is expressed by T, as well as the L.H.S. The fact that both sides of a physical equation have the same dimensions may be stated as follows: **Equations representing possible physical phenomena must be dimensionally homogeneous.** This property is extremely useful, as it sometimes enables us to predict the equations governing physical phenomena before we have determined them by experiment. As an illustration, suppose we wished to know how the time of oscillation t of a simple pendulum depended on its length l, the acceleration due to gravity g and the mass m of the pendulum bob. Then we assume that

$$t = f(m, l, g), \quad \cdots \cdots \quad (5.1)$$

where $f(m, l, g)$ is some function of the quantities involved. We then assume that this function may be expressed as an algebraic formula thus

$$t = m^\alpha l^\beta g^\gamma, \quad \ldots \ldots \quad (5.2)$$

where α, β and γ are the powers to which the quantities m, l and g are raised in the final expression. Now if equation (5.2) represents a possible state of affairs it must be dimensionally homogeneous. By equating, therefore, the dimensions of the two sides we obtain the required powers α, β and γ. Thus, writing (5.2) in dimensional form

$$T = M^\alpha L^\beta (LT^{-2})^\gamma, \quad \ldots \ldots \quad (5.3)$$

and equating indices of the dimensional quantities on both sides, we find

Mass	$0 = \alpha$,	
Length	$0 = \beta + \gamma$,	$\ldots \ldots \ldots$ (5.4)
Time	$1 = -2\gamma$,	

and hence from (5.4) $\alpha = 0$, $\beta = \frac{1}{2}$ and $\gamma = -\frac{1}{2}$, so that equation (5.2) becomes

$$t = l^{\frac{1}{2}} g^{-\frac{1}{2}}. \quad \ldots \ldots \quad (5.5)$$

We note that the time of oscillation is predicted to be independent of the mass of the bob, a fact which is borne out by experiment. It is clear that the process we have used, which is that of **dimensional analysis**, gives us no information about **dimensionless quantities** or **pure numbers** such as 2π. We therefore write (5.5) in the form

$$t = k \sqrt{\frac{l}{g}}, \quad \ldots \ldots \quad (5.6)$$

where k may represent some number. We note, however, that k may be determined by a *single experiment*, on substituting the measured value of t for a given length l and a known value of g.

Another use of dimensional analysis is the **testing of equations**. After a long mathematical analysis it is useful to check the final equation for dimensional homogeneity by substitution of the dimensional formulæ on both sides of the equation.

We shall come across various other applications of dimensional analysis in the course of this book, but we should warn the student here that the successful use of dimensional analysis involves a very wide knowledge and experience of Physics. Correct results depend upon the selection of the correct variables (m, l and g in our pendulum example), the choice of which is guided solely by physical analogy and intuition. Again, special methods of treatment must be used *if the number of variables is greater than the number of primary quantities.* Thus in the example chosen, there were three variables m, l and g, and three primary quantities, M, L and T, in which these could be expressed. Consequently three equations were obtained and the powers α, β and γ could be completely determined. Finally, besides dimensionless constants like 2π, there exist **dimensional constants** such as the gravitational constant G, discussed in the next chapter. Whether or not such dimensional constants should be introduced as additional variables when deducing formulæ by dimensional methods, often requires rather subtle considerations to decide.

EXERCISES

1. Explain what is meant by dimensional analysis, illustrating your answer by examples from different branches of physics.

2. A drop of liquid is suspended in another liquid of the same density but with which it is immiscible. If the drop is distorted from the spherical shape and then released, deduce by dimensional methods a formula for its period of oscillation, given that the latter depends on surface tension, density and drop radius. $[t = k\rho^{1/2}r^{3/2}T^{-1/2}.]$

3. Show by dimensional methods that the viscous retarding force on a sphere moving with slow uniform velocity through a viscous liquid is proportional to the velocity, the radius of the sphere and the coefficient of viscosity of the liquid.

CHAPTER VI

The Acceleration due to Gravity and the Gravitational Constant

The two quantities associated with the earth's gravitational field which are of particular importance are g, the acceleration due to gravity at the earth's surface and **G**, the Newtonian constant of gravitation.

1. Methods of determining g.

Any motion which involves the earth's gravitation field may be used to obtain a value of g, and several possible methods are tabulated below. It is important, however, that the student should realize that a large number of them are simply laboratory exercises and that in practice the only method which is used in an accurate determination of g is the one employing the compound pendulum.

(1) *Inclined plane.*
(2) *Body rolling in a concave mirror.*
(3) *Atwood's machine.*
(4) *Simple pendulum.*
(5) *Conical pendulum.*
(6) *Bifilar suspension.*
(7) *Compound or rigid pendulum.*
(8) *Vertical vibrations of a body on a spiral spring.*

The direct determination of g by observation on the free vertical fall of a body is necessarily extremely inaccurate, since over short distances the time of fall is too short, while over large distances, owing to the high velocity acquired, the determination of the instant that the body passes a fixed point becomes very uncertain. The other methods, therefore, are methods which allow of the " dilution " of gravity. For example, on an inclined plane the acceleration of a particle becomes $g \sin \theta$ down the plane, so that by making θ small the effective acceleration may be made small. In practice, a limit is set by the rising relative magnitude of frictional forces as θ is made small. This difficulty is almost eliminated by the use of a **pendulum,** which

3   (H 394)

may be regarded as the motion of a body on a frictionless inclined plane of continually varying angle.

2. Body Rolling Down an Inclined Plane.

Fig. 1 shows two positions P and Q of a body rolling down an inclined plane. By the principle of the conservation of energy, if we assume that no energy is lost through friction, the gain in the kinetic energy (partly translational and partly rotational) of the body at Q, if it starts from rest at P, is equal to its loss in potential energy. Hence

$$\tfrac{1}{2}mv^2 + \tfrac{1}{2}I\omega^2 = mgh, \quad \ldots \ldots \quad (6.1)$$

where I is the moment of inertia of the body about its axis, ω is its angular velocity of rotation about that axis, m is the mass of the body, v its linear velocity, h is the vertical distance fallen, and g is

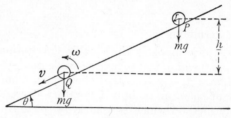

Fig. 1

the acceleration due to gravity. If mk^2 is written for I, where k is the radius of gyration about the axis of rotation through the C.G., (6.1) becomes

$$g = \frac{v^2 + k^2\omega^2}{2h}. \quad \ldots \ldots \quad (6.2)$$

If r is the radius of the body, $\omega = v/r$, also, from (2.16),

$$v^2 = 2ah \operatorname{cosec} \theta, \quad \ldots \ldots \quad (6.3)$$

where a is the acceleration down the plane.

Hence $$g = a\left(1 + \frac{k^2}{r^2}\right) \operatorname{cosec} \theta. \quad \ldots \ldots \quad (6.4)$$

If θ is small, a is correspondingly small, and by using a stop-watch and scale the distance-time curve may be obtained. The equation of this curve is $s = \tfrac{1}{2}at^2$, and a may be found by substituting any corresponding values of s and t in this equation; a better result is obtained from the average of several values of a, as so found. The radius r is obtained by direct measurement of the diameter, and k^2 can be shown mathematically to have the following values:

(1) *Solid sphere,* $k^2 = \frac{2}{5}r^2$.

(2) *Solid cylinder* or *disk,* $k^2 = \frac{1}{2}r^2$.

(3) *Hollow cylinder* or *hoop,* $k^2 = r^2$.

For a body rolling on a concave mirror we have the inclined plane replaced by an inclined plane of varying angle. It is left as an exercise to the student to show that for a sphere of radius r, oscillating to and fro in a concave bowl of radius R, the time of oscillation is given by

$$\tau = 2\pi \sqrt{\frac{7(R-r)}{5g}}. \qquad (6.5)$$

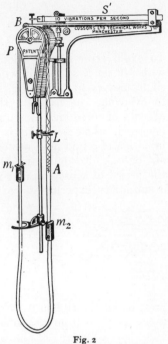

Fig. 2

3. Atwood's Machine.

In fig. 2 is shown the arrangement known as *Atwood's machine.* Two unequal masses m_1 and m_2 are joined by an endless ribbon A passing over a frictionless pulley P. When m_2 is released by removing the platform L, assuming m_2 greater than m_1, the former will commence to move down and the latter up with a uniform acceleration a. Suppose the vertical distance traversed is h, and the velocity then acquired by the masses is v. Then if the moment of inertia of the pulley wheel is I and its radius is r, we have, from the conservation of energy,

$$\tfrac{1}{2}I\omega^2 + \tfrac{1}{2}(m_1 + m_2)v^2 = (m_2 - m_1)gh, \quad . \quad . \quad (6.6)$$

where $\omega = v/r =$ angular velocity of rotation of the pulley. Hence

$$g = \frac{v^2(I/r^2 + m_1 + m_2)}{2(m_2 - m_1)h}. \quad . \quad . \quad . \quad . \quad (6.7)$$

Now if the actual acceleration of the system is a, $v^2 = 2ah$.

Hence

$$g = \frac{a(I/r^2 + m_1 + m_2)}{(m_2 - m_1)}. \quad . \quad . \quad . \quad (6.8)$$

It is usual to eliminate I by carrying out the experiment with two other masses m_2' and m_1', and observing the new acceleration a'. If this is done, we have

$$g = \frac{(m_1 + m_2) - (m_1' + m_2')}{\dfrac{(m_2 - m_1)}{a} - \dfrac{(m_2' - m_1')}{a'}}. \qquad \text{. . .} \quad (6.9)$$

To avoid error due to friction, the machine is loaded on one side with a mass w so that it will run with *uniform velocity* when given a slight movement. This occurs if the additional weight is just sufficient to overcome the friction; the absence of acceleration indicates the absence of force and consequently the frictional force has been compensated. The weight w is kept in position throughout the determination of g and does not of course form part of the masses m_1, m_2, m_1' or m_2'. To determine the acceleration, a flat vibrating strip S', the period of vibration τ of which has been timed by a stop-clock in a subsidiary experiment, carries a style B which marks a wavy im-

Fig. 2a

pression on the ribbon A. Now if x_1, x_2 and x_3 (fig. 2(a)) are the distances covered from rest in successive periods τ_0, $2\tau_0$, $3\tau_0$, we have:

$$x_1 = \tfrac{1}{2} a \tau_0^2,$$

$$x_2 = u\tau_0 + \tfrac{1}{2} a \tau_0^2 = \tfrac{3}{2} a \tau_0^2, \text{ since } u = a\tau_0,$$

$$x_3 = \frac{5}{2} a \tau_0^2,$$

so that $(x_2 - x_1) = (x_3 - x_2) = a\tau_0^2$, whence, τ_0 being known and the distances having been measured, a can be calculated.

4. Simple Pendulum.

The theory of this has already been given in Chap. III, § 9; the period, (3.7), is

$$\tau = 2\pi \sqrt{\frac{l}{g}}.$$

In practice, τ may be obtained accurately with a stop-clock; the error in g arises from the interpretation of l and from the ideal conditions assumed in the derivation of the formula. The distance l is usually taken to be the distance from the point of suspension to the centre of the suspended spherical bob. This would be fairly satisfactory if the bob and string moved rigidly; actually at the end of a swing the inertia of the bob will cause it to take up some such position as that shown in fig. 3. Again, the mass of the string has been neglected; in fact, string and bob really act as a compound pendulum of ill-determined rigidity.

In the **conical pendulum** (fig. 3a), the bob is made to describe a horizontal circle, instead of vibrating in a vertical plane. The forces

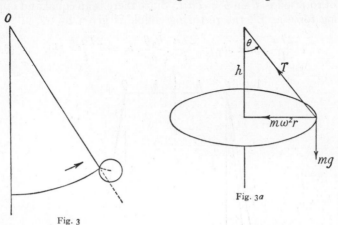

Fig. 3

Fig. 3a

acting on the bob are T along the string, and mg down. Their resultant balances the centrifugal face outwards, $m\omega^2 r$. Hence, by resolving, $m\omega^2 r = T\sin\theta$, and $mg = T\cos\theta$. Thus, $\omega^2 r/g = \tan\theta = r/h$; and $\omega = \sqrt{g/h}$, $\tau = 2\pi\sqrt{g/h}$.

5. Bifilar Suspension.

If a body is suspended by two strings the arrangement is called a *bifilar suspension*. In practice the strings are usually of equal length; when the suspended system is given a slight rotation in a horizontal plane forces are called into play which result in simple harmonic oscillations of the suspended body.

Consider the horizontal rod AB of fig. 4 supported symmetrically by two strings of length l. Let the distance between the two strings be $2b_1$ and $2b_2$ at the top and bottom respectively, and let the mass of the rod be m. When the rod is rotated through a small angle θ in a horizontal plane the rod takes up the position A'B'. Then, from the figure, if T is the tension in the strings before the bar is displaced, for vertical equilibrium

$$2T\cos\phi = mg, \quad \ldots \ldots \quad (6.10)$$

where $\cos\phi = (l^2 - a^2)^{\frac{1}{2}}/l$ and $a = (b_2 - b_1)$.

From the triangle AA'M

$$A'M^2 = a^2 + b_2^2\theta^2 - 2ab_2\theta \cos\left(90° - \frac{\theta}{2}\right);$$

therefore, since θ is small, we have approximately

$$A'M = a,$$

so that the $\angle A'PM = \phi$, and the restoring force along A'M in the plane of rotation is $T \sin\phi = Ta/l$. Since there is an equal and opposite restoring force at B', the restoring couple is given by

$$\frac{2Ta}{l} \cdot \sin a \cdot b_1 = \frac{2Ta}{l} \cdot \frac{b_2\theta}{a} \cdot b_1 = \frac{2Tb_2\theta}{l} \cdot b_1, \quad . \quad (6.11)$$

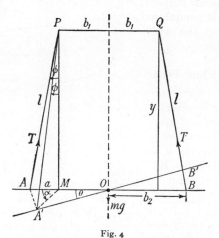

Fig. 4

where θ has been written for $\sin\theta$ and the sine formula has been applied to the triangle A'MO. From (6.10) and (6.11), the restoring couple becomes

$$mg \frac{l}{(l^2 - a^2)^{\frac{1}{2}}} \cdot \frac{b_1 b_2 \theta}{l}. \quad . \quad . \quad . \quad (6.12)$$

Hence, if I is the moment of inertia of the bar about a vertical axis through its centre of gravity, the equation of motion is

$$I \frac{d^2\theta}{dt^2} = - \frac{mgb_1 b_2}{(l^2 - a^2)^{\frac{1}{2}}} \theta. \quad . \quad . \quad . \quad (6.13)$$

If we denote the vertical distance of the bar from the points of suspension by y, $y = (l^2 - a^2)^{\frac{1}{2}}$, so that (6.13) may be written

$$I \frac{d^2\theta}{dt^2} = - \frac{mgb_1 b_2 \theta}{y}. \quad . \quad . \quad . \quad (6.14)$$

Equation (6.14) is of the well-known type of equation (4.22), and the solution for the time of oscillation is

$$\tau = 2\pi \sqrt{\frac{Iy}{mgb_1 b_2}}. \qquad \cdots \cdots \quad (6.15)$$

For the special case where the strings are vertical, $y = l$ and $b_1 = b_2 = b$, hence

$$\tau = \frac{2\pi}{b} \sqrt{\frac{Il}{mg}}. \qquad \cdots \cdots \quad (6.16)$$

Since the moment of inertia of a uniform rod can be calculated and its mass easily found, the acceleration due to gravity may be determined with the bifilar suspension. It suffers from the same disadvantages as the simple pendulum in that the mass of the strings has been neglected and that the whole constitutes a vibrating system of ill-determined rigidity.

6. Compound or Rigid Pendulum.

The accurate determination of g is carried out with a rigid pendulum, the theory of which has been given in Chap. IV, § 5. The type of pendulum commonly used is known as Kater's reversible pendulum and is shown in fig. 5. The pendulum consists of a uniform rod carrying a heavy bob at one end and two pairs of fixed knife-edges K_1 and K_2. An adjustable weight w is also provided, and oscillations are timed with the pendulum suspended first from K_1 and then from K_2. When this is done it is found that for a certain position of w, the period of oscillation τ is the same whether the pendulum is suspended from K_1 or K_2. In this position, the distance l between the knife-edges K_1 and K_2 is, as will be shown, exactly equal to the length of an ideal simple pendulum with the same period as the given rigid pendulum so that

$$t = 2\pi \sqrt{\frac{l}{g}},$$

Fig. 5

and, t and l being known, g is obtained.

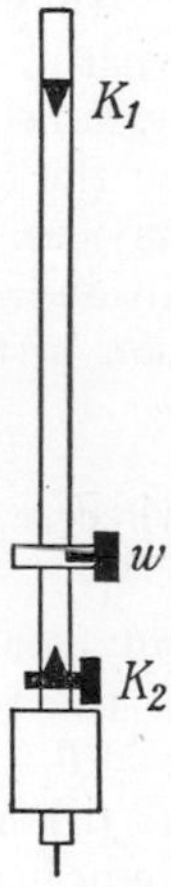

To prove that the distance between K_1 and K_2 is equal to the length of the **equivalent simple pendulum,** let the centre of gravity of the rigid pendulum, which lies between the knife-edges, be at distances l_1 and l_2 from K_1 and K_2 respectively. Then, by applying equation (4.23) to the two positions, we find

$$\tau = 2\pi \sqrt{\frac{I_1}{mgl_1}} = 2\pi \sqrt{\frac{I_2}{mgl_2}}, \qquad \cdots \quad (6.17)$$

where I_1 and I_2 are the moments of inertia of the rigid pendulum about the two axes respectively. Now by a well-known theorem, known as the theorem of parallel axes, the moment of inertia of a system about any axis is equal to that about its centre of gravity plus the product mr^2, where m is the mass of the body and r the distance from its centre of gravity to the axis in question. Hence if mk^2 is the moment of inertia of the rigid pendulum about its centre of gravity, equation (6.17) may be written

$$\tau = 2\pi\sqrt{\frac{m(k^2 + l_1{}^2)}{mgl_1}} = 2\pi\sqrt{\frac{m(k^2 + l_2{}^2)}{mgl_2}}, \quad . \quad . \quad (6.18)$$

whence
$$k^2 = l_1 l_2. \quad . \quad . \quad . \quad . \quad . \quad (6.19)$$

Resubstitution in (6.18) from (6.19) gives

$$\tau = 2\pi\sqrt{\frac{l_1 + l_2}{g}}. \quad . \quad . \quad . \quad . \quad (6.20)$$

But, for a simple pendulum of length l, the period is $2\pi\sqrt{(l/g)}$. Hence **the length of the equivalent simple pendulum is $l_1 + l_2$, the distance between the knife-edges.**

In practice, the distance between the knife-edges is determined with a scale and a travelling microscope. The period τ may be determined with a stop-clock, but the most accurate values are obtained by the method of coincidences, as explained in text-books of practical physics. It must be realized that equation (6.20) refers to ideal conditions. The observed period τ' will be connected with τ by an equation of the form

$$\tau = \tau'\{1 - (\alpha + \beta + \gamma + \delta + \epsilon + \sigma)\}, \quad . \quad . \quad (6.21)$$

where α, β, γ, δ, ϵ and σ represent small corrections.

(i) α arises from the fact that the theoretical equation (6.20) holds only for *infinitely small oscillations*. If the actual angular amplitude of the pendulum falls from θ_1 to θ_2 over the period of observation, $\alpha = \theta_1\theta_2/16$ approximately.

(ii) β is a correction to allow for the *buoyancy* due to the air surrounding the pendulum; this reduces its effective weight according to Archimedes' Principle, discussed in Chap. IX.

(iii) γ is to allow for the *kinetic energy imparted to the air* as the pendulum vibrates.

(iv) δ is a term to take into account the *friction of the air*, which tends to stop the pendulum vibrating.

(v) ϵ is a correction for *temperature rise*, since this would produce an increase in length of the pendulum, with consequent lowering of the centre of gravity and increase in the period of vibration.

(vi) σ is a correction to allow for possible *yielding of the support* on which the knife-edges are swinging. This support is generally an agate plane, and if it is screwed rigidly to a heavy beam the correction is small.

(vii) If the *knife-edges are not perfectly sharp* but are rounded cylinders a further correction is required. However, as Bessel first showed, if both pairs of knife-edges K_1 and K_2 are cylinders with the same radii of curvature the error is automatically eliminated.

The last method of determining g mentioned on p. 53 is discussed later on p. 90.

The measurement of g at sea formerly involved special and inaccurate methods, but the introduction of the submarine with its comparatively steady motion allows the use of the rigid pendulum with an accuracy approaching that obtained on land.

7. Newton's Law of Gravitational Attraction.

We shall now consider the nature of the **gravitational field,** and shall show that there is a close relation between G, the so-called Newtonian constant of gravitation, and g, the acceleration due to gravity at the earth's surface. We have already stated in Chap. II, § 8, that it was Kepler who first enunciated the laws of planetary motion. It was Newton who showed mathematically that the motion of the moon and planets, and the great bulk of the phenomena of celestial mechanics, could be accounted for if it was assumed that a force existed between two bodies of mass m_1 and m_2, inversely proportional to the square of their distance apart. **Newton's law of gravitational attraction** may therefore be written

$$\mathbf{F} = \mathbf{G}\,\frac{m_1 m_2}{d^2}, \quad \cdots \cdots \quad (6.22)$$

where F is the gravitational attractive force, and G is a universal constant termed the **Newtonian constant of gravitation.** Now a circle is a special or *degenerate* case of the ellipse, and we shall show that for the simple case of a circular orbit, Newton's law accounts for Kepler's third law. If we represent the mass of the earth by E and that of the sun by S, the gravitational force of attraction on the earth revolving in a circular orbit of radius d about the sun as centre is by Newton's law

$$F = G\frac{ES}{d^2}.$$

Since this gravitational force is equal to the product of the mass and the acceleration towards the centre, or in other words, balances the centrifugal force outwards, we have

$$E\frac{v^2}{d} = G\frac{ES}{d^2},$$

or
$$v^2 = \frac{GS}{d}$$

where v is the velocity of the earth in its orbit. Now the time of revolution is

$$t = \frac{2\pi d}{v},$$

so that
$$t^2 = \frac{4\pi^2 d^3}{GS},$$

or the square of the time of revolution is proportional to the cube of the distance, as required by Kepler's third law.

It should be noted that the interpretation of d requires careful consideration. For two solid attracting spheres, d is the distance between the centres of the two spheres; but for bodies of less regular shape, difficult integrations have sometimes to be evaluated. To show that a sphere, so far as gravitational action is concerned, behaves as though all its mass were concentrated at the centre, requires rather lengthy mathematical treatment. We shall content ourselves with observing that it is usual to prove the statement first for a thin spherical shell and then to consider a solid sphere as composed of a series of concentric spherical shells. It is important to note that it can also be shown that, for the inverse square law of attraction, a body placed *inside* a hollow gravitating sphere experiences no force. If the sphere is solid, and the body is inserted at a certain depth, the only resultant gravitational force on the body is therefore that due to the smaller sphere, concentric with the original sphere and having a radius given by the distance of the body from the centre of the sphere. This principle is involved in the mine experiments for finding the gravitational constant.

We may apply Newton's law of gravitation to find the force of attraction on a body of mass m at the surface of the earth, supposed spherical. Since, as stated above, the whole mass of the earth may be supposed to be concentrated at its centre, therefore

$$\mathbf{F} = G\frac{Em}{R^2}, \qquad \cdots \cdots \qquad (6.23)$$

where E is the mass of the earth and R is its radius. Now the attractive force of the earth is what gives rise to the weight of the body, and is therefore responsible for producing the acceleration g in the body if it is free to move. Hence

$$\mathbf{F} = mg, \qquad \cdots \cdots \cdots \qquad (6.24)$$

and from (6.23) and (6.24)

$$mg = G\frac{Em}{R^2},$$

or
$$g = \frac{GE}{R^2}. \qquad \cdots \cdots \cdots \quad (6.25)$$

Since g may be determined by experiment with the rigid pendulum and R may be found by trigonometrical survey, it follows that if G is known the mass E of the earth may be found.   Finally, if ρ is the mean density of the materials of which the earth is composed, and the earth is treated approximately as a sphere,

$$E = \frac{4}{3}\pi R^3 \rho. \qquad \cdots \cdots \cdots \quad (6.26)$$

Three important quantities, G, E and ρ are therefore related by equations (6.25) and (6.26), and the determination of any one of these allows the remaining two to be calculated.

The force of gravitational attraction with masses of ordinary size is extremely small.   For example, two equal spheres weighing together a million grammes exert a gravitational force of attraction of little over one dyne on each other when they are situated one metre apart. In order to determine G, therefore, either extremely large masses such as that of the earth itself must be used, or alternatively very sensitive balances must be used to measure the gravitational forces exerted by ordinary laboratory masses.   Both methods have been used, the former now being only of historical interest.   Discussing these briefly first we have:

(a) Bouguer's Mountain Experiment.

The basic idea of this experiment, which was first carried out by Bouguer on Mount Chimborazo in Peru in 1740, was to observe the deflection of a plumb-line from the vertical due to the side-ways gravitational attraction of a large mountain.   If the volume of the mountain is V and its mean density ρ, then the force of attraction on the bob of the plumb-line is $GV\rho m/d^2$, where d is a rather ill-defined distance, taken approximately as that between the centre of the mountain mass and the pendulum bob (of mass m).   The equilibrium of the pendulum is illustrated in fig. 6, whence

$$\tan\theta = \frac{G \cdot V\rho m}{d^2} \times \frac{R^2}{G \cdot Em} = \frac{V\rho}{E}\frac{R^2}{d^2}.$$

It is clear that neither V nor d can be determined with any accuracy, but the method was the first to give some idea of the magnitude of E.

The value of θ was determined from the different directions of the plumb-line with respect to that of a fixed star when its distance from the mountain was d, and when it was very great.

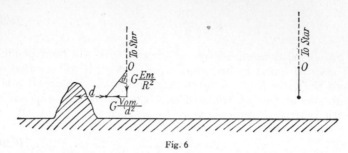

Fig. 6

(a) Airy's Mine Experiment.

In this experiment the times of oscillation of a pendulum at the top and bottom of a mine shaft of known depth were measured and found to be different. This difference is caused by the different accelerations due to gravity in the two positions, since, from (6.25),

$$g_1 = \frac{GE}{R^2}, \quad \cdots \cdots \cdots \quad (6.27)$$

and

$$g_2 = G\frac{(E - M)}{(R - h)^2}, \quad \cdots \cdots \quad (6.28)$$

where g_1 and g_2 are the accelerations at the earth's surface and at a depth h respectively, and M is the mass of the shell of the earth of thickness h. The value of M can be obtained from the expression $M = \frac{4}{3}\pi\{R^3 - (R - h)^3\}\rho$, the value of ρ being estimated from samples of rock taken from various levels down to a depth h. Hence, to a rough approximation, estimates of G and E may be obtained by combining (6.27) and (6.28).

All the laboratory methods depend upon the use of the torsion balance for estimating the effects of gravitational forces between bodies of laboratory dimensions.

(c) Boys' Apparatus.

The experiment was first carried out by Cavendish in 1798; the principle lay in fixing two small spheres to the ends of a rigid horizontal rod which was suspended by a thin metal torsion wire. Two large lead spheres were then placed on opposite sides of the suspended rod and spheres, and the gravitational forces produced a measurable twist in the suspension. The main difficulty in the original experiment of Cavendish lay in the avoidance of convection air currents, for the torsion beam was some 6 feet in length. By introducing the use of quartz fibres for the torsional suspension, Boys was able to reduce the size of the beam without loss of sensitivity. A form of Boys' apparatus is shown in fig. 7. A central vertical quartz fibre T is suspended from a metal disk H termed the torsion head. The fibre carries a horizontal glass beam; from grooves in both ends, other quartz fibres of unequal length hang vertically, each supporting a small gold sphere S. This suspension system is hung inside a glass tube, of internal diameter about 3·8 cm., and is thus protected from draughts. Outside the tube, two equal spheres of lead about 11 cm. in diameter are suspended at equal distances from the axis. The centres of these spheres are respectively situated in the same horizontal planes as the centres of the gold balls so that each lead sphere exerts a large attraction only on the gold sphere to which it is closest. The angular deflection θ is obtained by using a lamp, mirror, scale and telescope, the mirror being the horizontal glass beam itself. The large spheres are then swung to the reverse side of the gold spheres and the maximum deflection in the opposite direction is obtained.   If the couple required to produce unit angular deflection is C, then we have

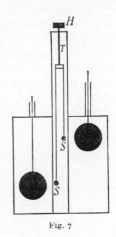

Fig. 7

$$C\theta = \frac{G \cdot mMl}{d^2}, \quad \ldots \ldots \quad (6.29)$$

where m and M are the masses of the gold and the lead spheres respectively, d the distance between the centres of two spheres attracting each other, in the final position of equilibrium, and l is the distance between the centres of the gold spheres, which is approximately the length of the torsion beam. The quantity C is found from the time of oscillation τ of the suspended system, since, if its moment of inertia (a quantity which is calculated for this symmetrical arrangement) is I, then

$$\tau = 2\pi\sqrt{\frac{I}{C}}. \quad \ldots \ldots \quad (6.30)$$

The most accurate value of G is probably that obtained by Heyl in 1930. A torsion balance was again used, but details of the method are beyond the scope of this book.

The dimensional formula for G is obtained from its definition in equation (6.22) and found to be $M^{-1}L^3T^{-2}$. Its value is

$$6 \cdot 67 \times 10^{-8} \text{ cm.}^3 \text{ gm.}^{-1} \text{ sec.}^{-2},$$

and hence the mean density of the earth is found to be about 5·5. Since the density of the surface crust is much less than this, the interior of the earth must consist of materials of high density.

8. Variations of g.

Equation (6.25) was deduced on the assumption that the earth is a perfect sphere, which it is not. The earth is more nearly a spheroid, being flattened at the poles and bulging at the equator. Hence the value of g varies from place to place on the earth's surface. We should expect it to be greater at the poles than at the equator. This is found to be so, although another cause, which we shall discuss in a moment, assists in making this difference greater than it would otherwise be.

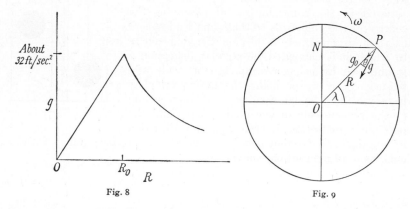

Fig. 8   Fig. 9

We may note here that although from equation (6.25) g varies inversely as the square of the distance from the centre of the earth (regarded as a sphere) for points outwards from the earth's surface, yet, for points in the interior of the earth, g varies directly as the first power of the distance. This behaviour, which is illustrated in fig. 8, may be explained from equations (6.25) and (6.26), for combination of these gives

$$g = \frac{4}{3} G \pi R \rho, \quad \ldots \ldots \quad (6.31)$$

so that for $R < R_0$, the radius of the earth, the acceleration due to gravity is proportionally less.

We must next consider the effect of the centrifugal force, arising from the rotation of the earth, on the apparent value of the acceleration due to gravity at different points on the earth's surface. Treating the earth once more as a sphere, consider with reference to fig. 9 the forces acting on a mass m situated at a point P on the earth's surface. Representing the uniform angular velocity of the earth by ω, the true acceleration due to gravity by g_0, the observed value by g and the angle of inclination between the apparent and true vertical by θ, if we resolve the forces parallel and perpendicular to OP, we have, since mg is the resultant of mg_0 and $m\omega^2$. PN outwards,

$$mg \cos \theta = mg_0 - mR\omega^2 \cos^2\lambda, \quad . \; . \; . \; (6.32)$$

and
$$mg \sin \theta = mR\omega^2 \cos \lambda \sin\lambda, \quad . \; . \; . \; . \; (6.33)$$

where λ is the latitude of P. Hence

$$\tan \theta = \frac{\omega^2 R \cos\lambda \sin\lambda}{g_0 - \omega^2 R \cos^2\lambda}, \quad . \; . \; . \; . \; (6.34)$$

or, eliminating θ,

$$g = g_0\left(1 - \frac{\omega^2 R \cos^2\lambda}{g_0}\right), \quad . \; . \; . \; (6.35)$$

where we have expanded by the binomial theorem and neglected higher powers of $\omega^2 R/g_0$, which equals $1/289$; otherwise: since θ is small, we may put $\theta = 0$ in (6.32).   Substitution of the appropriate values in equation (6.35) shows that the acceleration due to gravity will change by about 0·3 per cent, owing to centrifugal force alone, as we proceed from the poles to the equator. Local variations in the magnitude and direction of g will also occur, owing to irregularities in gravitational attraction such as that caused by the mountain in Bouguer's experiment.

9. Variations in G.

A great many experiments have been performed to test whether G is a universal constant or whether, for example, the interposition of different bodies between two gravitationally attracting masses causes the force of attraction to differ from that to be expected from the simple relation $F = Gm_1m_2/d^2$. We shall see in Part 5 that the force between two magnetic poles and between two electric charges is also that of the inverse square. For these forces, the magnitude of the force depends very much on the nature of the medium separating the centres of force. In the magnetic case, this is said to be due to the **permeability** of the intervening medium. We may state immediately that there is no experimental evidence for what might be termed gravitational permeability. All attempts to detect variation in G due to different materials, temperature change, orientation of crystallographic axes, and so on, have so far produced negative results.

EXERCISES

1. Enumerate methods for determining the acceleration due to gravity and discuss the accuracy obtainable by different methods.

2. Give an account of an accurate method for finding the acceleration due to gravity and point out the corrections to be applied if a very accurate value is required.

3. Write a short essay on Weighing the Earth.

4. Describe in detail Boys' method for finding the Newtonian constant of gravitation.

5. Explain clearly why the acceleration due to gravity is less at the equator than at the poles and deduce a general formula for the acceleration due to gravity in any latitude in terms of its value for a spherical non-rotating earth.

6. Find the acceleration of any solid sphere, rolling down a plane inclined at $20°$ to the horizontal. [$0·24g$.]

7. Determine the acceleration of masses of 200 and 210 gm. respectively attached to an Atwood's machine, neglecting friction and treating the pulley as a disk of mass 100 gm. [$g/46$.]

8. What is the length of the equivalent simple pendulum for a pendulum which consists of a sphere of radius 10 cm. suspended by a light string 50 cm. long? [$60·67$ cm.]

9. Find the time of oscillation of a cylindrical rod of length 100 cm. and radius 1 cm., suspended horizontally by two vertical strings of length 50 cm., attached to points on the rod 20 cm. from each end, the rod vibrating in a horizontal plane. [$0·683$ sec.]

10. Prove that the gravitational force acting on a particle inside a closed spherical mass-shell is zero (Gauss' theorem). Hence show that the shell behaves for external points as though all its mass were concentrated at the centre.

11. Using the results of Q. 10, show that a solid sphere, considered as a number of concentric spherical shells, exerts a gravitational force at external points as though all its mass were concentrated at the centre.

12. If a pendulum is released from rest with its centre of gravity in the same horizontal line as the axis of rotation, determine at what angle the pendulum is inclined to the vertical when the horizontal thrust on the axis is a maximum. [$45°$.]

CHAPTER VII

Gyroscopic Motion[*]

1. Conservation of Angular Momentum.

Consider the experiment illustrated in fig. 1. A man is seated in a chair which is free to revolve about a vertical axis. He holds a bicycle wheel which he supports by a short axle held in the hands. The wheel is given a spin by an outside observer, and the man then moves the axle of the rotating wheel in a sideways direction so that the plane of the wheel becomes vertical. He finds that it requires considerable strength to do this, and he also finds that his chair commences to rotate about its vertical axis. If he moves the wheel back again he finds that his chair rotates back again to its original position. The explanation of these phenomena is the conservation of angular momentum, mentioned briefly in Chap. IV, § 4. We have to consider the system of man, chair and wheel as a whole. Initially the system has a certain angular momentum about the axis of the chair. When the man turns the axle of the wheel so that it points horizontally, the wheel acquires angular momentum about a horizontal axis; this comes ultimately from an external couple applied at the bearings of the axis of the chair. But these bearings cannot communicate angular momentum about the axis of the chair itself, and therefore the angular momentum of the system of man, chair and wheel, about that axis, must retain its original value. It follows that the man and chair must rotate.

Fig. I

If the moment of inertia of the rotating wheel about the vertical axis of the chair is I_1 and its original angular velocity of movement about this axis was ω_1, then for the conservation of angular momentum about the axis of the chair,

$$I_1\omega_1 = I_2\omega_2, \quad \ldots \ldots \ldots (7.1)$$

where I_2 is the moment of inertia of the whole system about the axis of the chair and ω_2 is the final common angular velocity of rotation.

69

Since I_2 is much greater than I_1, the angular velocity of rotation of man and chair is correspondingly smaller than the original angular velocity of the wheel.

The conservation of angular momentum explains the ability of a cat always to land on its feet when it is dropped. The cat achieves this in the following manner. Suppose it is released lying on its back. It immediately swings its legs, head and tail sideways; this results in an oppositely directed rotation of the remainder of its body. Since the latter has greater moment of inertia than the former its angular velocity of rotation is not very large, but it is sufficient to produce a small rotation before the legs and tail have reached the end of their sideways swing. If now the cat were to swing its legs and tail back by the same route as it originally took, its body would rotate back again and the cat would once more be on its back. To avoid this the cat draws in its extremities *radially*. This process introduces no angular momentum and hence the body remains turned through a small angle. The cat then throws its legs sideways again in such a direction as to increase further the rotation of the body and then again draws the legs in radially. Proceeding in this way with sufficient rapidity the cat can rotate itself so as to be feet downwards for landing, for any depth of drop greater than a few feet. The whole process can be watched in detail by means of the slow motion camera. The student is now in a position to see why an acrobat can rotate so rapidly in a curled position, how a diver can perform double somersaults before reaching the water, and how a ballet dancer is able to pirouette so rapidly upon her toes. In all instances a certain angular momentum is imparted to the body by the operator when the body is in a position such that its moment of inertia about the axis of rotation is large. The moment of inertia about that axis is then made small by radial contraction and the angular velocity increases automatically so as to keep the angular momentum constant.

2. Gyroscopic Action.

One form of the **gyroscope** or **gyrostat** consists of a heavy flat metal wheel which can rotate freely about a central axle. This axle is supported in gimbals which are themselves supported on a point, and the whole is counterpoised so that the centre of gravity of the system lies at the point of suspension as shown in fig. 2. The whole

Fig. 2

constitutes a special form of top, and the wheel can be rotated at a high speed either by a string or as in the gyrostatic compass, by an electric motor. Suppose now the axle is held and the wheel is spun, the whole then being released. The system commences with a definite angular momentum about the axis of rotation of the disk, which we shall assume to be rotating in a vertical plane, so that the axis of the disk is horizontal. Suppose a small weight w is suspended on the horizontal axis on the side opposite to the wheel. The weight applies a couple G to the system, and had the wheel been at rest the loaded side would simply have fallen and continued to fall until it met some resistance; but now that the disk is rotating what is observed is a small descent of the weight, after which it ceases to fall. At the same time the whole apparatus commences to rotate or **precess** about the vertical axis of support. The reason for this precession is as follows. We may represent the angular momentum of the disk by the vector $OP = M$, and the couple due to the weight by G. The latter tends to produce angular momentum dM in a vertical plane about a horizontal axis in a time dt. The total angular momentum of the system therefore becomes represented by OP' in fig. 3, where $PP' = dM$. The reason for drawing PP' per-

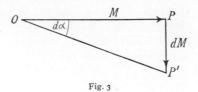

Fig. 3

pendicular to OP is that the angular rotation which the couple due to the weight attempts to produce is about a horizontal axis in the direction of PP', and it can be shown that angular momenta may be regarded as vectors and represented by lines drawn of length proportional to their magnitude and in the direction of the axes about which they operate. In time dt, therefore, the axis OP has rotated through an angle da, given by

$$M da = dM. \qquad \cdots \cdots \cdots (7.2)$$

Now if the angular velocity of precession is ω_p,

$$da = \omega_p dt. \qquad \cdots \cdots \cdots (7.3)$$

Also from equation (4.20) $G = \dfrac{dM}{dt}. \qquad \cdots \cdots \cdots (7.4)$

Hence, from (7.2), (7.3) and (7.4), the angular velocity of precession is given by

$$\omega_p = \frac{G}{M} = \frac{G}{I\omega}, \qquad \cdots \cdots \cdots (7.5)$$

where I is the moment of inertia of the wheel about its axis, and ω is its angular velocity about that axis. From (7.5), the greater the couple G, that is, the greater the weight w, the faster the rate of precession. On the other hand, the larger the angular velocity of the wheel the smaller the rate of precession. Owing to friction, the angular velocity ω of the wheel gradually decreases and consequently, as time goes on, the rate of precession increases, and the dip of the weight w becomes more pronounced.

Perhaps the most important practical application of the principle of the gyroscope is the gyrostatic compass. This instrument is used in the steering of ships and aeroplanes, the magnetic compass now taking secondary place, and being used chiefly as an emergency instrument. The gyrostatic compass consists essentially of a heavy disk which is driven by an electric motor and supported freely in frictionless gimbals. If it is set rotating with its axis in the meridian, then owing to the persistence of the direction in space of the angular momentum, the axis continues to point in this direction no matter how the supporting body moves. Actually, small deviations do arise due, among other things, to the rotation of the earth, with the result that tables of corrections have to be applied to deduce the true meridian at any latitude, just as for the magnetic compass. The gyrostatic compass, however, has the advantages of being free from magnetic disturbance due to the presence of iron, of possessing higher torsional rigidity and even of being able, by suitable coupling, to operate the steering-gear of the vessel.

EXERCISES

1. Explain the precession which occurs when a small weight is attached to the horizontal axis of a gyrostat. How has gyroscopic action been applied to replace the magnetic compass?

2. Describe experiments which demonstrate that angular momentum is a vector quantity. How is a cat able to land on its feet even when it is released lying on its back?

3. A circular disk is spinning about a diameter when suddenly it is held fixed at a point on the circumference midway between the ends of the diameter. Show that the new angular velocity of rotation is $\omega/5$, where ω was the original angular velocity.

CHAPTER VIII

Elasticity

1. Introduction.

The student is now in a position to appreciate the statement that advances in the understanding of nature are achieved by making abstractions. In elucidating the laws of dynamics we have seen that the concept of the material particle and of the rigid body have been of the utmost importance. However, experiment shows that in the vast majority of instances met with in practice actual results are not in exact agreement with those to be expected from a direct application of the laws deduced hitherto. These discrepancies are not due to the theory being at fault, but to over-simplification in our treatment of actual bodies.

No body, for example, is perfectly rigid. When a large weight is attached to a long, thin, horizontal bar gripped at one end, not only are certain forces called into action, but the bar is **bent.** Usually the bending is accompanied by vertical vibrations of the bar which gradually die away. The energy of vibration cannot, of course, by the principle of conservation of energy, have been destroyed; and careful measurements would show that the temperature of the bar had been raised.

We concentrate in this chapter on **elasticity,** the deformation of bodies when subjected to forces. If a body entirely recovers its original size and shape when the deforming forces are removed, it is said to be **perfectly elastic.** If it retains completely its new size and shape it is said to be **perfectly plastic.** Actual bodies lie between those two extremes, but most bodies are nearly perfectly elastic over a certain range of force, and it is with such ranges that we shall be mainly concerned. Some substances, especially single crystals, exhibit different elastic properties in different directions. Such bodies are said to be **anisotropic.** Their treatment is complicated, and we shall only consider substances whose elastic properties do not depend on direction; these are said to be **isotropic.** Fortunately, metal rods, bars and wires, which are the most important elastic bodies occurring in practice, are approximately isotropic in their elastic behaviour.

2. Strain and Stress.

The **strain** of an elastic body may be described in general terms as the change of shape or the fractional change of size (or both) which that body undergoes. It is therefore a dimensionless quantity. The forces which produce the strain are often loosely referred to as the

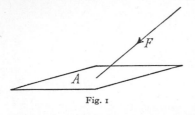

Fig. 1

stresses, but the correct description of **stress** is **force per unit area**. A stress, therefore, has dimensions $ML^{-1}T^{-2}$. It is usual to define the stress more exactly. If, in fig. 1, the force F is acting on the plane area A at an angle to its surface, the normal component of F divided by A is termed the **normal stress,** and the tangential component of F divided by the area is termed the **tangential stress.** The plane area A may be a surface in the interior of a body, separating two portions P and Q of the body. Then P acts on Q across A with a certain force per unit area, and Q acts on P with an equal and opposite force. The force per unit area, in this double aspect, is also called the **stress across** A.

With respect to stress and strain, a perfectly elastic body would exhibit the following properties:

(*a*) A given stress would always produce the same strain.

(*b*) Maintenance of a given stress would maintain the same strain.

(*c*) Removal of stress would result in complete disappearance of strain.

3. Hooke's Law.

We shall now consider the experiment shown in fig. 2. In this apparatus, due to Searle, a frame-work CC'D'D is supported by two vertical wires A, A' fastened to clamps at F. Inside the frame-work rests a spirit-level L supported by the horizontal bar H and the end of the thick screw S. A large graduated drum-head is attached to S and moves over a vertical scale R. From one side of the frame-work is suspended a heavy constant weight M and from the other a heavy scale pan P. The spirit-level is first adjusted to the horizontal position by turning the drum-head on S. A known load is then placed in P, whereupon, since K, K' are loosely pivoted, the increase in length of the wire A' results in tilting of the spirit-level. The distance through which S has to be turned to bring the level back to horizontal then gives directly the increase in length of the wire A'.

In fig. 3 are shown curves which are given by such an apparatus if the load is plotted against the extension. These curves are known as the load-extension, stress-strain, or briefly *p-e* curves for a material. Considering (*a*) we note that for a considerable distance from the origin the curve is a straight line, indicating that the extension is directly proportional to the load. This fact is known as **Hooke's Law.** It is observed to hold in fig. 3(a) up to the point P which is termed the **limit of proportionality.** Further increase in the load leads one to a point known as the **elastic limit.** Up to this point the wire will return to its original length once the load is removed. Beyond this point a

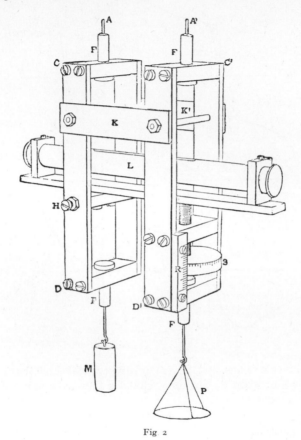

Fig 2

permanent set is produced. The extension is observed to increase very rapidly beyond the point S for only a small increase in load. The material of the wire actually *flows*, beyond S, the so-called **yield-point,** certain sections of the wire decreasing rapidly in diameter. Fracture occurs at the point Z, the value of p_z and e_z being termed the **breaking stress** and the **breaking strain** respectively. We note that the breaking stress in fig. 3(a) is less than the maximum stress at the point B; the latter is a point of unstable equilibrium.

By using suitable apparatus the behaviour of materials under compression instead of extension may be observed. Hooke's Law is again initially obeyed, but eventually fails, and the specimen finally collapses beyond the **crushing limit** S' (see lower part of fig. 3(a)).

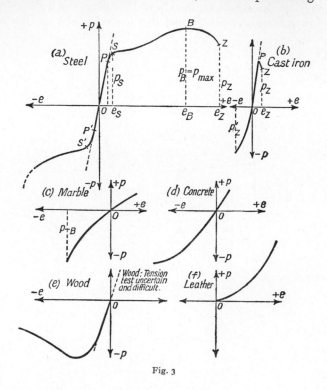

Fig. 3

Consideration of figs. 3(b), (c), (d), (e) and (f) will show that materials like marble and wood do not obey Hooke's Law over any appreciable range.

4. Moduli of Elasticity.

The slope of the p-e curve over the region of proportionality is characteristic of the material of the wire, and is termed **Young's modulus of elasticity** of the material. It is defined as

$$q = \frac{\text{stress}}{\text{strain}} = \frac{\text{Applied load per unit area of cross-section}}{\text{Increase in length per unit length}} = \frac{WgL}{\pi r^2 l},$$

(8.1)

where W is the load, g the acceleration due to gravity, L the original length of the wire, r its radius and l its extension (increase of length) under the load W.

If the load is expressed in grammes, and lengths in centimetres, the formula $WgL/(\pi r^2 l)$ gives Young's modulus in **dynes per sq. cm.** In Engineering, Young's modulus and other similar moduli are usually expressed in **tons per sq. in.**

There are two other moduli of elasticity in common use; these are the **rigidity modulus** and the **bulk modulus** respectively. There is also an elastic constant termed **Poisson's ratio.** These quantities are defined as follows. Consider a cube of side ABCD fixed at the base and under the action of tangential forces in the direction AA'BB' (fig. 4). Equal tangential forces are set up along the sides, CD, CB, AD. The cube takes up the form A'B'CD, that is the volume remains unaltered; such a strain is termed a **shear,** and is measured by the angular deformation θ. As the

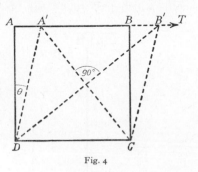

Fig. 4

tangential stress is increased, over a limited range the angular deformation θ increases proportionally and the *rigidity modulus* is defined by

$$n = \frac{\text{stress}}{\text{strain}} = \frac{\text{tangential force per unit area}}{\text{shear}\,\theta}. \quad . \quad (8.2)$$

Finally, if an isotropic body such as a sphere is uniformly compressed simultaneously in all directions it will retain its original spherical shape but undergo a reduction in volume. Over a limited range the fraction (diminution in volume/original volume) or *volume strain* is found to be proportional to the applied force per unit area, and the *bulk modulus* is defined by

$$K = \frac{\text{stress}}{\text{strain}} = \frac{\text{compressive or tensile force per unit area}}{\text{change in volume per unit volume}}.$$

$$(8.3)$$

Since strain has no dimensions, moduli of elasticity have the same dimensions as stress.

Returning to our experiment with the stretched wire, if careful measurements are made it is found that as the extension increases, the radius of the wire decreases. Further, the ratio (decrease in radius/original radius) is proportional to the longitudinal stress. *Poisson's ratio* is defined as

$$\sigma = \frac{\text{fractional change in radius}}{\text{fractional change in length}} = \frac{\Delta r}{r} \cdot \frac{l}{\Delta l}. \quad . \quad (8.4)$$

*5. Rigidity Modulus.

It is not usual to attempt to measure the rigidity modulus with the cubical arrangement used in its definition. The apparatus used is shown in fig. 5, which illustrates *Barton's statical method.* The specimen, which is in the form of a circular wire, hangs vertically, being clamped at A and having a brass cylinder attached firmly to it at B by means of a set-screw. A torsional couple is applied to the wire by cords which pass round the brass cylinder and carry weights in the

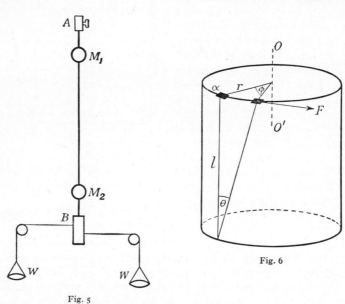

Fig. 5

Fig. 6

scale-pans W. The angular twist in the wire between points a distance l apart is obtained by fixing two mirrors M_1 and M_2 to the wire by means of set-screws and using the usual lamp and scale method. It remains to show that the rigidity modulus of the wire, n, is given by the equation

$$n = \frac{4l\mathrm{W}ag}{\pi\mathrm{R}^4\varphi}, \qquad \ldots \ldots \quad (8.5)$$

where a is the radius of the brass cylinder, R is the radius of the wire, and ϕ is the angle of twist. Referring to fig. 6, consider an element, area α, of the cross-section of the wire at a distance r from its axis of symmetry. Let the wire be fixed at its lower end which is a vertical distance l from α, and let α be twisted through an angle ϕ by an external couple Q. Then, if the tangential stress across a is F, the element of couple which this contributes about the axis is

$$dQ = Far. \quad \cdots \cdots \quad (8.6)$$

Now the tangential stress produces a shear θ in the wire and from fig. 6

$$r\phi = l\theta. \quad \cdots \cdots \quad (8.7)$$

Also, by definition, $n = F/\theta. \quad \cdots \cdots \quad (8.8)$

Hence, from (8.6) and (8.8),

$$dQ = \frac{n\phi}{l} ar^2,$$

so that the total couple Q about the axis is

$$Q = \int dQ = \frac{n\phi}{l} \int_0^R 2\pi r \, dr \, r^2 = \frac{\pi n\phi R^4}{2l}, \quad \cdots \quad (8.9)$$

for the element of area a over which the same force is experienced is the circular annulus $2\pi \, rdr$. Since Q is equal to the applied couple, $2Wag$, this proves (8.5).

*6. Bulk Modulus.

We shall see in Chap. IX that liquids have the property of transmitting equally in all directions any pressure which is applied to them. In determining the bulk modulus, therefore, the body is immersed in a liquid and subjected to a measured hydrostatic pressure. The pressure is usually produced by the action of a piston on a cylinder, that

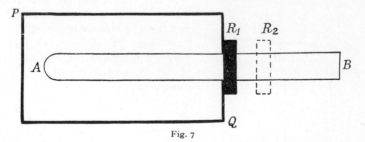

Fig. 7

is, a hydraulic ram. For many years it was possible only to use moderate pressures since at higher pressures the liquid escaped between the cylinder and the piston. In recent years a special packing device has been introduced by Bridgman which allows of pressures up to the bursting point of the container.

To find the bulk modulus of a solid an apparatus of the type shown in fig. 7 is placed inside a liquid and subjected to a high, measured pressure. The apparatus consists of a heavy steel cylinder PQ, enclosing the specimen AB, which is in the form of a rod. The contraction of the rod relative to the cylinder is measured by the movement of a fairly loose-fitting ring R_1, which during the contraction moves to R_2, in which position it remains after the pressure is removed. Correction amounting to a few per cent has to be applied for the increase in length of the container.

The method measures the *longitudinal* strain e, due to the applied hydrostatic pressure. The change in *volume* which a sphere of the material, of original volume unity, would experience under the same pressure as that applied to the rod would be $3e$ to a first order of approximation. This follows from consideration of a cube, the side of which before compression is unity. The decrease in volume is $1 - (1 - e)^3 = 3e$, approximately, since e is small. The high pressures are measured with the *free piston gauge* introduced by Amagat. This consists of a piston which is very accurately fitted to a vertical cylinder, the latter being let into the side of the main vessel in which the compressing liquid is placed. The pressure is then measured directly from the load which must be applied to the top of the piston in order to maintain equilibrium.

We may note that, if the rigidity modulus and Young's modulus have been measured for a specimen, the bulk modulus may be calculated from (8.14).

*7. Relations between the Elastic Constants.

The elastic constants are interdependent, since any change in the size and shape of a body may be obtained by first changing the size but not the shape, as in a volume strain, and then changing the shape but not the size by means of a shear or shears. To deduce the relation, consider a cube of material as shown in fig. 8, with axes of x, y and z parallel to the edges of the cube. Let the cube be subjected to stresses X, Y and Z along these three directions and consider the strains produced. We know from our experiment on Young's modulus and Poisson's ratio that any one of these forces results in an extension of the cube along the direction in which that force acts and a contraction in directions at right angles to this. Since the extensions and contractions are proportional to the forces, if λ represents the constant of proportionality for extensions and μ that for contractions, we have

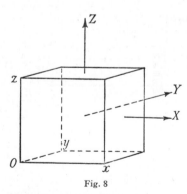

Fig. 8

for the total extensions of the cube in each of the three directions:

$$\left.\begin{aligned}
e_x &= \lambda X - \mu(Y + Z), \\
e_y &= \lambda Y - \mu(X + Z), \\
e_z &= \lambda Z - \mu(X + Y).
\end{aligned}\right\} \quad \cdots \cdots \quad (8.10)$$

We apply (8.10) to the three moduli of elasticity. For *Young's modulus* we are concerned with only one force X, the other two being zero. Hence

$$e_x = \lambda X.$$

But Young's modulus q is, from (8.1), equal to X/e_x, so that

$$q = \frac{1}{\lambda}. \quad \cdots \cdots \quad (8.11)$$

For the *rigidity modulus*, for reasons to be given in a moment, in equations (8.16–8.18), $Y = -X$, $Z = 0$, and $n = \frac{1}{2}X/e_x$, hence

$$e_x = (\lambda + \mu)X,$$

and

$$n = \frac{1}{2(\lambda + \mu)}. \quad \cdots \cdots \quad (8.12)$$

Finally, for the *bulk modulus*, since the forces are applied equally in all directions, $X = Y = Z$, and

$$e_x = (\lambda - 2\mu)X,$$

and, since the volume strain is three times the linear strain,

$$K = \tfrac{1}{3}X/e_x,$$

so that

$$\mathbf{K} = \frac{1}{3(\lambda - 2\mu)}. \quad \cdots \cdots \quad (8.13)$$

Eliminating λ and μ from equations (8.11), (8.12) and (8.13), we obtain

$$q = \frac{9n\mathbf{K}}{3\mathbf{K} + n}. \quad \cdots \cdots \quad (8.14)$$

Also *Poisson's ratio*, by definition, is

$$\sigma = -e_y/e_x, \text{ for the case } Y = Z = 0.$$

Hence from (8.10), $\sigma = \dfrac{\mu}{\lambda},$

or, in terms of K and n, $\sigma = \dfrac{3\mathbf{K} - 2n}{6\mathbf{K} + 2n}. \quad \cdots \cdots \quad (8.15)$

Equation (8.15) may be written $3K(1 - 2\sigma) = 2n(1 + \sigma)$. Since K and n are both positive, $1 - 2\sigma$ and $1 + \sigma$ must have the same sign, so that σ cannot be greater than $\frac{1}{2}$ nor less than -1; this deduction from theory is borne out by experiment.

It remains to show that the statements on which (8.12) is based are correct. We consider the cube in fig. 4 held at the base and experiencing the tangential stress X. It becomes strained through an angle θ into the figure A'B'CD, the diagonal DB increasing in length to DB' and the diagonal AC decreasing in length to A'C. Such extensions and compressions could be produced by the action of stretching and compressing forces Q and P acting in the directions of these diagonals. These forces would have magnitude $F \sec 45° = P = Q$ if F is the actual force producing the stress X in the x-direction, for P or Q resolved in the x-direction is to be equivalent to F, as we see

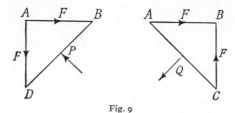

Fig. 9

by considering the equilibrium of the wedges ABD, ABC (fig. 9). Now the diagonal areas of the cube across which P and Q are acting are equal to $A \sec 45°$ where A is the top area of the cube across which the force F is acting. Hence the *diagonal stresses* produced by P and Q are proportional to $P/(A \sec 45°) = F \sec 45°/(A \sec 45°) = F/A = X$. The tangential stress X is therefore equivalent to two stresses X and $-X$ along the diagonals of the cube. If we identify the direction DB with the x-axis of the cube in fig. 8, and the direction AC with the y-axis, we obtain the first of the statements preceding (8.12), namely, $Y = -X$, $Z = 0$.

To show that $n = X/2e_x$, taking the diagonal of the unstrained cube as having unit length, we have

$$\tan \mathrm{DA'O'} = \frac{\mathrm{DO'}}{\mathrm{A'O'}} = \frac{1 + e_x}{1 + e_y}, \quad \cdot \ \cdot \ \cdot \quad (8.16)$$

where we shall insert the negative value of e_y later.

But $\theta = \angle \mathrm{DA'B'} - \angle \mathrm{DAB} = 2\angle \mathrm{DA'O'} - 90°$; hence

$$\tan \frac{\theta}{2} = \frac{\tan \mathrm{DA'O'} - 1}{1 + \tan \mathrm{DA'O'}} = \frac{e_x - e_y}{2 + e_x + e_y}. \quad \cdot \ \cdot \ \cdot \quad (8.17)$$

Now $e_x = -e_y$, so that (8.17) becomes for small angles

$$\tan\frac{\theta}{2} = \frac{\theta}{2} = e_x. \quad \ldots \ldots \quad (8.18)$$

Now, by definition, the rigidity modulus

$$n = \frac{X}{\theta} = \frac{X}{2e_x},$$

which is the other relation used in deriving (8.12).

*8. Bending of Beams.

The bending of loaded beams is of great practical importance in structural engineering; and conversely, observation of the depression of loaded beams in the laboratory gives an accurate method for measuring elastic moduli. When a beam is bent by an applied couple, the filaments of the beam are extended on the outside of the curve and compressed on the inside. The term **neutral axis** or **neutral filament** is applied to the central filament which experiences no change in length. Suppose the rod ABCD, shown in fig. 10, is bent into a circle and that the radius of curvature of the neutral axis PQ is ρ. Considering a filament P'Q' of the rod a distance z ($= $ PP') from PQ, we have

$$P'Q' = (\rho + z)\phi,$$

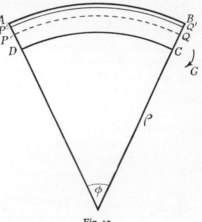

Fig. 10

so that the extension of this filament is

$$P'Q' - PQ = (\rho + z)\phi - \rho\phi = z\phi, \quad . \quad . \quad (8.19)$$

and the horizontal strain is $z\phi/\rho\phi = z/\rho$. If the area of cross-section of the filament is a, then if q is Young's modulus for the material of the beam,

$$q = \frac{\text{stress}}{\text{strain}} = \frac{X}{z}\rho,$$

so that the force across the area is

$$Xa = \frac{qza}{\rho}. \quad \ldots \ldots \ldots \quad (8.20)$$

Consider a cross-section of the beam perpendicular to the neutral axis and cutting it at a point K. The line through K at right angles to the plane of the paper (the plane of bending) lies in this cross-section, and is called its *axis*. The forces such as Xa across the cross-section combine to form a couple, the magnitude of which is found by taking the sum of the moments of the forces Xa about the axis of the section. The contribution of a single force Xa to the couple is $Xa \cdot z = qaz^2/\rho$; hence the total couple or **bending moment** exerted by the stresses in all the filaments which make up the rod is

$$G = \frac{q}{\rho}\Sigma az^2. \qquad \cdots \cdots \quad (8.21)$$

The quantity G must be just equal to the exterior bending couple which has been applied, when the rod is in equilibrium. The expression Σaz^2 is analogous to the moment of inertia as defined in (4.18). It differs in that the element of mass dm has been replaced by an element of area. It is therefore termed the **geometrical moment of inertia** of the cross-section of the beam about its axis. Just as Mk^2 is written for a physical moment of inertia, where M is the whole mass and k is the radius of gyration, so we may write Ak^2 for the geometrical moment of inertia, where A is the surface area. Equation (8.21) is therefore generally written

$$G = \frac{qAk^2}{\rho}. \qquad \cdots \cdots \quad (8.22)$$

We have only dealt with the simple case when the beam is bent into a circle, but the above theory applies to the most general type of bending, provided ρ is taken to be the radius of curvature of the neutral axis at the cross-section, the stress across which we are considering.

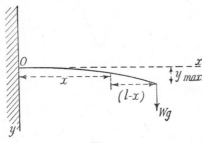

Fig. 11

We shall consider the simple **cantilever** shown in fig. 11. For simplicity we neglect the weight of the beam itself and suppose it to be clamped at one end, and loaded with a weight W at the other. We choose two axes, the x-axis lying horizontally in the position of the undeflected beam and the y-axis vertically downwards. The origin of co-ordinates is taken at O. Now by a well-known theorem in differential calculus, if the curvature is small,

$$\frac{1}{\rho} = \frac{d^2y}{dx^2}. \qquad \cdots \cdots \quad (8.23)$$

Hence, equation (8.22) becomes

$$G = qAk^2 \frac{d^2y}{dx^2}. \quad \cdots \quad \text{(8.24)}$$

Equation (8.24) is the fundamental equation for beam problems; since it is of the second order, we solve it by integrating twice. In this instance the couple, or bending moment, at any point x is $G = Wg(l - x)$. Hence

$$Wg(l - x) = qAk^2 \frac{d^2y}{dx^2}. \quad \cdots \quad \text{(8.25)}$$

Integrating twice, we have

$$A' + Wglx - \frac{Wgx^2}{2} = qAk^2 \frac{dy}{dx}. \quad \cdots \quad \text{(8.26)}$$

and

$$B + A'x + \frac{Wglx^2}{2} - \frac{Wgx^3}{6} = qAk^2y, \quad \cdots \quad \text{(8.27)}$$

where A' and B are constants of integration, the values of which depend on the problem in hand. With our simple cantilever, since there is no depression at the origin, $y = 0$ when $x = 0$. Substituting these values in (8.27), B $= 0$. Again, the cantilever is horizontal at the origin so that when $x = 0$, $dy/dx = 0$; hence from (8.26), A' $= 0$. For this case, therefore, the depression y at any point x along the beam is

$$y = \frac{Wgx^2(3l - x)}{6qAk^2}.$$

In particular at the end of the beam where $x = l$, the depression is given by

$$y_{max} = \frac{Wgl^3}{3qAk^2}. \quad \text{(8.28)}$$

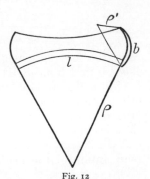

Fig. 12

For a beam of rectangular cross-section $Ak^2 = bd^3/12$, where b is the breadth and d the depth; for a circular cross-section it is $\frac{1}{4}\pi r^4$, where r is the radius. Since all the quantities in (8.28) except q may be measured, this affords a **method of measuring Young's modulus.**

If a bar of rectangular cross-section is used and bent by a symmetrical couple as shown in fig. 12, besides the curvature ρ in the plane of the paper there is an anticlastic curvature of radius ρ' developed in a plane perpendicular to this. It has been shown that the hori-

4

zontal strain e at any distance z from the neutral axis is z/ρ, where ρ is the radius of curvature of the axis. The *lateral contraction* f is similarly given by z/ρ'. Hence **Poisson's ratio** $\sigma = f/e = \rho/\rho'$. The radii may be determined directly by clamping pointers to the rod and observing the distances and angles traversed when a given couple is applied.

9. Energy in a Strained Body.

(a) A Stretched Wire.

The energy in strained systems is obtained by calculating the work done in straining the system. We suppose the strain to be produced in successive small steps, and apply to each step the general formula:

$$\text{Work done} = \text{force} \times \text{distance} = \text{stress} \times \text{area} \times \text{distance}, \quad (8.29)$$

so that the calculation in each case involves an integration. Applying (8.29) to a vertical wire, if the strain at any instant is e, the extension is Le where L is the unstretched length. The stress is qe. Hence the work done in stretching to the final strain e_0 is

$$V = \int_0^{e_0} qe \,.\, A \,.\, L\,de = \tfrac{1}{2}qLAe_0^2 = \tfrac{1}{2}\frac{qAl^2}{L}, \quad . \quad . \quad (8.30)$$

where A is the area of cross-section of the wire, and l is the final extension, given by $l = Le_0$. If the stretch is produced by a weight W, since $q = WgL/(lA)$, therefore

$$V = \tfrac{1}{2}Wgl = \tfrac{1}{2}\frac{W^2g^2L}{qA}. \quad . \quad . \quad . \quad (8.31)$$

Now the loss in potential energy which the weight experiences is Wgl, so that from (8.31) we see that the energy stored up in the wire is only half that lost by the weight. The reason for this is that the other half has been converted into vibrational energy as we shall see later in discussing the oscillations of a spiral spring in § 11(c). With the wire, these vibrations are very rapidly damped by internal friction, and the energy is converted into heat, a slight rise taking place in the temperature of the loaded wire.

*(b) Rod or Wire under Torsion.

If the couple applied to the wire in § 5 is Q, the work done in twisting the wire through a further angle $d\phi$ is

$$dV = Q\,d\phi. \quad . \quad . \quad . \quad . \quad . \quad (8.32)$$

Now from equation (8.9) $Q = \pi n\phi R^4/(2l)$, so (8.32) becomes

$$dV = \tfrac{1}{2}\frac{n\pi R^4}{l}\phi\,d\phi,$$

and the energy stored in the wire is

$$V = \int dV = \frac{n\pi R^4}{2l}\int_0^{\phi_0}\phi\,d\phi = \tfrac{1}{4}\frac{n\pi R^4 {\phi_0}^2}{l} = \tfrac{1}{2}Q_0\phi_0 = \frac{Q_0{}^2 l}{n\pi R^4},$$

(8.33)

where ϕ_0 is the final angle of twist, and Q_0 the final steady couple. If the steady couple Q_0 is applied from the start, the total external work done is $Q_0\phi_0$, which is twice the energy stored in the wire. The other half of the energy is exhibited as *angular* or *torsional oscillations* which are eventually damped by internal friction.

*(c) Bent Beam.

   Considering a filament of the beam of area a at a distance z from the neutral axis, and applying the same reasoning as in sections (a) and (b) we find for dV, the energy in the filament,

$$dV = \int_0^{e_0} qa \,.\, Le \,.\, de = \tfrac{1}{2}qL \,.\, a{e_0}^2, \quad \ldots \quad (8.34)$$

where e_0 is the final strain in the filament, and the unstretched length of the filament is L. Integrating (8.34) over the cross-section, and remembering that $e_0 = z/\rho$, we find

$$V = \int dV = \frac{qL}{2}\Sigma a{e_0}^2 = \frac{qL}{2\rho^2}\Sigma az^2; \quad \ldots \quad (8.35)$$

whence, since $\Sigma az^2 = Ak^2$, and from (8.22) the applied couple $G = qAk^2/\rho$,

$$V = \frac{qL}{2\rho^2}Ak^2 = \tfrac{1}{2}\frac{GL}{\rho}. \quad \ldots \ldots \quad (8.36)$$

The angle ϕ subtended by the beam at the centre of curvature equals L/ρ, hence (8.36) may be written

$$V = \tfrac{1}{2}G\phi, \quad \ldots \ldots \ldots \quad (8.37)$$

which shows its similarity with the torsional equation (8.33). In a similar manner the total work done on bending is $G\phi$, the remaining work $\tfrac{1}{2}G\phi$ being converted into oscillations which are eventually damped.

*10. Spiral Springs.

We require an expression for the depression x of a flat spiral spring when it is loaded with a weight W. If the radius of the cylinder on which the spring is wound is a, and the radius of the wire itself is R (see fig. 13), we may regard the spring, to a first approximation, as a long wire of length l, fixed at one end and subjected to a torsional couple Wga at the other. This torsional couple results in the end being twisted through an angle ϕ, and, from fig. 13, the depression $x = a\phi$. Now by equation (8.9)

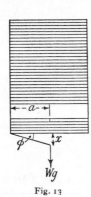

Fig. 13

$$Q = Wga = \tfrac{1}{2}\frac{n\pi R^4 \phi}{l},$$

and therefore

$$x = \frac{2Wga^2 l}{\pi n R^4}. \quad . \quad . \quad . \quad (8.38)$$

The student should realize that this treatment is only approximate, bending as well as torsion taking place in the wire of which the spring is composed.

*11. Vibrations of Stretched Bodies.

We shall consider the vibrations set up when a loaded cantilever, a twisted wire and a loaded spiral spring are given small displacements.

(a) Light Cantilever.

Let the cantilever on p. 84 suffer a displacement y at the end, and then be released. If y_1 is the displacement at time t after the release, then the force F which, if applied at the end, would keep the beam in equilibrium with this displacement is, from (8.28), given by the equation

$$y_1 = \frac{Fl^3}{3qAk^2}.$$

The *restoring force* acting on W is equal to F, but reversed.

Since the mass on the end is W, it experiences an acceleration given by

$$F = -W\frac{d^2 y_1}{dt^2}. \quad . \quad . \quad . \quad . \quad (8.39)$$

Hence (8.38) becomes

$$\frac{d^2 y_1}{dt^2} = -\frac{3qAk^2}{Wl^3}\, y_1, \quad . \quad . \quad . \quad . \quad (8.40)$$

and this equation is of the well-known type of (3.20) where $p^2 = 3qAk^2/Wl^3$. The time of oscillation is therefore

$$t = 2\pi/p = 2\pi\sqrt{\frac{Wl^3}{3qAk^2}}. \quad \ldots \ldots (8.41)$$

Equation (8.41) allows Young's modulus q to be determined for the beam if the remaining quantities in the equation are measured. It therefore affords a *dynamical method for Young's modulus.*

(b) Torsion Wire.

Consider a regular body fixed rigidly to the bottom of a torsion wire, the latter being fixed at the upper end. Then if the body is twisted through an angle ϕ in a horizontal plane, the *restoring couple* is by (8.9)

$$Q = \frac{\pi n R^4}{2l}\,\phi,$$

and hence from (4.17) the body will experience an angular acceleration given by

$$\frac{\pi n R^4}{2l}\,\phi = -I\,\frac{d^2\phi}{dt^2}, \quad \ldots \ldots (8.42)$$

where I is the moment of inertia of the body about the vertical axis of the wire. Since equation (8.42) is of the same type as (8.40), the period of angular vibration is given by

$$t = 2\pi\sqrt{\frac{2lI}{\pi n R^4}}, \quad \ldots \ldots (8.43)$$

an equation which allows the rigidity modulus n to be determined by a *dynamical method.*

(c) Loaded Spring.

The total work done in stretching the vertical spring in § 10 is Wgx, and as in the previous example of a stretched wire, the energy stored in the spring may be shown to be one-half of this. Hence the energy stored is $V = \frac{1}{2}Wgx$, or, from (8.38), by eliminating Wg,

$$V = \frac{\pi n R^4 x^2}{4la^2}. \quad \ldots \ldots (8.44)$$

When the spring is vibrating, the energy stored in the spring is continually being converted into kinetic energy of the vibrating mass and vice versa. We propose to write down the equation for the *total energy* of the vibrating system, a quantity which by the conservation of energy must remain constant throughout the motion. If the vertical velocity of the end of the spring is dx/dt when its displacement is x, the kinetic energy of the vibrating mass is

$$E_w = \tfrac{1}{2}W\left(\frac{dx}{dt}\right)^2. \quad \ldots \ldots \quad (8.45)$$

The spring itself possesses finite mass w, and it remains to calculate an expression for its kinetic energy. Since the upper end of the spring is at rest we assume that the velocity of the spring increases uniformly from a value zero at the upper end to dx/dt at the lower end. If the total length of the spring is l, the velocity at a distance s from the fixed end is $(s/l)(dx/dt)$, so that the kinetic energy of a small element of the spring at the point s is $\tfrac{1}{2}m\,ds(s/l)(dx/dt)^2$ where m is the mass per unit length of the spring. The total kinetic energy of the spring is therefore

$$E_s = \int_0^l \tfrac{1}{2}m\left(\frac{dx}{dt}\right)^2 \frac{s^2}{l^2}\,ds = \tfrac{1}{6}w\left(\frac{dx}{dt}\right)^2, \quad \ldots \quad (8.46)$$

where $w = ml$, the whole mass of the spring. Adding equations (8.44), (8.45) and (8.46), we find the total energy of the system, and since this is constant,

$$\tfrac{1}{2}(W + w/3)\left(\frac{dx}{dt}\right)^2 + \frac{\pi n R^4}{4la^2}\,x^2 = \text{constant.} \quad . \quad (8.47)$$

If we differentiate with respect to t, and divide by dx/dt, we obtain the equation of motion:

$$(W + w/3)\frac{d^2x}{dt^2} + \frac{\pi n R^4}{2la^2}\,x = 0. \quad \ldots \quad (8.48)$$

This is of the form $\dfrac{d^2x}{dt^2} = -p^2x$, and hence the time of vibration is

$$t = \frac{2\pi}{p} = 2\pi\sqrt{\frac{W + w/3}{\pi n R^4/(2la^2)}}, \quad \ldots \ldots \quad (8.49)$$

and we note that the *effective mass* of the spring is one-third of its total mass. Equation (8.49) gives yet another dynamical method for the *rigidity modulus*.

Finally, from equations (8.49), (8.44) and the one which precedes it,

$$t = 2\pi\sqrt{\frac{x}{g}} \quad\quad (8.50)$$

if we neglect the weight of the spring. Hence, measurement of the extension x of the spring together with the time of oscillation of the suspended mass allows an estimate of g, the acceleration due to gravity, to be made.

EXERCISES

1. Define *stress*, *strain* and *modulus of elasticity*. Give an account of the stress-strain relations for a number of substances subjected to longitudinal extension or compression.

2. Describe the experimental determination of Young's modulus of elasticity.

Find the energy stored in a stretched wire of area of cross-section 2 mm.^{2} and initial length 50 cm., if it is loaded with a mass of 1000 gm. and Young's modulus for the material of the wire is 10^{12} dynes/cm.^{2} [1203 ergs.]

3. How may the rigidity modulus be measured by (a) a statical method, (b) a dynamical method?

Obtain an expression for the period of torsional oscillation of a horizontal bar attached at its mid-point to a vertical torsion wire.

4. Deduce an expression for Poisson's ratio in terms of Young's modulus and the rigidity modulus for the material. Show also that for an isotropic material, Poisson's ratio must lie between $+\frac{1}{2}$ and -1.

5. How is the bulk modulus of a solid determined? Calculate the bulk modulus for a specimen of steel, given that Young's modulus and the rigidity modulus for the specimen are 21×10^{11} and 8×10^{11} dynes/cm.^{2}, respectively. [$18\cdot7 \times 10^{11}$ dynes/cm.^{2}.]

6. Obtain an expression for the bending moment acting on a uniform light rod when it is bent into an arc of a circle of radius ρ, in terms of its geometrical moment of inertia and Young's modulus for the material of the rod.

How may experiments based on this relation be used to determine (a) Young's modulus, (b) Poisson's ratio?

7. A light rod of length $2l$ rests symmetrically on two knife-edges a distance $2a$ apart. If a load W is placed at the centre, show that the ends of the rod rise a distance $\dfrac{Wg}{4qAk^2} \cdot a^2(l - a)$.

8. Show that if a vertical flat spiral spring is undergoing vertical oscillations with a mass M fixed to the end, the effective mass is increased above that for a spring of negligible mass by $m/3$ where m is the mass of the spring itself.

9. Find the maximum velocity with which a 500 gm. weight moves if it is attached to a light spiral spring and then released, given that the latter shows a steady extension of 1 cm. when loaded with 100 gm. [70 cm./sec.]

10. Find the period of oscillation of the 500 gm. mass in Q. 9 and the maximum extension of the spring. [0·45 sec.; 10 cm.]

CHAPTER IX

Hydrostatics

The essential property that distinguishes a fluid (that is, a liquid or a gas) from a solid is that the fluid cannot remain in equilibrium under a shearing stress. The force across any surface in the fluid, or across its boundary, must therefore be a normal pressure.

We shall begin with some of the properties of liquids at rest, leaving the properties of liquids in motion until a later chapter.

1. Fluid Pressure.

If we consider liquid contained in a hollow rectangular vessel as shown in fig. 1, the bottom of the container must be exerting an upthrust sufficient to balance the weight of the liquid down, since the forces exerted by the sides are everywhere horizontal. The same volume of different liquids will possess different weights, the ratio of the mass to volume being defined as the **density** of the liquid. Hence

$$\rho = \frac{M}{V}, \quad \ldots \ldots \ldots \quad (9.1)$$

where ρ is the density of the liquid, M its mass and V its volume. The force on the bottom of the container may therefore be alternatively expressed as

$$F = Mg, \quad F = \rho V g. \quad \ldots \ldots \quad (9.2)$$

Since pressure is defined as force per unit area, if the area of the base is A, the pressure on it is

$$p = \frac{F}{A} = \frac{Mg}{A} = \frac{\rho V g}{A},$$

and, since $V = Ah$, where h is the height of the liquid in the container,

$$p = \rho g h. \quad \ldots \ldots \ldots \quad (9.3)$$

The same proof may be applied to any vertical cylinder of fluid within the vessel. It follows that the vertical pressure at any depth d in a liquid is $\rho g d$, assuming that the density ρ remains constant at all depths. This is true for small depths, since liquids are not very compressible,

but at great depths the increase in density with depth must also be
taken into account.

Consider now the equilibrium of a small triangular prism of the
liquid shown in fig. 2. Let the average pressure on the three faces of

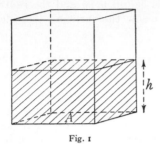

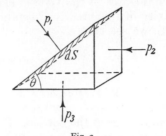

Fig. 1   Fig. 2

the prism be p_1, p_2 and p_3 as shown. Then for equilibrium, if we equate
forces horizontally and vertically,

$$(p_1 \, dS) \cdot \sin \theta = p_2 \cdot dS \sin \theta,$$

and $$(p_1 \, dS) \cdot \cos \theta = p_3 \cdot dS \cos \theta.$$

Hence $$p_1 = p_2 = p_3,$$

or the *liquid pressure is the same in all directions* and is therefore given
by ρgh at any depth h in a liquid of density ρ.

The formula $p = \rho gh$ shows that the liquid pressure is the same
at all points at the same level. This is easily proved independently by

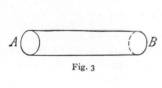

Fig. 3

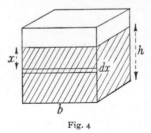

Fig. 4

considering a cylinder of fluid of small cross-section with its axis
horizontal (fig. 3); for the only forces having a component in the
direction of the axis are the forces on the ends A and B.

To calculate the total liquid pressure on one of the vertical sides
of the vessels in fig. 4, consider a small strip of the side of height dx
and breadth b at a depth x. The force on this, which will be normal
to the strip, will be

$$dF = \rho gx \cdot b \, dx$$

and the total force on the whole side will therefore be

$$F = \int dF = \rho g b \int_0^h x\,dx = \frac{\rho g b h^2}{2}. \quad \ldots \quad (9.4)$$

Now the area of the vertical side under liquid is bh and the centre of gravity of this area is a distance $h/2$ below the surface. Considering (9.4), we see that

$$F = \frac{\rho g h}{2} \cdot bh = \text{pressure at C.G.} \times \text{area of surface.} \quad (9.5)$$

Equation (9.5) represents a special case of a very useful general theorem. Suppose now the vertical side of the vessel were free to turn about a hinge at the bottom. Then, owing to the liquid pressure acting horizontally upon the side, unless the latter is held in position it will experience a couple about the horizontal axis of the hinge and will collapse outwards. To calculate this couple, we first consider the elementary couple dG due to the pressure on the small area $b\,dx$ at a distance $(h - x)$ from the base, that is

$$dG = \rho g x (h - x) b\,dx.$$

The total couple is therefore

$$G = \int dG = \rho g b \int_0^h x(h - x)\,dx = \frac{\rho g b h^3}{6}. \quad \ldots \quad (9.6)$$

Now from (9.4), the total horizontal force F on the side is $\rho g b h^2/2$. Hence the total force may be considered to act at a distance

$$d = \frac{G}{F} = \frac{h}{3},$$

from the base. The point where this force may be considered to act is termed the **centre of pressure**. We observe that the centre of pressure of the vertical side is below the centre of gravity of the immersed portion of the side. The student should therefore note that while to calculate pressures on surfaces the pressure at the C.G. is found and multiplied by the area immersed, to calculate couples introduced by the liquid pressure, the pressure at the C.P. is found and multiplied by the appropriate distance from that point to the axis in question.

2. Archimedes' Principle.

The definition of density given in equation (9.1) applies to solids as well as to liquids; that is, it is the ratio of the mass to the volume of a body. Since mass and volume are measured in (pounds, cubic feet) and (gm., c.c.) on the F.P.S. and C.G.S. systems respectively, different numbers are obtained for the density of a body according to the system of units applied. To avoid this complication, a quantity termed the **specific gravity** is sometimes used. This is defined as the ratio

$$S.G. = \frac{\text{weight of given volume of substance}}{\text{weight of an equal volume of water}},$$

and since the weights of both substance and water will be measured consistently in either pounds or grammes, the specific gravity will be a dimensionless number, independent of the units of measurements used. On the C.G.S. system, the gramme is defined as the mass of 1 c.c. of water at its temperature of maximum density. For this system, therefore, the density and specific gravity are numerically equal, although the former has dimensions ML^{-3}, whereas the latter is dimensionless.

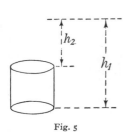

Fig. 5

Consider now the equilibrium of the immersed solid body of mass M and volume V shown in fig. 5. The immersion of the body will have resulted in a displacement of a volume of water V, equal to that of the body itself. If we take the simple case of a cylindrical body of uniform cross-sectional area A, its ends being horizontal, the vertical upthrust due to the difference in pressure on top and bottom will be

$$F = \rho g(h_1 - h_2)A. \quad \ldots \quad \ldots \quad (9.7)$$

But $(h_1 - h_2)A$ is the volume of the body v and $\rho g v$ is the weight of the water displaced. Hence we see that **the immersed body experiences an upward thrust equal to the weight of water displaced** by the body. This is Archimedes' Principle. It holds for a body of any shape; to prove this, consider the body removed and the space filled with the liquid. The liquid would be in equilibrium under the surrounding pressure, which would be the same as before. The surrounding pressure as a whole must therefore be just sufficient to maintain the liquid in equilibrium, and must therefore be statically equivalent to the weight of the liquid, which passes through its C.G. This same vertical upthrust will continue to act if the actual body is now placed in position. The condition of *equilibrium* of an immersed body is therefore that the weight of the body down shall equal the thrust of the displaced liquid up, and be in the same line. Hence, if the body, of mass M, floats with a volume v immersed,

$$Mg = v\rho g, \quad \ldots \quad \ldots \quad \ldots \quad (9.8)$$

and if σ is the density of the body and V its total volume, since $\sigma = M/V$,

$$V\sigma = v\rho,$$

or
$$\frac{v}{V} = \frac{\sigma}{\rho}. \qquad \ldots \ldots \ldots \quad (9.9)$$

Since ice has a density about 0·92 gm./c.c., and the density of sea-water is somewhat greater than unity, the fraction of an iceberg v/V which is immersed is about 9/10 the total volume of the iceberg.

3. Determination of Densities.

We shall consider the determination of the densities of gases and vapours in Part 2, confining our attention at present to the densities of liquids and solids.

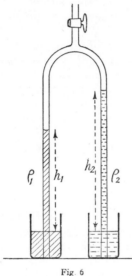

Fig. 6

(a) Liquids.

Of the many methods available, the determination of the relative masses of equal volumes of the liquid and of water respectively is the most direct. The vessel used is termed a **specific gravity bottle.** Another method involves the use of a vertical U-tube in the form known as **Hare's apparatus** shown in fig. 6. The liquid and water respectively are contained in two beakers into which dip the two arms of the inverted U-tube. Suction is then applied at the top, after which the top is closed. The two liquids will now be observed to stand at different heights, but since they are in equilibrium, their pressures down plus the common gas pressure on their meniscuses are equal in both cases to the external atmospheric pressure (see p. 105).

Hence
$$\rho_1 g h_1 = \rho_2 g h_2, \qquad \ldots \ldots \quad (9.10)$$

where ρ_1 and ρ_2 are the densities of the two liquids standing at heights h_1 and h_2 respectively.

The third method we shall describe involves the determination of the loss in weight of a body of known mass and volume suspended from a balance arm, when the body is surrounded by the liquid. The arrangement is shown in fig. 7. If the weights of the body in air and liquid are w_1 and w_2 respectively, the loss in weight $(w_1 - w_2)$ is, by Archimedes' principle, equal to the weight of liquid displaced, that is

$$(w_1 - w_2)g = \rho g v, \qquad \ldots \ldots \quad (9.11)$$

where ρ is the density of the liquid and v is the volume of the body. Such an arrangement is used to find the variation of the density of water with temperature, described in Part II. When the densities of a variety of liquids are known, an instrument known as the **common hydrometer** may be calibrated and used for determining densities. As shown in fig. 8 it consists of a uniform hollow glass tube at the end of which is a weighted bulb. The hydrometer is allowed to float in the liquid and according to the density of the liquid so the depth of the stem will change until the weight of the displaced liquid is sufficient to balance the constant weight of the hydrometer. The stem is then graduated with different densities corresponding to different depths of immersion.

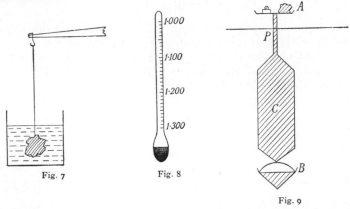

Fig. 7   Fig. 8

Fig. 9

To determine the density of a solid, variations of the specific gravity bottle method may be used. If the solid is insoluble in water, a certain mass of the solid is introduced into the specific gravity bottle, the remaining space being filled with water. The calculation is left to the student.

If the substance is soluble in water, its density may often be determined with reference to some liquid in which it is insoluble, say methylated spirit, after which the density of the latter may be compared with that of water.

The density of a solid which is insoluble in water may also be determined from (9.11), for since ρ is equal to unity and w_1 and w_2 may be measured, v can be calculated and the density of the solid $\sigma = w_1/v$. The experimental arrangement is sometimes made in a convenient form known as **Nicholson's hydrometer**. This consists, as shown in fig. 9, of a hollow cylindrical air-tight container C carrying upper and lower scale-pans A and B respectively. A fixed mark is made on the stem at some point P and the following measurements are made.

Let the weight which must be placed in the top scale-pan, which is in air, in order to sink the hydrometer so that the mark shall lie in the surface of the liquid, be w_1. Now replace w_1 by a given piece of the solid substance whose density is required, and note the weight w_2 which must be added again to sink the hydrometer to the mark. The weight of the body in air must then be $(w_1 - w_2)$. Finally, place the body in the water on the lower scale-pan and note the new weight w_3 which must be added to the top scale-pan again to sink the hydrometer to the mark. The weight of the body in water must then be given by $(w_1 - w_3)$. Hence the density of the body is

$$\sigma = \frac{(w_1 - w_2)}{(w_1 - w_2) - (w_1 - w_3)} = \frac{(w_1 - w_2)}{(w_3 - w_2)}, \quad . \quad (9.12)$$

for the denominator is the loss in weight of the body on being immersed in water, and this must equal the upthrust of the water which is the weight of water displaced, which in turn is equal to the volume of the body on the C.G.S. system. The density of a liquid can be found by Nicholson's hydrometer by observing the weights required to sink it to the mark in the liquid and in water respectively.

4. Stability of Floating Bodies.

Consider the floating body shown in fig. 10(a). It has been given a slight displacement and we observe that the two forces due to the weight of the body and the upthrust of the water respectively produce

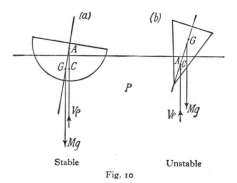

Stable   Unstable
Fig. 10

a couple which tends to rotate the body back to its original position. The floating body is therefore in stable equilibrium. This holds so long as the centre of gravity of the body lies below the point A, where the vertical line from the centre of gravity C of the displaced liquid cuts the line of symmetry passing through the centre of gravity. C is called the **centre of buoyancy**. The point A is called the **metacentre**; to ensure stable conditions the centre of gravity of the body must be as low as possible and the metacentre as high as possible.

With a completely submerged submarine, the volume of water displaced is the same for all orientations and the metacentre and the centre of buoyancy coincide. The condition for maximum stability is in this case simply that the centre of gravity shall be as low as possible.

The *metacentric height H* of ships, represented by AG in fig. 10, is found experimentally by observing the angle of tilt of the mast when weights are moved across the deck. If on moving a weight W a horizontal distance x, the ship heels through an angle a, then from fig. 10

$$Wxg = V\rho g \,.\, H \,.\, \sin a,$$

where V is the volume of immersion. Since a is small, the equation may be written

$$H = \frac{Wx}{V\rho a}.$$

It may be shown in the general case that

$$H = \frac{Ak^2}{V},$$

where A is the area of cross-section at the water-line, k is the radius of gyration of that area about the axis in it about which the body is displaced, and V is the original volume immersed before displacement.

5. The Hydraulic or Bramah Press.

This consists in principle of two vertical cylinders, one A of much larger area of cross-section than the other B, as shown in fig. 11. Its

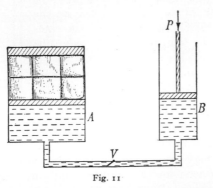

Fig. 11

purpose is to lift and sustain weights far greater than would otherwise be possible. The two cylinders are connected at the base by a horizontal tube containing a one-way valve V which allows liquid to flow from B to A but not vice versa. On applying a moderate load P to a cylinder moving in B, the liquid between B and A is subjected to a pressure p given by $p = P/B$. The liquid transmits this pressure in all directions and, in particular, over the whole surface of A. The latter therefore experiences a force $W = pA = PA/B$, and is therefore able to sustain a load A/B times the load applied at B. The **mechanical advantage** of this machine is therefore $W/P = A/B$. If, however, it is required to lift the weight W a vertical distance h, then, by the principle of the conservation of energy, P must be moved a much greater distance d given by

$$Wh = Pd,$$

or $$d = \frac{W}{P}h.$$

The ratio d/h is the **velocity ratio** (p. 38), and is clearly equal to the mechanical advantage.

6. Compressibility of Liquids.

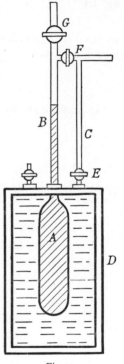

Fig. 12

We have so far assumed that liquids are incompressible, but at high pressures decrease in volume does occur. This was first shown by Canton in 1762, using an apparatus similar in principle to that shown in fig. 12, and termed a **piezometer**. The liquid is contained in the bulb A, and extends into the graduated capillary tube B, the upper end of which is connected to a compression pump and a manometer. The pressure is transmitted to the outside of A by liquid contained in the outer vessel D, which can be placed in communication with the compresser by the side-tube C and the tap E. This tap, together with the remaining taps F and G, allows the pressure to be communicated (1) to the outside only, (2) to the inside only, or (3) to the outside and inside simultaneously. While the last arrangement is all that is required to determine the compressibility, which is defined as the reciprocal of the bulk modulus K (see p. 77), it may be shown that if δv_o and δv_i represent the observed contractions under conditions (1) and (2) and δv_l under condition (3)

$$\delta v_l = \delta v_o + \delta v_i,$$

if the containing vessel is isotropic. This last condition must be satisfied if a correction for the compressibility of the container is to be applied in the simple form

$$\frac{\delta v_l}{v_l} = P\left(\frac{1}{K} - \frac{1}{k}\right),$$

where k is the bulk modulus of the material of the container, v_l is the uncompressed volume of the liquid, and P is the applied pressure. Canton's apparatus, which was improved by Regnault, gave for many years the most reliable values of the compressibility of liquids, but the conditions have since been shown to be subject to serious error, and the values of K accepted at present are those due to Bridgman using an apparatus very similar to that described in Chap. VIII, § 6. The cylinder PQ of fig. 7 (p. 79) contains liquid instead of solid and is compressed by a piston rod which replaces the specimen AB. The displacement R_1R_2 of the sliding piston ring, which takes place when pressure is applied, is almost entirely due to the compression of the contained liquid, the compressibility of liquids being much greater than that of the solids of which the container and piston are made.

EXERCISES

1. What is meant by centre of pressure?
An equilateral triangle lies in a vertical plane with its vertex downwards and its base in the surface of a liquid. Find the position of the C.P. of the triangle. [$\frac{1}{2}h$.]

2. A sphere is floating with one-eighth of its surface above water; find its specific gravity. [245/256.]

3. A thin cylinder of area of cross-section A is closed at its lower end and contains water to a depth a. If it floats vertically in water when immersed to a depth b, find the depth of immersion if the water is baled out of the cylinder and the work done in baling. [$(b - a)$; $Aa(b - a)$.]

4. Write a short account of the methods available for finding the densities of solids and liquids. Give examples of the measurement of important physical quantities where a knowledge of densities is essential.

5. What determines the stability of floating bodies?
A hollow rectangular vessel is closed at both ends and loaded internally so that it floats in equilibrium with its longest sides vertical, when immersed in a liquid to a depth of 20 cm. Find the period of vertical oscillation if the vessel is depressed a small farther distance into the liquid and is then released. [0·9 sec.]

6. Describe the action of a hydraulic press.
If the platform of a hydraulic press has an area of 10 square feet, find the largest weight which can be sustained, given that the materials of a connecting tube of the press will burst under a pressure of more than 15,000 Kgm./cm.^{2} [$1·37 \times 10^5$ tons.]

7. Write a short essay on the compressibility of liquids.

CHAPTER X

Properties of Gases and Vapours

1. Atmospheric Pressure.

The earth's surface is covered with a layer of air some forty miles high and the force per unit area which the weight of this air exerts is termed the *atmospheric pressure*. Unlike liquids, gases are highly compressible, and therefore the layer of air at the earth's surface, compressed by the weight of the superincumbent layers of air, is denser than the air above it. In fact, the density of the air decreases continually from the earth's surface upwards in an exponential manner. Owing to air currents, varying quantities of water vapour and other

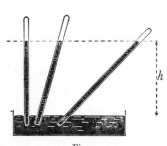

Fig. 1

irregularities, the pressure of the atmosphere is continually changing, varying on either side of its mean value by about five per cent. Consider now the experiment shown in fig. 1 in which a number of glass tubes, closed at one end, have been filled with mercury and then inverted in an open trough also containing mercury. If the tubes are more than about 76 cm. long it is found that mercury will run out of the tubes until the vertical height of mercury is about 76 cm. This statement holds for the inclined tubes as well as for the vertical tube, the tops of the mercury columns all being observed to lie at one horizontal level. Now by the principles of the preceding chapter, the mercury columns must be exerting a pressure given by $\rho g h$, where ρ is the density of mercury and h is the vertical height. This pressure is exerted down into the mercury in the trough, but this mercury will transmit the pressure equally in all directions. For equilibrium the pressure of the air downwards on to the general mercury surface, that is the atmospheric pressure, must therefore also be equal to $\rho g h$. This experiment was first carried out by Torricelli, and the space above the mercury, which contains nothing except a little mercury vapour, is termed a **Torricellian vacuum**.

In Chap. IX (at figs. 1 and 4, for example) nothing was said about

102

the effect of atmospheric pressure within the liquid. But it is easy to show, by the methods already used, that if a liquid is contained in an open vessel exposed to the atmosphere, and if p is the pressure at depth d, then

$$p = \Pi + \rho g d,$$

where Π is the atmospheric pressure.

It follows from this equation that the free surface is horizontal, for if $p = \Pi$, then $d = 0$. The equation may be regarded as stating that pressure applied at the surface of a liquid is communicated to every point within it.

2. Barometers.

The vertical tube in fig. 1 is termed a **simple barometer**, and the atmospheric pressure is usually expressed simply by h, the height of the mercury in the barometer tube. Owing to the variation of g, the acceleration due to gravity, the same barometric pressure may be balanced by different heights of the mercury column. Allowance has therefore to be made for this; the temperature must also be stated, for the density of the mercury decreases with rising temperature. It may be shown that if h_0 is the height which the mercury column would possess at 0° C. at sea-level in latitude 45°, then h_0 is connected with h, the observed height of the mercury column, by the equation

$$h_0 = h(1 - a\cos 2\lambda - \beta H - \gamma t), \quad . \quad . \quad . \quad (10.1)$$

where $a = 2 \cdot 65 \times 10^{-3}$, λ is the latitude, $\beta = 2 \times 10^{-7}$, H is the height in metres of the barometer above sea-level, γ is the coefficient of cubical expansion of mercury which is about $1 \cdot 82 \times 10^{-4}$ per °C., and t is the temperature in °C. An additional correction must also be applied for the **capillary depression** (see p. 119) of the mercury in the barometer tube. This varies with the width of the tube, and is a standard correction for barometer tubes of standard width. The standard barometer is the **Kew barometer**. The former standard was the **Fortin barometer** (fig. 2). This consists of a glass barometer tube dipping into a reservoir the bottom of which is flexible and usually made of chamois leather. As the barometric height fluctuates, so the level of the mercury in the reservoir fluctuates, and since we are concerned with the height of the top of the mercury column above the surface level of the mercury in the reservoir it is convenient to adjust this level always to a constant value. An adjustable screw is therefore used to move a base-plate vertically in contact with the chamois leather until the level of mercury in the reservoir is always such that it just touches a vertical, inverted, fixed ivory pin-point. Coincidence of pin-point and mercury surface is judged by observing when the actual pin-point appears just to be in contact with its inverted mirror image in the mercury surface.

The height of the column is noted from a vernier scale moving over a fixed scale. Contact of the base of the moving scale with the top of the mercury column is judged by observing against the background of a white tile placed vertically behind the column. The scales are usually made of materials whose temperature coefficient of expansion is very small. If brass or steel scales are used, allowance must be made for their expansion in deducing the true height of the mercury column.

It will be realized that the determination of the absolute value of the atmospheric pressure may require tedious corrections. Further, on board ship, the motion of the ship introduces further difficulties owing to the "bumping" of the mercury column. In practice, therefore, a secondary barometer such as the **aneroid barometer,** a diagram of which is shown in fig. 3, is usually used. This, of course, requires calibration against a Kew or Fortin barometer, at some base station. The aneroid barometer consists of a flexible metal vacuum box, shaped in the form of a short cylinder of large area of cross-section.

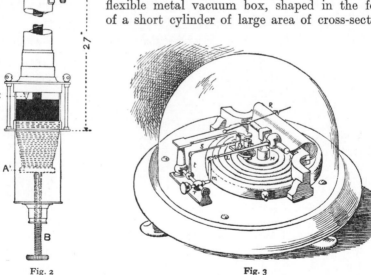

Fig. 2   Fig. 3

This metal container is exhausted of air and then sealed. It is subject to atmospheric pressure outside, and is in a state of considerable strain. Any variation in the external pressure will therefore cause the cylinder to expand or contract, and owing to the elastic properties of the metal of which it is composed, the movement of the cylinder accurately follows the change in atmospheric pressure. By a suitable system of levers the small changes in the movements of the cylinder are magnified sufficiently to move a pointer over a graduated scale so that the atmospheric pressure may be read off directly. The **barograph** is simply an aneroid barometer in which the movements of the cylinder are recorded by an attached pen on the surface of a rotating drum. A permanent record is thus obtained of the variations in atmospheric pressure throughout the day.

3. The Siphon.

The main reason for using mercury in barometer tubes is its high density, which allows the atmospheric pressure to be measured as a convenient height of about 76 cm. A tube containing water could be used, but its height would be about fourteen times that of the equivalent mercury column, while the pressure which its vapour would exert in the Torricellian vacuum would be inconveniently large. Consider now the behaviour of an inverted U-tube containing a liquid and having the shorter limb of the U dipping below the surface of a liquid contained in an open reservoir. Let the longer limb hang down as shown in fig. 4. It is found that liquid continues to run out of the longer

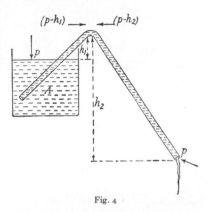

Fig. 4

limb until the level of the liquid in the reservoir falls below the end of the short limb. Such an arrangement is said to constitute a **siphon**. The pressure in the liquid just to the left of the bend is pressure transmitted by the liquid in A up the short limb of the tube. This will be the atmospheric pressure p which acts on A less the pressure of the vertical height h_1 of the liquid contained in the short limb. (For brevity we suppose p to be expressed as a height of the liquid.) Similarly the pressure at a point in the liquid just to the right of the bend will be that transmitted by the liquid up the longer arm of the siphon. This is the atmospheric pressure acting on the open end of the longer limb less the pressure of the vertical height h_2 of liquid in the longer limb. Since $(p - h_1)$ is greater than $(p - h_2)$ there is a resultant pressure driving the liquid along the tube, and this motion will continue until all the liquid in the reservoir has been emptied from above the bottom of the short limb. If the vertical height of the shorter limb is greater than the barometric height for the liquid used, that is, if $h_1 > p$, the siphon will cease to work since the driving pressure is, as we have seen, $(p - h_1)$.

4. Pumps for Liquids.

(a) Suction Pump.

The operation of a suction-pump is shown in fig. 5. The pump consists of a vertical cylinder in which slides a piston operated by the pump-handle. On raising the piston, a vacant space—actually a vacuum—would be left below the piston. The valve at B therefore

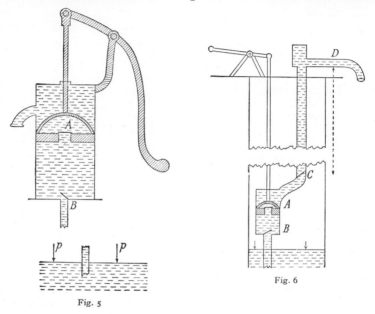

Fig. 5

Fig. 6

opens upwards admitting liquid, since while there is no pressure above it, atmospheric pressure is transmitted through the liquid from the surface of the well and acts on the under surface of the valve. This process continues until the piston reaches the top of its motion. When the piston moves down, the valve B is pushed down and closed by the pressure transmitted through the liquid, but the valve A in the piston is opened by the pressure underneath it, and the liquid is therefore pushed out through the spout. We note that the space above the piston must be open to the atmosphere, otherwise a vacuum would be created here as the piston moved down.

(b) Force Pump.

If the surface of the liquid in the well is lower than the barometric height for the given liquid, then the pump will not work, since the upward pressure is, as we have seen with the siphon, $(p - h)$, where p is the atmospheric pressure and h the height of the pipe above the surface of the liquid. There is therefore no point in making a water well deeper than about 34 feet if it is to be operated by a suction pump. On the other hand, by the use of a force pump the depth may be considerably increased. As shown in fig. 6 the force pump contains three valves A, B and C. The lower valve B is operated by atmospheric pressure just as for a suction pump, but the upper valve C is forced open by the upward movement of the pump rod controlled by the operator. This valve closes when the piston is moved down, owing to the weight of the head of water above it. The limit to the height which may be reached is determined by the strength of the operator, who has to overcome the downward pressure of the liquid column DC. If the pump is operated by a machine the limiting factor is the strength of the valves, and in practice the height through which water can be raised by a force pump is about 300 feet.

5. Boyle's Law.

Consider the apparatus shown in fig. 7. A quantity of dry air is enclosed in a glass tube and may be compressed by raising the mercury reservoir to which the glass tube is connected by indiarubber pressure tubing. When the level of the mercury is the same in both arms the pressure of the air enclosed in the tube must just equal the atmospheric pressure, otherwise the mercury would move under the pressure difference. If now the mercury is raised in the open reservoir it is found that the level of the mercury in the closed limb does not quite follow it, and in the position of equilibrium there is a steady difference in levels between the two columns of mercury. Calling this difference h, the pressure exerted by the enclosed air must be sufficient to sustain both atmospheric pressure p and also this height of mercury; it is therefore $(p + h)$. The volume of the enclosed gas may also be noted, if the tube has been calibrated; usually it is assumed that the tube is of uniform cylindrical bore, in which case the volume is proportional to the length of the air space. This is measured directly with a scale fixed to the apparatus:

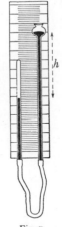

Fig. 7

the scale also allows the height of the mercury in the open limb to be measured. As the pressure $(p + h)$ is increased, the volume v decreases, and pressure-volume measurements show that

$$(p + h)v = \text{constant.} \quad \ldots \quad \ldots \quad (10.2)$$

Equation (10.2) expresses *Boyle's Law*, which states that the *volume*

*occupied by a gas is inversely proportional to its pressure, if the temper-
ature is constant.*

Since the mass m of the contained gas remains constant and the
density ρ is defined as m/v, the density must vary directly as the
pressure. In conducting the experiment, a moment or two must be
allowed to elapse between adjusting the pressure to a new value and
measuring the new volume. This is because alteration of the pressure
on a gas causes its temperature to change, and Boyle's law is true only
for constant temperatures. The temperature soon returns to its
original value, and in this way a series of values of $(p + h)$ and v are
obtained. It is usual to plot a graph of $(p + h)$ against $1/v$ whereupon
a straight line is obtained passing through the origin. If the atmospheric pressure is not known, then, since it will remain constant over
the time of the experiment, it is sufficient to plot h against $1/v$. A
straight line is then obtained which cuts the axis of $1/v$ at a point where
$h = -p$, thus allowing the atmospheric pressure to be determined
indirectly. If $(p + h)$ is plotted against v instead of against $1/v$, the
curve obtained is a hyperbola, since it corresponds to the curve
$xy = $ const. We shall describe the determination of the density of
gases and vapours in Part II, where also an account will be given
of the deviations of gases from Boyle's law.

6. Air Pumps.

(a) Mechanical Pumps.

The simplest type of mechanical pump works on identically the
same principle as the suction pump for liquids, described on p. 106,
a vessel filled with air, which it is desired to evacuate, taking the
place of the well. On raising the piston, a vacuum is created below it,
the air below the valve exerts sufficient pressure to raise the valve
and escapes into the cylinder space. This process continues until the
piston reaches the top of its motion. When it descends, the gas beneath it is compressed and therefore, by Boyle's law, its pressure rises.
The valve B therefore closes and as the pressure goes on rising it ultimately exceeds atmospheric pressure whereupon the valve A opens
and the gas is expelled. To ensure that the joint between the piston
and the cylinder shall be air-tight, liberal use is made of sealing oil.
The limit to the vacuum obtainable is reached when the compression
of the gas in the cylinder, which occurs at downstroke, is insufficient
to raise the pressure of the enclosed gas above atmospheric pressure.

Gas pressure is usually expressed in mm. of mercury; a simple
mechanical pump will not reduce the pressure much below 1 mm. of
mercury. Modern mechanical pumps are very much more efficient;
in fig. 8 are shown four stages in the process of evacuation by a Cenco-
Hyvac pump. A cylindrical metal rotor A is mounted excentrically

in a cylinder. Through the wall of the outer cylinder slides a vane C; it is pressed in contact with A by a spring arm D. The vessel to be exhausted is connected to E and the exhaust is through the outward-opening valve at L. The pump is immersed in oil. In the first position (*a*), gas has just been admitted via E to the crescent-shaped space. In the second position (*b*), the gas has been compressed as the excentric rotor revolves, and fresh gas is admitted behind the rotor. Further compression follows in the stage (*c*), and finally at the stage (*d*) the

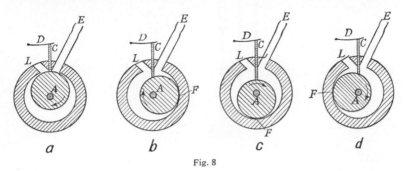

Fig. 8

valve L opens and the gas is expelled, for it has been compressed until its pressure is greater than atmospheric pressure. The pump is generally constructed in two parts, the first part exhausting directly to atmosphere and the second part supplying the gas to the first part. *The speed of pumping* is about 6 litres a minute and the vacuum obtainable about 10^{-3} mm. of mercury.

(*b*) Liquid Pumps.

In figs. 9, 10, 11 are shown diagrams of three pumps all of which depend on the motion of liquid past an orifice for their pumping action. In the **filter pump** the jet of water which issues from the tube A and passes down B entraps gas which has passed over from the vessel to be exhausted through the tube C. The process of trapping is continuous but the vacuum attainable is only a few cm. of mercury. This is partly due to the high vapour pressure of water.

A jet of mercury is much more efficient, and on this principle are based the Sprengel and Töpler pumps shown in figs. 10 and 11 respectively. In the **Sprengel pump** the arm A is raised so that mercury flows along the inverted U-tube. As the mercury passes the tube at the top of the U, which communicates with the vessel to be exhausted, it breaks up into pellets, and between the pellets is enclosed a small air-bubble. The exhausting process is extremely slow and laborious, as the mercury has to be collected and replaced in the reservoir periodically, but a vacuum as high as 10^{-5}mm. of mercury may eventually be obtained. The **Töpler pump** works on a similar principle, except that the gas is allowed to expand into a fairly large bulb B, so that

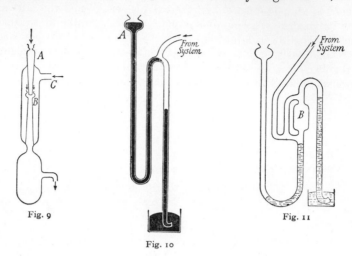

Fig. 9

Fig. 10

Fig. 11

the exhausting process is somewhat more rapid than with the Sprengel pump.

(c) Vapour Pumps.

For obtaining the highest possible vacua, such as are required in some wireless valves and X-ray tubes, instead of liquid as in the Sprengel and Töpler pumps, the passage of vapour past an orifice is used. In fig.

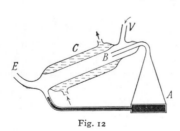

Fig. 12

12 is shown a simple form of **condensation pump.** Mercury is boiled in the vessel A and mercury vapour passes out through the jet B. This orifice is surrounded by a Liebig's condenser C so that the mercury vapour jet is condensed, but not before gas expanding over from V, the vessel to be evacuated, has been caught in the unidirectional jet of vapour. The mercury is returned to the boiler A, but the gas escapes through the exhaust E. Such a pump will not exhaust directly from atmospheric pressure; it is therefore used in conjunction with, say, a Cenco-Hyvac pump. The vapour pump therefore is supplied with an initial "backing" vacuum supplied by its "backing" pump. It is then able to carry the vacuum to 10^{-6} or 10^{-7} mm. of mercury.

(*d*) **Other Processes.**

To obtain vacua much higher than 10^{-6} mm. of mercury, **chemical processes** are usually used. Thus many gases are rapidly absorbed by coco-nut charcoal when the latter is surrounded by liquid air (see Part II). Hydrogen may be eliminated by its affinity for palladium or platinum black. Traces of oxygen and other gases are sometimes removed by " flashing ". In this process, which is largely used in wireless valve construction, a metal such as magnesium or calcium is placed on the filament and suddenly vaporized by passing a large electric current momentarily through the filament. Much of the vaporized metal condenses as a bright mirror on the glass walls of the valve, but at the same time the oxygen or other gas has combined with some of the metal to form a compound with negligible vapour pressure.

7. Measurement of Gas Pressures.

Large pressures of several thousand atmospheres may be measured with the free piston gauge described on p. 80, the pressure being transmitted by some liquid buffer between gas and gauge. *Secondary gauges* are often used in practice, for example, to measure steam pressure. The simplest of these is the **Bourdon spring gauge,** which consists of a plane spiral of metal tubing flattened at the closed end. When the pressure is transmitted down the tubing the spiral tends to straighten out, and a pointer may be made to register the pressure.

Moderate pressures are measured with **manometers.** The common manometer is a U-tube containing mercury. One side is left open to the atmosphere, and the other limb is connected to the vessel the pressure of whose contents is required. The difference in height of the mercury in the two limbs added to the atmospheric pressure gives the total pressure in the vessel. To obtain an appreciable difference in level when the pressure is not very different from that of the atmosphere, a liquid of small density, such as paraffin oil, is used in the manometer instead of mercury.

To measure low pressures, such as those produced by the vacuum pumps described in this chapter, a great many manometers are available, depending on the different physical properties of gases at low pressures. For example, gauges based on the viscous friction of gases and on their thermal conductivity are available. The discussion of these is beyond the scope of this book (but compare Part II). Fortunately, however, they are all secondary gauges. They are calibrated against the **McLeod gauge,** the operation of which the student will readily understand. In fig. 13 is shown Gaede's modification of the McLeod gauge. Gas from the system whose pressure is required enters the gauge through B and fills it down to the level of the mercury reservoir

G. The reservoir is then raised, cutting off the gas present in the bulb H and compressing it into the capillary extension which lies along the scale KK_1. The mercury rises faster in the left-hand arm, and may be made to stand at any arbitrary height in the tube A above that in the closed tube. If the required gas pressure is p, and the total volume of H and the capillary extension is V, then applying Boyle's law to the mass of gas enclosed in this bulb and eventually compressed in the capillary, we have

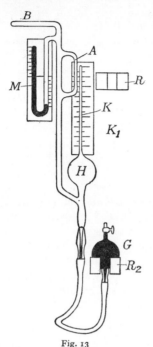

Fig. 13

$$pV = (p + h)V', \quad . \quad (10.3)$$

where h is the height of the mercury in the tube A above the level of the mercury in the capillary tube, and V' is the volume the gas now occupies in the capillary tube. Since h is a few cm. and p is much less than 1 mm., equation (10.3) may be written

$$pV = hV'$$

or

$$p = h \frac{V'}{V}. \quad . \quad (10.4)$$

Pressures from 100 mm. to 1 mm. can be read directly on the manometer M, which is simply an exhausted U-tube filled with mercury in the left-hand limb. Pressures from 1 mm. to 10^{-4} mm. may be read on the scale KK_1. We should note that the pressures registered by all gauges which contain liquids as the working substance register the vapour pressure of this liquid simultaneously with the pressure which it is desired to measure.

EXERCISES

1. Describe the construction of a standard mercury barometer, indicating what corrections are necessary to reduce the observed reading of atmospheric pressure to the accepted standard conditions.

2. Explain the action of (a) a force pump, (b) a suction pump.

Find an expression for the pressure inside a vessel of volume V (initially atmospheric pressure) at the end of the nth stroke of an ordinary mechanical air-pump, the volume of whose cylinder is v.

$$\left[P_n = p_1 \left(\frac{V}{V + v} \right)^n \right].$$

3. How may a very low gas pressure such as that required in a vacuum electric filament lamp be obtained? By what means is such a low gas pressure measured?

4. State Boyle's law, giving two examples of practical applications of the law involving quantitative results.

5. A spherical diving chamber contains air initially at atmospheric pressure and has a small opening at the bottom of its lower surface. How deep is the centre of the chamber below a water surface when the water has risen so as to half-fill the chamber? [10·34 m.]

6. If the chamber in Q. 5 is 10 m. in diameter, what volume of air at atmospheric pressure must be pumped into the chamber so as to expel the water completely? $\left[\dfrac{500\pi}{3} \cdot \dfrac{15\cdot34}{10\cdot34} \text{ c. metres.} \right]$

CHAPTER XI

Properties of Liquids at Rest

1. Surface Tension.

If a small quantity of mercury is dropped on to a wooden bench, it is found that it splits up into a number of different-sized globules. The larger globules are oblate spheroids, while the smaller are nearly perfect spheres. This spherical shape is also shown by small water drops issuing from a jet. If the mercury drops are distorted from their equilibrium shape by slight pressure from the finger, it is found that they return to their original shape when the pressure is released. This behaviour is so like that of a child's rubber balloon that the phenomenon is ascribed to **surface tension**; that is, the liquid drop behaves as though there were skin under a tension stretched over its surface. This assumption is very useful, as it enables us to predict the behaviour of the surface forces in liquids in a great many instances, but we shall now proceed to show from the molecular hypothesis that the apparent existence of forces and tensions *parallel* to the surface really arises from forces in the liquid which act *normal* to the surface.

2. Molecular Theory of Surface Tension.

We assume that the molecules of a liquid exert an attraction on each other somewhat analogous to the gravitational attraction that exists between all bodies. The forces are actually electrical and not gravitational, as the student will understand by reference to Part V; gravitational forces are far too small to produce the observed experimental effects. If we knew the precise law of force according to which each molecule attracted the others, it would be possible to calculate mathematically the behaviour of liquids. Unfortunately the liquid state is too vague (being somewhere intermediate between the solid state, where the molecules have no translational motion, and the gas state, where the molecules have almost free translational motion) to allow us to formulate a definite law of attraction, but Laplace introduced a working hypothesis based on the conception of a **radius of molecular attraction**. According to this idea, each molecule is considered to exert attractive forces on the molecules surrounding it for a certain radius c, but beyond this distance the force of attraction is

114

considered to be zero. In actual fact the force of attraction must fall off continuously as the distance increases, but the admittedly approximate assumption of the radius of molecular attraction provides a very useful tool in qualitative and, in some cases, quantitative work. For example, consider a molecule A situated in the first instance at a distance greater than the radius of molecular attraction below the surface of the liquid as in fig. 1(a), and in the second instance at a distance less than the radius of molecular attraction from the surface as in fig. 1(b). Then in the first case the molecule will experience no resultant force as it is attracted equally in all directions, but in the second case there will be more molecules attracting it from below than

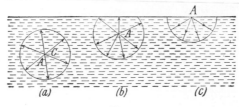

Fig. 1

from above. This downward force will be a maximum for molecules in the liquid surface since there is now a completely unbalanced hemisphere of forces acting from below on the molecule. The molecule will therefore experience a force normal to the surface of the liquid, and these normal forces acting over the whole surface of an isolated portion of the liquid such as constitutes a drop will cause that surface to take up a curved shape just as though there were an elastic skin producing a surface tension in the surface of the liquid (see end of § 3).

3. Definition of Surface Tension.

We shall use the convenient fiction of a tension acting in the surface of a liquid freely in our subsequent discussion. **Surface tension is defined as the force per unit length acting on either side of any line drawn in the surface of a liquid,** the direction of the force being tangential to the surface and perpendicular to the line. To illustrate this definition consider a soap-film supported by a wire frame as in fig. 2. If the frame is vertical and the wire AB is free to move, it will move down, stretching the film until the surface tension force up equals the weight of the wire down. Representing the mass of the latter by w, for equilibrium, we have

$$wg = 2Tl, \qquad \ldots \ldots \quad (11.1)$$

where l is the horizontal length of AB across which the surface tension T acts. The factor 2 is introduced since the film has two sides. From

(11.1) we see that surface tension is a *force per unit length*, and there-fore has dimensions MT^{-2}.

Consider next the rectangular frame-work shown in fig. 3, and let this frame-work be horizontal. Let the cross-wire PQ, of length l, be pulled a distance x along the frame-work, thus increasing the area of each side of the film by $A = lx$. The work done, W, against the surface tension forces is

$$W = 2Tl \cdot x = 2TA. \quad \ldots \ldots \quad (11.2)$$

We see that (11.2) gives a second definition of surface tension, for since the total increase in area of the film is $2A$, the **surface tension may be defined as the work done in increasing the area of the film by unit amount.** This work done is stored up as energy in the stretched film and can be regained if the film is allowed to contract. *Surface*

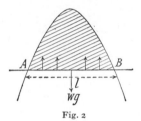

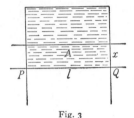

Fig. 2   Fig. 3

tension and **surface energy** are thus closely connected. However, it is found experimentally that unless special precautions are taken, the value for T obtained by methods based on (11.2) is different from the value obtained by methods based on (11.1). The reason is that the second is a dynamical method, and when contractions and expansions of a film take place, temperature changes occur and **thermal energy** is also involved. The two methods give the same result if we stipulate that the energy change must be arranged to take place without change of temperature, that is, under **isothermal conditions.**

The concept of surface tension as energy per unit area affords us an explanation why small drops of liquid are spherical. All systems tend to the condition where their **total potential energy is a minimum,** and the body which has the least surface area (corresponding to the least surface energy) for a given volume is the sphere. Large drops are flattened into oblate spheroids because their gravitational energy would be greater if the centre of gravity of the drop were at the centre of a sphere of the same volume as the spheroid.

4. Pressure Difference over a Curved Surface.

Consider a small curvilinear rectangle ABCD (fig. 4, *a* and *b*) of the curved surface of a film. Let the sides have lengths δl_1 and δl_2

and let the radii of curvature of these sides be R_1 and R_2. Suppose the film is in equilibrium with an excess pressure p on one side of the film. To find the relation between the surface tension T and the excess pressure p, we apply the principle of virtual work; that is, we suppose the film to expand, and equate the work done by the pressure to the work done against the surface tension of the film as its area is increased. If the sides of the film increase by the fractions of their lengths, a_1 and a_2, the increase in the area of *one side* is

$$\delta A = \delta l_1(1 + a_1) \cdot \delta l_2(1 + a_2) - \delta l_1 \cdot \delta l_2,$$

so that the work done against surface tension is

$$\delta W = T \delta l_1 \delta l_2 (a_1 + a_2), \quad \cdots \cdots \quad (11.3)$$

neglecting the small product $a_1 a_2$.

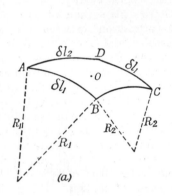

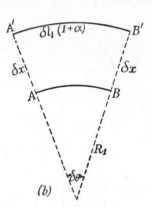

(a)

(b)

The work done by the pressure is

$$\delta W = p \cdot A \cdot \delta x = p \cdot \delta l_1 \delta l_2 \delta x. \quad \cdots \quad (11.4)$$

But, from fig. 4(b),

$$a_1 \cdot \delta l_1 = (R_1 + \delta x)\delta\theta - R_1 \cdot \delta\theta = \delta x \cdot \delta\theta = \delta x \cdot \frac{\delta l_1}{R_1};$$

hence $a_1 = \delta x / R_1$, and similarly $a_2 = \delta x / R_2$.

Substituting these values of a_1 and a_2 in (11.3), and comparing with (11.4), we find

$$p = T\left(\frac{1}{R_1} + \frac{1}{R_2}\right). \quad \cdots \cdots \quad (11.5)$$

5

(H 394)

Equation (11.5) is very useful and allows us to calculate, for example, the excess pressure which must exist inside a spherical soap-bubble. In this case $R_1 = R_2 = R$, and there are two sides to the film, so (11.5) becomes

$$p = \frac{4T}{R}. \qquad \ldots \ldots \quad (11.6)$$

The excess pressure therefore varies inversely as the radius of the bubble, and if two bubbles of different radii are connected by a common tube the larger bubble will grow at the expense of the smaller since the air pressure in the latter is greater than that in the former.

5. Angle of Contact.

If water is contained in a narrow vertical glass tube, it is found on examination that the surface of the water is not level, but is higher

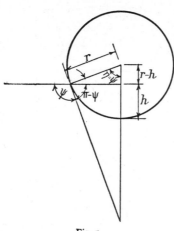

Fig. 5

at the edges where it is in contact with the glass than at the centre. The attraction between the water molecules and the glass is greater than the attraction between water molecules themselves. With mercury the reverse is true and consequently the surface is convex. If careful examination is made of the behaviour of the liquid where it meets the solid it is found that with mercury the two surfaces meet at an angle of about 160°. This angle is said to be the **angle of contact.** For a liquid like water which wets the surface the angle of contact is zero. Measurement of the angle of contact may be carried out with Ablett's apparatus shown in fig. 5. A cylinder with its axis horizontal is lowered into the liquid until the liquid surface appears horizontal at the line of contact with the cylinder. Then

$$\cos\psi = \frac{h - r}{r}, \qquad \ldots \ldots \quad (11.7)$$

where ψ is the angle of contact. Analogous measurements are taken with the cylinder rotating in clockwise and anticlockwise directions so that a mean of two values may be obtained, the values corresponding to liquid advancing or receding over the surface of the solid.

6. Methods of Measuring Surface Tension.

(a) Capillary Tube Method.

If a fine capillary tube is placed vertically with one end beneath the surface of a liquid, either a rise or a depression of the liquid in the tube occurs with respect to the general level of the liquid outside the tube. The rise occurs with liquids whose angle of contact ψ is less than 90°; a diagram of such a case is shown in fig. 6. When the liquid column is in equilibrium the weight of the liquid column acting downwards must be just balanced by the *surface tension force* or *capillary attraction* upwards. The liquid column consists of the cylinder of volume $V = \pi r^2 h$, and the meniscus, which may be shown by elementary mensuration to have a volume $v = \pi r^3$ $(\sec\psi + \tfrac{2}{3}\tan^3\psi - \tfrac{2}{3}\sec^3\psi)$. This assumes that the surface of the liquid is in the shape of a spherical cap.   Hence, equating the two forces, we have

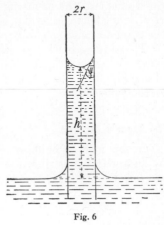

Fig. 6

$$2\pi r T \cos\psi = \pi r^2 h \rho g + \pi r^3 \rho g (\sec\psi + \tfrac{2}{3}\tan^3\psi - \tfrac{2}{3}\sec^3\psi), \quad (11.8)$$

where ρ is the density of the liquid.   This gives

$$T = \frac{r\rho g \sec\psi}{2}\{ h + r(\sec\psi + \tfrac{2}{3}\tan^3\psi - \tfrac{2}{3}\sec^3\psi)\}. \quad (11.9)$$

If the liquid wets the surface the meniscus is approximately a hemisphere, and $\psi = 0$, so (11.9) becomes

$$T = \frac{\rho r g}{2}\left(h + \frac{r}{3}\right). \quad \ldots \ldots \quad (11.10)$$

In carrying out the experiment the tube must be thoroughly cleansed before use.   The height h is determined with a vertically travelling microscope.   The radius of the capillary tube is usually found by drawing a thread of mercury into the tube, measuring the length l of the mercury column and then running the thread of mercury out into a watch-glass and finding its weight w.   Then, if σ is the density of mercury, $\pi r^2 l \sigma = w$.   As the radius particularly required is that at the point where the meniscus is formed, it is better to mark the tube at this point and then to break the tube here at the conclusion of the experiment. The radius is then found with a travelling microscope for several diameters mutually at right angles, the average value being taken. The method is fairly accurate for liquids which wet the tube; otherwise the angle of contact must be known. If very accurate values are required the exact shape of the meniscus must be examined. The curved surface of a liquid between its flat general level and the line of contact with the solid is sometimes referred to as the *capillary curve*.

The surface tension between two immiscible liquids is termed the *interfacial surface tension*. It may be determined by placing a layer of one liquid on top of the other and inserting a vertical capillary tube at the junction.

(b) Jäger's Method.

In this method bubbles are blown beneath the surface of the liquid by an apparatus as shown in fig. 7, the pressure at which the bubbles are formed being given by the manometer. If we assume that the

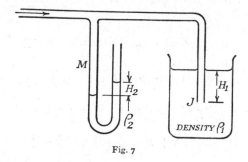

Fig. 7

bubbles become detached when they are just greater than hemispheres of radius r equal to that of the tube, then by equation (11.5) the pressure registered by the manometer is

$$p = \frac{2T}{r} = \rho_2 g H_2 - \sigma_1 g H_1, \qquad . \quad . \quad . \quad (11.11)$$

where ρ_2 is the density of the liquid in the manometer, and H_2 is the difference between its levels. The quantities σ_1 and H_1 are the density of the liquid in which the bubbles are being blown, and the depth of the bubble orifice below the surface of the liquid. The method has the advantage over the capillary tube method that the liquid-air interface is continually being renewed so that contamination of the surface, a factor which makes a great difference to the surface tension, is avoided.

The method may also be used to determine the surface tension of molten metals.

(c) Frame Method.

A vertical rectangular metal frame is supported from a rigid horizontal rod and dips into the liquid as shown in fig. 8. The rod is fixed to a horizontal torsion wire which acts as an axis, suitable counterpoise being placed on the other side of the rod. The dish containing the liquid is then lowered and the frame follows it, twisting the torsion

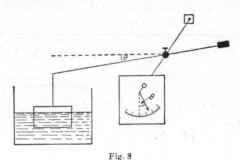

Fig. 8

wire through an observed angle θ. When the torsional couple is just greater than the pull down due to surface tension, the frame jerks out of the liquid. The maximum angle of twist is observed and then suitable weights are suspended in place of the balance arm to produce the same couple as that produced by the surface tension forces. If the equivalent effective mass is m,

$$2Tl = mg,$$

where l is the length of the horizontal wire of the frame. There are many variations of this type of apparatus, sometimes flat wire rings or horizontal disks being used instead of the wire frame.

(d) Drop Weight Method.

In this method, which is valued in industry for its simplicity and rapidity, liquid is allowed to drop from a circular orifice and the average weight of a drop is determined by counting a given number and finding the total weight of liquid collected. Then if we assume that the drop breaks away immediately after the issuing liquid becomes hemispherical, we have

$$T2\pi r = mg, \quad \ldots \ldots \quad (11.12)$$

where m is the mass of the drop, and r is its radius, which is taken to be that of the tube. Actually equation (11.12) does not exactly represent the true state of affairs, but for a given tube

$$mg = KT,$$

where K is a constant which must be determined for the tube by calibration with a liquid of known surface tension.

(e) Stationary Drops or Bubbles.

We consider either a stationary drop as shown in fig. 9(a), or a stationary bubble as shown in fig. 9(b), each being in contact with a horizontal surface. If the drop or bubble is large and flat, and we consider the equilibrium of the section shown in fig. 9(c), the total force per unit length to the right is $T(1 - \cos\psi)$. This balances the

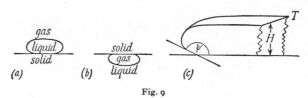

Fig. 9

hydrostatic pressure across the section of the drop, and if H is its mean thickness this gives rise to a force per unit length of $g\rho\dfrac{H}{2} \cdot H$. Hence

$$T(1 - \cos\psi) = \frac{g\rho H^2}{2}. \quad \ldots \ldots \quad (11.13)$$

This method involves a separate measurement of the angle of contact ψ; H is usually determined with a microscope.

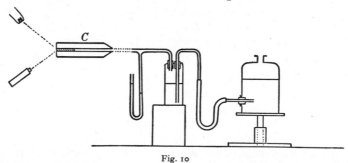

Fig. 10

(f) Ferguson's Method for a small quantity of Liquid.

The arrangement, which is a variation of the capillary tube method, is shown in fig. 10. The capillary tube C, which is very narrow, is arranged horizontally, and a pressure p is applied by raising the reservoir on the right until the liquid, which is placed in the capillary, has its surface forced plane. This condition is judged by the occurrence of regular planar reflection of light incident on the end of the tube. If the angle of contact of the liquid is ψ and the radius of the tube at the meniscus is r, then

$$2\pi r T \cos\psi = p \cdot \pi r^2 = \rho g h \cdot \pi r^2, \quad . \quad . \quad (11.14)$$

where ρ is the density of the liquid in the attached manometer, and h is the difference in levels of the arms. The required quantities in (11.14) are measured in the manner already described for the vertical capillary tube method.

* (g) Ripple Method.

This is an elegant dynamical method due to Lord Rayleigh. In fig. 11 is shown a section of a wave across the surface of a liquid. We assume the waves to be simple harmonic in form (see Part 1V); then the vertical displacement y at any point x is given by

$$y = a \sin\left(\frac{2\pi x}{\lambda} + b\right), \quad . \quad . \quad . \quad . \quad (11.15)$$

where a is the amplitude, λ is the wavelength, and b is a constant

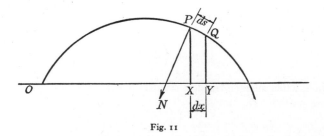

Fig. 11

termed the phase constant. If r is the radius of curvature of the portion of the wave at y, then using equations (8.23) and (11.15) we find

$$\frac{1}{r} = \frac{d^2y}{dx^2} = -\frac{4\pi^2 y}{\lambda^2}. \quad . \quad . \quad . \quad (11.16)$$

Now, if we consider the effect of surface tension, a pressure $p = T/r$ will by equation (11.5) act normally to the curve, the other radius being infinite since we treat the waves as cylindrical rollers. Hence, (11.16) becomes

$$p = -\frac{4\pi^2 y}{\lambda^2} T,$$

and the vertical *downward* force on an area of unit length perpendicular to the paper and of length dx in the x-direction is

$$p\,dx = +\frac{4\pi^2 y}{\lambda^2}T\,dx. \quad \ldots \ldots \quad (11.17)$$

Now the force arising from the hydrostatic pull downwards on this element of volume due to the action of gravity is $g\rho y\,dx$, where ρ is the density of the liquid. The total downward force on the element of volume is therefore

$$\rho y\,dx\left(g + \frac{4\pi^2 T}{\lambda^2 \rho}\right). \quad \ldots \ldots \quad (11.18)$$

Surface tension is therefore shown by equation (11.18) to increase the effective acceleration due to gravity by an apparent amount $4\pi^2 T/\lambda^2\rho$.

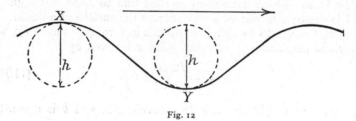

Fig. 12

Now the velocity of propagation c of purely gravitational waves is, as we shall show later, given by

$$c = \left(\frac{g\lambda}{2\pi}\right)^{\frac{1}{2}}, \quad \ldots \ldots \quad (11.19)$$

and hence, when surface tension is also operative, this must be changed to

$$c = \sqrt{\frac{\lambda}{2\pi}\left(g + \frac{4\pi^2 T}{\lambda^2 \rho}\right)}. \quad \ldots \ldots \quad (11.20)$$

In practice the ripples are produced by a dipper attached to the prongs of an electrically-driven tuning fork of known frequency n. Then since (see Part IV) the velocity $c = n\lambda$, equation (11.20) may be written

$$T = \frac{\lambda^3 n^2 \rho}{2\pi} - \frac{g\lambda^2 \rho}{4\pi^2}. \quad \ldots \ldots \quad (11.21)$$

The wave-length λ is found by observing the surface of the liquid with a stroboscopic slit (see Part IV) of the same frequency as the fork. The ripples then appear stationary, and the distance between a given number of them may be found with a travelling microscope.

To show that $c = (g\lambda/2\pi)^{\frac{1}{2}}$ for gravitational waves alone, we assume that, as shown in fig. 12, every particle of liquid in the wave describes a circular path in a vertical plane. Then the circles are described in an anticlockwise direction for waves which are proceeding from left to right. If the time of revolution of a particle in the circle is τ, the horizontal velocity at a crest X is

$$q_1 = c - \frac{2\pi r}{\tau}, \quad \ldots \ldots \quad (11.22)$$

while at the trough Y it is

$$q_2 = c + \frac{2\pi r}{\tau}. \quad \ldots \ldots \quad (11.23)$$

Now, assuming that the gain in velocity is due to the decrease in gravitational potential energy due to the particle falling a height $h = 2r$, we have

$$q_2{}^2 = q_1{}^2 + 2gh = q_1{}^2 + 4gr. \quad \ldots \quad (11.24)$$

Hence, from (11.22), (11.23) and (11.24), by eliminating $(q_2{}^2 - q_1{}^2)$,

$$c = \frac{g\tau}{2\pi} = \frac{g\lambda}{2\pi c},$$

or

$$c = \left(\frac{g\lambda}{2\pi}\right)^{\frac{1}{2}}.$$

7. Variations in Surface Tension.

The surface tension is very sensitive to small quantities of impurities on the surface, a state of affairs which is referred to as *contamination*. Solutions have a lower surface tension than the pure solvent, but no simple law of variation with concentration is observed. Rise of temperature results in a fall in the surface tension, and the surface tension disappears a few degrees below the critical temperature (see Part II). The variation with temperature is not a simple one; one of the more useful formulæ which have been proposed to represent the relation is the *Eötvös-Ramsay-Shields formula*:

$$T(Mvx)^{\frac{2}{3}} = K\,(\theta_c - \theta - d), \quad \ldots \quad (11.25)$$

where K is a constant, M is the molecular weight of the liquid, v its specific volume, that is the reciprocal of the density, θ_c its critical temperature, θ its actual temperature and d a constant equal numerically to about 7. The quantity x is the *degree of association* of the liquid; this is defined as the molecular weight of the liquid divided by the molecular weight of the unassociated liquid. For example, water contains groups of associated molecules nH_2O where n is 2,

3, &c., as well as ordinary H_2O molecules, and the relative fraction of the groups present with $n = 1, 2, 3$, &c., varies as the temperature changes.

8. Osmosis and Osmotic Pressure.

It was discovered by the Abbé Nollet in 1748 that if certain plant cells are placed in a solution of salt, they shrivel, owing to passage of water outwards through the cell membrane, but that they regain their original size if they are again placed in pure water. This passage of liquid through a cell-membrane in one direction only is termed **osmosis,** and is said to take place through a **semi-permeable membrane.** Some cells, such as red blood corpuscles, when placed in pure water receive

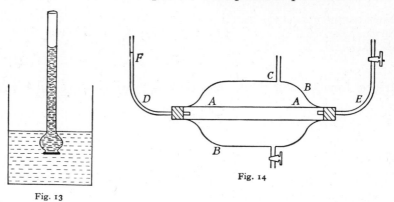

Fig. 13

Fig. 14

so much water through their semi-permeable membranes that they burst. This bursting is attributed to **osmotic pressure,** the existence of which may be simply demonstrated with the apparatus shown in fig. 13. A thistle funnel contains some sugar solution and is closed at the bottom with a sheet of parchment which acts as a semi-permeable membrane. The funnel is placed in a beaker of pure water, and as the latter passes through the semi-permeable membrane the height of liquid in the tube of the thistle-funnel continues to rise until the hydrostatic pressure down is just sufficient to balance the osmotic pressure on the membrane. A method of measuring the osmotic pressure is thus provided, but in practice the method is modified so that less strain is placed upon the semi-permeable membrane. The latter is usually made of a film of copper ferrocyanide, deposited in the walls of a porous pot by allowing copper sulphate to diffuse through one side of the pot and potassium ferrocyanide through from the other side. In fig. 14 is shown Berkeley and Hartley's method of measuring osmotic pressure. A horizontal porcelain tube A has a semi-permeable membrane of $CuFe(CN)_6$ deposited near the outer wall. The gun-metal case B enclosing A is filled with the solution under test by the side-tube C. The brass end-tubes D and E lead respectively to a vertical open graduated glass capillary tube, and to a tap. The solvent is placed in the inner tubes A, D, E, but is prevented from passing into the solution by a hydrostatic pressure applied through C. When the applied hydrostatic pressure is just equal to the osmotic pressure the meniscus at F remains stationary. Osmotic pressures up to 130 atmospheres may be measured in this way.

The fundamental quantitative laws of osmotic pressure are:

(a) The osmotic pressure is directly proportional to the concentration of the solution.

(b) The osmotic pressure is directly proportional to the absolute temperature.

(c) If a gramme-molecule of a non-electrolyte is dissolved in 22·4 litres of solvent an osmotic pressure equal to 76 cm. of mercury is produced at 0° C.

The first two laws may be summed up in the equation

$$p = nkT, \qquad \ldots \ldots \quad (11.26)$$

where n is the concentration, k is a constant, and T is the absolute temperature. This equation bears a striking resemblance to the gas equation (see Part II), and this, coupled with the fact that law (c) is the exact counterpart of Avogadro's hypothesis (see Part II) leads us to attribute osmotic pressure to the same mechanism as gas pressure. We shall see in Part II that the kinetic theory of gases gives us almost a perfect picture of gas pressure arising from the bombardment of gas molecules, so in a similar manner osmotic pressure is attributed to the bombardment of liquid molecules on the semi-permeable membrane. It is assumed that the membrane is permeable to molecules of the solvent but not to those of the solute. Consequently, since all the molecules which impinge on the membrane on the side containing the pure solvent are molecules of solvent, while the latter constitute only a fraction of the total number of bombarding molecules on the other side, there is a net number of solvent molecules passing through the semi-permeable membrane in the direction of solvent to solution. Owing to the complicated nature of the liquid state only partial success has attended this view of osmosis. Also the explanation of the behaviour of electrolytes has required the resources of modern electrical theory. We shall treat osmotic pressure from a different point of view in our Chapter on Thermodynamics (Part II, Heat).

Solutions which exert the same osmotic pressure are termed *isotonic*. Medical injections into the blood-stream must be isotonic with the contents of the blood corpuscles.

9. Diffusion.

Consider the simple experiment of placing a few crystals of copper sulphate at the bottom of a beaker containing water, and then awaiting events. A layer of copper sulphate solution is formed at the bottom of the beaker with a layer of water above it, but after a few months the blue colour is found to have spread uniformly throughout the entire volume of the liquid, indicating that the solution has the same concentration at all points. Now the copper sulphate solution had a much greater density than the pure water, so the question arises as to how the denser liquid can rise against gravity. The phenomenon is referred to as **diffusion** and is explained on the **kinetic theory of liquids.** Since the molecules in the liquid state are endowed with a certain amount of kinetic energy, which is actually proportional to their absolute temperature, this kinetic energy is shared by the molecules of solute present in the solution. The solute molecules therefore wander about in the liquid and owing to their thermal kinetic energy are able to rise against gravitational attraction. The basic **law of diffusion,** due to Fick, states that the *rate of transfer of solute across unit area in the solution is directly proportional to the concentration gradient.* Expressing this mathematically, we have

$$w = -D \frac{dn}{dx}, \qquad \ldots \ldots \quad (11.27)$$

where w is the weight of solute crossing unit area per second in the direction of the x-axis and dn/dx is the concentration gradient of the solution at the point in question. The negative sign is introduced because if the solute moves in the direction of increasing x, the concentration must *decrease* in this direction. The rate of transfer also depends on the nature of the solute, and the constant D is called the **coefficient of diffusion** or **diffusivity** for the substance in question.

Diffusion is not confined to the liquid state. Owing to the higher translational velocity of the molecules it is much more rapid in gases. It may be examined by placing two gases in a vertical gas jar, separated by a horizontal glass plate, which may be removed with a minimum of disturbance. For example, a dense gas such as carbon dioxide may fill the lower half of the jar and a lighter gas such as hydrogen may fill the upper half of the jar. If the plate is removed, after some time, it is found that the mixture which is formed by diffusion is of uniform density throughout the vessel. Various means may be employed to study the diffusion of the gas; while chemical analysis is the commonest method, other less disturbing processes, such as the measurement of the refractive index of the gas layers at various heights, may be employed.

Closely related to diffusion is *effusion*. This is the passage of a gas through a small aperture. If a porous pot, which may be regarded as a large number of very small apertures, contains two gases, the rate of effusion will differ and thus a method of separating gases becomes available. This method has been used in separating the isotopes of chlorine, and also heavy hydrogen, from a mixture with ordinary hydrogen (see Part V).

Graham's law of diffusion compares the velocities of diffusion of different gases, and states that the rate at which diffusion (or effusion) takes place through an aperture is inversely proportional to the square root of the density of the gas, that is,

$$v \propto \sqrt{\frac{1}{\rho}}. \quad . \quad . \quad . \quad . \quad . \quad (11.28)$$

This equation only holds for constant temperature, the rate of diffusion increasing rapidly as the temperature is raised. A simple apparatus for illustrating gas diffusion is shown in fig. 15. An inverted vertical porous pot containing air has a projecting tube dipping below the surface of liquid contained in a beaker. Over the outside of the porous pot is placed a beaker which has been filled with coal-gas by upward displacement. Bubbles are immediately observed to escape from the end of the tube, the coal-gas diffusing through the porous pot more rapidly than the air diffuses out and so giving rise to an increased pressure inside the pot.

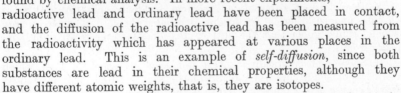

Fig. 15

Even solids show some ability to diffuse over a long period of time. In the experiments of Roberts-Austen, a small lead cylinder was fused to a thin gold plate at one end. After one month the lead cylinder was cut into slices and the quantity of diffused gold found by chemical analysis. In more recent experiments, radioactive lead and ordinary lead have been placed in contact, and the diffusion of the radioactive lead has been measured from the radioactivity which has appeared at various places in the ordinary lead. This is an example of *self-diffusion*, since both substances are lead in their chemical properties, although they have different atomic weights, that is, they are isotopes.

The phenomenon of *diffusion* is closely related with that of *osmosis*, for the latter may be regarded as diffusion in one direction through a semi-permeable membrane. In this connexion the process of **dialysis** is of interest. This is the name given to the passage of some substances termed **crystalloids,** and the non-passage of others termed *colloids,* through certain semi-permeable membranes. For example, mineral acids and salts may be separated from gum by placing a mixture of the two on one side of a membrane of gold-beater's skin. The former, being crystalloids, pass through the membrane while the latter, being a colloid, remains behind. However, the line of demarcation between crystalloids and colloids is very vague; sodium stearate, for example, acts as a colloid in aqueous solution and as a crystalloid in alcoholic solution.

EXERCISES

1. Define *surface tension* and *surface energy* of a liquid-gas interface. Describe an *accurate* method for measuring the surface tension of a liquid.

2. How may the interfacial surface tension between two non-miscible liquids be measured?
What variation in surface tension results from (a) temperature change, (b) presence of impurities?

3. Deduce an expression for the difference of pressure existing on opposite sides of a curved film which is subject to surface tension forces.
Calculate the energy latent in a soap-bubble of radius 5 cm., given that the surface tension of the soap-solution is 35 dynes/cm. [7000 π ergs.]

4. What is meant by the term *angle of contact* as applied to capillarity and how may the angle of contact be measured?
Describe the method of determining surface tension from measurements on stationary drops or bubbles.

5. Enumerate the methods available for measuring the surface tension of liquids and describe one method which is especially suitable when only a small quantity of liquid is available.

6. Distinguish between statical and dynamical methods of measuring surface tension and describe one dynamical method in detail.

7. Give an account of the ripple method for measuring the surface tension of a liquid.

8. If a globe of water of radius 2 cm. suddenly splits into 50 equal globules under isothermal conditions, determine the gain in surface energy which occurs, given that the surface tension of water is 75 dynes/cm. [3225 π ergs.]

9. Show mathematically that a homogeneous sheet of lava which contracts on solidifying will split into hexagonal flagstones (Giant's Causeway) because this geometrical figure is the one consistent with least work being done against surface tension forces.

10. State the main laws governing osmosis for substances which do not dissociate on solution. How may the osmotic pressure of a solution be measured?

11. Write a short essay on the phenomena of diffusion of matter.

CHAPTER XII

Properties of Fluids in Motion

It is true that the processes of osmosis and diffusion are due to motion, but it is only random *molecular motion*, the bulk of the fluid remaining at rest. We shall now discuss the properties of fluids in motion, considering first liquids and then gases.

* 1. Translational Flow of an Ideal Liquid.

We first neglect the relative motion of one layer of liquid over another, which produces *internal friction* or *viscosity*, and consider the behaviour of a frictionless, incompressible liquid. If such a liquid is acted upon by gravitational forces, it has a certain gravitational potential energy, and also a kinetic energy due to its motion. If the pressure in the liquid is p and the liquid is moving vertically in a cylinder the work done on the piston (see fig. 1) if the volume increases by V is pV. If the mass of liquid raised is m and the mean height through which it is raised is h, the work done against the gravitational field is mgh. Finally, if its velocity of movement is v, the kinetic energy imparted to the liquid is $\frac{1}{2}mv^2$. If the system is a conservative one, that is to say, if no energy either enters or leaves it, then by the principle of the conservation of energy

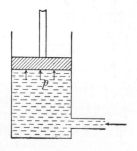

Fig. 1

$$pV + mgh + \tfrac{1}{2}mv^2 = \text{constant}, \quad . \quad . \quad . \quad (12.1)$$

or since the density of the liquid is $\rho = m/V$,

$$p + \rho gh + \tfrac{1}{2}\rho v^2 = \text{constant}. \quad . \quad . \quad (12.2)$$

This result is known as **Bernoulli's Theorem.** For a liquid which is moving *horizontally*, h is constant and therefore (12.2) becomes

$$p + \tfrac{1}{2}\rho v^2 = \text{constant}. \quad . \quad . \quad . \quad (12.3)$$

131

In equation (12.3) p is termed the *static pressure* and $\frac{1}{2}\rho v^2$ the *dynamic pressure* or *velocity pressure*; the equation therefore states that for an *ideal fluid*, moving horizontally, the sum of the static and dynamic pressures is constant. We may apply equation (12.2) to find the velocity of efflux of liquid escaping from an orifice under the action of gravity. If Π is the atmospheric pressure, and h is the height of the head of liquid above the orifice, then, just outside the orifice, $p = \Pi$, $h = 0$; and, at the upper surface, $p = \Pi$, $v = 0$. Hence

$$\Pi + \tfrac{1}{2}\rho v^2 = \Pi + \rho g h, \quad \cdots \quad (12.4)$$

so that
$$v = (2gh)^{\frac{1}{2}}. \quad \cdots \cdots \quad (12.5)$$

* 2. Rotating Ideal Liquid.

We next consider the shape of the surface of liquid contained in a beaker and rotated rapidly about a vertical axis of revolution. As

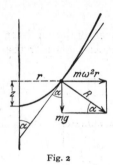

Fig. 2

shown in fig. 2, each small element of volume of the liquid is acted upon by the gravitational force downwards and centrifugal force outwards, so for equilibrium we have

$$\tan \alpha = \frac{mg}{m\omega^2 r}, \quad \cdots \quad (12.6)$$

where m is the mass of the element of liquid, r is the radius of its path, and ω the angular velocity of revolution. The angle is that made with the vertical by the tangent to the liquid surface at the point considered; the resultant force R, which is balanced by the atmospheric pressure, must be perpendicular to the liquid surface for the liquid to rotate steadily. Now $\tan \alpha = dr/dz$, so equation (12.6) may be written

$$dz = \frac{\omega^2}{g} r \, dr, \quad \cdots \cdots \quad (12.7)$$

which gives on integration

$$z = \frac{\omega^2}{2g} r^2 + \text{constant.} \quad \cdots \cdots \quad (12.8)$$

This is the equation to a parabola, so that the surface of the liquid is parabolic, for a uniform speed of rotation.

3. Viscosity.

The behaviour of liquids with translational and rotational motion is approximately described by the considerations of sections (1) and (2), but in practice, internal friction or viscosity must be taken into account. With reference to fig. 3, it is found that when liquid flows over a fixed surface such as AB, a layer at distance $(x + dx)$ from AB flows with a velocity greater than that at a layer C, distant x from AB. If the difference in the velocities at the two layers is dv, the *velocity gradient* between the two is dv/dx. **Newton's Law of Viscous Flow** states that the viscous force between the two layers is

$$F = \eta A \frac{dv}{dx}, \quad \cdot \quad \cdot \quad \cdot \quad \cdot \quad \cdot \quad (12.9)$$

F acting opposite to the direction of flow and A being the area of either layer. The quantity η is termed the **coefficient of viscosity,** and is characteristic of the liquid in question. From (12.9), η has dimensions $ML^{-1}T^{-1}$. If the velocity gradient is small it is found that the

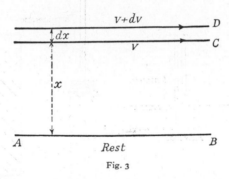

Fig. 3

layers of liquid flow continually parallel to the fixed surface AB. If, however, the velocity gradient is large, local eddies are set up. Newton's law applies only to the former condition, which is that of **streamline flow,** and not to the latter, which is termed **turbulent motion.**

4. Methods of Measuring η for Liquids.

The methods available for determining the coefficient of viscosity of liquids fall into two groups, the first involving the rate of flow of liquid through a capillary tube, and the second involving the motion of a solid body through a mass of the liquid. In both cases the conditions must be those of stream-line motion and this means that in general the velocity of the liquid or solid must be small.

(a) Poiseuille's Method.

An apparatus suitable for the measurement of η by this method is shown in fig. 4. The liquid flows down a horizontal tube of small diameter, the pressure difference between two points being measured by the manometer as shown. Then if Q is the volume of liquid collected in the measuring cylinder per second, we shall proceed to show that

$$Q = \frac{\pi p a^4}{8l\eta}, \quad \ldots \ldots \quad (12.10)$$

where l is the length of the tube over which the pressure difference p is acting, a is the mean radius of the tube, and η is the coefficient of viscosity. The liquid is flowing most rapidly at the centre of the tube and is at rest in contact with the walls of the tube. Let the velocities at the inside and outside of an annulus of the liquid between the radii r and $r + dr$ be v and $v + dv$ respectively, as shown in fig. 5. Then

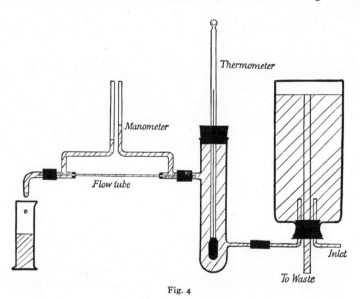

Fig. 4

the velocity gradient across this annulus is dv/dr and by Newton's law of viscous force a tangential stress will be produced, given by $\eta dv/dr$. Since the flow is proceeding with uniform velocity this tangential force exactly balances the accelerating force due to the pressure difference across the ends of the volume of liquid in the cylinder of area πr^2. Hence

$$p \cdot \pi r^2 = -\eta \cdot 2\pi r l \cdot \frac{dv}{dr},$$

or

$$\frac{dv}{dr} = -\frac{rp}{2\eta l}, \quad \ldots \ldots \quad (12.11)$$

so that the velocity gradient is proportional to r. At the wall of the tube $r = a$ and $v = 0$; therefore, integrating (12.11) from $r = a$ to $r = r$, we have

$$a^2 - r^2 = \frac{4\eta l v}{p}$$

or $$v = \frac{p}{4\eta l}(a^2 - r^2). \quad . \quad . \quad . \quad . \quad (12.12)$$

Equation (12.12) shows that $v \propto (a^2 - r^2)$, so that the profile of the advancing liquid is parabolic.

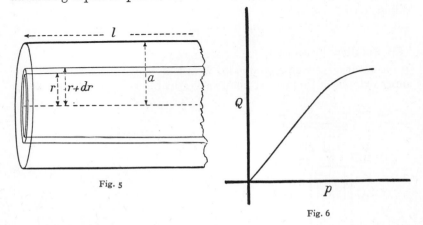

Fig. 5

Fig. 6

Now the volume of liquid dQ flowing per second through the annulus of the tube between r and $r + dr$, with velocity v, will be the volume of the annulus multiplied by v, that is

$$dQ = 2\pi r \, dr \cdot v. \quad . \quad . \quad . \quad . \quad (12.13)$$

Hence the total volume of liquid flowing through the tube per second is from (12.12) and (12.13),

$$Q = \int_0^a \frac{\pi p}{2\eta l}(a^2 - r^2) r \, dr = \frac{\pi p a^4}{8 l \eta}.$$

We have made no allowance in this deduction of **Poiseuille's equation** for the kinetic energy imparted to the liquid by the pressure difference. An expression for this may be deduced by application of Bernoulli's theorem, discussed on p. 131. However, the correction which results is only approximate, and other corrections of doubtful magnitude are also involved. A more correct formula is

$$\eta = \frac{\pi p a^4}{8Q(l + 1 \cdot 64a)} - \frac{mQ\rho}{8\pi(l + 1 \cdot 64a)}, \quad . \quad (12.14)$$

where ρ is the density of the liquid, and m is a value which varies with the conditions of the experiment, but which is not very different from unity.

The velocity at which turbulent flow sets in is termed the **critical velocity** V_c. It may be shown by dimensional analysis that $V_c = k\eta/\rho a$ where k is a quantity termed the **Reynolds number,** and generally has a value about 1000. The relation between the volume of liquid Q and the pressure p is shown in fig. 6. At low velocities Q is proportional to p, as indicated by Poiseuille's equation, but when the critical velocity is exceeded Q is proportional to $p^{\frac{1}{2}}$. The pressure difference is now occupied in communicating kinetic energy to the eddies as well as in overcoming internal friction.

(b) Rotation Viscometer.

A rotation viscometer due to Searle is shown in fig. 7(a). The inner cylinder a is pivoted about a vertical axis b, and rotates under

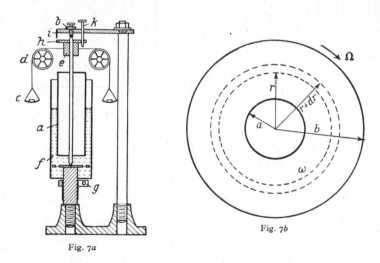

Fig. 7a

Fig. 7b

a couple provided by the weights in the scale-pans c. The couple is transferred by cords passing over the frictionless pulleys d to a drum e. The outer cylinder f can be raised or lowered by rotating the ring g. The speed of rotation is determined with a stop-watch by observing the transits of the point i over the circular scale h. The apparatus is stopped or released by raising or lowering the stop k. In considering the theory of the rotation viscometer, let the angular velocity of rotation increase by $d\omega$ across the annulus between radii r and $r + dr$ as shown in fig. 7(b) (in which it is the *outer* cylinder which is shown rotating). Then the velocity gradient across the annulus is $rd\omega/dr$, so that by Newton's law the viscous force round the annulus is, per unit length of the cylinder,

$$F = 2\pi r\eta \cdot r \frac{d\omega}{dr}, \quad \ldots \ldots \quad (12.15)$$

and the torque about the central axis is

$$Fr = 2\pi r^3\eta \frac{d\omega}{dr}. \quad \ldots \ldots \quad (12.16)$$

When the steady state is reached, this torque G, multiplied by the length of the cylinder, l, must equal the steady external couple on the inner cylinder; that is, $G dr/r^3 = 2\pi\eta l d\omega$; integrating, therefore, between the limits

$$r = a, \quad \omega = \Omega; \quad r = b, \quad \omega = 0,$$

we find, $$\mathbf{G = 4\pi\eta\Omega} \frac{a^2 b^2}{(b^2 - a^2)} l. \quad \ldots \ldots \quad (12.17)$$

To eliminate correction for the torque over the base of the cylinder, two lengths are employed. Then if $f(B)$ is the unknown torque over the base

$$G_1 = 4\pi\eta\Omega \frac{a^2 b^2}{(b^2 - a^2)} l_1 + f(B)$$

$$G_2 = 4\pi\eta\Omega \frac{a^2 b^2}{(b^2 - a^2)} l_2 + f(B)$$

so $$\eta = \frac{(b^2 - a^2)(G_1 - G_2)}{4\pi a^2 b^2 \Omega(l_1 - l_2)}. \quad \ldots \ldots \quad (12.18)$$

The velocity of rotation must be small so that the conditions are those of stream-line flow.

(c) Stokes's Falling-Body Viscometer.

This viscometer is extremely simple to use and therefore very convenient. It was shown by Stokes that if a sphere of radius a is moving with uniform velocity v through an infinite, homogeneous, incompressible fluid of coefficient of viscosity η, the retarding force F is given (compare Ex. 3, p. 52) by

$$F = 6\pi\eta av. \quad \ldots \ldots \quad (12.19)$$

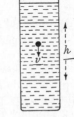

Fig. 8

In practice, the apparatus consists of a vertical glass tube containing the liquid as shown in fig. 8, in which spheres of radius a and mass m are dropped. After a short time the spheres acquire a uniform *terminal velocity v*, and this may be determined by timing the fall of the spheres over a fixed height *h* of the tube. Since the accelerating force down *m'g* must just equal the viscous retarding force when the spheres move with uniform velocity,

$$m'g = 6\pi\eta av, \quad \ldots \ldots \quad (12.20)$$

and hence η may be determined. The quantity *m'* is the mass of the sphere in the liquid, that is, the buoyancy of the liquid has been taken into consideration. If ρ and σ are the densities of spheres and liquid respectively, equation (12.20) may be written

$$\frac{4}{3}\pi a^3(\rho - \sigma)g = 6\pi\eta av, \text{ or } \eta = \frac{2}{9} \cdot \frac{a^2(\rho - \sigma)g}{v}. \quad (12.21)$$

This equation is of fundamental importance in Millikan's method for determining the electronic charge *e*, described in Part V.

Equation (12.21) must be divided by a factor $(1 + 2{\cdot}4\,A/R)$ where *A* and *R* are the radii of sphere and tube, if accurate valves of η are required. This correction arises from the finite extent of the tube.

*5. Viscosity of Gases.

Newton's law of viscous flow applies to gases as well as to liquids, with the same limitation to stream-line flow. One essential difference is that the high compressibility of gases must also be taken into account. Otherwise, with small modifications the methods of measuring the viscosity of gases are essentially the same as for liquids. The rotating cylinder method may be applied directly; it is usual to rotate the *outer* cylinder and measure the torque on the inner cylinder, which is suspended by a torsion wire. To allow for the compressibility of gases when the coefficient of viscosity is determined by a flow method, either a constant pressure or a constant volume is usually employed.

(a) Constant Pressure.

The experimental arrangement due to Schultze is shown in fig. 9. The gas is contained in the spheres *a* and *b* and is passed through the capillary flow tube *k* at constant pressure by raising the mercury *c* up the scale *d*. The volume of gas passed is recorded electrically as the mercury passes the metal points inserted at *f* and *g*.

To allow for the compressibility of the gas we have, by Poiseuille's equation, for a short length *dx* of the flow tube across which a pressure difference *dp* is acting,

$$Q = -\frac{\pi a^4}{8\eta} \cdot \frac{dp}{dx}. \quad \ldots \ldots \quad (12.22)$$

When a steady flow of gas is in progress the *mass* of gas crossing all cross-sections of the tube must be constant. This is an example of the **Equation of Continuity.** It holds for all fluids and for electric current. If it were not true at any point, there would be a continual generation or destruction of fluid at that point. Now the density of the gas is, by Boyle's law, directly proportional to the pressure, so that we have, for any cross-section of the tube,

mass crossing per sec. = constant = vol. per sec. × density.

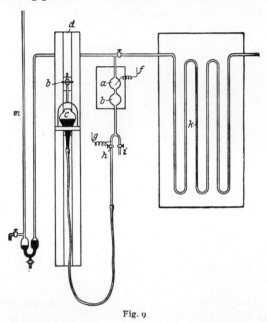

Fig. 9

Thus, if the volume of gas entering the flow tube per second is Q, and its pressure, as registered by the manometer m in fig. 9, is p, then

$$Q\rho \propto Qp. \qquad \ldots \ldots \quad (12.23)$$

Also
$$p_1Q_1 = pQ = -\frac{\pi a^4}{8\eta} p \cdot \frac{dp}{dx}, \quad \ldots \quad (12.24)$$

from equation (12.22). Hence, integrating over the whole length l of the flow tube,

$$\int_0^l p_1Q_1 \, dx = -\frac{\pi a^4}{8\eta} \int_{p_1}^{p_2} p \, dp,$$

or
$$p_1Q_1 = \frac{(p_1^2 - p_2^2)\pi a^4}{16\eta l}. \quad \ldots \quad (12.25)$$

All the quantities in (12.25) are known, except η, so that η may be determined. The pressure p_2 is, of course, atmospheric pressure; correction must be applied for the kinetic energy imparted to the gas, as in the corresponding experiment with liquids.

(b) Constant Volume.

In Edward's constant volume method, a diagram of which is shown in fig. 10, the gas is contained in a large bulb B at a pressure p, which is registered by the mercury in the arms of the manometer ab. The tap T_2 is then closed and T_3 opened to atmosphere for a certain time T.

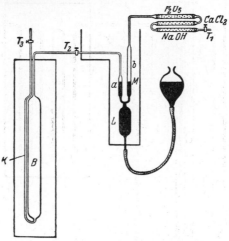

Fig. 10

Finally, T_3 is closed and the new gas pressure p_2 is observed. Let the volume of the bulb be Q; then if Q_1 is the volume of gas entering the capillary flow tube K per second at a time t when the pressure in the apparatus is p_1, for a slow rate of flow we may apply Boyle's law. During the interval dt the volume becomes $(Q + Q_1\,dt)$ while the pressure becomes $(p + dp)$, so

$$pQ = (p + dp)(Q + Q_1 dt), \quad \text{. . . . (12.26)}$$

and, neglecting the small quantity $Q_1\,dp\,dt$,

$$pQ_1 = -Q\frac{dp}{dt}.$$

Now by equation (12.25), if p_0 is the atmospheric pressure

$$pQ_1 = \frac{\pi a^4(p^2 - p_0{}^2)}{16\eta l}. \quad \text{. . . . . (12.27)}$$

Hence

$$\frac{\pi a^4 T}{16 \eta l Q} = -\int_{p_1 + p_0}^{p_2 + p_0} \frac{dp}{p^2 - p_0^2} = \frac{1}{2p_0} \log_e \left(\frac{p_2 + 2p_0}{p_1 + 2p_0} \cdot \frac{p_1}{p_2} \right). \quad (12.28)$$

6. Variations in the Viscosity of Fluids.

The coefficient of viscosity of liquids increases with rise of pressure, and decreases very rapidly with rise of temperature. The viscosity of solutions is irregular and bears no simple relation to the concentration. Singularly little success has attended the attempts to apply the molecular theory to explain the viscosity of liquids.

With gases, the coefficient of viscosity is independent of the pressure at ordinary pressures, a rather unexpected result indicated first theoretically from the kinetic theory of gases and subsequently verified experimentally, by Maxwell, by observation of the damping of an oscillating disk surrounded by gas at different pressures. At low pressures the viscosity varies directly as the pressure, a fact which forms the basis of *viscosity gauges* for measuring low gas pressures (see p. 111). The viscosity of gases, in contrast to that of liquids, increases with rise of temperature. We shall see in Part II that the behaviour of gases is well accounted for by the kinetic theory.

EXERCISES

1. Discuss Bernoulli's theorem concerning the translational flow of an ideal liquid and use it to deduce the velocity of efflux of liquid escaping from an orifice under the pressure of a constant head of water.

2. Show that the surface of an ideal liquid contained in a cylindrical vessel rotating about a vertical axis is a paraboloid of revolution.

A cylindrical vessel of diameter 30 cm. contains water and is rotating with uniform velocity about a vertical axis. If the vessel makes 50 revs/min., find the difference in level between the edges and the centre of the water surface. [3.1 cm.]

3. Liquid stands in a vertical cylinder attached to an automobile which is being accelerated. How will the level of the liquid in the cylinder be affected (a) if the cylinder is fixed rigidly to the floor, (b) if it is freely suspended from the roof?

4. Explain clearly what is meant by the term **coefficient of viscosity** of a fluid.

Describe one method for finding the coefficient of viscosity of a liquid experimentally.

5. Give an account of the rotation viscometer and indicate what advantages it possesses over Poiseuille's method in finding the coefficient of viscosity of gases.

6. How does the viscosity of fluids vary with temperature? Describe how Stokes's viscometer might be applied to examine this variation.

7. Describe a constant-volume flow method for determining the co-efficient of viscosity of a gas.

How does the viscosity of a gas vary with the pressure?

8. If water is flowing down a right-circular cylinder of radius 1 mm. under a pressure gradient of 10 dynes/cm.^{3}, find the velocity of flow at a point 0·5 mm. from the centre of the tube, given that the coefficient of viscosity of water is 0·01 gm./cm.$^{-1}$sec.$^{-1}$. [1·9 cm./sec.]

EXAMPLES

1. Use the method of dimensions to find how the time of oscillation of a simple pendulum varies with (a) the mass of the bob, (b) the length of the suspension, (c) the acceleration due to gravity.

2. Find by the method of dimensions how the volume of viscous liquid flowing per second with streamline motion through a cylindrical tube of circular cross-section depends on (a) the pressure gradient, (b) the radius of the tube and (c) the coefficient of viscosity of the liquid.

3. If a smooth sphere of mass M, moving with uniform velocity, collides with another sphere (initially at rest) of mass m, show that if translational energy and momentum are conserved in the collision, $M/m = \sin(\phi + 2\theta)/\sin\phi$, where ϕ and θ are the angles made by the directions of motion of M and m after collision, with the direction of motion of M before collision.

4. In a sand-blast, spherical particles each of mass 0·1 gm. are sent along a cylindrical tube of cross-section 9·5 cm.², the end of which is held in contact with a flat plate. If 100 particles impinge on the plate per sec. with a velocity of 5×10^3 cm. per sec., and the coefficient of restitution is 0·9, find the pressure exerted by the particles on the plate.

5. A particle starting from rest slides down a plane inclined at 30° to the horizontal. If the coefficient of friction between particle and plane is $\frac{1}{4}$, show that the ratio of the kinetic energy of the particle at any instant to its loss in potential energy is $(4 - \sqrt{3})/4$.

6. A spring balance hangs from the roof of a stationary lift and supports a weight of 5 lb. The lift starts to descend, whereupon the balance reads 4·5 lb. What is the downward acceleration of the lift, and what would the balance read if the lift fell freely under gravity?

7. A mascot hangs vertically in an automobile which is moving with a uniform velocity of 45 m.p.h. along a straight horizontal road. If the brakes are applied to give a uniform resistance and the mascot is observed to be deflected through an angle of 10°, determine the distance the car travels before coming to rest.

8. A flywheel of mass 100 lb. is mounted on a horizontal axle of diameter 2 in. Determine the radius of gyration of the wheel if a

mass of 1 lb., attached to the axle by a string, descends through 6 ft. from rest in 10 sec.

9. An aeroplane is approaching an air-port at a uniform speed u_1 when another plane leaves the port with a uniform speed u_2. Find the ratio of the distances of the aeroplanes from the port when they are closest to each other if the angle between the lines of motion of the planes is θ.

10. Taking the acceleration due to gravity (observed) as 981 cm./sec.^{2} at latitude 45°, determine its value at latitude 60° if the earth is regarded as a sphere of radius $6\cdot4 \times 10^8$ cm.

11. A propeller-driven ice-yacht is made to move in a circle on a rough plane inclined at an angle θ to the horizontal. If the coefficient of side-ways friction is μ, show that the greatest allowable velocity v_1 at the highest point of the circle is related to the greatest allowable velocity v_2 at a point midway between the top and bottom of the circle, by the equation $v_2{}^2/v_1{}^2 = \mu \cos\theta/(\sin\theta + \mu \cos\theta)$.

12. A small pellet is projected from the bottom of a circular hoop of radius 1 ft. with a speed of 12 ft./sec. If it just reaches the top of the hoop, determine the percentage energy loss due to friction.

13. A car is running round a curved track of radius 1000 ft. at a speed of 120 m.p.h. Determine the angle of banking so that there shall be no tendency to side slip.

14. Referring to Ques. 13, if the centre of gravity is 2 ft. from the ground and the wheel base is 5 ft. wide, find the maximum speed at which the car may safely take a corner on a very rough horizontal road, if the radius of the track is 20 ft.

15. A horizontal platform executes simple harmonic motion in a vertical plane, the total vertical movement being 10 cm. Find the shortest period permissible if objects resting on the platform are to remain in contact with it throughout the motion.

16. Show that if a short straight frictionless tunnel is driven through the earth from one point on the surface to another, then assuming the earth to be a sphere of radius 4000 miles, an object will travel along the tunnel under gravitational forces and will again reach the surface in about 42 min.

17. A uniform open U-tube contains very mobile liquid to a height of 50 cm. in each limb. If the liquid in one limb is depressed and then released, find the period of oscillation of the liquid in the tube.

18. What is the length of the equivalent simple pendulum for a pendulum which consists of a sphere of radius 15 cm., suspended by a light string 120 cm. long?

19. Show that in a reversible pendulum which has been nearly adjusted, except when the centre of gravity is very close to the point midway between the two knife-edges, g is given by $g = 8\pi^2 l/(T_1^2 + T_2^2)$, where l is the distance between the two knife-edges and T_1 and T_2 are the nearly equal times of oscillation.

20. A circular hoop is suspended by any number of vertical strings of length l, uniformly spaced around the hoop. Show that the period of a small rotational oscillation about the centre is that of a simple pendulum of length l.

21. A wire that breaks under a tension greater than 3×10^9 dynes carries a smooth ring which supports a weight of 4 kgm. If the wire is pulled in a horizontal direction, determine the angle the wire makes with the horizontal at the instant of fracture.

22. A given vertical light spiral spring is observed to stretch 1 cm. when loaded with a weight of 50 gm. Find the velocity with which a 1000 gm. weight is travelling if it is attached to the end of the spring and has then fallen through 10 cm.

23. In Ques. 22 determine the maximum extension of the spring and the period of oscillation of the 1000 gm. mass.

24. Given that Young's modulus for brass is 10^{12} dynes/cm.^{2}, find the energy stored up in a stretched brass wire of area of cross-section 1 mm.^{2} and initial length 1 m., when it is loaded with 2000 gm.

25. A load of 2 kgm. is observed to stretch a given wire through 1 mm. Determine the work done in stretching the wire through 5 mm. and the load required to do it.

26. Two vertical wires of copper and brass are initially of the same length, but the former has twice the diameter of the latter. If Young's modulus for the two materials has the ratio 12 : 11, find the ratio of the extensions when they are stretched by the same load.

27. If the bulk modulus for the compression of a liquid is k and its thermal coefficient of cubical expansion is γ, find the pressure that must be applied to the liquid to prevent it expanding when its temperature is raised $t°$.

28. A rectangular bar of length 20 cm. is supported at its extremities by a bifilar suspension of two vertical strings of length 100 cm. If the mass of the bar is 800 gm., determine the restoring couple acting upon it when it is twisted through 0·001 radian.

29. Find the time of oscillation of the bar in Ques. 28 if its breadth may be neglected in comparison with its length.

30. Determine the greatest weight that may be lifted by a person with the aid of a jack, given that the person can exert a maximum

force of 80 lb. on a 3-ft. lever attached to the screw which has 10 threads to the inch.

31. In an arrangement of pulleys, 3 are attached to an upper block which is fixed, the remaining 2 being attached to a lower movable block. If a man of weight 180 lb. stands on the lower block which weighs 20 lb., find the force which he must exert to raise himself with the aid of a rope attached to the lower block and passing round all the pulleys. How much work has been done when the free end of the rope has descended through 50 ft.?

32. If the gravitational constant $G = 6.66 \times 10^{-8}$ c.g.s. units and the acceleration due to gravity is 32 ft./sec.^{2}, find the mean density of the earth, taking the latter as a sphere of radius 4000 miles.

33. With a given Nicholson's hydrometer it is found necessary to add a weight of 50 gm. to the scale-pan in order to sink it to the required mark. On placing an insoluble solid in the top pan, the weight required is only 25 gm., whereas this has to be increased to 30 gm. when the solid is placed in the lower scale-pan immersed in the liquid. Find the volume and the density of the solid.

34. Two vertical cylindrical tanks have areas of cross-section 10 cm.^{2} and 5 cm.^{2} respectively, and are joined at the base by a U-tube of area of cross-section 1 cm.^{2}. Liquid of specific gravity 2 is then poured into the U-tube so as to half-fill it and water (immiscible with the liquid) is then added to both tanks until it stands well above the bottom of each tank. If the gas pressure above the two tanks is initially the same and that above the larger is then increased by an amount equal to 2 cm. of water, what is the change in the difference of height between the two columns of liquid in the U-tube?

35. A uniform wooden pole of length 10 ft., and specific gravity 0.6 lies with one end on the bank of a lake and the other end dipping into and supported by the water, the level of which is only a few inches below the edge of the lake. Find the immersed length of pole and show that within certain limits it is independent of the depth of the water surface below the bank.

36. Determine the greatest height h to which water may reach in a reservoir with rectangular ends of breadth a, if the end collapses when a couple greater than G acts about the bottom edge of the end of the reservoir.

37. A quarter of a circular cylindrical surface of radius r and length l is immersed in water with one edge of length l in the surface and the axis of the cylinder vertically below it. Show that the resultant force on the surface is about $0.54\, gr^2l$, and is inclined to the horizontal at about 23°.

38. A thin flat plate in the shape of a triangle of vertical height h is immersed in a liquid in a vertical plane with its base horizontal and at a distance $2h$ below the surface, the vertex being above the base. Show that the centre of pressure of the triangle is at a depth $17h/10$.

39. A cylindrical vessel contains water and a floating body. Show that provided that the body has constant volume, the water level in the cylinder is independent of the area of cross-section of the body.

40. In Ques. 39 if the height of the water in the cylinder before the introduction of the body is 30 cm. and the body weighs 20 gm., find the force required to submerge it, given that when it floats in the water the level rises to 34 cm. whereas when it is completely submerged the level reaches 36 cm.

41. Taking the density of air at a temperature of $0°$ C. and a pressure of 760 mm. of mercury to be $1·29 \times 10^{-3}$ gm./c.c., find to what depth a hollow metal sphere must be sunk in sea-water of constant density $1·03$, before the air will start to leak out through a crack in the bottom of the sphere. The temperature of the sea-water is to be taken as $0°$ C. and the density of mercury as $13·6$ gm./c.c.

42. A vertical closed cylinder is floating in equilibrium and is immersed to a depth of 10 cm. Determine the period of vertical oscillation of the cylinder if it is depressed a further small distance into the liquid and is then released.

43. Determine the osmotic pressure of 1 per cent solution of cane sugar at $100°$ C.

44. A circular rubber band has an unstretched diameter of 5 cm. and requires a tension of $910/\pi$ dynes to increase its length by 1 cm. It is placed on a soap-film and the film inside the ring is then broken. If the new diameter of the ring is observed to be $5·2$ cm., determine the surface tension of the soap-film.

45. A drop of liquid of surface-tension T is placed between two flat plates. Show that if the liquid is spread out into a circular patch of area A, the force required to separate the plates when the separation is d is $2TA/d$.

46. If the surface-tension of some soap solution is 35 dynes/cm., find the excess pressure inside a soap bubble of diameter 10 cm. Find also the work done in blowing this bubble.

47. A hollow vertical cylindrical tube of weight 20 gm. has a radius of 1 cm. and is closed at the base. Determine the length of the tube immersed in water if the surface tension of the latter is 75 dynes/cm. and the tube is floating in equilibrium.

48. Determine the difference in level between the surfaces of mercury in a U-tube having limbs of diameter 1 mm. and $0·5$ mm.

respectively, given that the surface tension of mercury is 550 dynes/cm., its density is 13·6 gm./c.c., and the angle of contact is 140°.

49. Two tubes A and B of lengths 100 cm. and 50 cm. have radii 0·1 and 0·2 mm. respectively. If liquid is passing through the two tubes, entering at A at a pressure of 80 cm. of mercury and leaving B at a pressure of 76 cm. of mercury, find the pressure at the junction of A and B.

50. Bubbles of the same diameter are blown at the end of a long narrow tube using successively two liquids A and B. If the times taken for the bubbles to collapse are 30 sec. and 20 sec. respectively, what is the ratio of the surface tensions of A and B?

ANSWERS AND HINTS FOR SOLUTION

1. $t = f(m, l, g)$; dimensionally $t = T$, $m = M$, $l = L$, $g = LT^{-2}$. Suppose $t \propto m^\alpha l^\beta g^\gamma$, so dimensionally $T = M^\alpha L^\beta L^\gamma T^{-2\gamma}$; equating indices, $\alpha = 0$, $\beta = \frac{1}{2}$, $\gamma = -\frac{1}{2}$; hence $t \propto (l/g)^{\frac{1}{2}}$.

2. $V/t = f(p/l, \ r, \ \eta) \propto (p/l)^\alpha \cdot r^\beta \cdot \eta^\gamma$; dimensionally η is given by: viscous force = area × velocity gradient × η; whence $\eta = ML^{-1}T^{-1}$; also $r = L$ and $p/l = ML^{-2}T^{-2}$; $V/t \propto p/l \cdot r^4 \cdot 1/\eta$.

3. If U and V are the velocities of M before and after collision and v is the velocity given to m, then (a) conservation of momentum along the initial direction of motion gives $MU = MV \cos\phi + mv \cos\theta$, (b) conservation of momentum perpendicular to previous direction gives $MV \sin\phi = mv \sin\theta$, and (c) conservation of translational energy gives $MU^2 = MV^2 + mv^2$. Eliminate U, V and v.

4. Momentum brought up per sec. = $100 \times 0\cdot1 \times 5 \times 10^3 = 5 \times 10^4$ and momentum taken away is $-0\cdot9 \times 5 \times 10^4$; total change in momentum per sec. is $9\cdot5 \times 10^4$, and by Newton's second law of motion, this is the force. Hence pressure = force/area = 10^4 dynes/cm.²

5. Loss in potential energy of particle after descending vertical distance h is mgh. Force on particle down plane is $mg \sin30° - \frac{1}{4}mg \cos30°$; gain in kinetic energy after travelling distance $h \cosec30°$ is therefore $(mg \sin30° - \frac{1}{4}mg \cos30°) . h \cosec30°$.

6. If downward acceleration of lift is f, considering forces on weight, $5g - 4\cdot5g = 5 . f$; $f = 3\cdot2$ ft./sec.²; zero.

7. Considering forces on deflected mascot, if horizontal deceleration of car is f, $f/g = \tan10°$; also $v^2 - u^2 = 2fs$; or $s = 386$ ft.

8. Moment of inertia × angular acceleration = applied couple. I × ang. acc. = $1 \times 32 \times 1/12$, since acceleration is small; also $s = ut + \frac{1}{2}ft^2$ or $f = 12/100$ ft./sec.². Hence ang. acc. = $12 \times 12/100 = 144/100$; therefore I $= 100/54$ and $k^2 = I/M = 1/54$ ft.²

9. Let distance of first plane from port be d at instant second plane starts from port, and let least separation of planes occur at subsequent time t. Then $s^2 = (d - u_1t)^2 + u_2{}^2t^2 - 2u_2t(d - u_1t) \cos\theta$; for s to be a minimum $ds/dt = 0$; hence $t = d(u_1 + u_2 \cos\theta)/(u_1{}^2 + u_2{}^2 + 2u_1u_2 \cos\theta)$, so required ratio $(d - u_1t)/u_2t = (u_2 + u_1 \cos\theta)/(u_1 + u_2 \cos\theta)$.

10. Angular velocity of rotation of earth is $2\pi/24 \times 60 \times 60$ radians per sec. Hence $r\omega^2 = 3\cdot4$ cm./sec.² Observed acceleration g is resultant of g_0 for a non-rotating earth and centrifugal acceleration due to rotation.

Hence $g^2 = g_0{}^2 + r^2\omega^2 \cos^2\lambda - 2g_0 r\omega^2 \cos\lambda$ or approximately $g = g_0 - r\omega^2 \cos^2\lambda$, neglecting $r^2\omega^4 \cos^2\lambda$ and expanding the R.H.S. by the binomial theorem. Hence $g_0 = 982\cdot7$ and $g_{60°} = 981\cdot85$ cm./sec.

11. At highest point, equation of motion in a circle gives $v_1{}^2/r = g(\sin\theta + \mu\cos\theta)$; at mid-point $v_2{}^2/r = \mu g \cos\theta$.

12. Kinetic energy of pellet is $m \times 144/2 \times 32 = 9m/4$ ft.-lb. Gain in potential energy is $2m$ ft.-lb. Hence loss in energy due to friction is $11\cdot1$ per cent.

13. Equation of equilibrium, neglecting friction, is

$$v^2 \cos\theta/r = g\sin\theta; \quad 44° \text{ approx.}$$

14. Taking moments about the line of contact of the off-side wheels and the road, $2v^2/r = 2\cdot5g$; $28\cdot3$ ft./sec.

15. Objects will leave platform if vertical acceleration of latter $> g$. Equation of motion of platform is $x = a\cos\omega t$; hence maximum value of acceleration is $d^2x/dt^2 = -a\omega^2$. Hence $\omega = (g/a)^{\frac{1}{2}}$ and $t = 2\pi/\omega = 0\cdot45$ sec.

16. Component of gravitational force along tunnel at any instant is mgx/r where x is distance along tunnel measured from its deepest point; hence motion is simple harmonic, and period is $t = 2\pi(r/g)^{\frac{1}{2}}$, and time taken is $t/2 = 42$ min.

17. If depression from equilibrium level is x, restoring force is $2x$. $A \cdot \rho \cdot g$, where A is area of cross-section and ρ is density. Motion is S.H., equation being $2xA\rho g + 100A\rho \times$ acceleration $= 0$. Period $t = 2\pi(50/g)^{\frac{1}{2}}$ $= 1\cdot42$ sec.

18. Equation of motion about point of suspension is $m[k^2 + (l + a)^2] \times d^2\theta/dt^2 + mg(l + a)\theta = 0$; length of equivalent simple pendulum is therefore

$$[2a^2/5 + (l + a)^2]/(l + a) = 135\cdot67 \text{ cm.}$$

19. If k^2 is radius of gyration of pendulum about axis through C.G., then $T_1 = 2\pi[(k^2 + h_1{}^2)/gh_1]^{\frac{1}{2}}$ and $T_2 = 2\pi[(k^2 + h_2{}^2)/gh_2]^{\frac{1}{2}}$, where h_1 and h_2 are the distances of the points of suspension from the C.G. Eliminate k^2; hence $4\pi^2/g = (h_1 T_1{}^2 - h_2 T_2{}^2)/(h_1{}^2 - h_2{}^2) = \frac{1}{2}(T_1{}^2 + T_2{}^2)/(h_1 + h_2) + \frac{1}{2}(T_1{}^2 - T_2{}^2)/(h_1 - h_2)$ by partial fractions. Since $T_1 \sim T_2$ but $h_1 \neq h_2$, the second term on the R.H.S. is negligible.

20. Let tension in each of n strings $= T = Mg/n$, where M is mass of hoop. Restoring force is $nT\theta$ where strings are inclined at θ to vertical, and couple about centre is $nT\theta a = nTa^2\phi/l$, where l is length of string, a is radius of hoop, and ϕ is rotation of hoop in horizontal plane. Equation of motion is $Ma^2 g\phi/l + Ma^2 \times$ ang. acc. $= 0$; hence $t = 2\pi(l/g)^{\frac{1}{2}}$.

21. Resolving forces vertically, if limiting tension in wire is T, $2T\sin\alpha = Mg$; $2\cdot25$ min.

22. Kinetic energy of mass $=$ loss in gravitational potential energy less potential energy stored in spring, that is $\frac{1}{2}mv^2 = mga -$ spring energy. To calculate spring energy, let $F =$ tension when extension is x; then

work done in stretching a further distance dx is F dx, and total work done in stretching spring through distance a is $\int_0^a$ F dx. Now F $= kx$, where k is constant; hence potential energy in spring is $\frac{1}{2}ka^2$. Actually $k = 50 \times 981$, $a = 10$ and $m = 1000$, hence $v = 121\cdot4$ cm./sec.

23. Maximum extension occurs when kinetic energy is zero; hence $mgh = \frac{1}{2}kh^2$; $h = 40$ cm.; $t = 2\pi(m/k)^{\frac{1}{2}} = 0\cdot9$ sec.

24. Energy stored in wire is $\frac{1}{2}qAa^2/l$, where a is extension, l is original length, A is area of cross-section, and q is Young's modulus. Alternatively, $a = Pl/qA$; hence E $= \frac{1}{2}P^2l/qA$, where P is the stretching force; $1\cdot9 \times 10^4$ ergs.

25. Since 2 kgm. weight stretches wire through 1 mm., a weight of 10 kgm. will be required to stretch the wire through 5 mm. Work done will be loss in potential energy of weight or $4\cdot9 \times 10^6$ ergs.

26. $Pl/A_1a_1 = q_1$, $Pl/A_2a_2 = q_2$. Hence $a_1/a_2 = 11/48$.

27. From definitions, $\gamma = (v_t - v_0)/v_0t$, P $= k(v_t - v_0)/v_0 = k\gamma t$.

28. If θ is angle at which strings are inclined to the vertical, $\theta = 10 \times 10^{-3}/100 = 10^{-4}$ rads. Resolving forces vertically, 2T $\cos\theta = 800$, or 2T $= 800$ approx.; horizontally, couple about vertical axis through centre of rod is $2T\theta \cdot 10 = 0\cdot8$ gm. cm.

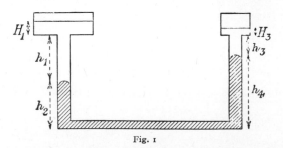

Fig. 1

29. Equation of motion about vertical axis through centre of rod is $1 \times$ ang. acc. $+ 2Tr\theta = 0$, or I $\times$ ang. acc. $+ Mgr^2\phi/l = 0$, whence time of oscillation $t = 2\pi(Il/Mgr^2)^{\frac{1}{2}}$. For rectangular bar of small width I $= Mr^2/3$, hence $t = 1\cdot16$ sec.

30. Let weight W be lifted 1 in.; then distance through which person exerts 80 lb. force is $2 \cdot \pi \cdot 3 \cdot 10$ ft., and work done is $4800\,\pi$ ft.-lb. Hence W $\times 1/12 = 4800\pi$; $180\pi/7$ tons.

31. 6T $= 200$, so T $= \dfrac{100}{3}$ lb.; $\dfrac{5000}{3}$ ft.-lb.

32. $mg = GmM/R^2$ or $\rho = 3g/4\pi GR$; $5\cdot43$ gm./c.c.

33. Weight of body in air $50 - 25 = 25$ gm. If V $=$ vol. of body, then for equilibrium when body is in lower pan $50 + V = 30 + 25$, so V $= 5$ c.c. Since $V\rho = 25$, $\rho = 5$ gm./c.c.

34. Let initial heights be as shown in fig. 1, and let final heights have primed values. For equilibrium, if initial gas pressure is p, $p + h_1 + H_1 + h_2\rho = p + h_3 + H_3 + h_4\rho$, or $\Delta h \cdot \rho = (h_1 + H_1) - (h_3 + H_3)$, where Δh is initial difference between levels of liquid. Finally $2 + (h_1' + H_1') - (h_3' + H_3') = \Delta h' \cdot \rho$. Equations of continuity give, since liquid is incompressible, $(h_1 - h_1')1 = (H_1' - H_1)10$, $(h_3' - h_3)1 = (H_3 - H_3')5$; also $(h_2 - h_2') = (h_4' - h_4) = \Delta H/2 = (h_1' - h_1) = (h_3 - h_3')$ where $\Delta H = \Delta h' - \Delta h$. Putting $\rho = 2$, $\Delta H = 40/23$ cm.

35. Taking moments about point of contact of pole and bank, if x is length immersed, $10 \times 0.6 \times 5 = x(10 - x/2)$ or $x^2 - 20x + 60 = 0$; 3·68 ft.

36. Pressure on side when depth is h is $ha \cdot \frac{1}{2}\rho gh$; this acts effectively at centre of pressure $h/3$ from base. Hence limiting height is given by $h^3 a \rho g/6 = G$ or $h = (6G/ag)^{1/3}$ for water.

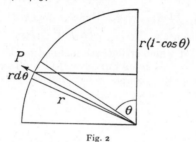

Fig. 2

37. Referring to fig. 2, force on an elementary strip of width $r\,d\theta$ and depth $r(1 - \cos\theta)$ is $\rho g r^2 l(1 - \cos\theta)\,d\theta$ normal to surface. Hence total vertical component of force $V = \int_0^{\pi/2} \rho g r^2 l(1 - \cos\theta)\cos\theta\,d\theta$, and total horizontal component $H = \int_0^{\pi/2} \rho g r^2 l(1 - \cos\theta)\sin\theta\,d\theta$.

38. Divide the triangle into elementary strips of width dx measuring x from the vertex; force on strip parallel to base is $2x\Delta \cdot dx \cdot \rho g(h + x)/h^2$, where Δ is area of triangle. Hence centre of pressure is distance x from vertex where

$$x = \int_0^h x^2(h + x)\,dx \Big/ \int_0^h x(h + x)\,dx = 7h/10.$$

39. If density of body is ρ and volume is V, then if equilibrium is reached when immersed volume is v, $V\rho = v$, which is independent of area of cross-section.

40. Let immersed volume of floating body $= v$. For equilibrium, $v = 20$. If area of cross-section of cylindrical vessel is A, $(34 - 30)A = v$ or $A = 5$ cm.^{2}. When completely submerged $(36 - 30)A = V$ or $V = 30$ c.c.; hence $\rho = 2/3$. Additional upthrust on complete immersion is $(V - v) = 10$ gm.

41. p/ρ = constant; air leaks out when its density exceeds 1·03; 8000 metres.

42. Restoring force for further depression x is $xA\rho g$; hence equation of motion is $10A\rho \times$ acc. $+ xA\rho g = 0$, where A is area of cross-section of cylinder and ρ is density of liquid; $t = 2\pi(10/g)^{\frac{1}{2}} = 0·63$ sec.

43. $C_{12}H_{22}O_{11}$ has molecular weight in gm. = 342, and this dissolved in $22·4 \times 10^3$ c.c. of water exerts an osmotic pressure of 76 cm. of mercury at $0°$ C. Hence a 1 per cent solution at $100°$ C. exerts an osmotic pressure $76 \times 22·4 \times 10^3 \times 373/342 \times 100 \times 273 = 68$ cm. of mercury.

44. To find relation between surface tension S and tension T in band, let radius be r and apply principle of virtual work. Then we have $2\pi\,dr$. T = $2 . 2\pi r$S . dr, or T = $2r$S. Also $T/0·2\pi = 910/\pi$ or T = 182 dynes. Hence S = $182/5·2 = 35$ dynes/cm.

45. Consider shape of film at edge; it has two radii of curvature in directions at right angles, $R_1 \approx d/2$ and R_2, where $\pi R_2^2 = A$; hence excess pressure acting over film is $p = T(1/R_1 \pm 1/R_2) = 2T/d$, since $R_2 \gg R_1$. Hence total force urging plates together is $pA = 2TA/d$.

46. $p = 4T/R = 28$ dynes/cm.^{2}. Work done in increasing radius from r to $r + dr$ is $p\,dV = 4T . 4\pi r^2\,dr/r$, and total work done in blowing bubble of radius 5 cm. is $16\pi T \int_0^5 r\,dr = 7000\pi$ ergs.

47. If immersed length is l, equilibrium occurs when $\pi . 1 . l = 2\pi . 1 . 75/981 + 20$; hence $l = 6·52$ cm.

48. Equation of equilibrium for each arm is $2\pi r T \cos\psi = \pi r^2 H\rho g + \pi r^3 \rho g(\sec\psi + \frac{2}{3}\tan^3\psi - \frac{2}{3}\sec^3\psi)$, where ψ is the angle of contact, and where first term on R.H.S. is due to volume of cylinder of supported liquid and second term is due to volume of meniscus; 1·342 cm.

49. Applying continuity equation, volume per sec. passing through tubes is $V = \pi(p_1 - p)r_1^4/8l_1\eta = \pi(p - p_2)r_2^4/8l_2\eta$; 76·12 cm. of mercury.

50. If Poiseuille's equation holds, $V \propto$ excess pressure $\propto T/R$, but time taken is inversely proportional to V; 2 : 3.

PART II

HEAT

CHAPTER I

Temperature and Thermometry

1. Introduction.

We commence our study of Heat with considerations of Temperature. Over a limited range, **temperature** is a concept which is directly appreciated as a sense perception and we may define it as the **degree of hotness of a body.** A more precise definition requires a considerable knowledge of heat phenomena and we shall not attempt it at this stage. We may note, however, that temperature receives a ready explanation on the molecular hypothesis (Chap. XI), where it is identified with the kinetic energy of the molecules.

2. Scale of Temperature.

Most people have little difficulty in distinguishing the temperatures of different bodies over a limited range if the temperature difference is large, but it requires great skill, experience and aptitude to detect a temperature difference of $\frac{1}{4}°$ C. Again, wood and metal, although actually at the same temperature, appear to be at different temperatures if they are judged by touch. We therefore need a means of estimating temperature which is (*a*) more reliable and objective, (*b*) more sensitive, than direct determination from the sense of touch. Any physical property which changes continuously with temperature, e.g. length, volume, gas pressure, electrical resistance, &c., may be used to measure temperature. Most of these physical properties increase in magnitude with increased temperature, but they do not all increase at the same rate or in the same way. For example, while we might define the temperature θ_2 at which a wire had twice the electrical resistance it possessed at a temperature θ_1 by the relation $\theta_2 = 2\theta_1$, we should not in general find that the volume or length of bodies was doubled on raising the temperature from θ_1 to θ_2. **Each physical property therefore has its own temperature scale.** Because of the interdependence of physical phenomena the different temperature scales are connected, and, as we shall see (section 6, Chap. XIII), it is even possible to define an **absolute scale of temperature.**

3. The Centigrade Scale.

The melting-point of ice and the boiling-point of water take place at definite temperatures if certain conditions are fulfilled. If these two temperatures are called 0° and 100° respectively, they are said to represent two *fixed points on the Centigrade scale.* Now the melting-point and boiling-point depend very much on the purity of the substance. They also vary with changes of external atmospheric pressure. As pure water is easily obtained it is suitable for giving the fixed points and accordingly **0° C. is defined as the temperature of melting ice under an external pressure of 760 mm. of mercury at sea-level and latitude 45°, while 100° C. is the boiling-point of water under the same conditions.**

When two fixed points have been determined, other temperatures are related to these by the *Centigrade definition,* namely

$$t° = (A_t - A_0)/\{(A_{100} - A_0)/100\}. \quad . \quad . \quad . \quad (1)$$

In equation (1), A_t is the magnitude at temperature $t°$ of the physical property which is being used to measure the temperature $t°$, A_0 is the magnitude of that quantity at 0° C. and A_{100} its value at 100° C. Equation (1) may therefore be expressed as

$$t° = \frac{\text{Change in magnitude of property}}{\frac{1}{100} \text{ (change in magnitude of property on raising from 0° to 100°)}}.$$

To fix ideas, let us suppose A represents the length of the mercury column in a mercury thermometer. Then from (1)

$$t_l = (l - l_0)/\{(l_{100} - l_0)/100\}, \quad . \quad . \quad (2)$$

where l_{100} is its length at 100° C., l_0 its length at 0° C., and l its length at t_l. Equation (2) therefore defines t_l and allows it to be calculated.

4. Common Mercury Thermometer.

The name **thermometer** is given to any instrument which is used to measure temperature. The name **thermoscope** is usually reserved for instruments which register a single temperature. For example, the action of an electric fuse depends on one temperature only, that of its melting-point, and thus it constitutes a typical discontinuous thermoscope. The commonest type of thermometer is the liquid-in-glass thermometer, the liquid usually being mercury.

The mercury thermometer, as shown in fig. 1, consists of a bulb blown at the end of a glass tube of

Fig. 1.—Mercury Thermometer

capillary bore. Clean dry mercury is introduced by alternate heating and cooling until all the air is expelled and the whole is filled with mercury. While the mercury is still hot and occupying the whole of the bulb and tube, the top end of the tube is sealed. On allowing the thermometer to cool, the mercury contracts until at room temperature it is standing a few centimetres above the bulb. The instrument is now calibrated by immersing the bulb first in melting ice as shown in fig. 2, and then **in the steam** from boiling water as shown in fig. 3. Scratches are made on the glass tube opposite the level of the mercury under the two conditions and the figures 0° and 100° are engraved on the tube. The space between the 0° and 100° is then subdivided into 100 equal parts, figures being engraved on the

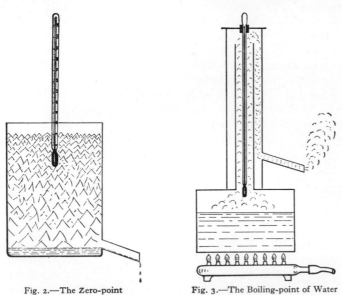

Fig. 2.—The Zero-point   Fig. 3.—The Boiling-point of Water

tube at suitable intervals. Such division is termed **interpolation;** the scale may also be **extrapolated** below 0° C. and above 100° C. by continuing the uniform divisions beyond these temperatures.

5. Some Temperature Scales.

One of the earliest thermometers on record was that devised by Galileo. It consisted of an inverted glass bulb containing air. The neck of the bulb dipped into a reservoir of coloured liquid. Rise of temperature resulted in expansion of the air and change in position of the level of coloured liquid in the neck. Galileo also made a liquid-in-glass thermometer, using alcohol as the working substance. For many years, however, temperature scales remained quite arbitrary, partly owing to the difficulty of obtaining pure working substances and partly because it was not realized that fixed points could be obtained simply from melting- and boiling-points of suitable materials.

Little progress was made until 1701, when Newton proposed a

scale of temperature, defining 0° on the scale from the melting-point of ice and 12° as the temperature of the blood of a healthy man. On this scale, the boiling-point of water, which was regarded as too variable to be suitable for a fixed point, came to 34°. The working substance used was linseed oil. In 1714, a great step forward was made when **Fahrenheit** introduced mercury as the working substance, for this is comparatively easily purified. Fahrenheit introduced at the same time a scale of temperature which is still widely used in meteorology and medicine. This persistence is unfortunate, since the fixed points on Fahrenheit's scale were most unsuitable for scientific work. The lowest temperature reached by an unrecorded mixture of ice and sal-ammoniac was taken as 0° F. and the warmth of the human body as 96° F. On the same scale, the melting-point of ice is 32° F. and the boiling-point of water is 212° F.

A third scale which is sometimes used is due to Réaumur. On this scale the fixed points are 0° R. at the melting-point of ice and 80° R. at the boiling-point of water.

To convert temperatures from one scale to another the ratios of two given intervals are equated; hence

$$\frac{C}{100} = \frac{F - 32}{180} = \frac{R}{80}. \quad \cdots \quad (3)$$

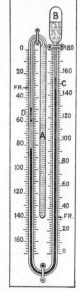

Fig. 4. — Six's Maximum and Minimum Thermometer.

6. Types of Thermometer.

(a) Liquid-in-glass Thermometers.

(i) *Six's Maximum and Minimum Thermometer.*

In this thermometer, a cylindrical bulb A as shown in fig. 4 is filled with alcohol which extends continuously up to the mercury column. More alcohol is situated beyond the mercury column, and finally an air and vapour space B exists at the far end of the tube, which is closed. Two small steel indices C and D are in contact with the ends of the mercury column. If the temperature rises, the volume of the alcohol in A increases and the mercury column is pushed round, driving the index C before it. If the temperature should now drop, the index C remains in its farthest position and thus indicates the **maximum** temperature which occurred. Conversely, the position of D indicates the **minimum** temperature reached. The indices are returned to the ends of the mercury column by the use of a magnet.

(ii) *Clinical Thermometer.*

This is an ordinary mercury thermometer except that it possesses a very fine constriction in the capillary bore, visible in fig. 5.

On inserting the bulb into the patient's mouth (say) the mercury
expands and indicates its appropriate temperature. On removal from
the patient, the mercury stays at its highest position, for the thread

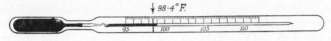

Fig. 5.—Clinical Thermometer

simply breaks at the constriction as the main bulk of mercury in the
bulb contracts. The entire scale is made to cover only some 10° F.,
so fractions of a degree are easily observed. The short
column of mercury is returned to the bulb by shaking.

(iii) *Beckmann Thermometer.*

This thermometer is designed to read **differences** of
temperature to $\frac{1}{100}$° C. As shown in fig. 6 it consists of
a large bulb A containing mercury and connected with
the usual capillary stem B, graduated with five or six
large divisions each corresponding to 1° C. and each
subdivided into 100 equal parts. So that the instrument
may be used over a large range of temperature, the bulb
C is constricted at the top end of the thermometer.
Mercury is then jerked over from A to C or vice versa
so that when the bulb A is immersed in the vessel whose
temperature **change** is required, the mercury stands at a
convenient height in the stem B.

We shall discuss other types of thermometer only
very briefly in this chapter. Their use depends upon a
knowledge of a variety of physical phenomena which are
discussed in detail in the chapters concerned.

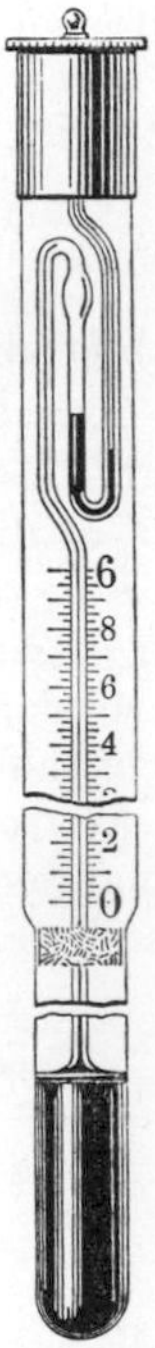

(*b*) **Gas Thermometers.**

These may be of the constant pressure or constant
volume type. In practice, the **constant volume thermometer** described in detail in Chap. VII constitutes the
basic thermometer against which all others are calibrated.
The scale of temperature defined by the constant volume
hydrogen thermometer is referred to as the **gas scale.** The relation
of the gas scale with the **absolute scale** is discussed in Chap. XIII.

Fig. 6.—Beck-
mann Thermo-
meter.

(*c*) **Platinum Resistance Thermometer.**

This thermometer is described in detail in Part **V.**

(*d*) Thermocouples.

These instruments are described in detail in Part V.

(*e*) Radiation Pyrometers.

The radiation pyrometers are instruments which depend for their action on the properties of Radiant Heat. They are therefore described in Chap. XIV. They are of two distinct types: (*a*) the *total radiation pyrometer* associated with Stefan's law, and (*b*) the *optical pyrometers* based on Planck's law.

(*f*) Vapour Pressure Thermometers.

These depend for their action on the variation of vapour pressure with temperature, which is discussed more fully in Chap. IX.

(*g*) Magnetic Susceptibility Thermometers.

The variation of the magnetic susceptibility (see Part V) with temperature has been used to measure temperatures near the absolute zero.

(*h*) Strain Thermometers.

These depend for their action on the unequal expansion of different materials for the same temperature rise. Two short bars of equal length but of different metals are placed side by side and attached rigidly to a metal cross-piece at one end. If the temperature is raised, one bar expands more than the other and a suitable system of levers may be actuated by the unequal expansion to move a pointer over a scale as in the " radiator " indicator attached to automobiles.

We conclude this chapter with a table stating some of the advantages and disadvantages of the various types of thermometer mentioned.

Type	Advantages	Disadvantages	Range
1. Liquid in glass	(1) Simple; (2) convenient size; (3) direct reading; (4) easy to read; (5) moderately quick in action.	(1) Restricted range; (2) zero changes with time owing to contraction of glass envelope: this reduced to a minimum by " aging " the glass naturally or artificially; (3) variation in reading with the length of the column exposed: correction can be calculated; (4) reading varies with changes in external and internal pressure: corrections obtained by calibration.	$-30°$C. to $400°$ C. with nitrogen above mercury. $30°$ C. to $-100°$ C. with alcohol.

Type	Advantages	Disadvantages	Range
2. Gas thermometer	(1) Enormous range; (2) no effective zero changes since expansion of envelope $\ll$ gas expansion; (3) accurate values owing to large gas expansion; (4) individual corrections not required since all permanent gases identical in behaviour.	(1) Complicated; (2) bulky; (3) slow in action; (4) uncertain corrections for the " dead space "; (5) not direct reading.	$-270°$ C. to $2500°$ C.
3. Platinum resistance thermometer	(1) Wide range; (2) no zero change; (3) reads easily to $1/50°$ C.; (4) quick reading.	(1) Complicated; (2) expensive; (3) not direct reading.	$-200°$ C. to $1200°$ C.
4. Thermocouples	(1) Wide range; (2) moderately cheap; (3) quick reading; (4) very low heat capacity and small size ensures minimum disturbance due to thermometer.	(1) Complicated; (2) requires frequent calibration as zero changes; (3) not direct reading.	$-270°$ C. to $2000°$ C.
5. Radiation Pyrometers (a) *Total radiation type*	(1) Large range; (2) otherwise as for thermocouples.	(1) Complicated; (2) requires calibration as T^4 law only applicable to black bodies (see Chap. XIV).	$500°$ C. upwards.
(b) *Optical type*	(1) Large range; (2) not so dependent as type (a) on black body conditions; (3) does not require such a large area of emitter as type (a).	(1) Complicated; (2) requires calibration as Planck's law is strictly true for black bodies only.	$600°$ C. upwards.
6 and 7. Vapour pressure thermometers and magnetic susceptibility thermometers	Useful at very low temperatures.	(1) Complicated; (2) require calibration against gas thermometer at higher temperatures and then have to be subjected to rather uncertain extrapolation down into the region where they are to be used.	$0°$ to $5°$ *absolute.*

EXERCISES

1. Explain clearly how a scale of temperature is established and discuss the choice of fixed points.

2. An accurate Fahrenheit thermometer and a Centigrade thermometer register 160° and 70° respectively when placed in the same enclosure, which is at uniform temperature.

What is the error in the Centigrade thermometer? [−1·1° C.]

3. Write a short essay on the methods of measuring temperature.

CHAPTER II

Thermal Expansion of Solids and Liquids

1. Introduction.

It is a matter of common observation that a change of size occurs when the temperature of a body is changed. In general the change is undesirable and allowances must be made for it. For example, railway lines are laid down in short lengths which are placed end to end but not quite in contact. Expansion consequent on rise of temperature does not then cause buckling of the rails. Similarly, long steam pipes are not made quite straight but have a loop or bend at intervals to provide " slack " which may be taken up or given out according as the temperature falls or rises.

2. Coefficients of Expansion.

When a rod is heated, its change in length is much larger than its change in breadth or depth. Considering only the change in length, we define the **coefficient of linear expansion** a of the material of the rod by the relation

$$a = \frac{l_t - l_0}{l_0 \, t}, \qquad \ldots \ldots \quad (2.1)$$

where
$$l_0 = \text{length of rod at its initial temperature,}$$
$$l_t = \text{length of rod when it has been raised } t°,$$
$$t° = \text{rise in temperature.}$$

The coefficient of linear expansion is therefore the increase in length divided by the original length for a rise in temperature of 1°. Equation (2.1) is often written in the form

$$l_t = l_0(1 + at). \qquad \ldots \ldots \quad (2.2)$$

Again, if a square plate as shown in fig. 1 is heated, the change in area is relatively larger than the change in thickness. If we concentrate on the change in area, we define the **coefficient of surface expansion** β by a relation similar to (2.1),

$$\beta = \frac{S_t - S_0}{S_0 \, t}, \quad \ldots \ldots \quad (2.3)$$

where S_0 = area of plate at its initial temperature,
            S_t = area of plate when it has been raised $t°$,
            $t°$ = rise in temperature.

Equation (2.3) may alternatively be written

$$S_t = S_0(1 + \beta t). \quad \ldots \ldots \quad (2.4)$$

Further, reference to fig. 1 shows that β and α are related, for $S_t = l_t^2$, so from equation (2.2)

$$S_t = l_0^2(1 + \alpha t)^2 = S_0(1 + 2\alpha t + \alpha^2 t^2)$$
$$= S_0(1 + 2\alpha t), \quad \ldots \ldots \ldots \quad (2.5)$$

for $S_0 = l_0^2$, and we may neglect the term involving α^2 except for

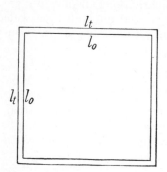

very large temperature changes since $\alpha \sim 10^{-6}$ per °C. Hence, comparing equations (2.4) and (2.5), $\beta = 2\alpha$, or the coefficient of surface expansion is twice the coefficient of linear expansion. The relation is sufficiently true to make it quite unnecessary to measure the coefficient of surface expansion for a material if its coefficient of linear expansion has been already determined.

Fig. 1.—Expansion of Square Plate

Finally, if a cube is heated it expands, the coefficient of volume expansion γ being defined by

$$\gamma = \frac{V_t - V_0}{V_0 \, t}, \quad \ldots \ldots \quad (2.6)$$

or, as it may be written,

$$V_t = V_0(1 + \gamma t). \quad \ldots \ldots \quad (2.7)$$

It is left as an exercise to the student to show that $\gamma = 3\alpha$ approximately.

These simple relations between the coefficients of expansion hold only for isotropic substances (see Chap. VIII, Part I). Some crystals expand by different amounts along their different crystallographic axes.

3. Timepieces.

The time of oscillation of a pendulum is governed mainly by the distance of the centre of gravity of the pendulum from the axis of suspension. Consequently, when a rise in temperature occurs the clock loses, for the length of the pendulum is increased and therefore the time of oscillation also (see Chap. III, Part I). To allow for this, pendulums are often constructed of wood, the coefficient of expansion of which is exceptionally small. More robust pendulums are made of **invar steel**, a nickel steel alloy, which also has a very small coefficient of expansion. Unfortunately invar has a sufficiently high magnetic susceptibility to be influenced by changes in the earth's magnetic field. Other alloys, such as **elinvar**, are less influenced and therefore more suitable. Before the introduction of these alloys, methods of compensation had to be used. Thus **Harrison's grid-iron pendulum** consisted of alternate bars of iron and brass connected as shown in fig. 2. Change of temperature resulted in a lowering of the pendulum bob due to the expansion of the iron rods and a rise due to the expansion of the brass rods. Clearly the height of the bob will not change if $l_1 a_1 = l_2 a_2$, where l_1 and l_2 are the **total** lengths of iron and brass rods respectively, and a_1 and a_2 are the coefficients of linear expansion of the two metals.

Fig. 2.—Harrison's Grid-iron Pendulum.

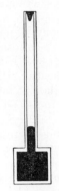

Fig. 3.—Graham's Hollow Iron Rod Pendulum.

An alternative pendulum designed by Graham consisted of a hollow iron rod as shown in fig. 3, attached to a reservoir containing mercury. Increase in length of the iron rod was compensated by a rise in the level of the mercury. By adjusting the quantity of mercury, exact compensation could be obtained.

In watches, the time is controlled by the **balance wheel**, the period of the oscillation of which is governed by the moment of inertia (see Chap. IV, Part I) of the wheel about its axis of oscillation. As the temperature rises the spokes of the wheel expand, the rim of the wheel is pushed farther from the axis and the moment of inertia is increased. The main contribution to the moment of inertia is from small

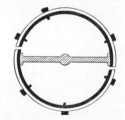

Fig. 4.—Balance Wheel

screw-weights situated on the rim of the wheel, and if these are kept at a constant distance from the axis compensation is attained. Accordingly, the rim of the wheel is made of two metals as shown in fig. 4, with different coefficients of expansion. The metal with the lower coefficient is placed on the inside and that with the larger coefficient on the outside. Consequently, when the temperature rises the curvature of the rim increases, and by suitable adjustment the amount by which the increased curvature of the rim brings the weights closer to the axis may be made exactly equal to the amount by which they are thrust outwards from the axis by the expansion of the spokes.

4. Useful Applications of Thermal Expansion.

Perhaps the most useful application of thermal expansion is the use of liquids as thermometric substances. Apart from this use, which we have already discussed in Chap. I, a number of other applications may be noted.

In former times, and to some extent to-day, cart-wheels are made of wood, bound by a steel hoop. The latter is fixed in position by heating the hoop until its internal diameter is sufficiently large to allow it to be slipped over the wheel. On cooling, the metal rim contracts and grips the wooden wheel firmly.

The S-shaped piece of iron seen on the outside of some farm-buildings is an indication of a tie-rod which runs through the rafters and is attached at each end to an S-shaped piece. The purpose is to strengthen the walls of the barn, and the arrangement is fixed in position by heating the rod in the centre and then screwing the S-shaped pieces as close as possible to the outside of the two opposite walls. When the tie-rod cools and contracts a large stress is set up tending to pull the two walls together and prevent outward collapse.

If it is desired to attach machine parts, such as a wheel and axle or gun barrels, without the use of set-screws, then the two parts may be " sweated " together by having the hole in the wheel slightly smaller than the diameter of the axle and then heating the former until it will slip over the axle. The method has the disadvantage that the metals may suffer by heat treatment. Accordingly, the more recent method of **shrinkage fits** is often used. For the example quoted above, the axle is immersed in " dry ice ", the trade name for solid carbon dioxide. The temperature of the axle is thus reduced to about $-80°$ C., and the axle contracts sufficiently to allow it to be inserted into the wheel.

We may also note that since platinum has approximately the same thermal coefficient of expansion as glass, platinum wires may be fused through holes in a glass vessel and no strain will occur when the whole returns to room temperature. It is also possible to fuse glass to other metals if the latter are made sufficiently thin so as to give easily and take the strain when the glass cools.

Another useful application of thermal expansion is the gas regulator and **thermostat**. One form of thermostat is shown in fig. 5. A long bulb B is filled with toluene (a liquid of exceptionally large expansion coefficient) which is in contact with a mercury column. Gas entering by the tube T_1 proceeds to the burner by the main tube T_2. If the temperature in the neighbourhood of B rises sufficiently, the toluene expands and pushes the mercury up the tube; the gas supply is thus cut off by the blocking of T_2. Actually a small bypass T_3 allows sufficient gas to pass to keep the flame burning, but the heat provided is insufficient to maintain the temperature of B. Consequently, the toluene contracts and more gas is again admitted through T_2. In this way the temperature in the neighbourhood of B is maintained constant to one or two degrees. A simple modification of the apparatus uses electrical heating, the moving mercury column being used to make and break electrical contacts.

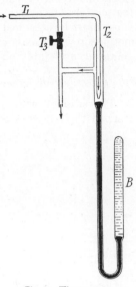

Fig. 5.—Thermostat

5. Measurement of Linear Expansion.

As the coefficient of linear expansion is very small, direct measurement with an ordinary scale is impossible. Various methods of magnification have therefore to be adopted. Mechanical and optical levers may be used, but the best methods are either comparator or interferometer methods.

(a) *Comparator Methods.*

In these methods the bar AB may rest freely on rollers as shown in fig. 6, the whole being enclosed in a double-walled box with glass

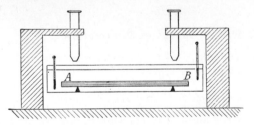

Fig. 6.—-Measurement of Linear Expansion

windows through which two scratches on the bar may be observed with microscopes containing calibrated scales in the eye-pieces. Water is then allowed to surround the bar, the temperature being thermostatically controlled. The temperatures are read from thermometers inserted in the water-bath and the changes in length are read directly on the scales in the eye-pieces of the microscopes which are focussed on the scratches on the bar. If the changes in length are too large for the scratches to remain on the scale in the eye-piece, the whole microscope must be attached to a carriage which may be moved by a micrometer screw. In all circumstances the microscopes must be firmly mounted, preferably on stone pillars.

*(b) *Fizeau's Interference Methods for Crystals.*

The student will appreciate this method fully only after having grasped the contents of Chap. VII, Part III, Light. In fig. 7, a lens

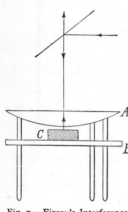

A is allowed to rest on three points above a polished metal table B, and the specimen C whose coefficient of expansion is required is inserted between A and B. A Newton's rings system is formed in the air-space between A and C and the temperature of the whole is then raised. Owing to the expansion of C, the thickness of the air-space changes, and this is accompanied by a movement in the Newton's rings system. In particular, rings appear to be born in the centre of the system and to expand outwards. Counting of the number of rings created allows changes in height of the specimen to be measured to 10^{-5} cm. Allowance must be made for the increased size of the apparatus as a whole and for the changes in refractive index of air

Fig. 7.—Fizeau's Interference Method

when the temperature is changed. This is achieved by performing a subsidiary experiment without the specimen in position.

6. Forces produced by Change of Temperature.

The student should read the articles on stress and strain in Chap. VIII, Part I, before proceeding with this section.

(a) *Force required to hold a Heated Bar Extended.*

Suppose a bar is allowed to cool but is prevented from contracting by being gripped at the ends. Then if l_t is the free length at the higher temperature and l_0 is the free length at the lower temperature, the rod is being kept in a state of increased length $(l_t - l_0) = l_0 a t$ from equation (2.2). The tension P set up in the rod is therefore that which would be required to increase the rod from a length l_0 by an amount $l_0 a t$.

From the definitions of stress and of Young's Modulus of Elasticity q we have therefore

$$q = \frac{\text{stress}}{\text{strain}} = \frac{P/A}{l_0 at/l_0},$$

or $$P = qAat. \quad \ldots \ldots \ldots \quad (2.8)$$

(b) *Force required to prevent a Heated Bar from Extending.*

The force required to prevent a bar extending when it is heated is clearly the force required to compress the rod back to its original length at the higher temperature after it has been freely allowed to expand. Hence

$$q = \frac{\text{stress}}{\text{strain}} = \frac{P/A}{l_0 at/l_t} = \frac{P/A}{l_0 at/l_0(1 + at)},$$

or $$P = \frac{qAat}{1 + at}. \quad \ldots \ldots \ldots \quad (2.9)$$

Since a is very small, the denominator of (2.9) is nearly unity so that (2.8) and (2.9) are in practice almost identical.

7. Cubical Expansion of Liquids.

Consideration of the thermal expansion of liquids leads to problems which do not occur with solids. For example, the liquid must be enclosed in a container, and in general the container will expand as well as the contained liquid, if a rise in temperature occurs. The apparent increase in volume which the liquid undergoes is therefore less than the true increase. Consequently, substitution in the expression (2.6)

$$\gamma = \frac{V_t - V_0}{V_0 t}$$

will only give an **apparent coefficient of expansion**. The true or **absolute coefficient of expansion** will be greater than this and we shall show immediately that

$$\gamma_{\text{absolute}} = \gamma_{\text{apparent}} + \gamma_{\text{container}}. \quad \ldots \quad (2.10)$$

The thermal expansion of liquids differs from that of solids in at least two other ways. First, while a given solid expands by equal amounts over almost any part of the temperature scale, liquids expand at different rates in different temperature regions. Some liquids, such as water, **contract** when the temperature is raised a few degrees at certain parts of the temperature scale. With liquids, therefore, it is usual to define a **mean coefficient of expansion**

$$\gamma_m = \frac{V_t - V}{V t}, \quad \ldots \ldots \quad (2.11)$$

where V is the volume at any temperature and V_t the volume of the same mass of liquid at a temperature $t°$ higher; and a **zero coefficient of expansion**

$$\gamma_0 = \frac{V_1 - V_0}{V_0}, \quad \cdots \cdots \quad (2.12)$$

where V_0 is the volume at 0° C. and V_1 the volume at 1° C.

Secondly, the thermal behaviour of liquids differs from that of solids in that their coefficient of cubical expansion is usually several hundred times larger than that of solids.

To deduce equation (2.10), we note the experimental fact that a hollow container such as a bottle expands just as though the bottle were solid.

Let $V_0 =$ initial vol. of bottle at lower temp.; $V_t =$ vol. of bottle when temp. is raised $t°$.

Then if the bottle contained a volume V_0 of the liquid at the lower temperature, suppose the observed volume of that liquid at the higher temperature is $V_{app.}$ and its true volume $V_{abs.}$ Then

$$V_{app.} = V_{abs.} - (V_t - V_0), \quad \cdots \cdots \quad (2.13)$$

since the expression in brackets represents the change in volume of the container. Applying equation (2.6),

$$\gamma_{app.} = \frac{V_{app.} - V_0}{V_0 t}, \quad \cdots \cdots \quad (2.14)$$

and

$$\gamma_{abs.} = \frac{V_{abs.} - V_0}{V_0 t}. \quad \cdots \cdots \quad (2.15)$$

Subtracting (2.14) from (2.15),

$$\gamma_{abs.} - \gamma_{app.} = \frac{V_{abs.} - V_{app.}}{V_0 t} = \frac{V_t - V_0}{V_0 t} = \gamma_{cont.},$$

from (2.13) and the definition of $\gamma_{cont.}$ This proves (2.10).

8. Variation of Density of Liquids with Temperature.

For a given mass m of liquid, from the definition of density (see Chap. IX, Part I),

$$m = \rho_0 V_0 = \rho_t V_t, \quad \cdots \cdots \quad (2.16)$$

where ρ_0, ρ_t are the densities at $0°$ and $t°$, and V_0 and V_t the corresponding volumes at these two temperatures. Hence, substituting in (2.6),

$$\gamma = \frac{\dfrac{m}{\rho_t} - \dfrac{m}{\rho_0}}{\dfrac{m}{\rho_0} \cdot t} = \frac{\rho_0 - \rho_t}{\rho_t t}, \quad \ldots \ldots (2.17)$$

or alternatively

$$\rho_0 = \rho_t(1 + \gamma t). \quad \ldots \ldots \ldots (2.18)$$

9. Variation of Density of Water with Temperature.

The thermal behaviour of water is exceptional in that it contracts fairly uniformly from room temperature down to $4°$ C., after which,

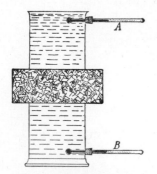

Fig. 8.—Hope's Apparatus for Density of Water

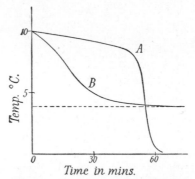

Fig. 9.—Temperature-time Curves

instead of continuing to contract it expands until it turns into ice at $0°$ C. The temperature $4°$ C. is said to be the temperature of the **maximum density of water,** and the existence of the phenomena is usually shown with an apparatus due to Hope. As shown in fig. 8, **Hope's apparatus** consists of a vertical hollow metal cylinder closed at the base, open at the top and surrounded round its centre by an annular tray. Pure water is placed in the cylinder and the temperature of the two thermometers A and B is observed to be the same. A freezing mixture is then introduced into the tray and temperature-time curves of A and B are then taken. The type of graph obtained is shown in fig. 9. The point where the two curves cross is the temperature of maximum density. The curves are explained as follows. As the layer of water at the centre of the cylinder is cooled by the mixture, its density is increased and consequently it sinks to the bottom of the cylinder. The temperature of the lower thermometer B therefore drops very rapidly, while that of the top thermometer A remains almost unchanged except for a slight lowering due to cooling by the very small conduction through the water from the cold layer at the centre. When the temperature of the central layer falls below 4° C., however, the cold layer becomes less dense than the water below it: consequently it tends to rise and thus cools the water *above* the central layer. The top thermometer A is therefore affected and shows a rapid lowering of temperature. Since the cold layers become less and less dense as their temperature approaches 0° C., they rise to the surface and freezing occurs first on the top of the water. The water at the bottom

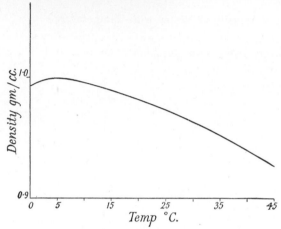

Fig. 10.—Density-temperature Graph of Water

of the vessel is still at a temperature of about 4° C. This behaviour is of great importance in nature, since it allows aquatic animals to exist at the bottom of the water in which they live. If the density of water continued to increase as the temperature fell to 0° C. the water would freeze from the bottom upwards and the organisms would be forced to the surface.

A graph of the variation of the density of water with temperature is shown in fig. 10. Note that the graph is not linear and the expansion is not uniform even after a temperature of 4° has been passed.

10. Measurement of the Thermal Expansion of Liquids.

(a) Volume Method.

By taking a flask with a long graduated neck and placing liquid inside it, the apparent coefficient of cubical expansion of the liquid can be found directly by immersing the flask in various temperature baths and noting the apparent volume of the liquid. The absolute coefficient of expansion of the liquid is then found by applying equation (2.10).

(b) *Weight Thermometer.*

In this method a bottle fitted with a perforated stopper (the weight thermometer) is first filled to the brim with liquid, weighed, and then heated through a known range of temperature. The liquid expands and some of it escapes from the bottle. The bottle is reweighed on cooling. Then if m_t and m_0 are the masses present at the higher and lower temperatures, and ρ_t, ρ_0, V_t, V_0 the corresponding densities and volumes respectively, then

$$\begin{aligned} V_0\rho_0 &= m_0, \\ V_t\rho_t &= m_t. \end{aligned} \qquad \dots \dots \quad (2.19)$$

Also, if γ is the coefficient of cubical expansion of the container,

$$V_t = V_0(1 + \gamma t), \quad \dots \dots \quad (2.20)$$

while from (2.18)

$$\rho_0 = \rho_t(1 + \gamma_{\text{liq.}}t). \quad \dots \dots \quad (2.21)$$

From (2.19), (2.20), and (2.21),

$$m_0/m_t = (1 + \gamma_{\text{liq.}}t)/(1 + \gamma t).$$

Hence
$$\gamma_{\text{liq.}} = \frac{m_0 - m_t}{m_t t} + \frac{m_0}{m_t}\gamma. \quad \dots \dots \quad (2.22)$$

Since the weight of a liquid may be determined with much greater accuracy than the volume, this method is superior to the previous one. However, it is not suitable for volatile liquids.

(c) *Method based on Archimedes' Principle.*

This method is a direct application of Archimedes' principle, and the experimental arrangement is that described in Part I, Chap. IX. For accurate results, a quartz cube whose expansion is negligible is suspended from one arm of a balance and dips into a vessel containing the liquid whose expansion coefficient is required. Then, as is shown in Part I, Chap. IX, the density of the liquid at any temperature may be obtained from a knowledge of the weight of the quartz cube in air and in the liquid respectively. To obtain absolute values of density, the volume of the cube must be known or some liquid of known density must be used to calibrate the instrument. If a sinker other than a quartz cube is used, allowance must be made for the increase in volume of the sinker as the temperature is raised.

(d) *Absolute Methods: Regnault's Apparatus.*

Dulong and Petit devised an elegant hydrostatic method which measures the absolute coefficient of expansion of a liquid without allowance being required for the expansion of the container. The liquid was introduced into a vertical U-tube, one arm of which was surrounded by a bath at constant temperature, the other arm being in a bath of variable temperature. When the two arms are at different temperatures the liquid is in equilibrium only if the column is higher in the arm at the higher temperature. This is because the density of the hot liquid is less than that of the cold. The condition for equilibrium is clearly that the hydrostatic pressure at the bottom of the U-tube shall be the same in both directions, from the left and from the right; that is,

$$h_t \rho_t g = h_0 \rho_0 g, \quad \cdots \cdots \quad (2.23)$$

where h_t and h_0 are the two heights respectively. Combining equation (2.23) with equation (2.18), we eliminate the densities and obtain

$$\gamma = \frac{h_t - h_0}{h_0 t}. \quad \cdots \cdots \quad (2.24)$$

The simple arrangement of Dulong and Petit is not quite satisfactory, since (1) a continuous circulation of hot and cold liquid takes place along the bottom of the U-tube, and (2) the quantity $(h_t - h_0)$ can be measured accurately only if the two levels are close together, and this is difficult to realize experimentally if they are to be maintained at different temperatures. Regnault therefore modified the original arrangement. His apparatus (fig. 11) consists of two wide vertical arms AB, CD, connected at the top by a narrow horizontal arm AC. At the base, AB and CD are each attached to a narrow horizontal tube which terminates in a narrow inverted U-tube from the top-end of which a tube leads to a compression air-pump. The liquid is then poured into AB and eventually fills AB and CD, but is prevented from rising too far in the ∩-tube by the compressed air. A small hole at E, open to the atmosphere, allows the top of the liquid to attain atmospheric pressure. The arm AB is then surrounded by a temperature bath, the other three arms all being at room temperature. If

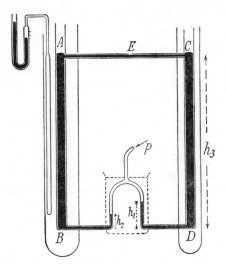

Fig. 11.—Regnault's Apparatus for Expansion of a Liquid

h_1, h_2 and h_3 are the heights shown in fig. 11, then the condition for equilibrium at the bottom of AB and CD is given by

$$h_3 \rho_0 g = p + h_1 \rho_0 g, \quad \cdots \quad (2.25)$$
$$h_3 \rho_t g = p + h_2 \rho_0 g, \quad \cdots \quad (2.26)$$

where p is the air pressure in the Ω-tube.

Subtracting (2.25) and (2.26) and combining with (2.18), thus eliminating the densities, we obtain

$$\gamma = \frac{h_1 - h_2}{(h_3 - h_1 + h_2)t}. \quad \cdots \quad (2.27)$$

The quantity $(h_1 - h_2)$ can be measured very accurately since the columns are at the same temperature and may be placed close together. The dimensions of Regnault's apparatus were 1 to 2 m. The effect has been magnified by later workers, particularly Callendar and Moss, by using six columns in series, each 2 m. long, but the principle remains the same.

EXERCISES

1. Define *coefficient of thermal expansion*. In what units may it be expressed?

Show that the coefficient of cubical expansion of a homogeneous solid is approximately three times its coefficient of linear expansion.

2. Describe an *accurate* method for measuring the coefficient of linear expansion of a rod.

Find the rise in temperature necessary to cause a pendulum clock to lose 1 sec. per day if the pendulum is made of brass of coefficient of linear expansion $1\cdot89 \times 10^{-5}$ per °C. [$1\cdot2$° C.]

3. Explain how clocks and watches are compensated for the thermal expansion resulting from temperature change.

What useful applications have been made of thermal expansion?

4. Show that provided the temperature change is not too large the force required to hold a heated bar extended, if it is allowed to cool from t_2° to t_1°, is approximately equal to the force such a rod would exert on rigid abutments if it is raised in temperature from t_1° to t_2°.

5. Enumerate methods for measuring the coefficient of cubical expansion of liquids, and describe in detail the method which you consider to be the best.

6. Show that the absolute coefficient of cubical expansion of a liquid is the sum of its apparent coefficient of expansion and the coefficient of cubical expansion of the material of the container.

Describe Regnault's method for measuring the absolute coefficient of expansion directly.

7. Describe how the variation of the density of a liquid with temperature may be determined.

A body floats in water at 4° C. and has 98 per cent of its volume immersed in the water. Determine the temperature of the water in which the body will be completely submerged, given that the mean coefficient of cubical expansion of water is to be taken as $2 \cdot 5 \times 10^{-4}$ per °C. and the expansion of the body may be neglected. [85·6° C.]

8. Describe Hope's apparatus for demonstrating the variation of the density of water with temperature and discuss the results as fully as possible.

9. Explain carefully the construction and use of a weight thermometer, deducing any formulæ which you may consider necessary.

A glass weight thermometer is just filled with 15 c.c. of mercury at 15° C. If the coefficient of cubical expansion of mercury is $1 \cdot 82 \times 10^{-4}$ per °C., and the coefficient of linear expansion of glass is $9 \cdot 00 \times 10^{-6}$ per °C., find the weight of mercury which escapes when the temperature is raised to 100° C., given that the density of mercury at 15° C. is 13·56 gm./c.c. [2·64 gm.]

10. The two arms of a vertical U-tube are at 0° C. and 100° C. respectively, and the difference in the height of the two columns of an enclosed liquid is 1·50 cm. If the cooler column is 60 cm. high, find the coefficient of cubical expansion of the contained liquid. [$2 \cdot 5 \times 10^{-4}$ per °C.]

CHAPTER III

Quantity of Heat

1. Introduction.

If we mix a given mass of water at, say, 60° C. with the same mass of water at 40° C. we shall find that the temperature of the mixture is 50° C. If, however, we take the same mass of some other substance, such as copper, at 60° C., and place it in the same mass of water at 40° C. we shall find that the temperature of the mixture is only about 42° C. We explain this by stating that the copper contained much less heat than the same mass of water. The quantity of heat H lost or gained by a substance is found to be proportional to the weight, the temperature change θ which it undergoes and the nature of the substance, that is,

$$H = ms\theta, \qquad \ldots \ldots \ldots \quad (3.1)$$

where s is a constant depending on the nature of the substance and is termed its **specific heat.** The specific heat of water is defined as unity, and the *unit quantity of heat* is obtained from (3.1) by putting $m = s = \theta = 1$. On the C.G.S. system therefore **the unit of heat or calorie is the amount of heat required to raise 1 gm. of water through 1° C.** Very accurate measurements show that the quantity of heat is not the same for different parts of the temperature scale. Consequently, for accurate work we must either specify the **mean calorie,** which is the average amount of heat per °C. over the temperature range considered, or else specify some definite temperature. Thus the **15° C. calorie** is the amount of heat required to raise 1 gm. of water from 14·5° C. to 15·5° C.

The calorie is a small quantity of heat, and for industrial purposes the **major calorie** is often used. This is defined to be 1000 times the ordinary calorie. On the F.P.S. system $m = 1$ lb. and $\theta = 1$° C. or 1° F. Hence we have also as units of quantity of heat *the lb.–°C. and the lb.–°F., the amounts of heat required to raise 1 lb. of water through 1° C. or 1° F. respectively.*

On the M.K.S. system, the unit of heat is the amount required to raise 1 kgm. of water through one degree Centigrade. It is therefore equivalent to 10^3 calories or one major calorie. Because of the equivalence between heat energy and mechanical energy discussed in Chap VI, specific heats may also be expressed as joules gm.$^{-1}$ °C.$^{-1}$ on the C.G.S. system or joules kgm.$^{-1}$ °C.$^{-1}$ on the M.K.S. system. The specific heat of water is therefore close to $4 \cdot 2$ joules gm.$^{-1}$ °C.$^{-1}$ or $4 \cdot 2 \times 10^3$ joules kgm.$^{-1}$ °C.$^{-1}$.

2. Specific Heat.

Let us suppose that a given mass of water requires a quantity of heat H_1 to raise its temperature by θ, and that the same mass of some other material requires an amount of heat H_2 for the same temperature range. Then, applying equation (3.1),

$$H_1 = m \times 1 \times \theta$$
$$\text{and} \qquad H_2 = m \times s \times \theta. \qquad \qquad (3.2)$$

Hence $s = H_2/H_1$ or the *specific heat of a substance is the ratio of the amount of heat required to raise the temperature of a given mass of the substance through a given temperature range to the amount of heat required to raise the same mass of water through the same temperature range.* Defined in this way, specific heat is a dimensionless quantity (see Part I, Chap. V.)   Alternatively, we may determine the dimensions from equation (3.1) alone, defining H and θ as new primary quantities, whereupon s has the dimensions $HM^{-1}\theta^{-1}$.

The product ms of equation (3.1) is often referred to as the **thermal capacity** or **water equivalent** of a body, since it gives the weight of water with the same thermal capacity as the given body. For example, the specific heat of copper is about $0 \cdot 1$: consequently the thermal capacity or water equivalent of 10 gm. of copper is $10 \times 0 \cdot 1 = 1$, and therefore 1 gm. of water is thermally equal to 10 gm. of copper.

3. Conservation of Heat.

When a body cools, the neighbouring bodies are observed to show a slight rise in temperature. It is therefore reasonable to assume that the heat lost by the cooling body is equal to the heat gained by those which are warmed. The quantity of heat present is therefore conserved and, in fact, as we shall see more clearly in Chap. VI, the Conservation of Heat is merely one particular case of the Conservation of Energy, since Heat and Energy are equivalent.   The conservation of heat forms the basis of the methods for measuring specific heats.

There are four main methods for determining specific heats: (a) *method of mixtures,* (b) *method of cooling,* (c) *electrical methods,* (d) *methods depending on latent heat.*

We discuss the first three methods in this chapter: examples of the last method are given in Chap. VI and VIII.

4. Method of Mixtures.

To determine the specific heat of an insoluble solid by the method of mixtures, a piece of the material M is attached to threads and is placed in a steam bath or **hypsometer,** as shown on the left in fig. 1, and allowed to take up the temperature of the steam. It is then dropped very quickly through a trap-door T into a copper vessel containing water. This vessel is placed in a larger vessel, though it is prevented from coming in contact with it by a layer of cotton-wool. Such an arrangement constitutes a simple form of **calorimeter,** and is shown on the right in fig. 1. The temperatures of the water in the calorimeter are noted with a thermometer inserted in the water, before and after the introduction of the specimen, stirring being effected with a small copper stirrer. Then if

w = mass of calorimeter,

m = mass of water in calorimeter,

θ_0 = initial temperature of water and calorimeter,

θ_f = final temperature of water and calorimeter,

s = specific heat of material (usually copper) of calorimeter;

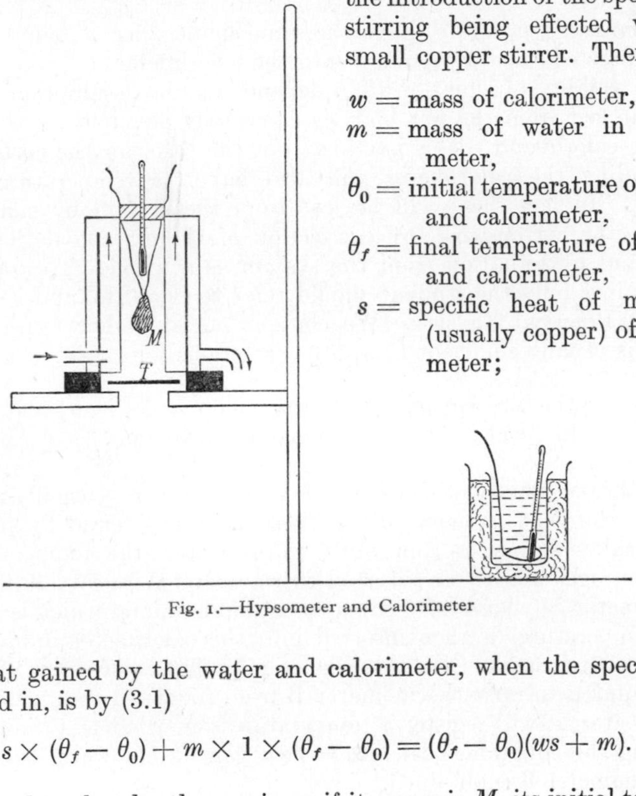

Fig. 1.—Hypsometer and Calorimeter

the heat gained by the water and calorimeter, when the specimen is dropped in, is by (3.1)

$$w \times s \times (\theta_f - \theta_0) + m \times 1 \times (\theta_f - \theta_0) = (\theta_f - \theta_0)(ws + m). \quad (3.3)$$

Now the heat lost by the specimen if its mass is M, its initial temperature θ_1 and its specific heat S, will be

$$MS(\theta_1 - \theta_f), \quad . \quad . \quad . \quad . \quad . \quad . \quad (3.4)$$

since its final temperature is that of the water and calorimeter. By the conservation of heat, (3.3) must equal (3.4); hence

$$MS(\theta_1 - \theta_f) = (\theta_f - \theta_0)(ws + m), \quad . \quad . \quad . \quad (3.5)$$

an equation by which, if the specific heat of the material of the calorimeter is known, S may be determined.

To find s for the calorimeter itself, a quantity of hot water at a known temperature is poured into the calorimeter containing cold water. It is left as an exercise to the reader to show that

$$s = \frac{M\theta_1 + m\theta_0 - (M + m)\theta_f}{w(\theta_f - \theta_0)}, \quad \ldots \quad (3.6)$$

where m, w, θ_0, θ_1 and θ_f have the same significance as before and M is the mass of *hot* water poured into the calorimeter.

The validity of equation (3.5) depends on the assumption that *all* the heat lost from the hot body is eventually acquired by the water and the calorimeter. This is clearly not the case, for the cotton-wool surrounding the calorimeter will also have its temperature raised slightly. In fact, heat will be lost from the system by conduction through the cotton-wool, by convection of the air above the calorimeter and by radiation from the system as a whole. To appreciate these points fully the student should refer to Chap. IV and to a text-book of Practical Physics. We content ourselves here with noting that it is usually sufficient to apply corrections for

(1) heat capacity of thermometer and stirrer,
(2) heat lost by radiation and convection.

The heat capacity of the stirrer is known since it is usually made of copper: the heat capacity of the thermometer is found by taking a very small calorimeter containing warm water, the temperature of which as registered by an inserted thermometer A is, say, $30°$ C. The thermometer B, whose heat capacity is required, and which is reading room-temperature, is then inserted into the calorimeter immediately after the withdrawal of the thermometer A. Then since heat will have been required to raise thermometer B from room temperature to that of the water, it will register a temperature somewhat less than $30°$ C. Applying the equation, heat lost = heat gained, the water equivalent of thermometer B is obtained.

Heat is lost by radiation and convection during the time taken for thermal equilibrium to be reached after the specimen has been introduced into the calorimeter. For example, it may take over a minute before the temperature rises to its final steady value θ_f. During this time, heat is being lost from the system to the room and hence θ_f is smaller than it would otherwise be. To correct for this, a **cooling curve** is plotted, that is, the temperature of the whole system is raised until it is some $5°$ above θ_f; it is then allowed to cool by radiation and convection and a cooling curve or graph of temperature-time is constructed. This curve passes through θ_f, and the rate of cooling in degrees per minute is obtained directly by drawing a tangent to the cooling curve at this temperature. Now the *average* rate of cooling during the main experiment was

$$\tfrac{1}{2}(\text{rate of cooling at } \theta_f + \text{rate of cooling at } \theta_0).$$

If θ_0 is room temperature, the rate of cooling at this temperature is zero. Consequently, the correction to be added to θ_f is

$$\delta\theta_f = \tfrac{1}{2} \text{ (rate of cooling at } \theta_f) \times \text{time taken for temperature to rise from } \theta_0 \text{ to } \theta_f \text{ in main experiment.}$$

The above treatment of the heat loss is only approximate: for more accurate methods the student should consult a textbook of Practical Physics. The radiation and convection correction is smaller the smaller the difference between θ_0 and θ_f. While a small temperature rise is therefore desirable, the limited sensitivity of the thermometer makes a very small rise difficult to measure accurately. If the water in the calorimeter was initially as much below room temperature as it was finally above it, no radiation and convection correction is necessary. This method was introduced by Rumford: it holds only over a small temperature range.

5. Method of Cooling.

The specific heat of a solid soluble in water may be found by using in the calorimeter some liquid in which it is insoluble (cf. *Determination of Densities*, Part I, Chap. IX). The specific heats of liquids are easily found by pouring the warmed liquid into a copper calorimeter either empty or containing some of the liquid already but at a lower temperature. Another method known as the **method of cooling** is, however, particularly applicable to liquids. The apparatus consists of two small aluminium calorimeters, equal in all respects and carried at their top edge by ebonite bushes. Equal *volumes* of water and of the liquid whose specific heat is required are introduced into the two calorimeters, and each is fitted with a cork and a thermometer. Both calorimeters are raised some degrees above room temperature by immersion in a water-bath. They are then removed and placed in a draught-free enclosure as shown in fig. 2. If

$$m = \text{mass of water,}$$
$$s(=1) = \text{specific heat of water,}$$
$$m' = \text{mass of liquid,}$$
$$s' = \text{specific heat of liquid,}$$

and $t, t' = $ times taken for water and liquid to cool through the same temperature range respectively,

then

$$\frac{ms}{m's'} = \frac{t}{t'}. \quad \cdot \quad \cdot \quad \cdot \quad \cdot \quad \cdot \quad \cdot \quad (3.7)$$

To prove (3.7), let dQ be the heat lost, per unit area, from the surface of the first calorimeter in a short time dt. Then if the area of the surface is A, and the dependence of heat loss on temperature is represented by some unknown function $f(\theta)$,

$$dQ = A\, f(\theta)\, dt. \quad \cdots \cdots \quad (3.8)$$

The temperature at time $t + dt$ is $\theta + d\theta$. Here $d\theta$ is negative, and hence, if the mass of the water is m,

$$dQ = -m\, s\, d\theta. \quad \cdots \cdots \quad (3.9)$$

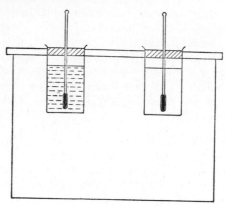

Fig. 2.—Method of Cooling

From (3.8) and (3.9)

$$dt = -\frac{ms}{A}\frac{d\theta}{f(\theta)}. \quad \cdots \cdots \quad (3.10)$$

Integrating (3.10) and writing $F(\theta)$ for the temperature integral, we obtain

$$t = -\frac{ms}{A}\, F(\theta). \quad \cdots \cdots \quad (3.11)$$

Now, since the calorimeters are identical, A is the same for the liquid as for the water; also the temperature ranges are equal, so $F(\theta)$ is the same. Hence, by analogy with (3.11),

$$t' = -\frac{m's'}{A}\, F(\theta), \quad \cdots \cdots \quad (3.12)$$

and dividing (3.11) and (3.12) we obtain (3.7).

Equation (3.7) should strictly be written

$$\frac{ms + W}{m's' + W} = \frac{t}{t''}$$

where W is the water equivalent of either of the aluminium calori-meters. As these are very light and aluminium has a low specific heat, W is usually much less than ms or $m's'$. The method of cooling has the advantage that it involves no mixing and is suitable though only small quantities of the liquid are available.

6. Method of Electrical Heating.

This method is applicable to solids, liquids and gases, and is based simply on equation (3.1). A measured quantity of electrical energy is converted into heat H and the rise in temperature of a known mass of material is observed. We shall concentrate on its application to liquids as the apparatus is the simplest in this case. With liquids the electrical method is applied in two distinct forms:

(a) Joule's Method.

In this method, a coil of wire is inserted into a given mass of the liquid contained in a calorimeter, and a known amount of electrical energy is supplied. If

$m =$ mass of liquid present,
$s =$ specific heat of liquid,
$w =$ water equivalent of calorimeter,
$R =$ heat loss due to radiation and convection,
$t =$ time of passage of current,
$I =$ mean current,
$E =$ mean potential difference,
$J =$ Joule's Equivalent of Heat (see Chap. VI),
$\theta =$ rise in temperature,

then $$H = \frac{EIt}{J} = (ms + w)\theta + R. \quad . \quad . \quad . \quad . \quad . \quad (3.13)$$

The quantity R may be allowed for by plotting a cooling curve as described on pp. 182-3. However, it is usually eliminated by repeating the experiment with a potential difference E' and current I', for a dif-ferent mass of liquid m' but for the same time t over the same tem-perature range θ. The heat loss R' is therefore approximately equal to R, and rewriting (3.13) for the second experiment and subtracting the two equations, we find:

$$\frac{t(EI - E'I')}{J} = (m - m')s\theta. \quad . \quad . \quad . \quad (3.14)$$

We note that the water equivalent of the calorimeter has also been eliminated. The method is very accurate and may be used to measure J, the mechanical equivalent of heat, as described on p. 208.

(b) *Continuous Flow Method.*

This method was introduced by Callendar and Barnes and was shown by them to be susceptible of a high degree of accuracy. As shown in fig. 3, the apparatus consists of a narrow glass or quartz capillary tube, down the centre of which is placed a fine platinum wire which is electrically heated. The liquid is flowing continuously down the tube and the temperatures of entrance and exit, θ_1 and θ_2, are recorded. The temperature θ_2 becomes steady when the liquid carries the heat away as fast as it is generated by the electric current.

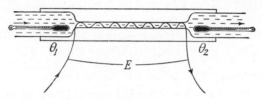

Fig. 3.—Continuous Flow Method of Callendar and Barnes

In this condition, which must be absolutely steady for accurate results,

$$H = \frac{EIt}{J} = ms(\theta_2 - \theta_1) + R, \quad . \quad . \quad . \quad (3.15)$$

where $m =$ total mass of liquid flowing along tube in time t,
$\quad s =$ specific heat of liquid,
$\quad E, I =$ average values of potential difference and current during the experiment,
$\quad J =$ Joule's equivalent of heat,
$\quad R =$ heat losses due to radiation and convection.

As in the previous electrical method, to eliminate R, the experiment is repeated with different values of E, I and m but with the same values of t and $(\theta_2 - \theta_1)$. Subtraction gives the equation for s, free from corrections. Heat losses are much reduced by surrounding the flow tube with an exhausted tube or vacuum jacket. Platinum resistance thermometers or thermocouples are used in accurate work, rather than mercury thermometers as shown in fig. 3.

7. Variation of Specific Heat with Temperature.

By means of the continuous flow method it may be shown, by taking different ranges of temperature for $(\theta_2 - \theta_1)$, that the specific heat of water varies with its temperature. If the specific heat is plotted

as a function of the temperature, a minimum is observed at about
37° C. as shown in fig. 4.   The liquid state is still not well understood
and satisfactory explanations are likely to be complicated.   Change of
state affects the specific heat profoundly; for example, ice has a specific

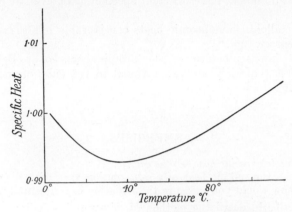

Fig. 4.—Temperature Variation of Specific Heat of Water

heat of about 0·5.   At room temperature, many solids have an approximately constant specific heat over a moderate temperature range.
At low temperatures, however, all show a marked decrease in the
specific heat.   In fig. 5, the **atomic heats** of some elements are plotted
against the temperature (atomic heat = atomic weight multiplied by
specific heat).   The following points are of especial interest:

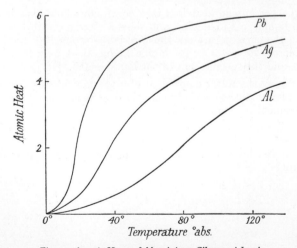

Fig. 5.—Atomic Heats of Aluminium, Silver and Lead

(i) Most elements approach the value 6·4 for their atomic heat at higher temperatures. This is **Dulong and Petit's law,** and was used in former times to determine the atomic weights of rare elements.

(ii) Elements which occur in different allotropic forms, such as gas carbon and diamond, have different specific heats, even at room temperature.

(iii) Metalloids have atomic heats considerably less than 6·4, even at room temperature.

(iv) At low temperatures, the atomic heats obey **Debye's law** which states that they are proportional to the cube of the absolute temperature.

EXERCISES

1. Define (a) *specific heat,* (b) *the calorie.*

How does the specific heat of a salt solution vary with the concentration, and how would you measure the variation experimentally?

2. Describe in detail the method of mixtures for finding the specific heats of substances, indicating clearly how corrections are applied for heat losses.

3. By what methods may the specific heat of liquids be determined?

Describe in detail the method of cooling, and find the specific heat of a liquid which has a mean density 3 gm./c.c., and which takes twice as long as an equal volume of water to cool through the same temperature range. [2/3.]

4. How have electrical methods been applied to determine the specific heats of liquids?

Find the percentage heat loss in a continuous flow experiment if 216 gm. of the liquid pass in 1 min., and show a steady rise in temperature of 1° C. when the current through the wire is maintained at 2 amp. and the potential across it at 4·2 volts. Joule's equivalent may be taken as 4·2 joules/cal., and the specific heat of the liquid as 0·5. [10 per cent.]

5. How may the water equivalent of a thermometer be determined?

What advantage has a thermocouple over a mercury thermometer in the measurement of temperature?

6. Describe suitable methods for finding the specific heat of (a) solids soluble in water, (b) strongly corrosive liquids like nitric acid.

What do you know of the variation of the specific heat of solids with temperature?

CHAPTER IV

Heat Transference and Convection

1. Introduction.

When a body cools it loses heat, or heat transference takes place, by three distinct processes, conduction, convection and radiation. We shall discuss convection in detail in this chapter, conduction and radiation being dealt with in Chap. V and XIV respectively.

If, for example, a hot piece of metal is laid on a wooden bench, heat is lost in the following manner. Conduction takes place where the metal is in contact with the wood and to a very small extent through the air. Radiation would take place even if the metal was suspended inside a vacuum. The main loss of heat, however, in the example considered is due to convection. It is important that the student should realize that conduction and radiation are essentially atomic and molecular phenomena, whereas convection is due to streaming of comparatively large masses of fluid. In fact, convection is confined to fluids, although conduction and radiation occur with both solids and fluids.

2. Convection.

The layer of air immediately above the metal in the above example is heated by conduction and radiation. Consequently, its density is decreased (see Chap. VII) and it rises, its place being taken by cold air which comes in at the sides. This cold air is in its turn warmed by the metal, its density is decreased and it rises also, and so the whole process is repeated until the metal is cooled to air temperature.

Such convection is termed *natural convection*, and is due to the fact that at the same pressure equal volumes of air have different densities at different temperatures. If a fan is used to circulate the air, cooling is due to *forced convection*.

3. Convection in Gases.

We may demonstrate convection in gases by the simple apparatus shown in fig. 1. A lighted candle is placed at the bottom of the opening in a bell-jar and it is found that after a short time the flame is extinguished. This is because the products of combustion are heavier than air; consequently they collect at the bottom of the jar and extinguish

189

the flame. For burning to continue indefinitely there must be a continual supply of fresh air. This is easily achieved by inserting a divider in the neck of the jar. If the candle is slightly to one side of the opening, the hot air rises out of the division above it and the heavier, cold fresh air passes down on the opposite side. That such a circulation is taking place may be shown by placing a small piece of smouldering rag near the down current of air. The smoke from the rag is carried down, thus showing visibly the direction of the air current.

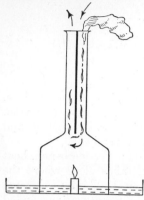

Fig. 1.—Convection in Gases

Convection plays an important part in the **ventilation** of rooms. Hot air is continually passing up the chimney above a coal-fire and fresh cold air passes in under the door or at the windows.

On a large scale, convection is basically responsible for the **systems of winds**. Of these we shall consider:

(a) Land and Sea Breezes.

It is observed at the coast that on an otherwise still, fine day there is a breeze which blows from sea to land in the morning and from land to sea in the evening. In the morning, the land having a lower specific heat than the sea is warmed more quickly by the sun's rays. Consequently, the air above the land is warmer than that above the sea. The former air therefore rises and the cool air from the sea flows in to take its place. In the evening the reverse process occurs. The land has acquired less heat than the sea since its specific heat is less; it therefore cools more quickly and the air above it becomes colder than that above the sea. The air above the sea now rises and the cool air above the land flows out to take its place.

(b) Trade Winds.

The air is hottest along the equator. It is therefore continually rising, and air flows in from either side, creating a northerly and southerly wind from the northern and southern hemispheres respectively. Owing to the rotation of the earth the winds are N.E. and S.E. and conditions are, of course, often complicated by local variations.

4. Convection in Liquids.

That convection occurs in liquids in readily shown by placing a few crystals of a coloured salt such as copper sulphate at the bottom of a flask containing water and heating locally at the centre of the base of the flask. Streams of blue liquid arise from the bottom at the centre and travel upwards, returning down the sides, showing that the less dense, heated liquid is rising in the centre and the cold, denser liquid is flowing in from the sides to take its place.

Domestic hot-water systems are operated by convection as shown in fig. 2. Water heated by the fire rises to the top of the boiler B and proceeds along the upper exit pipe to the storage tank T. Cold fresh denser water enters the boiler by the lower entrance pipe. In this way a continuous circulation is set up. Hot-water " radiators ", both domestic and for automobiles, act in the same way. We may note,

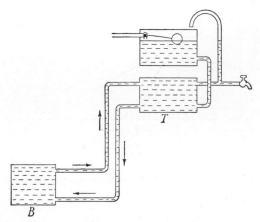

Fig. 2.—Domestic Hot-water System

however, that " convectors " would be a better name for " radiators ", since heat is given to the room mainly by convection of the air which takes place as the heated air rises continually from above the hot " radiator ".

5. Newton's Law of Cooling.

If in the experiment described on p. 183, on specific heat by the method of cooling, a cooling curve is plotted of temperature against time, its shape will be as ABC shown in fig. 3. Suppose now that tangents are drawn at various places on the curve to determine from the slopes of the tangents the rate of cooling, and another curve is plotted showing the variation of the rate of cooling with the excess temperature of the body above that of its surroundings. It will be found that provided the excess temperature is not too large the second curve is a straight line as shown in fig. 4. The *rate of cooling is proportional to the excess temperature*: this is **Newton's Law of Cooling.** The student should note that it applies to cooling by convection and radiation, and therefore differs from Stefan's Law of Radiation (see Chap. XIV), which refers to radiation alone.

Since, according to Newton's law, the rate of cooling is proportional to the excess temperature, it follows that $f(\theta) = C\theta$ in equation

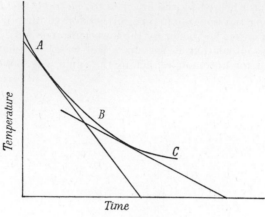

Fig. 3.—Cooling Curve

(3.8), where C is some constant depending on the nature of the surface of the calorimeter. Hence (3.8) becomes

$$dQ = CA\theta\ dt,$$

and since the area A is fixed for a given body, if we write $CA = D$, where D is a new constant,

$$dQ = D\theta\ dt. \quad . \quad . \quad . \quad . \quad . \quad . \quad (4.1)$$

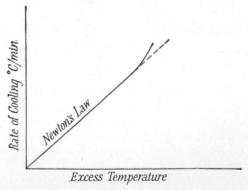

Fig. 4.—Newton's Law of Cooling

Combining equations (3.9) and (4.1),

$$dt = - \frac{ms \, d\theta}{D\theta}.$$

Integrating, we obtain

$$t = - \frac{ms}{D} \log_e \theta + B, \quad \ldots \ldots \quad (4.2)$$

where B is a constant of integration.

To determine B we note that when $t = 0$, $\theta = \theta_1$, the initial temperature from which cooling starts. Hence

$$B = \frac{ms}{D} \log_e \theta_1,$$

and (4.2) becomes

$$t = - \frac{ms}{D} \log_e \frac{\theta}{\theta_1},$$

or

$$\theta = \theta_1 \exp. \left(- \frac{D}{ms} t \right), \quad \ldots \ldots \quad (4.3)$$

where $\exp. (x) \equiv e^x$.

The cooling curve is therefore an **exponential curve** in the region over which Newton's law is obeyed. At higher temperatures the cooling is more rapid than Newton's law would indicate and no simple relation holds.

EXERCISES

1. Distinguish between natural and forced convection, and give examples to illustrate the part played by convection in atmospheric phenomena.

2. Describe how a cooling curve is constructed experimentally, and discuss the validity of Newton's Law of Cooling.

3. Distinguish between Newton's Law of Cooling and Stefan's Law of Radiation. Show that the former law follows algebraically from the latter for small temperature differences between a body and its surroundings. Is any theoretical significance to be attached to this agreement?

CHAPTER V

Thermal Conductivity

1. Introduction.

The fact that heat flows from one body to another when they are placed in contact, if a temperature difference exists between them, is attributed to **thermal conductivity.** On molecular theory, the temperature of a solid is proportional to the kinetic energy of the molecules. These molecules vibrate about fixed centres, and a higher temperature simply implies a larger amplitude of vibration. Thus if one end of a bar is heated, the molecules at this end are given a larger amplitude of vibration. The molecules impinge on the molecules in their immediate neighbourhood and cause them also to vibrate with larger amplitude. This process spreads along the whole bar, and is exhibited as the passage or conduction of heat down the bar.

2. Simple Experiments illustrating Thermal Conductivity.

If a piece of paper is wrapped round a roller consisting partly of wood and partly of iron, then on rotating the roller in a large flame a clear line of demarcation is observed, on one side of which the paper is badly charred while on the other it is scarcely singed. The charred side is found to cover the wooden portion and the uncharred the iron portion. The behaviour is attributed to the good thermal conductivity of iron and the poor thermal conductivity of wood. The iron conducts the heat away before the temperature can rise sufficiently to scorch the paper, whereas the wood is unable to conduct the heat away and therefore the paper burns.

That **liquids are poor conductors of heat** may be shown by sinking a small piece of ice with a lead weight to the bottom of a test-tube containing water. On applying a flame to the water at the top of the tube, the water may be boiled there for a considerable period before sufficient heat is conducted down through the water to melt the ice at the bottom.

The operation of the **Davy safety lamp** depends on the poor thermal conductivity of gases. The lamp consists of a metal gauze frame completely enclosing the naked flame. Should inflammable gas be present, the flame ignites the gas inside the gauze enclosure, but the heat from the flaming gas is conducted away along the metal gauze, which is a good conductor. Consequently, as the **thermal conductivity of gas is poor,** its temperature does not rise sufficiently to ignite it outside the gauze enclosure. Of course, if the heat continues for long enough the gauze becomes red-hot and the outside gas is then ignited.

Many domestic applications of good and bad conductors will occur to the student, such as the introduction of badly conducting ivory rings into the handle of a metal teapot and the use of wooden knobs on kettle lids.

The best conductors are usually metals: in fact, the general rule that **good conductors of heat are good conductors of electricity** is well obeyed. However, there are no heat insulators of comparable efficiency with that of insulators of electricity.

3. Coefficient of Thermal Conductivity.

If we consider heat flowing normally across a flat slab of area A and small thickness dx, as shown in fig. 1, then it is found that the quantity of heat dq which flows normally across, in the direction in which x increases, in a small interval of time dt, is given by

$$dq = -k\,A\,\frac{d\theta}{dx}\,dt, \quad \ldots \quad \ldots \quad (5.1)$$

where $d\theta$ is the small temperature difference existing between the two faces of the slab. The *minus* sign indicates that the flow of heat takes place in the direction in which θ decreases. In fig. 1, $d\theta$ is therefore *negative*. The quantity k depends on the nature of the substance and is termed the coefficient of thermal conductivity. From equation (5.1), if $A = dx = dt = 1$, and $d\theta = -1$, then $k = dq$, so k may also be defined as the *quantity of heat flowing per second across a cube of unit length of side, when the opposite faces are at unit difference of temperature.* However, the last definition implies that the **temperature gradient** $d\theta/dx$ is constant over a distance equal to the side of the cube, a state of affairs that may be difficult to realize.

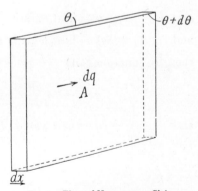

Fig. 1.—Flow of Heat across a Slab

When a rod is heated, the rate at which the far end becomes warm depends on the thermal capacity of the rod as well as on its thermal conductivity. If different rods of the same size are heated and we note the times taken for points at the same distance from the source to acquire the same temperature, these times will be inversely proportional to the **thermal diffusivities** of the rods. The **coefficient of thermal diffusivity**, κ, is defined by the equation

$$\kappa = \frac{k}{\rho s}, \quad \cdots \cdots \cdots \quad (5.2)$$

where k is the thermal conductivity of the rod, ρ its density, and s its specific heat. The thermal diffusivity is therefore the thermal conductivity divided by the heat capacity per unit volume of the material. In all problems on thermal conductivity, unless the contrary is expressly stated, *steady conditions must be reached*: otherwise the thermal diffusivity and not the thermal conductivity may be involved.

All methods for both good and bad conductors depend on the application of (5.1) under certain conditions. The conditions are usually determined by the necessity to keep dq/dt a quantity of convenient magnitude: this is accomplished by making the area large and the thickness small for poor conductors, and conversely for good conductors. The former are therefore usually in the form of a slab and the latter in the form of a bar or rod.

* 3. Thermal Conductivity along Bars of Good Conductors.

Consider an element, length δx, of a bar as shown in fig. 2. If

$$\theta = \text{temperature of one face at plane } x,$$

then $\left(\theta + \dfrac{d\theta}{dx}\,\delta x\right) = $ temperature of opposite face at plane $x + \delta x$;

and if $\qquad q = $ heat entering first face in *unit time*,

and $\qquad (q + \delta q) = $ heat leaving second face in unit time,

then by equation (5.1)

$$q = -kA\,\frac{d\theta}{dx},$$

and $\qquad q + \delta q = $ new value of q when x becomes $x + \delta x$

$$= q + \frac{dq}{dx}\,\delta x$$

$$= -kA\left(\frac{d\theta}{dx} + \frac{d^2\theta}{dx^2}\,\delta x\right).$$

Hence the element would gain an amount of heat δq given by

$$\delta q = kA\,\frac{d^2\theta}{dx^2}\,\delta x. \quad \cdots \cdots \quad (5.3)$$

Since the temperature of the rod is steady, this heat must be lost to the room in unit time. If we define the **emissivity** α of the rod *as the amount of heat lost per second per unit area of exposed surface per degree excess of temperature θ of the bar above its surroundings*, then

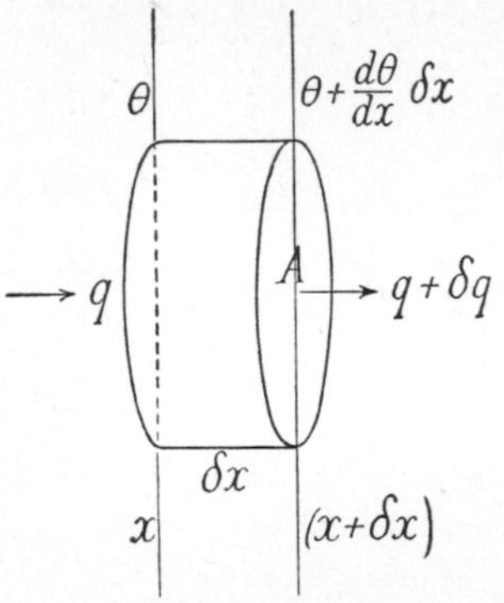

$$\delta q = p \, \delta x \, \theta \, \alpha, \quad . \quad . \quad (5.4)$$

where $p =$ perimeter of the rod.

Equating (5.3) and (5.4), we obtain

$$kA \frac{d^2\theta}{dx^2} = p \, \theta \, \alpha. \quad . \quad (5.5)$$

Two cases usually present themselves experimentally. If the bar is lagged with a poor conductor, there is no loss of heat to the room from the sides of the rod, all the heat which enters one face of the bar being transmitted down the bar. Under these conditions

$$kA \frac{d^2\theta}{dx^2} = 0. \quad . \quad . \quad . \quad . \quad . \quad (5.6)$$

Integrating equation (5.6) with respect to x,

$$kA \frac{d\theta}{dx} = \text{constant} = K, \quad . \quad . \quad . \quad . \quad (5.7)$$

which shows that the temperature gradient is constant. A graph of θ against x is therefore a straight line as shown in fig. 3, so that $d\theta/dx = (\theta_1 - \theta_2)/(x_1 - x_2)$.

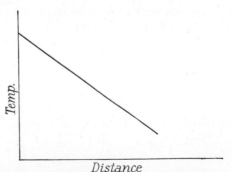

Fig. 3.—Uniform Flow of Heat along a Rod

Fig. 2.—Flow of Heat across an Element of a Rod

From equation (5.1), $K = -dq/dt$; substituting this value in (5.7), we have

$$\frac{dq}{dt} = -kA\,\frac{(\theta_1 - \theta_2)}{(x_1 - x_2)}. \quad \cdots \quad (5.8)$$

Finally, integrating q with respect to t,

$$q = -kA\,\frac{(\theta_1 - \theta_2)}{(x_1 - x_2)}\,t. \quad \cdots \quad (5.9)$$

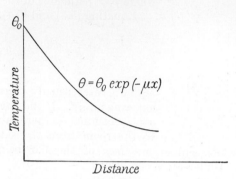

$$\theta = \theta_0\,exp\,(\text{-}\mu x)$$

Fig. 4.—Temperature-Distance Curve for Exposed Bar

On the other hand, if the bar is freely exposed at the sides, equation (5.5) may be written

$$\frac{d^2\theta}{dx^2} = \frac{pa}{kA}\,\theta = \mu^2\theta, \quad \cdots \quad (5.10)$$

where $\mu^2 = pa/(kA)$.

Integration of (5.10) gives

$$\theta = C\,\exp.\,(-\mu x) + D\,\exp.\,(+\mu x). \quad \cdots \quad (5.11)$$

To find C and D we note that for $x = \infty$ the temperature of the end of the bar will be that of the room, that is $\theta = 0$; hence $D = 0$. Finally, if θ_0 is the excess temperature above its surroundings at the high temperature end ($x = 0$) of the bar, substitution in (5.11) shows that $C = \theta_0$.

Hence

$$\theta = \theta_0\,\exp.\,(-\mu x). \quad \cdots \quad (5.12)$$

The temperature-distance curve for an exposed bar is shown in fig. 4.

4. Experimental Methods for Good Conductors.

(a) *Searle's Method.*

In this method the material is in the form of a rod about 20 cm. long and 5 cm. diameter. Heat is supplied at one end by a jet of steam and the other end is cooled by contact with ice, as shown in fig. 5. Two thermometers are inserted symmetrically in the bar at a distance apart of about 10 cm.: if accurate results are required, thermocouples must be used so as to reduce the disturbance of the heat flow to a minimum. The whole bar is lagged with some bad conductor, such as cotton-wool, and when *steady conditions have been reached*, the rate

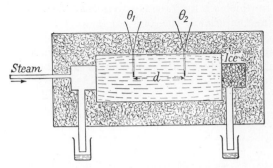

Fig. 5.—Searle's Method for Conductivity

of condensation of steam and the rate of melting of ice are observed, together with the temperatures θ_1 and θ_2 of the two thermometers. From fig. 5, the apparatus is seen to be so constructed that only the central portion of the bar is used. This is an example of the **guard-ring method** (we discuss this again in Part V). In this region the heat flow, as indicated by the broken lines, is normal to the restricted area A; consequently we may apply (5·9) or (5·1) directly and we have

$$q = m_1 L_1 = m_2 L_2 = kA \frac{(\theta_1 - \theta_2)}{d} t, \quad . \quad . \quad (5.13)$$

where m_1 and m_2 are the masses of steam and ice collected in a time t, L_1 and L_2 are the latent heats of condensation of steam and melting ice respectively, d is the distance between the two thermometers, and A is the area of the central portion as shown in fig. 5.

(b) *Forbes's Bar Method.*

In this method, a bar some six feet long is taken and freely exposed to the air. One end of the bar is immersed in a constant temperature bath, while thermometers or, better, thermocouples are inserted in the bar at regular intervals. When a steady state has been reached, the thermometers show the temperature distribution directly, and a curve is plotted of θ against x, which is the same as that shown in fig. 4. Tangents at any point of the curve give $d\theta/dx$ at that point. If we consider what becomes of the heat which crosses any cross-section of the bar at P, part of that heat travels down to the end of the bar, while the remainder is radiated from the sides. The quantity of heat q which flows across the bar at this point in one second is, by (5.1),

$$q = -kA \frac{d\theta}{dx}, \quad \ldots \ldots \quad (5.14)$$

an equation in which q is unknown as well as k. To determine q, a short bar of the same material as the long bar is taken and heated to a temperature considerably above that of the point P in the first experiment, and a cooling curve is obtained. Now if another curve is constructed with rates of cooling $(-d\theta/dt)$ as ordinates and corresponding values

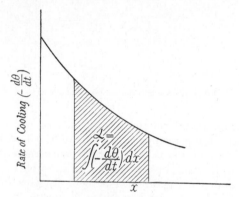

Fig. 6.—Forbes's Bar Method for Conductivity

of x as abscissæ as shown in fig. 6, the area a under the graph between any two values of x represents $\int \left(-\frac{d\theta}{dt} \right) dx$. But the amount of heat lost by an element of the rod of length dx in the neighbourhood of P in one second is

$$dq = \text{mass} \times \text{specific heat} \times \text{fall of temp.}$$

$$= \text{volume} \times \text{density} \times s \times \left(-\frac{d\theta}{dt} \right) \times 1$$

$$= A \, dx \, \rho s \left(-\frac{d\theta}{dt} \right).$$

Hence the total amount of heat lost beyond P between any two values of x is

$$q = A\rho s \int \left(-\frac{d\theta}{dt}\right) dx = A\rho s a. \quad . \quad . \quad . \quad (5.15)$$

But in the steady state (5.15) is equal to (5.14): hence

$$k = \frac{\rho s a}{(-d\theta/dx)}. \quad . \quad . \quad . \quad . \quad (5.16)$$

(c) *Ingenhausz's Experiment.*

For comparing thermal conductivities of metal rods an apparatus devised by Ingenhausz may be used. A number of metal rods of the

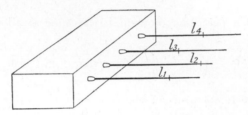

Fig. 7.—Ingenhausz's Experiment

same length and diameter are coated with the same material, say lamp-black, and then arranged with one end in a common temperature bath as shown in fig. 7. The rods are also coated with wax, and when steady conditions are reached it is found that the wax has melted for different lengths l_1 and l_2 on rods of different materials. If k_1 and k_2 are the thermal conductivities of the two rods,

$$\frac{k_1}{k_2} = \frac{l_1^2}{l_2^2}. \quad . \quad . \quad . \quad . \quad . \quad (5.17)$$

To show this, if we apply equation (5.12) to each rod we have

$$\theta_{\text{wax}} = \theta_0 \exp. (-\mu_1 l_1),$$
$$\theta_{\text{wax}} = \theta_0 \exp. (-\mu_2 l_2),$$

where θ_{wax} is the melting-point of the wax.

Hence

$$\frac{l_1}{l_2} = \frac{\mu_2}{\mu_1},$$

and from (5.10), since p, a and A are the same for both rods, $k_1/k_2 = l_1^2/l_2^2$.

5. Thermal Conductivity of Bad Conductors.

(a) *Tube Method.*

If the conductor (for example, rubber) can be made in the form of a tube, a convenient arrangement is to coil the tube inside a calorimeter containing water and to pass steam through the tube. The heat passing through the tube is measured by the rise in temperature of the calorimeter. For this case, equation (5.1) gives, for the heat crossing unit length of a section of radius r,

$$dq = -k(2\pi r)\frac{d\theta}{dr}\,dt,$$

or

$$\frac{1}{r}\frac{dr}{d\theta}\frac{dq}{dt} = -2\pi k.$$

Since dq/dt at a particular moment is the same at all sections, integration gives

$$\left(\log_e\frac{r_2}{r_1}\right)\frac{dq}{dt} = 2\pi k(100 - \theta'),$$

where θ' is the temperature of the tube next the water, i.e., approximately, of the water itself; we may assume for simplicity that θ' increases uniformly with the time. A further integration with respect to t then gives for k the equation

$$\left(\log_e\frac{r_2}{r_1}\right)\frac{q}{t} = 2\pi k\left(100 - \frac{\theta_1 + \theta_2}{2}\right), \quad . \quad . \quad . \quad (5.18)$$

where θ_1, θ_2 are the initial and final temperatures of the water. The value of $q = W(\theta_2 - \theta_1)$, where W is the water equivalent of the calorimeter and contents, and $(\theta_2 - \theta_1)$ is the rise in temperature during the time t. The method is not very satisfactory since r_2 is nearly equal to r_1; also the conditions are not steady, the temperature rising from θ_1 to θ_2 on one side of the tube during the experiment.

(b) *Lees's or the Slab Method.*

A good form of this apparatus is shown in fig. 8. It consists of a flat slab of the material X whose thermal conductivity is required, enclosed between two flat metal sheets. Next in the "sandwich" is a flat spiral heating coil, and finally, covering this, another flat metal disk. The whole is covered with shellac and suspended in a uniform temperature enclosure by the wires which serve to supply current to the heating coil. Energy is supplied to the coil and steady excess temperatures θ_1, θ_2 and θ_3 are registered by thermocouples in contact with the appropriate surfaces as shown in fig. 8. Then if we define the emissivity a of the shellacked surface as on p. 197, when equilibrium is established

$$H = \frac{EI}{J} = aS_1\theta_1 + aS\frac{(\theta_1 + \theta_2)}{2} + aS_2\theta_2 + aS_3\theta_3, \quad (5.19)$$

where H is the rate of heat supply, E and I are the average potential difference across and current through the heating coil, J is Joule's mechanical equivalent of heat, and S, S_1, S_2 and S_3 are the exposed areas of the specimen and disks respectively. Equation (5.19) determines the emissivity a.

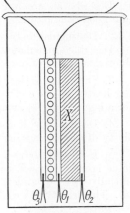

Fig. 8.—Lees's Method for Conductivity

If attention is now concentrated on the heat which passes *normally* through the specimen X per second, this heat q is the average of the heat entering and the heat leaving X. In the steady state the heat entering is the total amount of heat which leaves the surface of X and the lower disk, while the heat leaving is that which leaves the lower disk: hence

$$q = \frac{kA}{d}(\theta_1 - \theta_2) = \tfrac{1}{2}\left[\left\{aS\frac{(\theta_1 + \theta_2)}{2} + aS_2\theta_2\right\} + aS_2\theta_2\right]$$

$$= aS\frac{\theta_1 + \theta_2}{4} + aS_2\theta_2, \quad \cdot \quad \cdot \quad \cdot \quad (5.20)$$

where　　　　　　$k =$ thermal conductivity of the specimen,
　　　　　　　　　$A =$ area of cross-section of specimen,
　　　　　　　　　$d =$ thickness of specimen,

and　　　$\dfrac{(\theta_1 + \theta_2)}{2} =$ mean excess temperature of specimen.

Since a has been determined from (5.19) all the quantities in (5.20) are known except k.

The method may be applied to find the thermal conductivity of liquids and gases. The slab X consists of a hollow flat cylindrical box of glass. This is filled with the liquid or gas under test and the heating coil is arranged to be vertically above X to avoid convection currents. The box X is then evacuated and the experiment repeated to provide a correction for the heat conducted down the sides of the container. The thermal conductivity of gases is of particular interest on the kinetic theory as shown in Chap. XI. At *low* pressures, the thermal conductivity varies directly as the pressure, and this fact forms the basis of thermal conductivity pressure gauges.

EXERCISES

1. What factors govern the design of apparatus for measuring the thermal conductivity of solids?

Describe an *accurate* method for measuring the thermal conductivity of a good conductor.

2. Distinguish between thermal conductivity and thermal diffusivity.

Describe Ingenhausz's experiment for comparing the thermal conductivities of substances, and indicate how the required formula is derived.

3. Show theoretically that the distribution of temperature along a bar heated at one end and subject to steady conditions is (*a*) a straight line for a lagged bar, (*b*) an exponential curve for a bar which is freely exposed.

4. Describe the Forbes's bar method of measuring the thermal conductivity of a metal, giving the theory of the method.

5. If the air above a lake is at a steady temperature of $-1°$ C., determine how long it will be before it is safe to skate, given that the water is initially at $0°$ C. and that safe skating requires a thickness of 10 cm. of ice. The density of ice is 0·92 gm./c.c., its thermal conductivity is 5×10^{-3} cal. cm.$^{-1}$ °C.$^{-1}$ sec.$^{-1}$, and the latent heat of solidification is 80 cals./gm. [204·4 hr.]

6. How may the coefficient of thermal conduction of a liquid be measured?

What is the explanation of thermal conduction on the kinetic theory of matter?

7. Describe the tube method for finding the thermal conductivity of a poor conductor.

Two flat metal plates are placed with their surfaces in contact, and these surfaces are maintained at temperatures of $100°$ C. and $0°$ C. respectively. If the thicknesses of the plates are 2 cm. and 1 cm. and their thermal conductivities are 0·1 and 0·2 C.G.S. units, find the temperature of the common surface. [$20°$ C.]

CHAPTER VI

Heat, Energy, and Joule's Law

1. Forms of Energy.

We have already discussed briefly the nature of energy in Part I, Chap. III, section 6. We may note here that energy can occur in at least ten different forms, namely:

(1) *Kinetic energy.*
(2) *Potential energy.*
(3) *Heat energy.*
(4) *Strain energy.*
(5) *Sound energy*—compounded of (1), (2), and (4).
(6) *Light and radiant energy.*
(7) *Electrical energy*
(8) *Magnetic energy*
(9) *Chemical energy*   } not directly detected by the senses.
(10) *Sub-atomic energy*

Whenever energy disappears from one of these forms it reappears in another form. In this chapter we give the evidence on which this qualitative fact is transformed into a strict quantitative relation for the transformations, *mechanical energy → heat energy*, and *electrical energy → heat energy*. That is, we proceed to show that it is found experimentally that whenever a given quantity of mechanical or electrical energy disappears, a definite quantity of heat energy makes its appearance. This relation is sometimes termed the **First Law of Thermodynamics**, and is expressed mathematically as

$$W = JH, \qquad \ldots \ldots \ldots \quad (6.1)$$

where W is the mechanical energy which disappears and H is the corresponding quantity of heat energy formed. The ratio J is termed **Joule's equivalent of heat** and has a value of $4 \cdot 18 \times 10^7$ ergs per calorie.

2. Joule's Determination of J.

One form of the apparatus used by Joule about 1848 is shown in fig. 1. Two masses M_1, M_1 were attached to a cord passing round a vertical drum, rotation of the drum taking place when the weights were allowed to descend vertically. The axle of the drum was attached to a paddle system which stirred water contained in a cylindrical calorimeter. Radial stops in the calorimeter were staggered with the paddles, so that churning of the water took place and the liquid did not rotate as a whole. The suspended masses were between 10 and 30 lb. and the mass of water stirred was about 8 lb. The calorimeter was of copper and there were 8 paddles made of brass. The height through which the masses fell was 5 ft., and they were allowed to fall 20 times in succession. The rise in temperature of the water was then measured

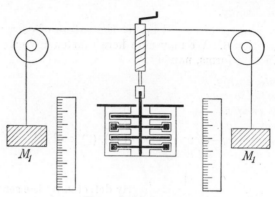

Fig. 1.—Joule's Apparatus

and found to be about 0·5° F. Since the mechanical energy destroyed was $W = nmgh$, where

n = number of times of fall,
m = mass of both weights,
g = acceleration due to gravity,
h = distance fallen,
and $H = C\theta$, where
C = water equivalent of calorimeter and contents,
θ = rise of temperature,

it follows from equation (6.1) that

$$J = \frac{W}{H} = \frac{nmgh}{C\theta}. \qquad \cdots \cdots \quad (6.2)$$

Several corrections were necessary to obtain an accurate result. These were:

(1) The potential energy of the weights was converted partly into kinetic energy as well as into heat. The terminal velocity of fall of the weights was determined to be about 1 in. per second. The corre-

sponding kinetic energy had to be subtracted from W to give correct results in equation (6.2).

(ii) To allow for the energy lost in overcoming the friction of the pulleys, a small additional weight had to be attached to the masses to give steady motion. This method of allowing for friction is the same as that used on p. 56, Part I, in determining g with Atwood's machine.

(iii) All the usual corrections for loss of heat in calorimetry, as discussed in Chap. III, p.182, had to be taken into account. The small rise in temperature tended to make these corrections small, but this advantage was offset to some extent by the comparatively long time of the experiment.

To show that J was a fundamental quantity, independent of the method used, Joule carried out many other experiments. Thus he used iron paddles moving in mercury and, in another experiment, two iron rings rubbing together under mercury. He also used electrical methods, his first method being to find the heat generated in a wire carrying the electric current from a dynamo which was consuming a measured quantity of mechanical energy to drive it. Electrical methods now give the most accurate value of J, but at the time Joule worked the electrical units of current, resistance and potential difference were only approximately defined.

Finally, Joule obtained a value for J from the heat developed in a gas when mechanical work is done in compressing the gas suddenly. The work done on adiabatic compression could be calculated as shown in Chap. XII, section 5, but the heat could not be measured accurately owing to the relatively large heat capacity of container and thermometers, compared with that of the gas itself.

3. Later Mechanical Experiments.

In 1879, Rowland carried out some accurate measurements of J, using a steam-engine to drive the paddle. In this way, with a rate of working of 2200 kg. metres/min. a rise in temperature of 25° C. was obtained in 40 min. Mercury thermometers were used, but these were calibrated against a standard hydrogen gas thermometer. Rowland's experiments were sufficiently accurate to show the existence of a variation in the specific heat of water with temperature.

Some years later, Callendar used a somewhat similar method, an electric motor being used to drive a rotating cylindrical calorimeter mounted on a horizontal axis, the heat being produced by the friction of a silk band pressing against the outer surface of the calorimeter. The mechanical energy used was determined by using the band as a brake tester as described in Part I, pp. 42-43.

4. Electrical Methods.

We have already described the electrical methods briefly in Chap. III, section 6. Joule's electrical method was carried out accurately by *Griffiths* in 1894 and by *Jaeger* and *Steinwehr* in 1921. In Griffith's experiment, the potential difference E and the resistance of the wire R were determined, and a vacuum jacket was used to reduce heat losses. A platinum wire 33 cm. long and of about 9 ohms resistance was used in a cylindrical calorimeter about 8 cm. high and 8 cm. diameter. Electrical energy was supplied by 3 and 6 Clark cells respectively; if E is the E.M.F. of one cell, equation (3.14) becomes

$$\frac{E^2}{R}\frac{1}{J}(4t_2 - t_1) = (m - m')s\theta, \quad \ldots \quad (6.3)$$

where s was unity for water, and t_2 was the time of the second experiment and was approximately equal to t_1 so that the heat losses were approximately the same in the two experiments. The quantity $(m - m')$ was about 120 gm.; a disadvantage of the method lies in the variation of R with temperature.

Callendar and *Barnes* determined J by the continuous flow method which has also been described in Chap. III, section 6. *Thermocouples* were used to measure the inlet and outlet temperatures and a very accurate value of J was obtained.

Recently Hercus and Laby have used a combination of Joule's first method and the continuous flow method. A copper tube stator conveying water is used as the flow tube, and a magnetic field rotates around this. Electrical energy is produced by electromagnetic induction and is converted into heat, the mechanical energy absorbed being determined with a brake tester.

5. J by the Reverse Process.

Equation (6.1) is strictly reversible, and it is possible to obtain a value for J by measuring the quantity of mechanical energy resulting from the transformation, heat energy → mechanical energy. The accuracy of the measurements does not approach that of the preceding methods, so we shall simply describe very briefly one experiment carried out by Hirn about 1860. A measured quantity of heat Q was taken from the boiler of a steam-engine and it was found that a smaller quantity q was given up to the condenser (see Chap. XIII). If W was the mechanical work performed by the steam-engine during this process, it was found that J satisfied the relation

$$W = J(Q - q - R), \quad \ldots \quad (6.4)$$

where R was a correction applied for the heat losses suffered by the engine. As the efficiency of a steam-engine is only a few per cent, the correction R was very large.

EXERCISES

1. Write a short essay on the Conservation of Energy, with special reference to the First Law of Thermodynamics.

2. Describe Joule's apparatus for measuring the mechanical equivalent of heat, pointing out the corrections necessary to obtain an accurate value.

3. Describe an electrical method for finding Joule's equivalent of heat.

Find the percentage heat lost if 100 gm. of liquid of specific heat 0·3, contained in a copper calorimeter of mass 200 gm. and specific heat 0·094, is raised in temperature by 10° C. in 150 sec. when an immersed coil of wire carries a current of 4 amp. under a potential difference of 4 volts. [15 per cent.]

4. Taking the specific heat of lead as 0·03, find the rise in temperature of a lead bullet if it remains embedded in a fixed, badly-conducting block. The initial velocity of the bullet was 100 cm./sec., and 95 per cent of its kinetic energy was converted into heat. Joule's equivalent of heat is $4\cdot2 \times 10^7$ ergs/cal. [$3\cdot8 \times 10^{-3}$° C.]

CHAPTER VII

Thermal Properties of Gases

1. Deviations from Boyle's Law.

As we have seen in Part I, Chap. X, section 5, at constant temperature, the pressure of a given mass of gas is inversely proportional to its volume. This statement constitutes Boyle's law, and within the limits of the experiment described on p. 107, Part I, it would be found to be true for what are sometimes termed the " permanent "

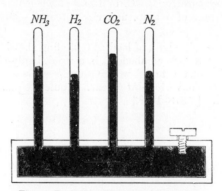

Fig. 1.—Deviation of Gases from Boyle's Law

gases, of which examples are hydrogen, oxygen, nitrogen, and the rare gases. Actually, Despretz showed as early as 1827 that gases such as carbon dioxide and ammonia were more compressible than if they had strictly obeyed Boyle's law. The apparatus, as shown in fig. 1, consisted of a number of barometer tubes cemented into a closed cistern containing mercury. Initially, the volume of different gases contained in the tubes was the same, but on raising the pressure by screwing a plug into the cistern the mercury rose much faster in the tubes containing the carbon dioxide and ammonia than in the tubes containing the " permanent " gases.

The simple Boyle's law apparatus hitherto described is clearly not capable of great accuracy at high pressures, since the volume of gas becomes very small indeed. Accordingly, in 1847 Regnault introduced the apparatus shown in fig. 2. The gas is contained in a vertical glass tube fitted at the top with a tap which communicates with a compression pump. A mark at the centre of the tube indicates the half-volume position; pressure is applied by a mercury column which is attached to a force-pump. Let us suppose the gas is initially at atmospheric pressure p, when it just fills the tube. The tap T is then closed and the pressure increased until the volume is halved. If Boyle's law is exactly obeyed the new pressure p_2 will be exactly equal to twice p_1, that is, the ratio $2p_1/p_2$ should equal unity. In the first pair of readings with permanent gases this is approximately true. The experiment is continued by pumping more gas in through T so as to depress the mercury back to its original position; then T is again closed. The gas will now be at some new pressure p_3, and we may again halve the volume by raising the pressure to p_4. If Boyle's law were still true $2p_3/p_4$ will also equal unity, but that is not found experimentally. In fig. 3 is shown a graph exhibiting the variation of pv with p. As the pressure is increased, most gases at room temperature show a value of

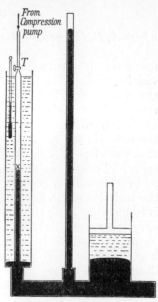

Fig. 2.—Regnault's Apparatus for testing Boyle's Law

pv which decreases as the pressure increases. A minimum value is eventually reached, after which pv increases indefinitely with rise of pressure. On the other hand, hydrogen and helium, *at room temperature*, show a steady increase in the value of pv from very low pressures.

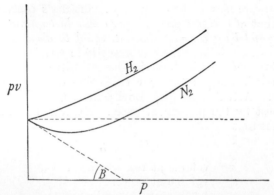

Fig. 3.—Graphs of pv against p for Hydrogen and Nitrogen

For very accurate work Boyle's law must be replaced by some more general equations. Of those which have been proposed we note first an empirical relation suggested by Holborn and Otto, namely

$$pv = A + Bp + Cp^2 +, \&c., \quad \ldots \quad (7.1)$$

where A, B, &c., are constants at constant temperature and are termed *virial coefficients*. Such an equation has no theoretical basis and is useful simply as a method of expressing the experimental results. The virial coefficients are such that $A \gg B \gg C$ and so on. At low pressures, therefore, Boyle's law is approximately true, whereas as the pressure is increased more and more terms become necessary in equation (7.1). We may note that $d(pv)/dp$ is the slope of the tangent to the curve in fig. 3. Differentiating (7.1) and putting $p = 0$, we find that the slope of the tangent at the commencement of the curve is the virial coefficient B. Since this slope is negative for most gases at room temperature, B is usually negative. Graphs are available showing the variation of B with temperature; the temperature for which $B = 0$ is termed the *Boyle temperature*, for at this temperature Boyle's law is obeyed for a considerable range of pressure.

As we shall see in Chap. XI, the deviations of gases from Boyle's law receive a ready explanation on the kinetic theory. Again, in Chap. X, we discuss Van der Waals' equation as a more satisfactory description of real gases than the perfect gas equation.

2. Thermal Expansion of Gases.

When gases are heated they show much more expansion than solids and liquids. In general, not only the volume increases but also the pressure. If the gas is heated in a closed vessel the volume perforce remains constant and the pressure increase is then a maximum. Conversely, if the gas is allowed to expand by a suitable amount then the pressure may be kept constant. **Charles's constant pressure law** states that *at constant pressure, for a rise in temperature of 1° C., all gases expand by a constant amount, equal to about 1/273 of their volume at 0° C.* This behaviour of gases is in striking contrast with that of solids and liquids, both in the magnitude of the expansion coefficient and in the fact that the expansion coefficient of all gases is the same. Actually, as with Boyle's law, Charles's pressure law is obeyed best by the permanent gases. Expressed mathematically, the law states that

$$v = v_0(1 + \gamma t), \quad \ldots \ldots \quad (7.2)$$

where $v =$ volume at temperature $t°$ C.,
               $v_0 =$ volume at 0° C.,
               $\gamma = 1/273$ approximately.

Equation (7·2) is formally similar to equation (2·7), but the difference lies in the fact that in the latter v_0 refers to the volume at any lower temperature, whereas, for gases, $\gamma = 1/273$ only if v_0 is the volume at 0° C. Equation (7·2) shows the surprising result that if $t = -273°$ C., $v = 0$, or the gas would contract to zero volume if it continued to obey Charles's pressure law. Actually, the gas liquefies and solidifies before this temperature is reached, but it is convenient to adopt $-273°$ C. as the natural zero for a **gas scale of temperature** for an ideal gas. If instead of keeping the pressure constant and allowing the volume to change the volume is kept constant, it is found that the pressure changes by a law exactly similar to (7.2), namely

$$p = p_0(1 + \gamma t). \quad \ldots \ldots \quad (7.3)$$

This expresses **Charles's constant volume law,** viz. *if the volume is kept constant, all gases undergo an increase in pressure equal to 1/273 of their pressure at 0° C. for each degree Centigrade rise of temperature.* The fact that the coefficient of pressure increase is numerically equal to the coefficient of volume increase shows that, on the pressure scale also, the natural zero of temperature would occur at $-273°$ C., for then the pressure as well as the volume would become zero. We represent temperatures on the gas scale by θ, so 0° C. $= 273°$ on the gas scale. In particular, equations (7.2) and (7.3) become

$$v = v_0 \frac{(273 + t)}{273} = \frac{\theta}{\theta_0},$$

or

$$\frac{v}{v_0} = \frac{\theta}{\theta_0}, \quad \ldots \ldots \quad \ldots \ldots \quad (7.4)$$

and

$$\frac{p}{p_0} = \frac{\theta}{\theta_0}, \quad \ldots \ldots \ldots \quad (7.5)$$

where θ corresponds to $t°$ C. and θ_0 to 0° C.

On the gas scale, therefore, the volumes and pressures are directly proportional to the temperatures, provided one or the other quantity is kept constant. Now since by Boyle's law, at constant temperature, $pv = $ constant, the only equation expressing that this law and Charles's two laws hold for one and the same gas is

$$pv/\theta = \text{constant}.$$

The value of the constant depends on the kind of gas and on its mass. If, however, the mass is 1 gram-molecule (i.e. μ grams, where μ is the molecular weight of the gas), the constant is the same for all gases. Thus, *for 1 gram-molecule of any gas*, we have the relation

$$\mathbf{pv} = \mathbf{R\theta}. \quad \ldots \ldots \ldots \quad (7.6)$$

Equation (7.6) is the most important relation in gas phenomena, and is sometimes termed the **Gas Equation**. The **universal** constant **R** is called the **gas constant**. Its value is $83 \cdot 15 \times 10^6$ ergs per gram-molecule.

If the mass of the gas is m grams, and its molecular weight is μ, equation (7.6) is replaced by

$$pv = \frac{m}{\mu} \mathbf{R}\theta. \quad . \quad . \quad . \quad . \quad . \quad . \quad (7.7)$$

The student should note that the equation $pv = R\theta$ is frequently used loosely with reference, not to a gram-molecule, but to any mass of the gas, e.g. 1 gram. In this usage, the value of R is not the same as in (7.6) and (7.7).

Of course the gas equation applies strictly only to ideal gases; besides deviating from Boyle's law in the way we have already discussed, real gases also deviate from Charles's laws. Consequently, to represent actual gases with greater accuracy some more complicated expression such as Van der Waals' equation (Chap. X) must be used. From equation (7.7), for a given mass of gas, $pv/\theta = A$, a constant: consequently if pressure, volume and temperature change simultaneously for a gas, we can find p_2, v_2, or θ_2 if we know *two* of these quantities and their initial values (p_1, v_1, θ_1) because

$$\frac{p_1 v_1}{\theta_1} = A = \frac{p_2 v_2}{\theta_2}.$$

3. Constant Volume Thermometer.

The term gas thermometer is usually understood to refer to an instrument of the constant volume type, as shown in fig. 4, and not to the constant pressure type as described in the next section. The standard gas thermometer consists of a cylindrical bulb of platinum-iridium alloy, about 100 cm. long and of capacity about 1 litre. The bulb contains hydrogen, and is placed in the temperature bath with a window for observing the mercury thermometers if the latter are being calibrated against the gas thermometer. A tube leads from the bulb to a manometer containing mercury with which is combined a barometer, so that the total pressure of the gas can be read directly from the manometer. The temperature scale is constructed by immersing the bulb first in melting ice. The mercury is brought back to a constant mark M on the manometer scale for all readings, the corresponding pressure being observed: then any temperature θ is given by the observed pressure p, since

$$\frac{p_0}{273} = \frac{p}{\theta}, \quad . \quad . \quad . \quad . \quad . \quad . \quad (7.8)$$

where p_0 is the pressure at $0°$ C. ($= 273°$ on the gas scale), and p is the pressure at $\theta°$ on the gas scale.

For accurate values, corrections must be applied for (a) the expansion of the bulb, (b) the existence of a " dead space " in the tube connecting the bulb to the manometer. The gas in this tube is at some temperature intermediate between those of the bulb and the manometer. If

$$V_1 = \text{vol. of bulb at } \theta_1,$$
$$V_2 = \text{vol. of bulb at } \theta_2,$$
$$v_1 = \text{vol. of connecting tube at } \theta_1,$$
$$P_1 = \text{pressure at } \theta_1,$$
$$P_2 = \text{pressure at } \theta_2,$$

we may apply equation (7.7) to the gas in the bulb, and also to the gas in the tube. Since the *total mass* of the gas is constant, we have by addition

$$\frac{P_1 V_1}{\theta_1} + \frac{P_1 v_1}{\theta_1} = \frac{P_2 V_2}{\theta_2} + \frac{P_2 v'}{\theta'}, \quad . \quad . \quad . \quad . \quad (7.9)$$

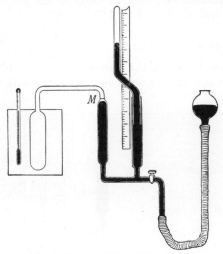

Fig. 4.—Constant Volume Thermometer

where v' corresponds to the volume of the connecting tube at some temperature θ' intermediate between θ_1 and θ_2, which may be defined by

$$\frac{1}{\theta'} = \frac{1}{2}\left(\frac{1}{\theta_1} + \frac{1}{\theta_2}\right). \quad . \quad . \quad . \quad . \quad (7.10)$$

In equation (7.9) θ_1 is known if the initial temperature is fixed by immersing the thermometer in melting ice; the desired quantity is

θ_2. Now P_1 and P_2 are measured directly; V_1 and v_1 are known, but V_2 can be calculated only if θ_2 is known, and similarly v' only if θ' is known, which also involves a knowledge of θ_2. Consequently, a method of *successive approximation is used*. Initially V_2 is put equal to V_1 and v' to v_1. Application of equation (7.9) then gives an approximate value of θ_2. Hence (1) an approximate value of V_2 can be calculated, knowing the coefficient of cubical expansion of the container, (2) an approximate value of θ' can be obtained from equation (7.10) and hence an approximate value of v' calculated. Substituting these values in equation (7.9) a new value for θ_2 is obtained. The quantities V_2, θ' and v' are again calculated and resubstituted in equation (7.9) to obtain a still better value of θ_2. Proceeding in this way, after a few successive approximations the value of θ_2 approaches a constant value, which is the true value of θ_2. It is essential that the mercury column should be some distance from the heated bulb, so that variations in the density of the mercury do not occur. The " dead-space " v_1 may be inconveniently large and Callendar and Bottomley inserted a U-tube of concentrated sulphuric acid to act as a buffer and thus reduce the dead-space. The advantages and disadvantages of the gas thermometer are discussed at the end of Chap. I, p. 163.

4. Constant Pressure Thermometer.

A thermometer based on the variation of gas volume at constant pressure is not as accurate as one based upon the variation of pressure

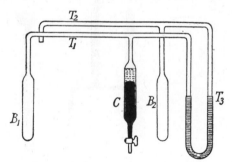

Fig 5.—Constant Pressure Thermometer

at constant volume. The chief reason is the difficulty of maintaining a continuously increasing volume of gas at constant temperature. In fig. 5 is shown an improved compensating constant-pressure thermometer due to Callendar. The gas is contained in the bulb B_1, and increases in volume are measured, and the pressure maintained constant, by allowing mercury to run out of the graduated container C. The compensating bulb B_2 is equal in volume to B_1 and has a dummy connecting tube T_2 equal in volume to the connecting tube T_1 and placed beside it. The two bulbs are joined through a U-tube T_3 which contains concentrated sulphuric acid. The whole instrument is first placed in melting ice, and C is filled with mercury. The bulb B_1 is then immersed in the bath at temperature θ and mercury is run out of C until the pressures in B_1 and B_2 are equal as shown by the levels of T_3. If

$$V_1, V_1' = \text{vol. of } B_1 \text{ at } \theta_0 \text{ and } \theta \text{ respectively,}$$
$$V_2 = \quad \text{,,} \quad B_2 \text{ ,, } \theta_0,$$
$$v_1 = \quad \text{,,} \quad T_1 \text{ ,, } \theta_0,$$
$$v_2 = \quad \text{,,} \quad T_2 \text{ ,, } \theta_0,$$
$$v_1' = \quad \text{,,} \quad T_1 \text{ at } t \text{ where } \frac{1}{t} = \frac{1}{2}\left(\frac{1}{\theta_0} + \frac{1}{\theta}\right)$$
$$v_2' = \quad \text{,,} \quad T_2 \text{ ,, } \quad \text{,,} \quad \text{,,} \quad \text{,,} \quad \text{,,}$$
$$P = \text{initial pressure in system,}$$
$$P' = \text{final } \quad \text{,,} \quad \text{,,} \quad \text{,,}$$
$$V = \text{vol. of gas expelled into C,}$$

then, by applying equation (7.7) to the two systems as at (7.9),

$$\frac{P'V_1'}{\theta} + \frac{P'v_1'}{t} = \frac{PV}{\theta_0} + \frac{PV_1}{\theta_0} + \frac{Pv_1}{\theta_0}, \quad . \quad . \quad (7.11)$$

and

$$\frac{P'V_2}{\theta_0} + \frac{P'v_2'}{t} = \frac{PV_2}{\theta_0} + \frac{Pv_2}{\theta_0}. \quad . \quad . \quad . \quad (7.12)$$

Now $V_2 = V_1$, $v_2 = v_1$, and $v_2' = v_1'$, since the tubes are similarly placed: hence from (7.11) and (7.12),

$$\frac{\theta}{\theta_0} = \frac{V_1'}{V_1 - V}. \quad . \quad . \quad . \quad . \quad (7.13)$$

5. Specific Heats of Gases.

If a gas is heated at constant pressure and is therefore allowed to expand, it is found that to produce the same rise in temperature more heat must be supplied than if the gas is heated at constant volume. Representing the specific heat of a gas at constant pressure by c_p and at constant volume by c_v respectively, $c_p > c_v$. We discuss this more fully in Chap. XI and XII; here we state briefly that in the former case external work is done by the expanding gas, and hence heat energy must be supplied to do this as well as to raise the temperature of the gas.

(a) Constant Volume.

The specific heats of gases at constant volume were determined by Joly with the differential steam calorimeter shown in fig. 6. Two additional scale-pans are suspended from the arms of a delicate balance, and are placed in an enclosure into which steam can be admitted. Two identical copper spheres are taken and placed in each scale-pan, one sphere being completely exhausted and the other filled with the gas whose specific heat is required. To magnify the effect the gas is at a pressure of several atmospheres. The steam condenses on the apparatus, and according to the principles discussed in Chap. VIII the temperature is raised from room temperature to approximately 100° C. by the latent heat given out when the steam condenses. Eventually a steady temperature is reached, and it is found that more water has

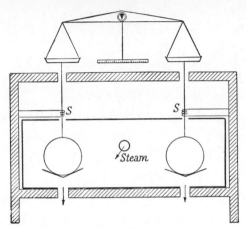

Fig. 6.—Joly's Differential Steam Calorimeter

condensed on the gas-filled sphere than on the evacuated sphere. This is because the former requires heat for raising the temperature of the gas as well as that of the container. The excess weight w of water is determined by calibrating the deflection of the pointer of the balance with a small weight. If

L = latent heat of condensation of steam,
c_v = specific heat of gas at constant volume,
θ = initial temperature of gas,
100° C. = final temperature of gas,
W = mass of gas present,

then $wL = Wc_v (100 - \theta)$. . . . . (7.14)

Various factors such as the greater expansion of the sphere containing the gas have to be taken into consideration. It is usual to prevent condensation at the small holes through which the suspending wires pass by encircling them with electrically heated spirals S as shown in fig. 6.

In modern determinations, a *Nernst calorimeter* is used. The detailed description of this apparatus is beyond the scope of this book, but the principle consists in supplying electrically a known quantity of heat to gas in a closed container. The relatively large heat capacity of the container is sometimes reduced by carrying out the experiment at low temperatures, since, as we have seen on p. 187, the specific heat of solids falls rapidly when the temperature is reduced.

(b) *Constant Pressure.*

In fig. 7 is shown the method due to Regnault; it is simply the method of mixtures adapted to gases. Gas whose pressure is controlled

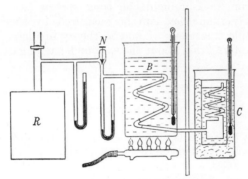

Fig. 7.—Regnault's Constant Pressure Method for c_p

and kept constant by continual adjustment of the needle valve N is allowed to flow from the reservoir R through a spiral immersed in a hot oil bath B, to the calorimeter C. Pressures are read on the manometer; the mass M of gas which has passed is known by reading the pressure of the reservoir before and after the experiment. Application of Boyle's law, together with a knowledge of the density of the gas, allows the mass to be calculated. Then if

θ = temp. gas acquires in oil bath,
θ_1 = initial temp. of calorimeter and contents,
θ_2 = final temp. of calorimeter and contents,
W = water equivalent of calorimeter and contents,

it follows that

$$Mc_r\left(\theta - \frac{\theta_1 + \theta_2}{2}\right) = W(\theta_2 - \theta_1). \quad . \quad . \quad (7.15)$$

Corrections must, of course, be applied to equation (7.15) to allow for heat losses as in the ordinary method of mixtures.

Modern determinations of the specific heat at constant pressure use the continuous flow method of Callendar and Barnes, already described for liquids on p. 186.

It should be noted that the **ratio γ of the specific heats of a gas at constant pressure and constant volume** occurs in many experiments. Hence if *either* c_p or c_v is known, an experimental determination of the ratio allows the third quantity to be determined. For example, Clement and Désormes' experiment, described on p. 262, allows the determination of γ. Much more accurate is the determination of γ from the velocity of sound in the gas, an experiment described in detail in Part IV.

Finally the student may note that the theory of gases is so well understood that the values of c_p and c_v may be calculated *purely theoretically* from measurements on *band spectra* (see Part III) far more accurately than they can be measured by thermal methods. Even our simple treatment of kinetic theory in Chap. XI gives us a great deal of information about the specific heats of gases.

EXERCISES

1. Describe experiments which have shown the deviations of gases from Boyle's law. What theoretical attempts have been made to account for these departures?

2. In what way do the pressure and volume of a gas vary with temperature on the Centigrade scale? Explain carefully the nature of the gas scale of temperature.

3. Discuss the origin and applicability of the Gas Equation governing the pressure, volume and temperature relations for a perfect gas. Three gases at initial pressures, volumes and temperatures (p_1, V_1, T_1), (p_2, V_2, T_2), and (p_3, V_3, T_3) are allowed to mix in an enclosure at temperature T. If the final pressure in the enclosure is p, what is the volume of the enclosure?

$$\left[\frac{T}{p} \left\{ \frac{p_1 V_1}{T_1} + \frac{p_2 V_2}{T_2} + \frac{p_3 V_3}{T_3} \right\} \right].$$

4. Describe an *accurate* form of gas thermometer, indicating clearly any corrections which may be necessary. How is the effect of the connecting tubes of a constant volume gas thermometer estimated?

5. Give an account of some form of constant pressure thermometer. Compare the advantages and disadvantages of this instrument with one of constant volume type.

6. If no particular attention is paid to the pressure-volume variations of a gas when it is heated, its specific heat is found to vary from experiment to experiment. Explain this and find an expression for the difference

in the two extreme values of the specific heat in terms of R, the gas constant. $[c_p - c_v = \mathbf{R}/\mu.]$

7. Describe the experimental determination of the specific heats of a gas at constant pressure and constant volume respectively.

8. Given that the specific heat of a gas at constant volume enclosed in one sphere of a Joly differential steam calorimeter is 0·3, find the excess mass of water which will condense on this sphere if its volume is 1000 c.c., its initial and final temperatures 15° C. and 100° C., and the gas is at a density of $8\cdot00 \times 10^{-3}$ gm./c.c. Latent heat of condensation of water = 540 cal./gm. [0·38 gm.]

CHAPTER VIII

Change of State

1. Introduction

If a mixture of ice and water is heated, it is found that the temperature of the mixture remains constant at 0° C. until all the ice has disappeared. Since heat has been supplied unaccompanied by any rise in temperature, it follows that it has probably been used in changing the state of the material from solid to liquid. Conversely, if heat is abstracted from a mixture of ice and water, no depression of temperature below 0° C. is observed until all the water has solidified. Heat phenomena which accompany change of state are said to be due to **latent heat**. The two laws of **latent heat of fusion** may be stated thus:

I. *For a given pressure, the temperature of fusion of a crystalline mass is fixed and is the same as for solidification. Consequently, while fusion or solidification is taking place, the temperature of the mixture remains constant.*

II. *During fusion, heat is absorbed by the substance, and an equal quantity of heat is evolved by the substance during solidification.*

2. Determination of Melting-points.

If a cooling curve (see Chap. IV) is plotted for water by inserting a thermometer in water contained in a beaker and surrounded by a freezing mixture, its appearance will be as shown in fig. 1. When the freezing-point is reached, heat is evolved according to Law II above; consequently the temperature remains at 0° C. until freezing is complete. The horizontal portion of the curve therefore shows the melting-point or freezing-point. If a substance like paraffin-wax is used, a similar curve is obtained except that the horizontal portion is less well-defined. The melting-point can therefore only be fixed approximately about 52° C. Mixtures or even the presence of small impurities strongly affect the sharpness of definition of the melting-point, and during the preparation of organic compounds their purity is tested by this property.

If only a small quantity of the material is available, it is tapped into a fine glass capillary tube, and the tube is attached directly to the stem of a thermometer by rubber bands. The thermometer is then immersed in a temperature bath and the temperature is raised very slowly. Melting is indicated by the formation of a few drops of liquid in the capillary tube; the temperature at which this occurs is noted. After all the material has melted it is allowed to cool and the temperature noted at which solid first appears, as indicated by slight opacity. The mean of the temperatures is taken as the melting-point.

In general, only crystalline substances have a definite melting-point, the remainder becoming plastic and melting over a considerable range of temperature. Even crystalline substances may be temporarily **super-cooled.** If great care is taken to avoid disturbances of the liquid and a smooth container is used, it is possible to cool the liquid considerably below its accepted freezing-point. Immediately,

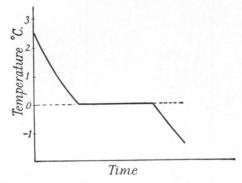

Fig. 1.—Cooling Curve for Water

however, a particle of the solid is formed in or dropped into the super-cooled liquid, the whole mass freezes and the temperature rises to the normal freezing-point owing to the latent heat evolved on solidification. Alloys and mixtures occupy an anomalous position. For example, *Rose's metal*, which consists of an alloy of two parts of bismuth (m.-pt. 271° C.), one part of lead (m.-pt. 327° C.), and one part of tin (m.-pt. 232° C.), melts at 94° C.

3. Effect of Pressure on the Melting-point.

As the temperature is reduced, most liquids contract fairly uniformly in volume. This contraction continues at the change of state, the volume of the solid being less than that of the same mass of liquid. As we have seen in Chap. II, water is an exception in that an expansion occurs when the temperature is reduced below 4° C.: this expansion is continued on solidification, the volume increasing by about 10 per cent. The metals, iron and antimony, also expand on solidification, and they are therefore useful in making sharp casts from a mould. Ordinary molten rock contracts on solidification, and the process may lead to remarkable results if the molten magma is homogeneous. Thus, the Giant's Causeway on the north-east coast of Ireland exhibits a series of basaltic columns which show almost perfect hexagonal section. The reason for this is that, on contraction, work has to be done against the surface tension forces. The hexagon is the geometrical figure which gives the maximum of area with the minimum of perimeter, together with perfect packing.

The effect of pressure on the melting-point may be easily deduced if it is known whether an increase or a decrease in volume occurs on solidification. If the volume increases, added pressure will tend to prevent the solid forming. Consequently, *the freezing-point of water*

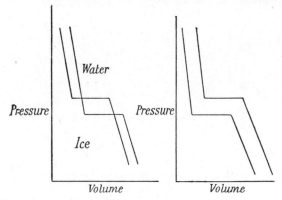

Fig. 2.—Isothermals near Freezing-point: (left) Water; (right) Substance
contracting on Freezing

is lowered by a rise in pressure. Strictly speaking, therefore, the pressure must be specified when a melting-point is stated. The depression in freezing-point may be calculated theoretically by the application of thermodynamics as in Chap. XIII. Familiar examples of depression of the freezing-point of ice occur in the making of snowballs, in skating, and in the regelation experiment.

With *snowballs* it is found that the snow will not " bind " under pressure from the hands, if the temperature is much below freezing-point. Binding is due to momentary melting under the increased pressure accompanied by freezing when the pressure is relaxed. If the temperature of the snow is very low, the pressure is insufficient to cause melting.

In *skating*, if the weight of the skater is sufficient to melt the ice, a layer of water is formed beneath the skates and lubrication is good. Since the edge of the skates is fine, the pressure, which is force per unit area, is generally sufficiently great to cause momentary melting.

In the *regelation* experiment two equal weights are attached to a fine wire and slung across a block of ice so as to hang down on either side of the block. Owing to the pressure the ice beneath the wire melts and the wire goes through. In this way the wire sinks through the block but the block is not permanently divided. When the wire has passed through, the pressure is released, and consequently the water above the wire refreezes.

The isothermals (see Chap. XII) of substances which expand and those which contract on solidification are different, inasmuch as the former intersect each other, while the latter do not, as shown in fig. 2.

4. Behaviour of Solutions.

We saw that with alloys, the melting-point of the alloy was considerably less than that of the constituents. Similarly, solutions in water and other liquids exhibit a *depression in freezing-point* below that of the pure solvent. With substances which do not dissociate (see Part V), the depression in the freezing-point is (a) directly proportional to the concentration, (b) inversely proportional to the molecular weight of the solute. For further details the student should consult a textbook of Physical Chemistry.

5. Measurement of Latent Heat of Fusion.

The latent heat of fusion is usually determined by the method of mixtures already described for specific heat measurement in Chap. III. For example, a quantity of ice is dried on blotting-paper and added to water contained in a calorimeter, the temperature of which is sufficient to melt all the ice added. The mass m of ice added is determined from the total weight of water present at the end of the experiment. Then if L is the latent heat of fusion, usually expressed in calories per gram,

$$mL + m\theta = W(\theta_1 - \theta), \quad . \quad . \quad . \quad . \quad (8.1)$$

where θ = final temperature,
         θ_1 = initial temperature of calorimeter and contents,
and W = water equivalent of calorimeter and contents.

Radiation corrections must be applied as usual.

If the ice is initially below $0°$ C., an additional term must be added to the L.H.S. of (8.1) to represent the heat required to warm the ice to $0°$ C. The specific heat of a substance may be profoundly changed by change of state, that of ice, for example, being only about 0·5.

If L is known, specific heats may be measured with an **ice-calorimeter**. In *Black's ice-calorimeter*, which is only of historical interest, a cavity in a block of ice was fitted with an ice lid and a known mass of material, previously heated to a known temperature, was dropped into the cavity. The water formed was removed with a sponge and weighed. The calculation is left to the reader.

A much more delicate apparatus was devised by Bunsen, who used it to determine the specific heat of the rare metal indium. As shown in fig. 3, *Bunsen's ice-calorimeter* consists of a glass test-tube T which fits into a larger tube containing pure distilled air-free water. This is surrounded by an air space, the whole being enclosed in a jacket of melting ice. The latter is in contact with a mercury column C, the end of which moves along a fine capillary tube by the side of a scale. The position of the mercury can be adjusted by manipulation of the screw

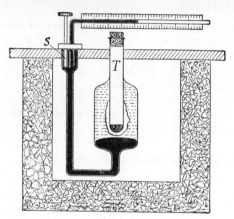

Fig. 3.—Bunsen's Ice Calorimeter

S. Initially, ether is placed in the test-tube and a current of air is blown rapidly through the ether. Owing to the latent heat absorbed in vaporization (see opposite), a crust of ice forms round the test-tube. This ice occupies a larger volume than the water, and the mercury moves along the capillary tube to some new position. As the heat in the room melts the ice, a steady creep is observed along the scale, and allowance must be made for this in estimating the zero readings of the instrument. To calibrate the apparatus, a small mass of water m_1 is introduced into the tube T at a known temperature θ_1, and the contraction d_1 is observed as this water is reduced in temperature by the melting ice to 0° C. If, then, a mass m_2 of the material at temperature θ_2 is introduced and the new contraction is d_2, then

$$m_1(s_1 = 1)\theta_1 = kd_1,$$

and

$$m_2 s_2 \theta_2 = kd_2,$$

whence

$$s_2 = \frac{d_2}{d_1}\frac{\theta_1}{\theta_2}\frac{m_1}{m_2},$$

where s_2 is the specific heat required, k being a constant of the apparatus which is eliminated by calibration. The radiation losses are included in the correction which is applied for the drifting zero. The disadvantages of the instrument are: (a) it is difficult to make and use, (b) thermal equilibrium takes a long time to establish itself. It has the advantage of high sensitivity.

6. Latent Heat of Vaporization.

The change of state from liquid to vapour is accompanied by phenomena which bear a general similarity to the transition from solid to liquid. Thus, a thermometer immersed in a boiling liquid shows no elevation of temperature after the boiling-point is reached, the heat being used to effect the change of state. The two laws of vaporization state that:

I. *For a given pressure, the temperature of vaporization is fixed and is the same as for condensation. Consequently, while condensation or boiling is taking place, the temperature remains constant.*

II. *During vaporization, heat is absorbed and an equal quantity of heat is evolved during condensation.*

The latent heat of vaporization is much greater than that of fusion, since the amount of energy which must be given to effect the former change is much greater than for the latter. For example, the latent heat of vaporization of water is about 540 cal./gm. whereas the latent heat of fusion of ice is only about 80 cal./gm.

There are no exceptions to the rule that all substances expand on transition from the liquid to the vapour state. Consequently, since the volume of a given mass of vapour is always greater than the volume of the same mass of liquid, increased pressure favours the liquid state and the boiling-point is always raised. In Chap. XIII we calculate an expression for the elevation in the boiling-point from thermodynamics. The presence of impurities, or of dissolved substances, in the liquid always results in an elevation of the boiling-point. As in the transition from solid to liquid, the change in the fixed point, for a dissolved substance which does not dissociate, is (a) proportional to the concentration, (b) inversely proportional to the molecular weight of the solute. For further experimental details the student must refer to a textbook of Physical Chemistry.

The change of state from liquid to vapour is discussed more fully in Chaps. IX and X.

7. Ebullition.

Even at low temperatures liquids are always undergoing a certain amount of evaporation, but as the temperature is raised a point is reached when the surface of the liquid is unable to afford the means of sufficiently rapid escape of the vapour. Bubbles of vapour are then formed in the interior of the liquid, and these throw the liquid into the familiar state of unrest termed boiling or ebullition. If the containing vessel is very clean and smooth, the temperature of a liquid may be raised considerably above its boiling-point without ebullition occurring. This phenomenon of **superheating** is clearly analogous to that of a super-cooled liquid. Dufour made experiments in which drops of water were suspended in oil of cloves and heated to 178° C. without boiling. If boiling commences locally in a superheated liquid, it spreads with explosive violence throughout the liquid, and normal boiling does not set in until the excess heat present has all been removed as latent heat of vaporization. The ease with which vaporization occurs if small rough surfaces are present is well known, and is the reason for adding small pieces of porous pot to the contents of a flask if gentle boiling is desired.   Ordinary ether contained in a test-tube will boil momentarily at room temperature if a small ball of paper or a piece of fine wire is inserted into the liquid. The explanation lies in the provision of vaporization nuclei. The dependence on the liquid and on the radius of the nuclei is treated in Chap. IX.

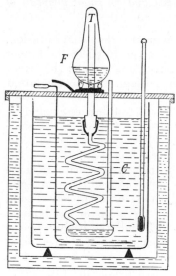

Fig. 4.—Method of Mixtures for Latent Heat

8. Experimental Determination of Latent Heat of Vaporization.

(a) *Method of Mixtures.*

In fig. 4 is shown a modification of the method of mixtures due to Berthelot for the measurement of latent heat of condensation. The liquid is contained in the boiling flask F up the centre of which passes a hollow tube **T** which conducts the vapour down into the calorimeter C. Then if m is the mass of vapour condensed and L is its latent heat of condensation, an equation similar to (8.1) is directly applicable.

(b) *Electrical Method.*

This method is a modification of the electrical method for specific heat determination described on p. 185. The liquid is heated by an immersed wire spiral to its boiling-point and allowed to boil vigorously. Then if m is the loss in weight due to evaporation and L is the specific heat of the liquid,

$$I^2Rt = mL + \text{heat losses},$$

where t = time of boiling,
                        I = current strength,
                        R = resistance of heating coil.

Suitable correction for heat losses is carried out as in ordinary calorimetry.

EXERCISES

1. Define (a) *latent heat of fusion*, (b) *melting-point of a substance*. What is the effect of (a) external pressure, (b) presence of impurities, on the melting-point of solids?

2. State the Laws of Fusion and describe in detail how the latent heat of fusion of a metal such as lead might be determined.

3. Describe Bunsen's ice-calorimeter and give the theory of its action. If the mercury recedes 20 divisions when 10 gm. of a substance are cooled from 50° C. to 0° C., find its specific heat, given that the mercury recedes 15 divisions when 20 gm. of copper of specific heat 0·094 are cooled from 100° C. to 0° C. in the same Bunsen ice-calorimeter. [0·501.]

4. A top of moment of inertia 10^4 gm. cm.^{2} rotates about its vertical cylindrical axis on a block of ice, with an initial speed of 1000 revs./min. Assuming that air resistance may be neglected and that the latent heat of fusion of ice is 80 cal./gm., find the depth to which the axis of the top will eventually sink into the ice owing to the heat generated by friction. The top is initially at 0° C., its axis is 1 mm.^{2} in cross-section, and Joule's equivalent is 4·2 × 10^7 ergs/cal. The density of ice is 0·92 gm./c.c. [1·8 cm.]

5. State the Laws of Vaporization and describe an *accurate* method of measuring the latent heat of condensation of a liquid.

6. Explain the process of ebullition. In what way does the condensation of vapour depend on the presence of electrical charges, and how has this dependence been applied to investigations in atomic physics?

7. A calorimeter contains a liquid immersed in which is a coil of wire carrying a current of 2 amp. under a potential difference of 2·5 volts. After the liquid has been boiling briskly for 4 min., the weight of the liquid is reduced by 5 gm. Find the latent heat of vaporization of the liquid. [57 cal./gm.]

CHAPTER IX

Vapour Pressure, Vapour Density and Hygrometry

1. Vapour Pressure: Statical Measurement.

We have already mentioned that a liquid is always undergoing slow evaporation even when well below its boiling-point. This vapour exerts a definite gas pressure, termed the vapour pressure of the liquid. At ordinary temperatures the vapour pressure may conveniently be measured by introducing a small quantity of the liquid into the Torricellian vacuum of a barometer tube, as shown in fig. 1 (a) (b). The liquid evaporates in the Torricellian vacuum, and the vapour pressure may be read directly from the depression of the mercury in

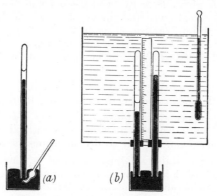

Fig. 1.—Measurement of Vapour Pressure

the barometer tube. As more liquid is introduced, the vapour pressure increases but eventually a layer of unvaporized liquid remains on the mercury. Addition of further liquid fails to increase the observed vapour pressure, which is then said to be the **saturated vapour pressure.** This quantity is characteristic of the material, having a definite value at a definite temperature.

If the tube is surrounded by a water bath and the temperature is raised, the saturated vapour pressure increases as in fig. 2, which shows the variation of the saturation vapour pressure of water with temperature. Ultimately, the vapour pressure reaches the external atmospheric pressure and at this temperature the liquid is observed to boil. In fact, the best **definition of boiling-point** is *that temperature at which the vapour pressure is equal to the external pressure.*

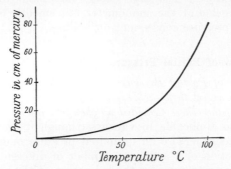

Fig. 2.—Saturation Pressure of Water Vapour

2. Dynamical Method for Vapour Pressure.

The simple statical apparatus already discussed is not suitable for measuring vapour pressures above atmospheric pressure. In fig. 3 is shown an apparatus of the type due to Regnault; it is based on a

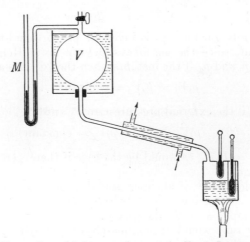

Fig. 3.—Regnault's Apparatus for measuring Vapour Pressure

dynamical principle. The liquid is boiled in a closed reservoir which leads to a Liebig's condenser and a large vessel V. The vessel V communicates with a manometer M, which allows the pressure in the system to be measured. By adjusting the manometer the pressure is raised to various values and the liquid is then boiled under these different pressures. The thermometers indicate steady boiling-points corresponding to the different external pressures, which, since the system is in equilibrium, must be the vapour pressures corresponding to those temperatures. The large vessel V is a buffer inserted between the boiling vessel and the manometer, to smooth out the violent fluctuations in pressure consequent on boiling.

3. Dalton's Law of Partial Pressures.

Dalton's law of Partial Pressures states that when two or more gases occupy the same vessel then each exerts the pressure which it would exert in the absence of the others provided no chemical interaction is occurring. This law is also applicable to vapours, though it holds only over a limited range, as otherwise an unlimited pressure might be produced by the introduction of a sufficient number of different liquids.

It is instructive to consider the behaviour of vapours and gases in the simple Boyle's law apparatus described in Part I, p. 107. If the gas is mixed with saturated vapour, a condition secured by having a small quantity of liquid always present above the mercury, the vapour pressure remains constant when the volume is altered. Thus, if the pressure due to the vapour is p, and that due to the gas present is p_1, while the external pressure at any instant is P,

$$P = p + p_1. \qquad \ldots \ldots \ldots \quad (9.1)$$

But whereas p is constant, p_1 is inversely proportional to the volume at any instant, since the gas obeys Boyle's law. Hence if the gas pressures are p_1 and p_2 at the instants when the volumes are V_1 and V_2,

$$p_1 V_1 = p_2 V_2 = \text{constant}, \quad \ldots \ldots \quad (9.2)$$

or from (9.1), if the external pressures are P_1 and P_2,

$$(P_1 - p)V_1 = (P_2 - p)V_2 = \text{constant}, \quad \ldots \quad (9.3)$$

and not $P_1 V_1 = P_2 V_2$, as would be the case if there were no saturated vapour present.

On the other hand, if an unsaturated vapour is not too near the condition for condensing it will behave approximately as a perfect gas. For example, a *small* quantity of water vapour introduced into a Boyle's law tube would approximately obey Boyle's law.

4. Vapour Density.

Vapour density is defined as the mass of unit volume of the vapour. It depends on the pressure and temperature of the vapour, and different methods are used for its determination according as the vapour density is required at ordinary or at high temperatures. We tabulate below various methods which are available:

(a) Gay-Lussac's and Hofmann's methods;
(b) Dumas's method;
(c) Victor Meyer's method.

As vapour densities are often involved in evaluating molecular weights, the subject has been investigated by physical chemists, and the student should consult a textbook of Physical Chemistry.

*5. Effect of Curvature of the Surface on Vapour Pressure.

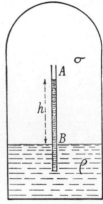

Fig. 4.—Effect of Curvature on Vapour Pressure

Reference to Part I, Chap. XI, section 6, shows that when a capillary tube is inserted vertically into a liquid, in many cases the liquid stands in equilibrium above the general level, the curvature of the surface at A in fig. 4 being concave upwards. Now the liquid and its vapour are in equilibrium at A and at B; the pressure across the surface at the former point must clearly be less than that at the latter by an amount equal to σgh where σ is the density of the vapour (assumed constant with height) and h is the height AB. If p is the vapour pressure at B and p' its value at A, then

$$p - p' = \sigma gh. \quad \ldots \ldots \quad (9.4)$$

Now from Part I, Chap. XI, equation (11.5), the pressure just under the curved surface at A is $\left(p' - \dfrac{2T}{r}\right)$, where T is the surface tension of the liquid and r is the radius of curvature of the surface. Hence, if the density of the liquid is ρ, the liquid pressure at B, the bottom of the column, is P where

$$P = \left(p' - \frac{2T}{r} + \rho gh\right). \quad \ldots \ldots \quad (9.5)$$

Now for equilibrium $P = p$. Hence, from (9.4) and (9.5),

$$\frac{2T}{r} = gh(\rho - \sigma), \quad \ldots \ldots \quad (9.6)$$

or, eliminating h,

$$p - p' = \frac{2T}{r} \frac{\sigma}{(\rho - \sigma)}, \quad \ldots \ldots \quad (9.7)$$

or, representing the difference in vapour pressure over a level and a curved surface by Δp,

$$\Delta p = \frac{2T}{r} \frac{\sigma}{(\rho - \sigma)}. \quad \cdots \cdots \quad (9.8)$$

If the variation of vapour density σ with the height h is taken into account, it can be shown that equation (9.8) becomes

$$\log_e \frac{p}{p'} = \frac{2T}{r} \frac{\sigma}{p\rho}. \quad \cdots \cdots \quad (9.9)$$

Consideration of equation (9.8) leads us to important conclusions concerning the processes of evaporation, boiling and condensation. For example, if r is very small, Δp becomes very large. This explains the comparative ease with which fogs occur in dust-laden atmospheres. The dust particles act as nuclei of appreciable radii of curvature; consequently, the supersaturation Δp, due to cooling of the atmosphere laden with water vapour, does not have to be so large as under dust-free conditions. Besides dust-particles, electric charges facilitate the formation of drops, and this fact forms the basis of the Wilson cloud method for examining atomic particles, discussed in Part V.

The student will also now appreciate more fully the process of ebullition discussed in section 7, Chap. VIII. If moderately large pieces of porous pot are present, vapour can form around them as nuclei, and the excess pressure present is of moderate amount since the radii of the nuclei are large. If no, or only very small, nuclei are present, the excess pressure generated when the vapour starts to grow will be extremely large, and the equilibrium between hydrostatic pressure and vapour pressure in the liquid will be very unstable.

6. Hygrometry.

Hygrometry is that branch of physics which relates to the water vapour in the atmosphere.

The **relative humidity** of the atmosphere is defined as

$$\frac{\text{pressure of water vapour actually present}}{\text{saturated vapour pressure of water at the same temperature}} = \frac{p_1}{p_2}.$$
$$(9.10)$$

Condensation of water vapour occurs if the vapour pressure rises above the saturation vapour pressure at the given temperature. If, for example, a beaker is cooled by passing a current of air through ether contained in the beaker, at a certain stage of the cooling dew will form on the beaker. The temperature of the beaker at which this occurs is termed the **dew-point**. The dew-point is therefore the temperature at which the actual vapour pressure in the atmosphere is the saturation vapour pressure. The condensation of water which is easily seen on mirrors, spectacles, &c., when they are suddenly introduced into a warm room is simply due to the cooling of the air and water vapour in contact with the cold object. The actual pressure of water vapour in the room is greater than the saturation vapour pressure at the temperature of the mirror, and condensation therefore occurs on the latter.

Solids as well as liquids exert a vapour pressure. Sometimes, as in the case of " dry ice " or solid carbon dioxide, the vapour pressure is so large that, on heating, the substance passes directly into the vapour state (or *sublimes*), without passing through the liquid stage at all. To a lesser extent snow and ice evaporate directly and, in the formation of hoar-frost, water vapour passes directly into the solid state without liquefying in the process.

Most hygrometers depend upon the measurement of the dew-point for the determination of the relative humidity. From previously constructed tables showing the variation of the saturation vapour pressures of water with temperature, the pressures p_1 and p_2 appropriate to t_1 and t_2, the temperatures of the dew-point and of the room respectively, are obtained directly.

(a) Regnault's Hygrometer.

In this apparatus, as shown in fig. 5, two identical glass tubes have metal thimbles attached to the bottom and hold thermometers T_1 and T_2. One of the tubes is cooled by drawing air through ether contained in the tube. The other thermometer remains at room temperature. The observer notes the dew-point, that is, the temperature at which dew collects on the cold thimble, taking care, by interposing a sheet of glass between his breath and the thimble, not to add to the humidity of the air.

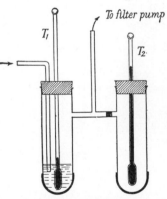

Fig. 5.—Regnault's Hygrometer

(b) Wet and Dry Bulb Hygrometer.

This hygrometer has the advantage of great simplicity, and is therefore widely used in meteorology. Two thermometers are mounted side by side; around the stem of one is wound a piece of cotton waste which dips into a small vessel containing water. Owing to the continuous evaporation from the cotton waste, the wet bulb shows an appreciably lower reading than the dry bulb. Empirical tables are constructed connecting the dew-point with the difference in reading of the wet and dry bulbs, and hence the relative humidity is obtained. An approximate theoretical treatment is as follows:

P = pressure of water vapour in the air,
p = saturation vapour pressure at temp. of wet bulb,
t = temp. of dry bulb,
t' = temp. of wet bulb.

The air over the wet bulb becomes saturated, and its vapour pressure therefore rises from P to p, and latent heat is taken up proportional to this rise, say $A(p - P)$. This heat comes from the wet bulb, which is cooled through $(t - t')$, and the heat given up is proportional to this, say $B(t - t')$. Hence

$$A(p - P) = B(t - t').$$

Actually, $P = p - 0 \cdot 011(t - t')$ when the barometer is about 29·4 in., and the relation is valid for a moderate range of pressure round this value.

(c) Chemical Hygrometer.

Since the density of the vapour is approximately proportional to the vapour pressure, an alternative definition of relative humidity is

$$\frac{\text{mass of water vapour actually present (per c.c.)}}{\text{mass of water vapour present (per c.c.), if saturated}}.$$

On this definition is based the chemical hygrometer shown in fig. 6. A given volume of air is drawn through a weighed drying tube T_1 by

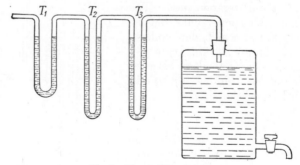

Fig. 6.—Chemical Hygrometer

means of an aspirator. Connected to T_1 are two additional tubes T_2 and T_3; the former absorbs any water vapour which has failed to be caught in T_1; the tube T_3 prevents water vapour from the aspirator from reaching the weighing tubes. The method is accurate but cumbersome.

(d) *Hygroscopes.*

Changes in humidity may be registered automatically by instruments termed hygroscopes, an example of which is shown in fig. 7. They depend for their action on the fact that the human hair or other fibre changes in length when a variation occurs in the humidity of the atmosphere. The small change in length is magnified by suitable levers to operate a pointer moving over a calibrated scale.

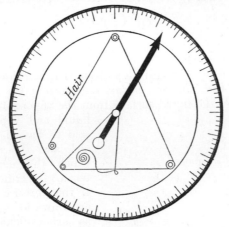

Fig. 7.—Hygroscope

EXERCISES

1. Describe statical and dynamical methods for measuring the vapour pressure of liquids at different temperatures, indicating the conditions under which each method is applicable.

2. State Dalton's Law of Partial Pressures.

The space above the mercury in a simple Boyle's law apparatus contains some air and saturated vapour. If the volume of the space is doubled when the external pressure is reduced from 76 cm. to 50 cm. of mercury, find the vapour pressure of the liquid. [24 cm.]

3. Explain clearly what is meant by *unsaturated* and *saturated vapour pressure* of a liquid.

Find the volume occupied by dry gas at N.T.P. if 500 c.c. of the gas are subject to an initial pressure of 75 cm. of mercury at 15° C., and are situated over a liquid whose saturation vapour pressure at this temperature is 18 mm. of mercury. [456·5 c.c.]

4. Enumerate methods for finding the vapour densities of substances and describe one method in detail.

Of what particular importance is a knowledge of vapour density for the theory of physics and chemistry?

5. Define the term *relative humidity*, and describe the use of a reliable instrument for determining the hygrometric state of the atmosphere.

CHAPTER X

Continuity of State and Liquefaction of Gases

1. Continuity of State.

It was shown by Cagniard de la Tour that if a liquid is heated in a closed vessel, then, above a certain temperature, the meniscus which normally divides the liquid surface from the vapour disappears. The liquid and vapour states are said to have become continuous, and the temperature at which the merge occurs is termed the **critical temperature.** If the pressure-volume curves are drawn for a substance such as carbon dioxide, the appearance is as in fig. 1. These curves were originally obtained by Andrews and are said to be the isothermals (see p. 258), since each curve shows the appropriate (*p-v*) relation for constant temperature. Taking the isothermal for 21·5° C., we see that when the volume is very large and the vapour therefore far from its condensation point, the vapour obeys Boyle's law, as shown by the approximately hyperbolic shape of the curve. As the pressure is increased the vapour eventually liquefies and a sudden contraction in volume takes place, represented by the horizontal portion of the curve. Since liquids are only slightly compressible, further increase in pressure results in an almost vertical line for the (*p-v*) relation.

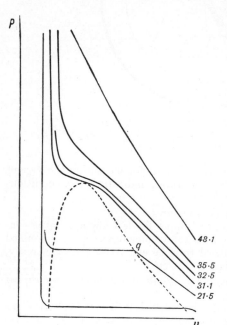

Fig. 1.—Isothermals of Carbon Dioxide

If, however, we consider the isothermal for 48·1° C., we find that

the curve approximately obeys Boyle's law even up to the highest
pressures; no transition to the liquid state takes place. Investigation
of intermediate isothermals shows that between 15° C. and 31° C.
the horizontal portion indicating the transition from vapour to liquid
grows shorter and shorter while it vanishes completely at about 31° C.
This temperature is the critical temperature of carbon dioxide. We
may therefore take as an alternative definition: **critical temperature
is the temperature above which a gas
cannot be liquefied simply by increasing
the pressure.**

If a curve is drawn between the
transition points, as shown in the dotted
line in fig. 1, this dotted curve just
touches the isothermal for 31° C., the
latter exhibiting a point of inflexion at
this point. The values p_c and v_c at
this point of inflexion are said to be
the **critical pressure** and **critical volume**
of the substance, and the isothermal
at 31° C. is termed the **critical isothermal.**

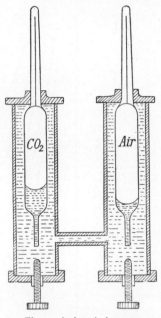

The term gas is usually reserved
for substances above their critical temperatures, and the term vapour for the
same substances below that temperature. Carbon dioxide is therefore a gas
above 31° C. and a vapour below 31° C.
" Permanent " gases like nitrogen and
hydrogen are simply substances which
at room temperature are much above

Fig. 2.—Andrews's Apparatus

their critical temperatures. They
become vapours when they are below their critical temperatures
(−147° C. for nitrogen, −240° C. for hydrogen).

The apparatus used by Andrews in obtaining the isothermals for
carbon dioxide is shown in fig. 2. The substance was compressed in a
fine capillary tube which was surrounded by a water bath. The pressure was supplied by a screw working into a reservoir as in Despretz's
experiments on the deviations from Boyle's law (see p. 210). Great
care had to be taken to eliminate air from the carbon dioxide tube by
working with a current of pure carbon dioxide over a long period before
sealing the tube.

2. Van der Waals' Equation of State.

Since the liquid and vapour states are essentially continuous, a more general equation than Boyle's law is required to cover the complete field of phenomena. Such an equation was proposed by Van der Waals on the kinetic theory of gases: we give a deduction in Chap. XI. Briefly, we may state here that a real gas differs from an ideal gas in two particulars:

(a) When a gas " occupies " a volume v, the space in which the molecules are free to move is less than v owing to the volume occupied by the molecules themselves; if we represent this occupied volume by b, the effective volume is reduced to $(v - b)$.

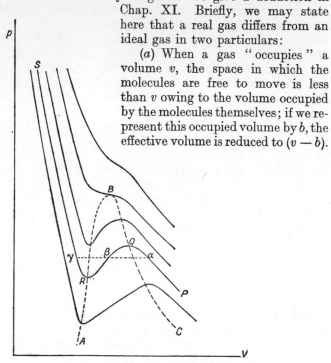

Fig. 3.—Isothermals according to Van der Waals' Equation

(b) The molecules exert a mutually attractive force on each other. This will be greater, the greater the density ρ of the gas. If we imagine two layers of gas attracting each other, the force of attraction will be proportional to the product ρ^2. For a fixed mass of gas the density is inversely proportional to the volume, so the force may be represented by a/v^2, where a is a constant. Now this will tend to reduce the volume just as if the external pressure had been increased. Consequently, the gas equation for an ideal gas must be changed from $pv = R\theta$ to

$$\left(p + \frac{a}{v^2}\right)(v - b) = R\theta. \quad . \quad . \quad . \quad (10.1)$$

Equation (10.1) is a cubic in v, and when plotted gives a curve as shown in fig. 3. It will be observed that the general shape of this curve agrees very well with the shape of the experimental isothermals except that the straight, horizontal portion of the latter is replaced by an oscillation as shown. It is now believed that the experimental curve also follows this humped course, but at the transition point from vapour to liquid the experimental conditions become so unstable that it is impossible to examine the situation in detail. Consequently, the change appears as an abrupt transition in the experimental curve. Other comparisons of Van der Waals' equation with experiment will now be given.

We propose to find expressions for p_c, v_c and θ_c in terms of the **Van der Waals' constants**, a and b. The condition for finding v_c is obtained from Van der Waals' equation by noting that v_c occurs at a point of inflexion on the critical isothermal. Consequently, we differentiate Van der Waals' equation twice with respect to v and equate to zero:

$$p = \frac{R\theta}{(v-b)} - \frac{a}{v^2},$$

$$\frac{\partial p}{\partial v} = 0 = -\frac{R\theta}{(v-b)^2} + \frac{2a}{v^3}, \quad \ldots \quad (10.2)$$

and
$$\frac{\partial^2 p}{\partial v^2} = 0 = \frac{2R\theta}{(v-b)^3} - \frac{6a}{v^4}. \quad \ldots \quad (10.3)$$

Elimination of θ between equations (10.2) and (10.3) gives $v_c = 3b$, and resubstitution gives $p_c = a/27b^2$ and $\theta_c = 8a/27Rb$. Hence, according to Van der Waals' equation, for all gases the ratio $p_c v_c / R\theta_c = 3/8$. This relation is only in approximate agreement with experiment. Again, in Chap. XI, we shall see that the expression $v_c = 4b$ is more nearly true than $v_c = 3b$. On the whole, however, Van der Waals' equation is as satisfactory as any of the other equations of state which have been proposed. Of these we shall only mention the *equation of Dieterici*, namely,

$$p(v-b) = R\theta \exp(-a/R\theta v), \quad \ldots \quad (10.4)$$

where a is a constant.

3. Joule-Thomson Experiment.

If a gas is allowed to expand, then, as shown in Chap. XII, it does external work. Besides this *external* work, however, it also does *internal* work. This follows from considerations of the correction introduced in the first term of Van der Waals' equation. The term a/v^2 was inserted to account for the mutual attraction between the molecules. If a gas is allowed to expand, its density decreases and the molecules in the expanded state are, on the average, a greater distance apart than before the expansion took place. Now energy must have been consumed to do the work of separating the molecules against their mutual attraction. This energy is abstracted from the heat energy of the gas and consequently, even when no *external* work is done, a gas cools slightly on expansion. Joule carried out an experiment to test this suggestion, but the results were negative owing to the insensitivity of the apparatus. Later, Kelvin carried out the **porous plug experiment,** which gave a positive result. The gas was allowed to stream from a region of high density on one side of a porous plug to a region of low density on the other. Thermometers inserted in suitable positions showed that a cooling occurred in all cases examined except hydrogen. If the experiment is carried out below —80° C., hydrogen also cools on expansion. In fact, there is a definite temperature for all gases, below which they cool on expansion and above which they heat. This temperature is termed the **inversion temperature,** and is as important a characteristic of the gas as its critical temperature.

4. Liquefaction of Gases.

(a) Cascade or Pictet Process.

It was Faraday who first liquefied what had hitherto been accepted as one of the permanent gases. The apparatus was extremely simple, consisting of a bent closed tube as shown in fig. 4. At one end chlorine

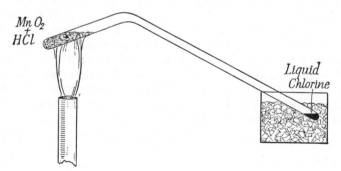

Fig. 4.—Faraday's Liquefaction Experiment

was generated by heating manganese dioxide and hydrochloric acid, while the other end was immersed in a freezing mixture. Since the critical temperature of chlorine is about 146° C., when the pressure in the tube became moderately high, liquid chlorine was formed at the cold end. One general process for the liquefaction of gases therefore consists in cooling the gas below its critical temperature and then applying sufficient pressure. To take a definite case, we consider the production of liquid oxygen. The critical temperature of oxygen is about —118° C.; it cannot therefore be liquefied by compression at ordinary temperatures. The method used is termed the cascade or Pictet process. First, some gas such as methyl chloride whose critical temperature is well above room temperature is liquefied by compression. If the liquid is poured into a Dewar flask (see Chap. XIV), it will evaporate comparatively slowly even if the pressure above the liquid is reduced to one atmosphere. This is because heat cannot reach the liquid, and latent heat of vaporization must be supplied for the liquid to evaporate.

If, now, a second vessel containing another gas, say ethylene, is immersed in the liquid methyl chloride, heat will be abstracted from the vessel and the ethylene by the methyl chloride, some of which will now evaporate. The ethylene is thereby cooled to about —30° C., and since its critical temperature is about +10° C., the ethylene in its turn may now be easily liquefied by compression. Continuing in this way, the liquefied ethylene boiling at atmospheric pressure will abstract heat from an immersed vessel containing oxygen, reducing the temperature of the latter to about —160° C., which is well below its critical temperature. The oxygen may now be liquefied by compression.

The production of liquid air may be carried out by a similar process, since nitrogen has a critical temperature of —146° C. As the liquid air boils off it becomes richer in oxygen since the nitrogen boils off more easily.

(b) Linde-Joule Process.

The previous method involved the conception of the critical temperature. The Linde-Joule process involves the conception of the inversion temperature. The apparatus is shown in fig. 5. Gas at high pressure, and cooled by previous passage through tubes immersed in calcium chloride solution at about —30° C., passes down a spiral which terminates in a very fine nozzle.

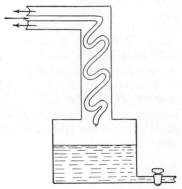

Fig. 5.—Linde-Joule Process

The gas expands through this orifice into an outer vessel, the gas pressure in which is kept low by pumping the gas away and returning it to the compressors for repassage through the spiral. The gas cools slightly on expansion, as in the Joule-Thomson porous plug experiment, and this cooled gas sweeps back over the outside of the spiral. Consequently, it cools the down-coming gas, and the whole process is regenerative, the temperature of the gas becoming lower and lower until it eventually liquefies and is drawn off from the base of the apparatus.

It is not possible to produce liquid hydrogen or liquid helium by the cascade process since their critical temperatures are below the lowest temperatures reached by the boiling gases which would precede them in the cascade process. They can, however, be liquefied by the Linde-Joule process if their temperatures are first reduced below their inversion temperatures. Since the inversion temperatures of gases are always much higher than their critical temperatures, there is no difficulty in the initial cooling of hydrogen and helium in preparation for the Linde-Joule process.

5. Production of Low Temperatures.

The history of the production of low temperatures is of considerable interest. In 1898, Dewar used the Linde-Joule process to produce liquid hydrogen. Ten years later, Onnes succeeded in liquefying the last remaining gas, helium, by the same process. With helium boiling under reduced pressure a temperature of −272° C. was eventually produced, but still the liquid helium did not freeze. It was not until 1926 that Keesom succeeded in producing solid helium. The transition from liquid to solid is usually observed by placing the liquid inside a nest of transparent Dewar flasks, the outer flasks containing liquefied gases of higher boiling-point. Thus the liquid helium was surrounded by flasks of liquid hydrogen and liquid air. On freezing, a change in the refractive index is usually observed, but in the case of helium the refractive index of liquid and solid helium is almost the same. Eventually a metal stirrer which could be operated magnetically from outside was installed, and sticking of the stirrer indicated the freezing of the helium.

Temperatures which are within a fraction of the absolute zero may now be obtained by first cooling with liquid helium and then demagnetizing certain crystals adiabatically (see Chap. XII). Magnetic energy leaves the system and the temperature is reduced to less than 0·01° absolute.

EXERCISES

1. Explain clearly what is meant by the term *continuity of state* as applied to liquids and gases.
How has the gas equation for perfect gases to be modified?

2. Define *critical temperature* as applied to the liquid-vapour transition of a substance. Describe the experiments of Andrews on the critical temperature of carbon dioxide.

3. What equations have been proposed to replace the equation of state for perfect gases and how far are they in agreement with experiment?

4. Give an account of the liquefaction of gases by the cascade process. How would you measure the boiling-point of liquid oxygen boiling steadily in a vacuum flask at atmospheric pressure?

5. Describe and give the theory of the Joule-Kelvin porous plug experiment. How have the ideas been applied to the liquefaction of gases on a large scale?

6. Write a short essay on the production and measurement of low temperatures.

7. Show that, under certain conditions, Dieterici's equation of state reduces to that proposed by Van der Waals.

8. Prove that for all gases $p_c V_c / R T_c = 3/8$ if Van der Waals' equation is obeyed, p_c, V_c, T_c being the critical pressure, volume and temperature of a gas, and R the gas constant referred to a gram-molecule.

9. Explain the difference between critical temperature and inversion temperature. Upon which concept is the liquefaction of hydrogen and helium based?

CHAPTER XI

Kinetic Theory of Gases

1. Introduction.

Since all gases obey, at least approximately, the simple gas laws of Boyle and Charles, it is reasonable to suppose that they all possess a common and simple structure. It was suggested first by Bernoulli that the pressure of a gas could be explained if the molecules, of which the gas is composed according to chemical theory, were endowed with considerable translational velocity. Bernoulli actually deduced Boyle's law, but it was not until Joule carried out in 1848 his classical work on the equivalence of mechanical work and heat that the kinetic theory could expand and assume its present comprehensive form.

In 1857, Clausius formulated the following basic postulates for a kinetic theory of gases:

(a) The molecules of a given monatomic gaseous element are regarded as identical solid spheres which move in straight lines until they collide with one another or with the wall of the containing vessel.

(b) The time occupied in collision is negligible; the collision is perfectly elastic, and there are no forces of attraction or repulsion between the molecules themselves.

(c) The molecules are negligible in size compared with the size of the container.

Clausius also introduced the important conception of the **mean free path** of a gas molecule; it is defined as the average distance traversed by a molecule between successive collisions. The quantities required for a knowledge of the properties and condition of a gas are (1) the velocity of the molecules, (2) the mean free path at S.T.P. (standard temperature and pressure), (3) the number of molecules per unit volume at S.T.P., (4) the diameter of a gas molecule regarded as a hard elastic sphere.

2. The Gas Laws and Avogadro's Hypothesis.

Consider a cubical volume of side l containing n gas molecules. Then if V_1 is the velocity of any one molecule and m is its mass, its momentum is mV_1. If this molecule strikes the face ABCD in fig. 1, it communicates a force to the face, but the only component of velocity which is effective is the component normal to the face. Calling this component u_1 and the other two components at right angles to it and to each other v_1 and w_1, then

$$V_1^2 = u_1^2 + v_1^2 + w_1^2. \quad \ldots \ldots \quad (11.1)$$

If the collision is perfectly elastic, the molecule rebounds with velocity V_1, and consequently the component momentum of recoil in a direction perpendicular to ABCD is $-mu_1$. Hence the change in momentum produced by impact is $mu_1 - (-mu_1) = 2mu_1$ perpendicular to ABCD. After recoil, if the direction of impact was almost normal to the surface, the molecule will travel to the opposite face, collide with it and rebound again to the face ABCD, the time between the successive collisions on ABCD being $2l/u_1$. Hence the average number of collisions per second which this molecule makes with ABCD is $u_1/2l$, and the average

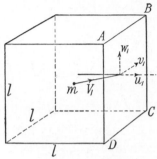

Fig. 1.—Components of Velocity

rate of change of momentum is $2mu_1 \cdot u_1/2l = mu_1^2/l$. For some other molecule with velocity V_2 and components u_2, v_2 and w_2, the change of momentum per second due to impact with ABCD will be mu_2^2/l.

Now by Newton's Second Law of Motion

Rate of Change of momentum $\equiv$ impressed force,

so the force on ABCD is

$$F_x = \frac{m}{l}(u_1^2 + u_2^2 + u_3^2 + \ldots u_n^2).$$

Since pressure is force per unit area, the average pressure on ABCD due to the molecular bombardment is

$$p_x = \frac{F_x}{A} = \frac{F_x}{l^2} = \frac{m}{l^3}(u_1^2 + u_2^2 + u_3^2 + \ldots u_n^2). \quad (11.2)$$

Similarly, if p_y and p_z represent the pressures on the faces of the cube, perpendicular to the y- and z-axes respectively,

$$p_y = \frac{m}{l^3}(v_1^2 + v_2^2 + v_3^2 + \ldots v_n^2), \quad \ldots \quad (11.3)$$

$$p_z = \frac{m}{l^3}(w_1^2 + w_2^2 + w_3^2 + \ldots w_n^2). \quad \ldots \quad (11.4)$$

Hence the average pressure p produced by the gas is

$$p = \frac{p_x + p_y + p_z}{3} = \frac{m}{3l^3}\{(u_1{}^2 + v_1{}^2 + w_1{}^2) + (u_2{}^2 + v_2{}^2 + w_2{}^2) +$$
$$\cdots (u_n{}^2 + v_n{}^2 + w_n{}^2)\}. \quad \cdots \quad (11.5)$$

Now $l^3 = v =$ volume of cube, and substituting also from equation (11.1), equation (11.5) becomes

$$pv = \tfrac{1}{3}m(V_1{}^2 + V_2{}^2 + V_3{}^2 + \cdots V_n{}^2). \quad \cdots \quad (11.6)$$

Now the **mean square velocity** of the molecules V^2 is defined by

$$V^2 = \frac{(V_1{}^2 + V_2{}^2 + V_3{}^2 + \cdots V_n{}^2)}{n}. \quad \cdots \quad (11.7)$$

Hence (11.6) may be written

$$pv = \tfrac{1}{3}nmV^2, \quad \cdots \cdots \quad (11.8)$$

or alternatively,
$$p = \tfrac{1}{3}\rho V^2, \quad \cdots \cdots \quad (11.9)$$

where $\rho = nm/v =$ density of the gas.

Now it is reasonable to assume, from the equivalence of heat and energy, that the energy of the molecules is a measure of the temperature θ of the gas, that is,

$$\tfrac{1}{2}nmV^2 = C\theta, \quad \cdots \cdots \quad (11.10)$$

where C is some constant of proportionality. Hence, from (11.8) and (11.10),

$$pv = R\theta, \quad \cdots \cdots \quad (11.11)$$

where $R = \tfrac{2}{3}C =$ constant, which is the *Gas Equation* obtained by combining Boyle's and Charles' laws as on p. 213.

To deduce **Avogadro's hypothesis** that, at the same temperature and pressure, equal volumes of different gases contain the same number of molecules, we have to make the further assumption, which can be proved by complicated mathematical analysis, that the average kinetic energy of the molecules of two different gases is the same when they are at the same temperature. Expressed mathematically, this is written

$$\tfrac{1}{2}m_1V_1{}^2 = \tfrac{1}{2}m_2V_2{}^2. \quad \cdots \cdots \quad (11.12)$$

Since p and V are the same for both gases, (11.8) and (11.12) give

$$n_1 = n_2,$$

which is Avogadro's hypothesis.

Equation (11.9) allows us to determine the root mean square velocity for a gas molecule directly, viz.

$$V = \sqrt{\frac{3p}{\rho}}. \qquad \cdots \cdots \quad (11.13)$$

For hydrogen at S.T.P. this velocity is about 10^5 cm./sec.

3. Specific Heats of Gases on Kinetic Theory.

If we consider a gram-molecule of the gas, then equation (11.8) becomes

$$pv = \tfrac{1}{3}MV^2, \qquad \cdots \cdots \quad (11.14)$$

where $M = nm = $ molecular weight of the gas.   Now the kinetic energy of the gas $E = \tfrac{1}{2}MV^2$. Hence, from (11.14)

$$pv = \tfrac{2}{3}E. \qquad \cdots \cdots \cdots \quad (11.15)$$

But $pv = R\theta$, so from (11.15)

$$E = \tfrac{3}{2}R\theta, \qquad \cdots \cdots \cdots \quad (11.16)$$

where R refers to a gram-molecule.   This equation allows us to define *the gas constant R as $\tfrac{2}{3}$ of the kinetic energy of a gram-molecule of gas at one degree absolute.*

If the gas is heated through 1°, its energy becomes

$$E_1 = \tfrac{3}{2}R(\theta + 1). \qquad \cdots \cdots \quad (11.17)$$

Now the heat required to raise one gram-molecule of the gas one degree is the **molecular heat** of the gas, where molecular heat = specific heat × molecular weight.   Further, if all the energy is assumed to go to raising the kinetic energy of the molecules and none is used in doing external work, it is the molecular heat at constant volume C_v which is involved.   Hence

$$C_v = E_1 - E = \tfrac{3}{2}R, \qquad \cdots \cdots \quad (11.18)$$

an equation which shows that the molecular heat of a gas at constant volume is $\tfrac{3}{2}$ (the gas constant).

We show, in Chap. XII, that

$$C_p - C_v = R. \qquad \cdots \cdots \cdots \quad (11.19)$$

Hence, from (11.18) and (11.19)

$$C_p = \tfrac{5}{2}R, \qquad \cdots \cdots \cdots \quad (11.20)$$

and from (11.20) and (11.18)

$$C_p/C_v = \gamma = \tfrac{5}{3}. \qquad \cdots \cdots \quad (11.21)$$

According to the kinetic theory, therefore, the ratio of the specific heats of monatomic gases is constant and equal to 5/3. This is in good agreement with experiment for such monatomic gases as helium, neon and the other rare gases.

It may be shown that for diatomic and polyatomic gases the ratio of the specific heats should be progressively less, approaching unity for high atomicity of the molecule. This is also found experimentally.

*4. Mean Free Path and Molecular Radius.

In order to account for the deviations of gases from the ideal gas laws it is necessary, as we saw in developing Van der Waals' equation on p. 240, to take into account the finite size of the molecules. Let s be the diameter of a molecule; then this quantity represents the closest distance to which two molecular centres can approach. To simplify

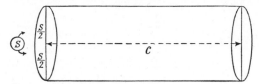

Fig. 2.—Molecular Collisions

calculations, let us endow one particular molecule with an **effective radius** s, treating the others as points. We proceed to calculate an expression for the average number of collisions made by this molecule in one second. If c is the velocity of the molecule, it sweeps out an effective cylindrical volume (fig. 2), per second, equal to $\pi s^2 c$. Hence, if there are ν molecules per unit volume, the number of collisions n per second is

$$n = \pi s^2 c \nu. \quad \ldots \ldots (11.22)$$

Now the average distance between successive collisions is the mean free path λ: hence the effective distance traversed by the molecule per second is $n\lambda = \pi s^2 c \nu \lambda$. But the distance traversed by the molecule per second is its velocity c. Hence

$$c = \pi s^2 c \nu \lambda,$$

or
$$\lambda = \frac{1}{\pi s^2 \nu}, \quad \ldots \ldots (11.23)$$

an important equation deduced by Clausius, connecting the mean free path λ, the molecular diameter s and the number of molecules ν per unit volume.

*5. Viscosity of Gases on the Kinetic Theory.

If we consider a unit cube situated in a gas, then the average number of molecules moving towards any one face of the cube at any instant will be $\nu/6$, where ν is the total number of molecules in the cube. The total number of molecules passing through one face of the cube per second is therefore $\nu c/6$, where c is the average velocity of the molecules. Referring to fig. 3, Chap. XII, Part I, p. 133, let us consider the molecules crossing unit area of a plane drawn parallel to and a distance x from the fixed surface, where the velocity of drift of the gas is v. The molecules which cross from below will have a lower drift velocity than those from above. They will, of course, have the same gas kinetic velocity since the whole gas is at uniform temperature. Consequently there is a net transfer of drift momentum across the area, and by Newton's Second Law this change in momentum will be equal to the viscous force F, where

$$F = \eta \frac{dv}{dx}, \quad \ldots \ldots \quad (11.24)$$

η being the coefficient of viscosity and dv/dx the velocity gradient as discussed on p. 133, Part I. Now of the molecules which start moving towards the area at x, only those which on the average are not farther away than the mean free path will cross the area. We therefore assume that the mean velocity of the molecules crossing from below is $\left(v - \lambda\frac{dv}{dx}\right)$, and of those from above $\left(v + \lambda\frac{dv}{dx}\right)$. Hence the net transfer of momentum per second is

$$G = \frac{mcv}{6}\left\{\left(v + \lambda\frac{dv}{dx}\right) - \left(v - \lambda\frac{dv}{dx}\right)\right\}$$

$$= \tfrac{1}{3}vmc\lambda\frac{dv}{dx}. \quad \ldots \ldots \ldots \quad (11.25)$$

From (11.24) and (11.25),

$$\eta = \tfrac{1}{3}vmc\lambda,$$

or $$\eta = \tfrac{1}{3}\rho c\lambda, \quad \ldots \ldots \ldots \quad (11.26)$$

where ρ is the density, for ν is the number of molecules per unit volume, since we are considering transfer across unit area.

Now from equation (11.23) $\lambda \propto 1/\rho$, and since c is dependent only on the temperature, according to equation (11.26) **the viscosity η is independent of the pressure.** This law was first deduced by Maxwell, who proceeded to show that it was obeyed experimentally. The apparatus consisted of a flat disk suspended from a torsion wire and allowed to undergo torsional oscillations close to a parallel flat plate. The pressure of the surrounding gas was changed, but no change in the rate of damping of the oscillating disk occurred, indicating that the viscosity was independent of the pressure. Now in equation (11.26) η may be measured experimentally as in Chap. XII, Part I, ρ is easily determined, and the average velocity c can be shown theoretically to be equal to $(8/3\pi)^{\frac{1}{2}}V$, where V is the root mean square velocity which can be calculated from (11.13). Hence λ may be determined from (11.26), and in this way Maxwell showed that for hydrogen at S.T.P. λ is about 2×10^{-5} cm.

*6. Thermal Conductivity of Gases from Kinetic Theory.

If we have contiguous layers of gas at different temperatures, there will be a net transfer of heat due to the gas-kinetic motion of molecules. By a similar argument to that used in the preceding section, we take the temperature to be θ and the temperature gradient $d\theta/dx$ at some layer x from a given boundary. Then the net transfer of heat per second across unit area of the layer x will be

$$Q = \frac{vc}{6} mc_v \left\{ \left(\theta - \lambda \frac{d\theta}{dx} \right) - \left(\theta + \lambda \frac{d\theta}{dx} \right) \right\}$$

$$= -\tfrac{1}{3} vmc\lambda \frac{d\theta}{dx} c_v, \quad \cdots \cdots \cdots \quad (11.27)$$

where c_v is the specific heat at constant volume.

Now by our definition of the coefficient of thermal conductivity in equation (5.1)

$$Q = -k \frac{d\theta}{dx}. \quad \cdots \cdots \cdots \quad (11.28)$$

Hence, from (11.27) and (11.28),

$$k = \tfrac{1}{3} vmc\lambda c_v$$
$$= \tfrac{1}{3} \rho c\lambda c_v. \quad \cdots \cdots \cdots \quad (11.29)$$

The thermal conductivity of a gas is therefore also independent of the pressure. At *low* pressures, however, both the viscosity and the thermal conductivity of gases are proportional to the pressure, and this relation forms the basis of some low-pressure gauges. The behaviour of gases at low pressures can receive very satisfactory treatment on kinetic theory, but it is beyond the scope of this book.

From equations (11.26) and (11.29), we deduce

$$k = \eta c_v, \quad \cdots \cdots \cdots \quad (11.30)$$

a relation which shows the great generality of the kinetic theory, for it connects the diverse physical phenomena of heat conduction, specific heat and viscosity.

XI]   THERMAL CONDUCTIVITY OF GASES   253

We have now described methods for evaluating V and λ; it remains to describe how the two remaining fundamental quantities,
ν the number of gas molecules per unit volume at S.T.P., and s the
molecular diameter, are determined. By equation (11.23), if one of
these quantities is known, then the other may be calculated.

The number of molecules ν *per unit volume* at S.T.P. is correctly
termed **Loschmidt's number**; its value is $2 \cdot 69 \times 10^{19}$. **Avogadro's
number** N is the number of molecules *in a gram-molecule*. Since a gram-
molecule of any gas occupies $22 \cdot 4 \times 10^3$ c.c., it follows that Avo-
gadro's number $= 2 \cdot 69 \times 10^{19} \times 22 \cdot 4 \times 10^3 = 6 \cdot 06 \times 10^{23}$. The name
Avogadro's number is often applied to both numbers. The best method
for determining N requires a knowledge of electricity. After studying
Part V, the student will realize that

$$N = \frac{Q}{e}, \quad \ldots \ldots \ldots \quad (11.31)$$

where Q is the charge given up to an electrode during electrolysis, by
a gram-molecule of a monovalent ion, and e is the charge on that
ion, which is the electronic charge. However, we describe in the
next section a method of finding N, which, although it is not as accurate as the electrical method, provides an elegant example of the
application of kinetic theory.

*7. Brownian Movement.

In 1827, a botanist named Brown observed that if pollen grains
about 10^{-3} mm. diameter were in suspension in a liquid, then examination with a microscope showed the pollen grains to be in incessant
random motion. Initially the phenomenon was ascribed to vital
forces, but subsequent work showed that it was also exhibited by
small particles held in suspension in the liquid inclusions in granite
and other rocks of great age. Not until nearly fifty years after its
discovery was it suggested that the Brownian movement is a visible
demonstration of the validity of the kinetic theory of liquids. In any
small interval of time, a particle will receive more impacts from molecular bombardment on one side than another. If the particle is sufficiently small, it will therefore execute a small motion under the resultant
force until its path is altered by further impacts. The essential feature
from the point of view of the kinetic theory is that the particles will
be sharing the average kinetic energy of the liquid molecules at the
particular temperature under consideration. The particles may therefore be considered to represent visibly the molecular motion of gas
molecules, the particles being regarded as molecules of gigantic size.

Now the equilibrium of the atmosphere on the earth's surface is
due to two opposing forces, gravitational attraction downwards and

gas pressure upwards. Only a few molecules succeed in reaching the upper regions against the gravitational attraction, and therefore the density decreases rapidly with height. In exactly the same way, if a tube containing small particles in suspension is examined with a microscope, there is seen to be a *sedimentation equilibrium*, most of the particles clustering at the bottom of the tube but a certain number reaching higher regions. The particular particles at any one horizontal layer are continually changing, but after the liquid has been undisturbed for some time, on the average the number present per layer remains constant. In fig. 3, if v is the number of particles per unit volume at a height h above the bottom of the container, and p the particle-bombardment-pressure on the section at height h, then

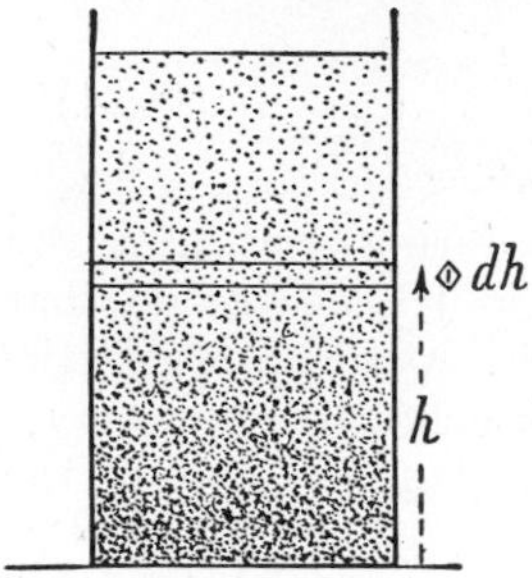

Fig. 3.—Particles in Suspension

if equilibrium has been reached, the small extra pressure $(-dp)$ must balance the weight of the particles in the height dh. Hence

$$dp = -vmg\,dh, \quad . \quad (11.32)$$

where m is the *reduced* mass of one particle (that is, its weight in air less the buoyancy in the surrounding fluid), and g is the acceleration due to gravity. Now if we treat the particles as a perfect gas they must obey the Gas Equation, namely,

$$pv = R\theta,$$

where R refers to a gram-molecule. The pressure which such a gas would exert if all the N molecules in a gram-molecule were compressed into *unit* volume would be

$$P = R\theta. \quad . \quad . \quad . \quad . \quad . \quad . \quad (11.33)$$

For the particles in suspension, the pressure is p when the number of particles per unit volume is v. Hence

$$P/p = N/v. \quad . \quad . \quad . \quad . \quad . \quad (11.34)$$

From (11.33) and (11.34),

$$p = \frac{vR\theta}{N}. \quad . \quad . \quad . \quad . \quad . \quad (11.35)$$

If we differentiate (11.35) to find the variation of p with v, we obtain

$$dp = dv\frac{R\theta}{N}. \quad . \quad . \quad . \quad . \quad . \quad (11.36)$$

Eliminating dp from (11.32) and (11.36), we get

$$\frac{dv}{v} = -\frac{mgN}{R\theta}\,dh. \quad . \quad . \quad . \quad . \quad (11.37)$$

From (11.37), by integration, if ν_1 and ν_2 are the numbers of particles per unit volume at heights h_1 and h_2,

$$\log_e \frac{\nu_2}{\nu_1} = -\frac{mg}{R\theta} N(h_2 - h_1), \quad \ldots \ldots \quad (11.38)$$

an equation from which N may be determined.

To evaluate N, Perrin used particles of gamboge in water. A drop of the emulsion, centrifuged to obtain particles of one size only, was placed on a microscope slide so as to form a column about 1/10 mm. high, which was then observed with a powerful microscope. Owing to the high power of the microscope, the thickness of the layer in focus was about that of the diameter of the particles: consequently only the number present in a very thin layer was observed for one position of the microscope. The microscope was then racked up a distance d measured on an accurately graduated vernier and another count was made, the distance $(h_2 - h_1)$ being equal to μd, where μ is the refractive index of the emulsion. (See Part III, on real and apparent depth.) The mass of the grains m in equation (11.38) was determined by finding:

(a) the density of the gamboge;

(b) the volume of the grains, obtained by noting their rates of fall through the solution and applying Stokes's law (see Part I and Part V). The viscosity of the solution had to be determined separately. From observations of many thousands of grains, the final value $N = 6 \cdot 8 \times 10^{23}$ molecules per gram-molecule was obtained. The electronic method gives the now accepted value of $6 \cdot 06 \times 10^{23}$ mol./gm. mol. Moderately good values of N have also been obtained by observation of Brownian movement of fine particles suspended in gases. Indeed, very small drops in Millikan's experiment (see Part V) are difficult to keep in focus owing to wandering due to Brownian movement.

*8. Van der Waals' Equation and Kinetic Theory.

To deduce Van der Waals' equation from the kinetic theory we consider first the effect of the finite size of the molecules. Since two molecular centres cannot approach closer than the molecular diameter s, if a molecule makes n collisions per second, its effective distance of action in this time is $c + ns$ instead of simply c. Actually such an increased distance of action would only occur if all the molecular collisions were head on. Taking into account that some are only glancing collisions, the effective distance covered may be shown to be $(c + \frac{2}{3}ns)$. The effect of the molecular diameter is to change

(11.9) to

$$p = \tfrac{1}{3}\rho V^2 \frac{(c + \tfrac{2}{3}ns)}{c}, \text{ approx.}$$

$$= \tfrac{1}{3}\rho V^2\Big(1 + \tfrac{2}{3}\frac{ns}{V}\Big), \quad \cdots \cdots \quad (11.39)$$

where c is put equal to V.

Substituting for n from (11.22),

$$p = \tfrac{1}{3}\rho V^2(1 + \tfrac{2}{3}\pi s^3 \nu)$$
$$= \tfrac{1}{3}\rho V^2(1 + \tfrac{4}{6}\pi s^3 \nu).$$

Since $\tfrac{4}{6}\pi s^3 \nu << 1$, this may be written approximately

$$p(1 - \tfrac{4}{6}\pi s^3 \nu) = \tfrac{1}{3}\rho V^2,$$

or $\qquad\qquad p v(1 - \tfrac{4}{6}\pi s^3 \nu) = \dfrac{M}{3} V^2, \quad \cdots \cdots \quad (11.40)$

where the total mass of gas is M.

Now the volume of ν spheres of radius $s/2$ is $\tfrac{1}{6}\pi s^3 \nu = d$. Hence equation (11.40) becomes

$$p v(1 - 4d) = \frac{M}{3} V^2,$$

or $\qquad\qquad\qquad p(v - b) = \dfrac{M}{3} V^2, \quad \cdots \cdots \quad (11.41)$

where b is equal to four times the volume of the total number of molecules present.

To find the effect of a finite time of collision due to the attractive forces between the molecules, let the average time of collision of two molecules be τ. Then the time spent in mutual encounter is time lost in bombarding the walls of the container. Hence the effective gas pressure is reduced in the ratio

$$p = \frac{M V^2}{3(v - b)} \cdot \frac{1}{1 + n\tau},$$

where n is the number of molecular collisions per second. Hence, by substituting for n from (11.22),

$$p(1 + \pi s^2 c\nu\tau) = \tfrac{1}{3}\frac{M V^2}{(v - b)};$$

and if we multiply out the L.H.S., substitute the approximate relation $p = \tfrac{1}{3}\rho V^2$ in the small second term, and put V for c, we find

$$p + \tfrac{1}{3}\rho V^3 \pi s^2 \nu \tau = \tfrac{1}{3}\frac{M V^2}{(v - b)}. \quad \cdots \cdots \quad (11.42)$$

Also, since $\nu = \rho/m$, and $\tfrac{1}{3}V^3\pi s^2\tau/m$ is constant, say equal to a', for a given gas and temperature, (11.42) gives

$$(p + a'\rho^2)(v - b) = \tfrac{1}{3}MV^2,$$

or
$$\left(p + \frac{a}{v^2}\right)(v - b) = R\theta, \quad \ldots \ldots \text{(11.43)}$$

where $a'\rho^2 = a/v^2$, where a is constant and $R\theta$ is proportional to the kinetic energy of the molecules.

EXERCISES

1. Deduce the Gas Equation from the kinetic theory of gases, explaining clearly the assumptions made in your deduction.

2. Explain the physical significance of the gas constant R on the kinetic theory of gases.

If the density of a gas at N.T.P. (temperature 0° C., pressure 760 mm. of mercury) is 9×10^{-4} gm./c.c., find the root mean square velocity of the gas molecules under these conditions. [$5\cdot8 \times 10^4$ cm./sec.]

3. Deduce an expression for the ratio of the specific heats of a monatomic gas at constant pressure and constant volume on the basis of the kinetic theory. What is the effect on the ratio of increasing the atomicity of the molecule?

4. Define *mean free path of a gas molecule* and *molecular diameter*.

Deduce Clausius' relationship connecting these quantities and find the effective diameter of a hydrogen molecule given that Avogadro's number is $6\cdot06 \times 10^{23}$ mols./gram. mol. and the mean free path of a hydrogen molecule at N.T.P. is 2×10^{-5} cm. [$2\cdot43 \times 10^{-8}$ cm.]

5. How are viscosity and thermal conductivity explained on the kinetic theory of gases?

Deduce an expression for the coefficient of viscosity in terms of the density of a gas and the mean free path and mean velocity of the gas molecules.

6. Deduce an expression for the thermal conductivity of a gas on the kinetic theory of gases and show that the thermal conductivity, the coefficient of viscosity and the specific heat of a gas at constant volume are very closely connected.

7. Enumerate methods for determining Loschmidt's number and describe in detail one method with which you are familiar.

8. What is meant by Brownian movement? Describe an experiment by which Avogadro's number may be deduced from observations on sedimentation equilibrium.

9. Write a short essay on Brownian Motion.

10. Explain how the kinetic theory may be made to take account of the actual (as opposed to the ideal) properties of gases, illustrating your answer by deducing Van der Waals' equation from the kinetic theory.

CHAPTER XII

Isothermal and Adiabatic Expansions

1. Introduction.

A change is said to take place **isothermally** if the temperature remains constant throughout the change. An **adiabatic** change is defined as one in which heat energy is neither gained nor lost by the system. In gas phenomena changes generally take place in practice under some intermediate condition where the temperature is not constant and where heat is transferred either to or from the surroundings.

2. Work Done by a Gas on Expansion.

We first consider the special conditions shown in fig. 1, where the gas is contained in a cylinder fitted with a piston of area of cross-

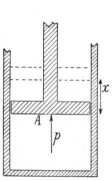

Fig. 1.—Work done by a Gas on Expansion

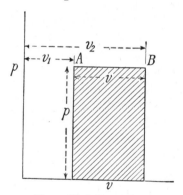

Fig. 2.—Work done at Constant Pressure

section A. Suppose the pressure p of the gas is kept constant and the gas is allowed to expand, thereby moving the piston through a distance x. Then

$$\text{work done} = \text{force} \times \text{distance} = pA \cdot x = pv, \quad (12.1)$$

where v is the increase in volume of the gas.

We can represent the expansion graphically by the horizontal line AB in fig. 2, where the increase in volume v is $(v_2 - v_1)$. Now the area between AB and the volume axis is pv: hence the *work done is represented by the area between the (p-v) curve and the volume axis.*

This statement holds also when the pressure does not remain constant on expansion, the work done in fig. 3 being equal to the area ABCD or, in the notation of the integral calculus, $\int p\,dv$, where integration extends over the limits of the volume change.

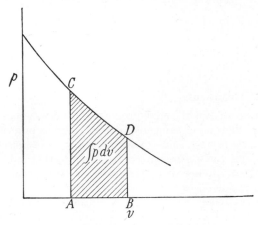

Fig. 3.—Work done represented by an Area

3. Specific Heats of Gases and External Work.

It follows from the First Law of Thermodynamics (Chap. VI) that heat absorbed by a body is equivalent to the external work done + the increase of internal energy.

Now, for gases, Joule proved experimentally that the internal energy approximately depends on the temperature only; and for a perfect gas the property is assumed to hold exactly. Consider, then, two changes in the state (p, v, θ) of a gram-molecule of a perfect gas, the one change at constant pressure, the other at constant volume, and the change of temperature $d\theta$ the same in both cases. If J is Joule's equivalent, we have

$$C_p\,d\theta - \frac{p\,dv}{J} = C_v\,d\theta, \quad \ldots \quad (12.2)$$

for each side represents the change in internal energy, which depends, as we have just seen, on $d\theta$ only.

Now, from the gas equation,

$$pv = R\theta.$$

Hence, at constant pressure, differentiating to obtain the small increase in volume dv accompanying the small rise in temperature $d\theta$,

$$p\,dv = R\,d\theta. \qquad \ldots \ldots \quad (12.3)$$

From (12.2) and (12.3) we derive the important expression

$$C_p = C_v + \frac{R}{J}. \qquad \ldots \ldots \quad (12.4)$$

If R is expressed in calories, the equivalent J is, of course, not introduced. Equation (12.4) has been used to determine Joule's equivalent from experiments on C_p, C_v and R. We have also used (12.4) in deducing $\gamma = 5/3$ for an ideal monatomic gas on p. 249.

4. Isothermal Expansions.

Consideration of the thermal properties of substances soon shows that strictly isothermal expansions cannot occur in practice. As soon as a gas expands it does some external work; consequently its temperature falls and the expansion is no longer isothermal. By making the walls of the container of material of very high conductivity, and letting the expansion occur very slowly, an approximation to isothermal conditions occurs when heat energy is supplied through the walls as rapidly as it is used in performing mechanical work by the expanding gas. If a gas expands *isothermally* from volume v_1 to volume v_2, the work done is

$$W = \int_{v_1}^{v_2} p\,dv = k \int_{v_1}^{v_2} \frac{dv}{v}, \qquad \ldots \ldots \quad (12.5)$$

since for an isothermal change, Boyle's law, that is $pv = k$ (constant), is obeyed. Integrating (12.5), we get

$$W = k \log_e \frac{v_2}{v_1},$$

which, by the gas equation $pv = R\theta$, may be written

$$W = p_1 v_1 \log_e \frac{v_2}{v_1} = p_2 v_2 \log_e \frac{v_2}{v_1} = R\theta \log_e \frac{v_2}{v_1}$$

$$= R\theta \log_e \frac{p_1}{p_2}. \qquad \ldots \ldots \quad (12.6)$$

5. Adiabatic Expansions.

For a perfect adiabatic expansion the gas would have to be contained in a perfect heat insulator so that no energy transfer took place to the surroundings. These conditions are realized by allowing the gas to expand rapidly inside a poor conductor. The expansion has then occurred before any appreciable quantity of heat has leaked through from the surroundings. Since external work is done by the gas when it expands, the loss in energy results in a cooling of the gas. Conversely, a heating occurs during an adiabatic compression.

We proceed to show that the equation between pressure and volume governing adiabatic expansions is

$$pv^\gamma = \text{constant,}$$

where γ is the ratio of the specific heats of the gas at constant pressure and constant volume respectively. Suppose a gram-molecule of gas is allowed to undergo a small adiabatic expansion dv; and let the changes of temperature and internal energy be $d\theta$ and du_1. Hence

$$du_1 = -p\,dv. \qquad \cdots \cdots \quad (12.7)$$

If the same change of temperature took place at constant volume, the change of internal energy in that case being du_2, then

$$du_2 = C_v\,d\theta. \qquad \cdots \cdots \quad (12.8)$$

But, from Joule's experimental law just cited, $du_1 = du_2$. Hence

$$p\,dv = -C_v\,d\theta. \qquad \cdots \cdots \quad (12.9)$$

Now, during the adiabatic expansion, pressure, volume and temperature change. Hence, differentiating the gas equation, we have

$$p\,dv + v\,dp = R\,d\theta. \qquad \cdots \cdots \quad (12.10)$$

Since we require a relation between p and v, we eliminate θ between (12.9) and (12.10), and obtain

$$p\,dv = -C_v \frac{(p\,dv + v\,dp)}{R}. \qquad \cdots \cdots \quad (12.11)$$

From (12.4), if R is in heat units, $R = C_p - C_v$. Hence (12.11) becomes

$$p\,dv = -C_v \frac{(p\,dv + v\,dp)}{C_p - C_v},$$

which gives

$$C_p p\,dv = -C_v v\,dp,$$

or

$$\gamma \frac{dv}{v} = -\frac{dp}{p}, \qquad \cdots \cdots \quad (12.12)$$

where $\gamma = C_p/C_v$. Integrating (12.12), we obtain

$$\gamma \log_e v = -\log_e p + \text{constant,}$$

or

$$\log_e pv^\gamma = \text{constant,}$$

whence

$$pv^\gamma = \text{constant.} \qquad \cdots \cdots \quad (12.13)$$

Proceeding as in the previous section, we may find the work done by a gas in an adiabatic expansion, remembering that $pv^\gamma = k$, instead of $pv = k$ when Boyle's law is obeyed and the expansion is isothermal. Equation (12.5) therefore becomes in the adiabatic case,

$$W = \int_{v_1}^{v_2} p\, dv = k \int_{v_1}^{v_2} \frac{dv}{v^\gamma} = \left[\frac{k\, v^{1-\gamma}}{1-\gamma}\right]_{v_1}^{v_2}. \quad \dots \quad (12.14)$$

Since
$$p_1 v_1{}^\gamma = p_2 v_2{}^\gamma = k,$$
$$p_1 v_1 = R\theta_1,$$
and
$$p_2 v_2 = R\theta_2,$$

equation (12.14) may be written in a variety of forms, thus:

$$W = \frac{p_1 v_1{}^\gamma}{(\gamma - 1)} \left(\frac{1}{v_1{}^{\gamma-1}} - \frac{1}{v_2{}^{\gamma-1}}\right) = \frac{1}{(\gamma - 1)} \left(\frac{p_1 v_1{}^\gamma}{v_1{}^{\gamma-1}} - \frac{p_2 v_2{}^\gamma}{v_2{}^{\gamma-1}}\right)$$

$$= \frac{(p_1 v_1 - p_2 v_2)}{\gamma - 1}, \quad \dots \dots \quad (12.15)$$

or
$$W = \frac{R}{(\gamma - 1)}(\theta_1 - \theta_2). \quad \dots \dots \quad (12.16)$$

6. Clement and Désormes' Experiment.

Since the equation $pv^\gamma = \text{const.}$ governs adiabatic changes, the student will realize that the exact knowledge of the ratio of the specific heats is quite as important as the knowledge of the individual values of c_p and c_v. The ratio γ is obtained directly from the velocity of sound in the gas, as described in Part IV; it can now be calculated more accurately from the theory of band spectra than it can be measured by direct experiment.

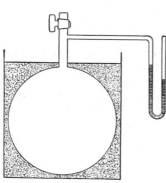

Fig. 4.—Clement and Désormes' Experiment

An interesting experimental determination, now only of historical and laboratory interest, is the determination of γ by Clement and Désormes' apparatus. As shown in fig. 4, a large container is fitted with a manometer containing some liquid of low density such as paraffin. Pressures differing little from atmospheric pressure may thus be easily read. The container is surrounded by cotton wool and fitted with an inlet valve through which air may be forced by a pump. A large outlet valve at the top of the container allows the air to expand sufficiently suddenly for the expansion to be approximately adiabatic. A pressure slightly above atmospheric, as indicated by a difference h_1 in the arms of the manometer, is first established. The gas is then expanded adiabatically by opening the outlet valve just sufficiently long to allow the pressure to fall to atmospheric. The valve is then closed. On allowing the apparatus to stand for five or ten minutes, the pressure rises to some new steady value h_2. This is because the gas in the container cools on the adiabatic expansion and finally regains room temperature with consequent rise of pressure. We proceed to show that approximately

$$\gamma = \frac{h_1}{h_1 - h_2}. \quad \cdots \quad \cdots \quad (12.17)$$

Referring to fig. 5, let $p_3 v_3$ be the final pressure and volume in the container. The gas which now occupies v_3, initially occupied a smaller

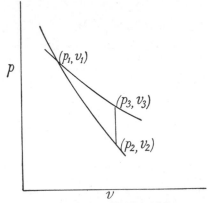

Fig. 5.—Adiabatic and Isothermal Curves

volume v_1 at the initial pressure p_1. On expanding adiabatically the pressure fell to p_2 (atmospheric) and the volume increased to v_2. When the gas had regained room temperature, the pressure rose to p_3 and the volume increased to v_3. Since the increase to volume v_3 from v_2 is only due to the rise in the level of the manometer, and is negligible compared with the volume of the container, v_3 is almost equal to v_2, and is put equal to it in the following calculation. For the adiabatic expansion

$$p_1 v_1{}^\gamma = p_2 v_2{}^\gamma = p_2 v_3{}^\gamma. \quad \cdots \quad \cdots \quad (12.18)$$

In the initial and final state the gas is at the same (room) temperature. Hence these two states are connected isothermally and consequently

$$p_1 v_1 = p_3 v_3 \quad \cdots \quad \cdots \quad \cdots \quad (12.19)$$

by Boyle's law.

Eliminating v_1 and v_3 from (12.18) and (12.19), we get

$$\left(\frac{p_1}{p_2}\right) = \left(\frac{p_1}{p_3}\right)^{\gamma},$$

or
$$\gamma = \frac{\log p_1 - \log p_2}{\log p_1 - \log p_3}$$

$$= \frac{p_1 - p_2}{p_1 - p_3} \quad \cdots \cdots \quad (12.20)$$

approximately, since p_1, p_2 and p_3 are not very different from each other.

But
$$p_1 = p_2 + h_1 \text{ and } p_3 = p_2 + h_2;$$

hence
$$\gamma = \frac{h_1}{h_1 - h_2}.$$

7. Expansion of Gases in Practice.

Since in general an expansion is neither purely isothermal nor purely adiabatic, the equation governing pressure and volume changes

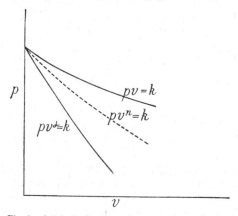

Fig 6.—Adiabatic, Isothermal and Intermediate Curves

may be taken to be $pv^n = $ const., where n lies between γ and unity. We represent the three types of expansion and compression in fig. 6. The curve governing the adiabatic change is always steeper than the corresponding isothermal, the intermediate type of change being shown by the dotted curve.

EXERCISES

1. Show that the work done when a gas expands is given by the area enclosed between the p-v curve and the v-axis. What are indicator diagrams?

2. Distinguish between *isothermal* and *adiabatic* expansions.

Obtain an expression for the relation between pressure and volume of a gas during an adiabatic change.

3. A gram-molecule of xenon at 15° C. is suddenly expanded to 10 times its original volume. Find the final temperature momentarily attained. [−212° C.]

4. Describe an experiment by which the ratio of the specific heat of a gas at constant pressure to its specific heat at constant volume may be obtained directly.

Why may a gas be considered to possess a variable specific heat between certain limiting values?

5. Obtain an expression for the work done when a gas undergoes isothermal expansion, and find the work done when a gram-molecule of gas at 183° C. expands isothermally until its volume is doubled. [628 cal.]

6. Give practical examples of gases undergoing adiabatic changes.

What is the work done when a gram-molecule of helium at 0° C. is suddenly compressed to a pressure twenty times its initial value? [1883 cal.]

CHAPTER XIII

*Elementary Thermodynamics

1. Carnot's Cycle

If a gas is submitted to a series of changes of pressure and volume and is ultimately brought back to its initial conditions, it is said to undergo a **cycle** of operations. A cycle of particular importance is that examined by Carnot and represented in fig. 1. Imagine a gas with initial pressure p_1 and volume v_1, represented by the point A. Let the

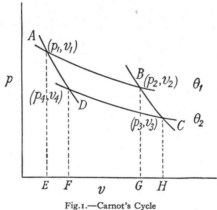

Fig.1.—Carnot's Cycle

gas expand isothermally down the isothermal at θ_1 until it reaches condition B, when its pressure and volume are p_2, v_2. Let the expansion now proceed adiabatically down the adiabatic BC to C, where the pressure and volume are p_3 and v_3. Now compress the gas isothermally along the isothermal CD at temperature θ_2 until it reaches D (on the adiabatic through A), where p_4 and v_4 represent its pressure and volume. Finally, compress the gas adiabatically from D to A until it regains its initial pressure and volume (p_1, v_1).

The net amount of work done by the gas in the cycle will be the difference between the work done by the gas in expanding from A to B, and B to C, and the work done in compressing the gas from C to D, and D to A. Now by our statement in Chap. XII, section 2, the work done is represented by the area between the (p-v) curve and the

v-axis. The net work done is therefore the difference in the areas (ABGE + BCHG) − (CDFH + DAEF), which is the area ABCD. In Carnot's cycle, therefore, *the net work done is equal to the area enclosed between the adiabatic and the isothermal curves.*

2. Reversible Cycles.

We could clearly have traversed the cycle in the preceding section in the reverse direction ADCBA, when we should have arrived at the same conclusions. Carnot's cycle is therefore strictly reversible. If we examine the cycle in more detail, we see that such a cycle cannot be exactly traversed by any real substance because (*a*) purely isothermal and adiabatic changes are not possible owing to the imperfect heat conduction and insulation of the container, (*b*) there is always a certain amount of heat lost irreversibly in any real cycle.

An example of irreversible heat loss is the heat generated by friction when a piston moves in a cylinder. When the gas expands and pushes the piston out, a certain amount of mechanical energy is provided plus a certain amount of frictional heat produced. Now for a strictly reversible movement of the piston, when the gas is compressed to its original state, frictional heat should be absorbed. This never occurs in practice, where friction always evolves heat.

3. Heat Engines.

The apparatus implied in traversing the cycle ABCD is said to be a *heat engine*. During the change from A to B, heat is taken in from some source maintained at θ_1. This supply is cut off at B, and the gas expands doing external work under its own energy down the adiabatic BC. Consequently its temperature falls; at C the compression stroke is commenced, and heat is removed during the compression so that the latter takes place isothermally at θ_2 from C to D. Finally, the compression is completed adiabatically, so that the temperature rises to θ_1 when we return to A.

4. Efficiency of a Reversible Cycle.

We define the efficiency of a cycle as

$$E = \frac{\text{net mechanical work done in the cycle}}{\text{heat taken in at the higher temperature}}. \quad (13.1)$$

Since the net work done is the area ABCD, if H_1 and H_2 are the heats taken in and given out along AB and CD respectively,

$$E = \frac{\text{ABCD}}{H_1} = \frac{H_1 - H_2}{H_1}. \quad \ldots \quad (13.2)$$

Equation (13.2) states that the net mechanical energy available is the difference between H_1, the heat absorbed by the engine from the source at θ_1, and H_2, the heat given up to the **condenser** at θ_2. This is simply an application of the principle of conservation of energy, for the initial and final states of the gas are the same, so that there is no change in the internal energy.

From equation (12.6),

$$H_1 = R\theta_1 \log_e \frac{p_1}{p_2}, \qquad \cdots \cdots \quad (13.3)$$

and

$$H_2 = R\theta_2 \log_e \frac{p_4}{p_3}.$$

Hence, from (13.2) and (13.3),

$$E = \frac{\theta_1 \log_e \dfrac{p_1}{p_2} - \theta_2 \log_e \dfrac{p_4}{p_3}}{\theta_1 \log_e \dfrac{p_1}{p_2}}. \quad \cdots \cdots \quad (13.4)$$

Now, since A and D, B and C lie on adiabatics,

$$p_1 v_1{}^\gamma = p_4 v_4{}^\gamma, \qquad \cdots \cdots \cdots \quad (13.5)$$

and

$$p_2 v_2{}^\gamma = p_3 v_3{}^\gamma.$$

Also, since A and B, C and D lie on isothermals,

$$p_1 v_1 = p_2 v_2, \qquad \cdots \cdots \cdots \quad (13.6)$$

and

$$p_3 v_3 = p_4 v_4.$$

Hence, from (13.5) and (13.6),

$$p_1/p_2 = p_4/p_3, \qquad \cdots \cdots \cdots \quad (13.7)$$

so (13.2), (13.4) and (13.1) become

$$E = \frac{H_1 - H_2}{H_1} = \frac{\theta_1 - \theta_2}{\theta_1} = \frac{\text{external work done}}{\text{heat taken in at higher temperature}}.$$

$$(13.8)$$

Equation (13.8) is of great importance, and we shall use it to deduce many physical results in later sections of this chapter.

5. Second Law of Thermodynamics.

If we have a large mass of a given substance at a temperature slightly lower than that of a small mass of the same substance, although the total energy contained in the former is much greater than that contained in the latter, it is quite impossible experimentally to liberate this energy by using the former as source and the latter as condenser in a heat engine. The flow of heat is governed entirely by the temperature. This fact is one way of putting the **Second Law of Thermodynamics,** which states that *no self-acting machine will operate using a body of lower temperature as source and giving up heat to a body at higher temperature.*

From this law we can show that the efficiency of all reversible heat engines is the same. Consider two reversible heat engines A and B, working between the same temperatures; it is sufficient if we show that E_B cannot be greater than E_A. Let B drive A backwards; and let B absorb heat H_{1B} at the higher temperature θ_1 and give out heat H_{2B} at θ_2. Then

$$E_B = \frac{H_{1B} - H_{2B}}{H_{1B}}.$$

Similarly, let the heat given out by A at the high temperature be H_{1A}, and that absorbed at the lower temperature be H_{2A}. Then

$$E_A = \frac{H_{1A} - H_{2A}}{H_{1A}}.$$

If it were possible that $E_B > E_A$, then

$$\frac{H_{1B} - H_{2B}}{H_{1B}} > \frac{H_{1A} - H_{2A}}{H_{1A}}. \quad \cdots \quad (13.9)$$

Now the work done by B is done on A: hence

$$H_{1B} - H_{2B} = H_{1A} - H_{2A}. \quad \cdots \quad (13.10)$$

Hence, from (13.9),

$$H_{1A} > H_{1B}, \quad \cdots \cdots \quad (13.11)$$

and consequently, by substituting from (13.11) in (13.10),

$$H_{2A} > H_{2B}. \quad \cdots \cdots \quad (13.12)$$

Now, if (13.11) and (13.12) were true, a net amount of heat would be extracted from the condenser at θ_2 and given to the source at the higher temperature θ_1. This is contrary to the second law of thermodynamics; consequently E_B must equal E_A.

This result, that the efficiencies of all perfectly reversible engines are the same, is one aspect of a very important part of thermodynamics; for it implies that, provided a cycle is reversible, its *behaviour is independent of the nature of the working substance.* Hitherto, we have only considered perfect gases as working substances; in later sections we propose to extend the applications of thermodynamics to such diverse physical phenomena as surface tension and thermo-electricity.

6. Absolute or Work Scale of Temperature.

Consider two adiabatics ACE, BDF, crossed at regular intervals by isothermals AB, CD, EF, as in fig. 2. Suppose the work done in the cycles ABDC, CDFE, &c., is the same: then we may introduce a new temperature scale *defining* the temperature intervals $(T_1 - T_2)$, $(T_2 - T_3)$ to be equal if equal work is done in the cycles ABDC, CDFE, &c. Such a scale is termed an *absolute* or *work scale of temperature*. As we proceed to lower and lower temperatures we may ultimately arrive at a temperature where no heat remains to be given to the condenser, all the heat taken in at the higher temperature being con-

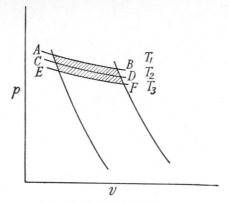

Fig. 2.—Absolute Scale of Temperature

verted into mechanical work. Such a temperature would constitute a natural *absolute zero*.

The efficiency of all the reversible cycles such as ABDC, CDFE is the same, and is defined by (13.1), where

$$E = \frac{H_1 - H_2}{H_1} = \frac{(T_1 - T_2)}{a}, \quad \ldots \quad (13.13)$$

where T_1 and T_2 are temperatures on the absolute scale and a is some function of T_1. Now for the last cycle above absolute zero, all the heat is converted into mechanical work. We therefore have $E = 1$; also $T_2 = 0$, so equation (13.13) gives $a = T_1$. Hence, the efficiency equation becomes

$$E = \frac{H_1 - H_2}{H_1} = \frac{T_1 - T_2}{T_1}, \quad \ldots \quad (13.14)$$

which is identical with (13.8), thus showing that **the absolute scale coincides with the perfect gas scale.**

7. Effect of Pressure on the Freezing-point of a Liquid.

In fig. 3, let ABCD be one complete isothermal covering the change of state at temperature $(\theta + d\theta)$ and EFGH the corresponding isothermal at temperature θ. Then if we draw adiabatics through B and C, we may regard the path BCPQ as a heat cycle. If we work with unit mass of material, the heat taken in along BC is $H_1 = L$, where L is the latent heat of fusion. Again, the work done in the cycle is the area BCPQ, which is approximately equal to $dp \cdot (v_2 - v_1)$, where

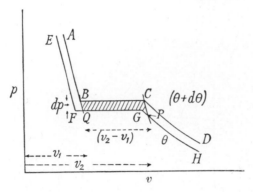

Fig. 3.—Effect of Pressure on the Freezing-point

$(v_2 - v_1)$ is the change in volume which occurs when unit mass of the material changes from liquid to solid at a pressure p. Hence, applying (13.8),

$$E = \frac{(\theta + d\theta) - \theta}{\theta} = \frac{dp(v_2 - v_1)}{L},$$

or

$$d\theta = \frac{dp(v_2 - v_1)}{L}\,\theta, \quad \cdots \cdots \quad (13.15)$$

an equation which gives the elevation $d\theta$ in freezing-point consequent upon a rise dp in pressure. Since $v_2 < v_1$ for water and ice, $d\theta$ comes out negative when dp is positive, as is observed.

8. Temperature Dependence of the Osmotic Pressure of a Dilute Solution.

We mentioned in Part I, p. 127, that the mechanism of osmotic pressure is still not well understood. Since, however, the application of thermodynamics is not concerned with the mechanism involved, provided we can construct a reversible cycle we may apply the principles of thermodynamics to deduce some of the laws of osmosis. We consider a quantity of dilute solution enclosed in a cylindrical vessel as shown in fig. 4, fitted with a frictionless piston, the top of which is semi-permeable, allowing pure solvent only to pass through it. Let the volume of the solution be V, its osmotic pressure P, and its absolute temperature θ. As the piston moves, pure solvent may pass through the piston-head into the region above or vice versa. The system is now taken round the reversible cycle LMNO of fig. 5. The point L represents the condition (P_1, V_1, θ), when the piston is at AB. The piston then moves slowly upwards admitting a volume dV of solvent through the piston; the system therefore moves to the point M of fig. 5, the operation having been carried out at constant

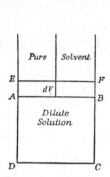

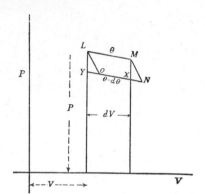

Fig. 4. – Osmotic Pressure

Fig. 5.—Carnot Cycle

temperature. Continue the cycle to N, allowing the solvent to pass through adiabatically from M to N; this is accompanied by a drop in temperature $d\theta$. Next depress the piston until the conditions are represented by O; this compression takes place isothermally along NO. Finally, complete the cycle by a small adiabatic compression represented by the path OL.

Applying the efficiency equation (13.8),

$$\frac{d\theta}{\theta} = \frac{dP \cdot dv}{P \cdot dv},$$

or

$$\int \frac{d\theta}{\theta} = \int \frac{dp}{P},$$

whence by integration

$$\log P = \log \theta + \text{constant},$$

or

$$P = a\theta,$$

where a is a constant. We have therefore deduced from thermo-dynamics the experimental law stated in Part I, p. 127, that the osmotic pressure of a dilute solution is proportional to the absolute temperature.

9. Surface Tension and Surface Energy.

To examine the relation between surface tension and surface energy (see Part I, p. 116), consider a heat engine consisting of a rect-angular soap-film as in fig. 6. Sup-pose, as actually occurs, when the film is stretched it absorbs heat from the surroundings, whereas when the film contracts this heat is evolved re-versibly. Let the film now be taken round a cycle in which:

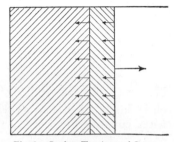

Fig. 6.—Surface Tension and Surface Energy

(1) It is increased by area A, isothermally at temperature θ, when its surface tension is S. Assume the heat absorbed reversibly is h per unit area. The work done by the film is $(-SA)$.

(2) Now place the film in an enclosure at temperature $\theta + \delta\theta$, keeping the area constant. The surface tension changes to $\left(S + \dfrac{dS}{d\theta}\delta\theta\right)$.

(3) Now let the film return isothermally to its original area. The work done on the film is $(-)\left(S + \dfrac{dS}{d\theta}\delta\theta\right)A$.

(4) Finally, replace the film in the enclosure at θ so that it returns to its original condition.

Applying the efficiency equation, we have

$$E = \frac{\theta - (\theta + \delta\theta)}{\theta} = \frac{-SA + \left(S + \dfrac{dS}{d\theta}\delta\theta\right)A}{hA},$$

or
$$h = -\theta\frac{dS}{d\theta}. \quad \ldots \ldots (13.16)$$

10. Action of Reversible Primary Cells.

In Part V we shall see that a certain amount of chemical action in a cell corresponds to a certain amount of electrical energy liberated. It was therefore suggested, on the basis of the conservation of energy, that the excess of chemical energy was exactly equal to the electrical energy liberated. We proceed to show that this relation requires correction if any heat is absorbed or evolved reversibly during the operation of the cell.

Let h be the heat absorbed thermodynamically for passage of unit quantity of electricity through the cell, and let H be the corresponding heat formed in the chemical reaction and V the electrical energy liberated. Then

$$V = H + h. \quad \ldots \ldots \quad (13.17)$$

Proceeding as in the preceding sections, let a quantity of electricity q be passed by the cell in an isothermal enclosure at θ when the E.M.F. of the cell is E. Then the work done by the cell is Eq. At the same time a quantity of heat hq is absorbed thermodynamically. Now place the cell in an isothermal enclosure at $\theta - \delta\theta$, when its E.M.F. changes to $\left(E - \dfrac{dE}{d\theta}\delta\theta\right)$, and pass a quantity of electricity q through the cell. The work done on the cell is $\left(E - \dfrac{dE}{d\theta}\delta\theta\right)q$. Hence, if the cell is finally allowed to return to its original temperature θ, the efficiency equation gives

$$\frac{\delta\theta}{\theta} = \frac{dE}{d\theta}\delta\theta\frac{q}{hq},$$

or

$$h = \theta\frac{dE}{d\theta}.$$

Hence equation (13.17) becomes

$$V = H + \theta\frac{dE}{d\theta}, \quad \ldots \ldots \quad (13.18)$$

or, since $V = E$,

$$E = H + \theta\frac{dE}{d\theta}.$$

The simple relation between chemical energy and electrical energy $V = H$ holds therefore only if $dE/d\theta$ is zero, that is, the cell has zero coefficient of change of E.M.F. with temperature. This happens to be approximately true for the Daniell cell, and hence the treatment given in Part V is approximately correct.

11. Entropy.

If we subtract unity from each side of the efficiency equation (13.8), we obtain

$$\frac{H_2}{H_1} = \frac{\theta_2}{\theta_1},$$

or, if H stands for heat *absorbed*, so that heat given out is negative,

$$\Sigma\frac{H}{\theta} = \text{zero}, \quad \ldots \ldots \quad (13.19)$$

in a reversible cycle. The expression $\Sigma \dfrac{H}{\theta}$ or $\displaystyle\int_{\theta_1}^{\theta_2} \dfrac{dH}{\theta}$ is said to represent the *change in entropy* of a system. For real systems, which are not exactly reversible, the change in entropy is always positive. Entropy defined as above is a mathematical rather than a physical conception. It allows the Second Law of Thermodynamics to be stated in the form that the entropy of a real system always increases. On examination this statement is found to imply (cf. section 5) that although the total amount of energy in a system remains constant, that energy becomes so distributed as time proceeds that it becomes less and less able to do work. In fact, a dead level of temperature is eventually attained. It is in this sense that the Universe is said to be " running down ".

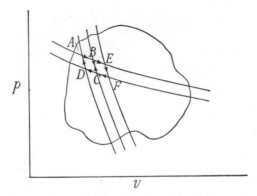

Fig. 7.—Entropy Equation for any Cycle

If we have a cycle with the outline shown in fig. 7, then provided the cycle is reversible it still obeys the entropy equation $\Sigma \dfrac{H}{\theta} = 0$.

We can see this by dividing the area into a large number of small Carnot cycles by drawing adiabatics and isothermals. Then in traversing each infinitesimal Carnot cycle part of the work done *on* the gas in one cycle exactly neutralizes part of the work done *by* the gas in the adjacent cycle. Thus, in fig. 7, the side BC is common to the cycles ABCDA, BEFCB, but it is oppositely traversed. When all the infinitesimal cycles are considered, this mutual cancelling occurs for all interior sides. Hence, in the limit, the net work done is that done in describing the circumference of the area.

12. Effect of Pressure on the Boiling-point of a Liquid.

Consider the transition from liquid to vapour for two isothermals at θ and $(\theta + d\theta)$ as shown in fig. 8. Then considering the reversible cycle ABCD, if s_1 is the specific heat of the fluid while traversing BC, and s_2 its specific heat while traversing DA, the First Law of Thermodynamics applied to unit mass of the substance gives

$$\left(L + \frac{dL}{d\theta}\delta\theta\right) - L + s_2\delta\theta - s_1\delta\theta = \text{work done in cycle}$$
$$= \text{ABCD} = \delta p(v_1 - v_2),$$

where $L = $ latent heat of vaporization at θ,

$$\left(L + \frac{dL}{d\theta}\delta\theta\right) = \text{latent heat of vaporization at } (\theta + \delta\theta),$$

$\delta p = $ pressure change,

$v_1, v_2 = $ volume of unit mass of vapour and liquid respectively at pressure p.

Hence $$\frac{dL}{d\theta} + (s_2 - s_1) = (v_1 - v_2)\frac{dp}{d\theta}. \quad . \quad . \quad . \quad (13.20)$$

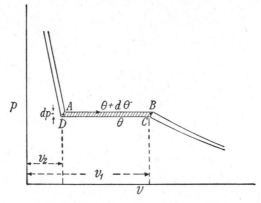

Fig. 8.—Effect of Pressure on Boiling-point

Next, by applying the Second Law of Thermodynamics to the cycle,

$$\left\{\frac{L}{\theta} + \frac{d}{d\theta}\left(\frac{L}{\theta}\right)\delta\theta\right\} - \left(\frac{L}{\theta}\right) + \frac{s_2 \cdot \delta\theta}{\theta} - \frac{s_1 \cdot \delta\theta}{\theta} = 0,$$

or $$\frac{dL}{d\theta} - \frac{L}{\theta} + (s_2 - s_1) = 0. \quad . \quad . \quad . \quad . \quad (13.21)$$

Hence, from (13.20) and (13.21), we have

$$\frac{L}{\theta} = (v_1 - v_2)\frac{dp}{d\theta},$$

or the elevation in boiling-point, $d\theta$, is given by

$$d\theta = \frac{\theta}{L}dp\,(v_1 - v_2). \quad . \quad . \quad . \quad . \quad (13.22)$$

Again, from (13.21), we have

$$s_1 = s_2 + \frac{dL}{d\theta} - \frac{L}{\theta}. \quad \cdots \quad (13.23)$$

As the critical temperature is approached, L decreases and its graph cuts the temperature axis at right angles; hence $\frac{dL}{d\theta} = \infty$, and so the specific heat of a saturated vapour approaches infinity as the critical temperature is approached.

13. Constants of the Thermoelectric Circuit.

The student should read the chapter on this subject in Part V before proceeding with this section. Consider two different metals A and B constituting a thermoelectric circuit with one junction at a temperature θ and the other at temperature $(\theta + \delta\theta)$. Then, if σ_A, σ_B are the Kelvin coefficients, and the Peltier coefficient at θ is P, applying the two laws of thermodynamics when a charge q is taken round the circuit, we have

$$\left(P + \frac{dP}{d\theta}\delta\theta\right)q - Pq + \sigma_A q\,\delta\theta - \sigma_B q\,\delta\theta = q\frac{dE}{d\theta}\delta\theta,$$

or

$$\frac{dP}{d\theta} + (\sigma_A - \sigma_B) = \frac{dE}{d\theta}, \quad \cdots \quad (13.24)$$

and

$$q\left\{\frac{P}{\theta} + \frac{d}{d\theta}\left(\frac{P}{\theta}\right)\right\} - \frac{qP}{\theta} + \frac{\sigma_A q\,\delta\theta}{\theta} - \frac{\sigma_B q\,\delta\theta}{\theta} = 0, \quad (13.25)$$

where $\frac{dE}{d\theta}\delta\theta$ is the thermoelectric Seebeck E.M.F. for a temperature difference $\delta\theta$ between the junctions. Eliminating σ_A and σ_B, we have

$$P = \theta\frac{dE}{d\theta},$$

and, eliminating P, we have

$$(\sigma_A - \sigma_B) = -\theta\frac{d^2E}{d\theta^2}.$$

These equations give a method of calculating the Peltier and Kelvin coefficients if $dE/d\theta$ and $d^2E/d\theta^2$ are known.

EXERCISES

1. Give an account of Carnot's cycle. Under what ideal conditions is a cycle strictly reversible?

2. Show that the efficiency of all strictly reversible cycles is the same. What important bearing has this fact on the generality of thermodynamical arguments?

3. State the Second Law of Thermodynamics. Upon what experimental facts is it based? Give one important example of its application.

4. Distinguish between the absolute scale of temperature and the gas scale. Show that for an ideal gas these are identical.

5. Deduce an expression for the change in freezing-point of a pure solvent with external pressure.

Find the change in the melting-point of ice when the external pressure is raised from one to two atmospheres, given that its latent heat of fusion is 80 cal./gm. and that the density of ice remains constant at 0·92 gm./c.c. [−0·007° C.]

6. Obtain an expression for the heat absorbed or evolved reversibly when a film subject to surface tension is taken round a reversible thermodynamical cycle.

Under what conditions are surface tension and surface energy per unit area equal?

7. Discuss the action of reversible primary cells from the thermodynamical standpoint. In what respects is a Daniell cell exceptional in its behaviour?

8. State briefly what you know concerning the nature of entropy, and deduce an expression for the difference in the specific heats of a liquid and its vapour at the boiling-point, in terms of its latent heat of vaporization.

CHAPTER XIV

Radiation

1. Introduction.

We have already stated in Chap. IV that if a hot body is placed in a vacuum so as to eliminate conduction and convection, it still loses heat. This is said to be due to **radiation.** It is supposed in elementary theory that the molecules, owing to their own heat vibration, send out waves which carry away energy; consequently the body eventually cools. Heat from the sun must reach the earth by radiation, since no material medium exists between the two bodies. Now during an eclipse of the sun, heat is cut off simultaneously with the light radiations. This indicates that light and heat radiations are similar and, in fact, heat radiation obeys the same general laws as light. If a spectrum is thrown on to a screen, with a powerful arc as a light source, and a thermometer with its bulb coated with lamp-black is moved across the spectrum, it will be found that little effect occurs when the thermometer is near the violet end of the spectrum. As, however, the red end is approached, the thermometer begins to rise, and this effect continues when the thermometer is placed beyond the red end and no *visible* radiations are falling upon it. It is then receiving heat radiation only, and is said to be in the **infra-red** portion of the spectrum (see Part III).

2. Simple Laws of Heat Radiation.

(i) *Angle of Incidence equals Angle of Reflection.*

To show that the angle of incidence equals the angle of reflection for heat rays, an apparatus is used as in fig. 1. A plane mirror M of speculum metal is equally inclined to the axes of two tubes. Opposite the end of one tube is placed a white-hot piece of platinum foil F, a thermopile T (see Part V) being used to receive the radiation reflected from the mirror. The galvanometer connected to the thermopile shows a large deflexion only when the mirror is turned so that the angle of incidence equals the angle of reflection.

(ii) *Inverse Square Law.*

To demonstrate that the intensity of the radiation falls off inversely as the square of the distance from the source, an apparatus is used as in fig. 2. A cubical metal container, known as *Leslie's cube*, contains water, and is raised to a suitable temperature, the thermocouple being presented to it at various distances as shown. The thermocouple is fitted with a conical hood so that radiations are received from definite circular areas of the cube. It is then found that the deflexion

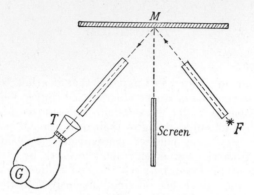

Fig. 1.—Law of Reflection for Heat Rays

of the galvanometer is independent of the distance of the thermocouple from the cube over a moderate range. We proceed to show that this is consistent with an inverse square law.

If d is the perpendicular distance, the effect on the thermocouple will be of the form kA/d^n, where A is the effective area cut off by the hood, k is some constant of the apparatus, and n is the exponent we

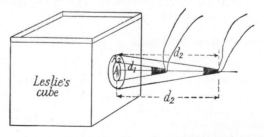

Fig. 2.—The Inverse Square Law

wish to find. For any two positions, the experiment shows that the effect is constant, so

$$kA_1/d_1^n = kA_2/d_2^n,$$

whence　　　　　　　　$A_1/A_2 = (d_2/d_1)^n.$　　. . . . . (14.1)

Now the two conical figures in fig. 2 are similar, and by the properties of similar cones

$$A_1/A_2 = (d_2/d_1)^2. \quad \cdots \cdots \quad (14.2)$$

But (14.1) and (14.2) can only hold simultaneously if $n = 2$.

If the thermocouple is so far away from the cube that the side of the cube is smaller than the projection of the hood, the result no longer follows. Similarly, for very close distances the agreement is not good, since the intensity of emission decreases as the rays become highly inclined to the emitting surface.

(iii) *Focussing Properties.*

If two parabolic mirrors are set up as shown in fig. 3 on a common axis several metres apart and a hot platinum foil is placed at the focus

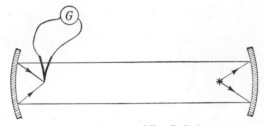

Fig. 3.—Focussing of Heat Radiation

of one mirror, an intense effect is produced in the thermocouple only when the latter is at the focus of the second mirror. It is striking to observe the deflexion of the galvanometer G decrease as the thermocouple is moved nearer the source but out of the focus.

3. Emission and Absorption of Radiation.

If the various sides of a Leslie's cube are coated with different materials such as lamp-black, highly polished metal, paper, and so on, it will be found on rotating the cube that although all the sides are at the same temperature some faces emit more radiant heat than others. Conversely, if a thermopile is covered with lamp-black, it is found to be far more sensitive to radiant heat than if its elements are highly polished. The general fact emerges that some substances emit and absorb radiant heat far more easily than others. Further, good radiators are good absorbers. A simple experiment to illustrate this is shown in fig. 4, which describes an apparatus due to Ritchie. A vertical U-tube containing coloured liquid is sealed at the ends to two equal cylinders A and B containing air. These cylinders have their faces coated with silver and lamp-black respectively, as shown. A third cylinder C is coated on one face with silver and on the other with lamp-black, and C may be filled with hot water and inserted between A and B. Now, if the apparatus is arranged so that the silvered face of C radiates to the blackened face of B and consequently the blackened face of C radiates to the silvered face of A, it is found that no movement of the liquid occurs in the U-tube. This shows that although there is little heat radiated from C to B, what there is is all absorbed by B; conversely, although a large quantity of heat is radiated from C to A the latter, being silvered, absorbs very little. On rotating C so that silver radiates to silver and lamp-black to lamp-black, a large deflexion shows the superior radiating and absorbing properties of lamp-black.

A perfect absorber is one that absorbs all the radiant heat incident upon it and reflects none. Lamp-black constitutes the nearest approach to such a hypothetical substance, which is called a **perfectly black body.**

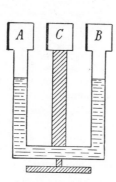

Fig. 4.—Absorption and
Radiation

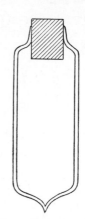

Fig. 5.—Dewar Vacuum
Flask

4. Applications of the Laws of Radiant Heat.

The student will be familiar with the use of brightly polished surfaces to minimize radiation and absorption. For example, teapots are usually highly polished. The most important example is perhaps the Dewar vacuum flask, in which heat losses by conduction, convection and radiation are reduced so much that liquid air, 200° C. below room temperature, may be kept in an ordinary room for over a day without completely evaporating. As shown in fig. 5, the Dewar flask consists of a double-walled glass vessel of cylindrical shape fitted with a long tapering cork. The inner sides of the glass walls are silvered, and the space between them finally evacuated. Heat conduction can occur then only along the top rim of the badly conducting glass or down the long tapering cork. Since air is prevented from reaching the inner walls of the vessels, convection is almost non-existent. Radiation is reduced to a minimum by the silvering, which reflects the heat waves.

5. Stefan's Law of Radiation.

From experiments with different surfaces at different temperatures, Stefan was led to the conclusion that the quantity of heat radiated by a surface was proportional to the fourth power of the absolute temperature. This is **Stefan's Law of Radiation.** It is only strictly true for perfectly black bodies, the power varying for real bodies between 3 and 4 or more according to the nature of the surface. Boltzmann first placed the law on firm theoretical grounds. In mathematical terms, a body at absolute temperature T_2 is losing heat to its surroundings at temperature T_1 according to the relation

$$H = \sigma(T_2{}^4 - T_1{}^4), \quad \ldots \ldots \quad (14.3)$$

where σ is a constant termed *Stefan's constant.* The quantity $\sigma T_1{}^4$ is introduced since the body will be *receiving* heat from the surroundings equal in magnitude to this amount.

6. Planck's Radiation Law.

We have indicated that radiant heat is similar in behaviour to light. If radiant heat is passed through a prism, a spectrum is formed, just as for light. The prism must, however, be made of some material such as rock salt or fluor-spar, since glass absorbs the greater part of heat radiation. That substances may be transparent to visible light but opaque to heat radiation is shown by the glass fire-screen, by which the light rays are transmitted while the heat rays are absorbed. The converse is true in fogs, where infra-red radiation is transmitted under conditions where visible radiation is absorbed. This fact forms the basis of infra-red photography under misty conditions over large distances. Substances which absorb radiant heat are sometimes said to be **athermanous,** while those which transmit it are termed **diathermanous.**

Now it has long been known (see Part III, Chap. IX) that light consists of a wave motion and radiant heat is the same type of wave motion but of longer wave-lengths. It is of particular interest to examine how the heat energy contained in the radiant heat is distributed among the various wave-lengths present. The experiment was carried out by Lummer and Pringsheim, who detected the heat from the variation in electrical resistance of a platinum wire on which the heat was allowed to fall. The wire was included in one arm of a Wheatstone bridge; such a general arrangement is termed a **bolometer.** Radiant energy deviated by a fluor-spar prism was focussed by a mirror on the bolometer. The prism had previously been calibrated with a diffraction grating (see Part III, Chap. VII), so the wave-length of the radiation was known for a given angle of deviation. The type of curves obtained is shown in fig. 6. A prominent feature of these curves is the hump indicating a maximum energy, which moves towards the region of shorter wave-lengths as the temperature of the black body radiator is increased. **Wien** showed that the radiation obeyed a **displacement law,**

$$\lambda_m \theta = \text{constant}, \quad \ldots \ldots \quad (14.4)$$

where λ_m is the wave-length of the maximum energy for a given absolute temperature θ. He also showed that the energy was distri-

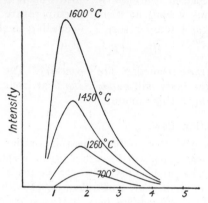

Fig. 6.—Spectrum of Radiant Heat

buted among the wave-lengths in accordance with the relation

$$E_\lambda d\lambda = c\lambda^{-5} f(\lambda\theta) d\lambda, \quad \ldots \ldots \quad (14.5)$$

where c is a constant. (In fig. 6, the abscissæ are wave-lengths, the unit being 1μ, or 10^{-4} cm.)

It was **Planck** who finally obtained the complete law, namely,

$$E_\lambda d\lambda = \frac{C_1 \lambda^{-5}}{e^{C_2/\lambda\theta} - 1} d\lambda, \quad \ldots \ldots \quad (14.6)$$

where C_1 and C_2 are constants.

The energy distribution observed experimentally by Lummer and Pringsheim was directly contradictory to what was expected theoretically from all previous physical principles, that is, from what is termed **classical theory.** Planck obtained his formula on the revolutionary theory that radiant heat is not emitted by the radiator nor absorbed by the absorber in continuous waves but in discrete packets of energy termed **quanta.** Thus, in 1900, the **quantum theory** and the era of Modern Physics were born.

7. Pyrometers for Measuring High Temperatures.

(i) *Féry Total Radiation Type.*

The pyrometers for measuring high temperatures depend on the heat absorbed, usually by a thermocouple, from a source radiating at high temperature, together with either Stefan's law or Planck's law. In the Féry total radiation type a concave polished copper mirror (fig. 7) focuses the radiations from an aperture in the side of the furnace, say, on to a thermocouple connected to a galvanometer. The thermocouple is usually calibrated by noting the deflexion of the galvanometer under the same conditions of standard distance when the temperature of the source is known by direct measurement. Of course, for very high temperatures this is not possible, and then Stefan's law must be extrapolated, that is, σ is given some average value for the source under consideration and Stefan's law is assumed to hold up to the highest temperatures to be determined. In this way, the **solar constant**, that is, the heat radiated per unit area per second by the sun's surface, indicates that if the conditions are those of Stefan's law, the mean temperature of the sun's surface is about 6000° C.

Fig. 7.—Féry Total Radiation Pyrometer

We may note that a small hole in the side of a furnace emits radiations which are likely to be very similar to those emitted by a perfectly black body at the same temperature. This is generally known as the *Law of Cavity Radiation.* We illustrate its validity as follows. Consider a ray passing *into* a small hole in a furnace. After incidence on the inner wall of the furnace, a certain portion of the radiant energy will be absorbed and a certain portion will be reflected. A perfectly black body would have absorbed all the radiation; the enclosure eventually approximates to this, for the reflected ray will strike the inner wall of the enclosure and again be partially absorbed. The chance of any appreciable portion of the radiant energy emerging again from the enclosure is extremely small, so the interior behaves as a perfectly black body. Conversely, the totality of rays which are emitted from the inner wall of the furnace and escape from the small aperture will be similar to those emitted by a perfectly black body.

(ii) *Disappearing Filament Pyrometer.*

This type depends on the use of Planck's law. A certain region of the spectrum is isolated by simply interposing a sheet of red glass which limits the spectrum to a small range of wave-lengths. Then for the eye to estimate as equal the brightness of two sources compared simultaneously, the energy in the same range of wave-lengths, and consequently, by Planck's formula, the temperatures, must be the same.

In the disappearing filament pyrometer, a diagram of which is given in fig. 8, the filament of an electric lamp is seen against the background of the image of the opening in the furnace. If the temperature of the filament is less than that of the furnace, the filament

Fig. 8.—Disappearing Filament Pyrometer

appears darker than the background. By using a variable resistance, the current through the filament is adjusted until it becomes invisible or disappears against the background. The ammeter has been calibrated already against surfaces of known temperature, so that the temperature is read off directly.

EXERCISES

1. Write a short essay on Radiant Heat.

2. By what experiment may it be shown that the intensity of heat radiated from a source falls off inversely as the square of the distance from the source?

What laws govern the emission and absorption of heat radiation and on what experiments are they based?

3. Describe the Dewar vacuum flask, explaining carefully how heat losses are reduced to a minimum.

4. State Stefan's Law of Radiation and describe some form of total radiation pyrometer.

5. Give an account of the distribution of energy in the spectrum of black-body radiation. What is the particular importance of this investigation?

6. Describe the disappearing filament pyrometer, explaining carefully the physical principles upon which it is based.

7. What is meant by *Wien's displacement law*?

How would you determine the solar constant?

EXAMPLES

REQUIRED CONSTANTS

The numbers in brackets at the end of each question indicate which constants are to be used from the Table given below

1. Coefficient of linear expansion of wrought iron, 1.19×10^{-5} per °C.
2. Coefficient of linear expansion of brass, 1.89×10^{-5} per °C.
3. Coefficient of linear expansion of copper, 1.67×10^{-5} per °C.
4. Coefficient of linear expansion of aluminium, 2.55×10^{-5} per °C.
5. Coefficient of linear expansion of steel, 2.00×10^{-5} per °C.
6. Coefficient of linear expansion of glass, 9.00×10^{-6} per °C.
7. Coefficient of cubical expansion of mercury, 1.82×10^{-4} per °C.
8. Coefficient of cubical expansion of ether, 1.63×10^{-3} per °C.
9. Young's Modulus for brass, 10^{12} dynes/sq. cm.
10. Young's Modulus for steel, 2×10^{12} dynes/sq. cm.
11. Density of glycerine at 15° C., 1.26 gm./c.c.
12. Density of mercury at 15° C., 13.56 gm./c.c.
13. Density of steel at 15° C., 8.00 gm./c.c.
14. Specific heat of lead, 0.03.
15. Specific heat of rubber, 0.50.
16. Latent heat of fusion of ice, 80 cal./gm.
17. Latent heat of condensation of steam, 540 cal./gm.
18. Melting-point of rubber, 310° C.
19. Melting-point of lead, 335° C.
20. Joule's mechanical equivalent of heat, 4.18×10^7 ergs/cal.

1. A Fahrenheit thermometer and an accurate Centigrade thermometer register 161° and 70.5° respectively when placed in the same enclosure, which is at uniform temperature. What is the error in the Fahrenheit thermometer?

2. A simple compensated pendulum consists of two wrought-iron rods and a brass rod with horizontal connecting pieces. Draw a diagram of the vertical arrangement of the rods and calculate the total length of the iron rods, given that the brass rod is 3 ft. long at 15° C. (1, 2.)

3. Find the fall in temperature required to cause a clock to gain 1 sec. per hour if the pendulum is made of wrought iron. (1.)

4. If a shrinkage fit is just obtained when a copper ring and an aluminium disk are both immersed in "dry ice" (solid carbon dioxide), find the temperature of the latter, assuming that the contraction is uniform and that the ratio of the radius of the disk to the internal radius of the ring at 20° C. is $(1\cdot00510/1\cdot00334)^{\frac{1}{2}}$. (3, 4.)

5. A thick vertical glass rod is held rigidly at its base. A horizontal brass rod of cross-section 1 sq. cm. has one end fixed rigidly in a wall, while its free end is clamped to the end of the glass rod. If the glass rod fractures under a horizontal pull of more than 100 lb., determine whether it will fracture if the brass rod is suddenly cooled through 10° C. (2, 9.)

6. Prove that the coefficients of surface and volume expansion of a solid are equal approximately to twice and three times the coefficient of linear expansion.

7. A steel rod of length 50 cm. and area of cross-section 1 sq. cm. has concentrated masses each of 2000 gm. attached to its ends. Neglecting the weight of the rod, find the speed at which the rod must be rotated about a vertical axis passing through its middle point so that the tension in the rod shall equal that produced by clamping the two masses rigidly and then cooling the rod through 100° C. (5, 10.)

8. In Ques. 7, find the error, in the tension at the middle point, introduced by neglecting the weight of the rod. (13.)

9. Two rods of length l_2 and coefficient of linear expansion a_2 are connected freely to a third rod of length l_1 and coefficient of linear expansion a_1 to form an isosceles triangle, and the arrangement is suspended on a knife-edge at the mid-point of l_1 which is horizontal. What relation must exist between l_1 and l_2 if the apex of the isosceles triangle is to remain at a constant distance below the point of suspension as the temperature changes?

10. A copper cylinder has a small hole in the side at a height of 10 cm. from the base. It is filled with ether to within 1 mm. of the hole. What must be the rise in temperature for the ether to commence to escape from the hole? (3, 8.)

11. A glass weight thermometer contains 79·4 c.c. of glycerine at 15° C. If 4·10 gm. of glycerine escape when the thermometer is raised to 100° C., find the absolute coefficient of cubical expansion of glycerine. (6, 11.)

12. A barometer stands at a height of 76·00 cm. when the room temperature is 15° C. Find the height registered when the tempera-

ture sinks to 5° C., the external barometric pressure remaining un-altered. (7.)

13. A narrow L-shaped silica tube is of uniform cross-section and is closed at the ends, the longer limb being twice the length of the shorter. It is freely suspended at the bend, and the shorter limb is just filled with a liquid the coefficient of cubical expansion of which is 3×10^{-3} per °C. rise of temperature. If the mass of the liquid is nine times that of the shorter limb and the apparatus is cooled through 100° C., show that the relation between the angles at which the shorter limb is inclined to the vertical at the two temperatures is given by $\tan a_1 : \tan a_2 :: 157 : 130$.

14. A silica sinker which weighs 100 gm. in air is suspended from a balance arm and immersed in water at 4° C., whereupon a loss in weight of 37·59 gm. is observed. On raising the water to 80° C. the loss in weight changes to 36·49 gm. Find the density of the water at 80° C. and the mean coefficient of cubical expansion of water between 4° and 80° C.

15. A piece of iron and a piece of copper each of weight 50 gm. are soldered together and placed in a hypsometer at 100° C. They are then removed and dropped quickly into a copper calorimeter of weight 50 gm. containing 50 gm. of water at 15° C., whereupon the temperature rises to 28·35° C. On repeating the experiment, but with 100 gm. of water in the calorimeter, the temperature rises to 22·55° C. Find the specific heat of iron and of copper.

16. A small cylindrical copper calorimeter of weight 10 gm. and specific heat 0·094 contains 10 gm. of water at 35° C., the temperature being registered by a thermometer inserted in the calorimeter. This thermometer is removed as a second thermometer which is register-ing a room temperature of 15° C. is inserted. The final temperature registered by the second thermometer is 33·35° C. The first ther-mometer is then replaced and shows a temperature of 32·00° C., while the second thermometer shows a temperature of 32·05° C. Find the water equivalent of the second thermometer.

17. A given volume of fresh water is placed in a calorimeter A, and an equal volume of sea-water is placed in an identically similar calorimeter B. Taking the density of the fresh water as unity and that of the sea-water as 1·05 gm./c.c., find the specific heat of the latter if the times taken for the two liquids to cool through 20° C. are 1800 sec. and 1776 sec. respectively.

18. In a Joly differential steam calorimeter, the volume of each sphere is 500 c.c. and the excess weight of water condensed on the sphere containing the gas is 0·1 gm. Find the specific heat of the gas at constant volume if its initial temperature was 15° C. and its den-sity is $6·00 \times 10^{-3}$ gm./c.c. (17.)

19. From the following data obtained by using Regnault's apparatus for the specific heat of a gas at constant pressure, find the specific heat of dry air at constant pressure: mass of air passed 32·00 gm., temperature of oil bath 150·00° C., initial temperature of calorimeter 15·00° C., final temperature of calorimeter 25·40° C., water equivalent of calorimeter and contents 100·00 gm.

20. A metal cube of side 10 cm. is maintained at a uniform temperature. It is supported from below by an exactly similar cube of wood and suspended from above by a metal wire 10 cm. long and of cross-section 1 sq. mm. Compare the amounts of heat conducted through wood and wire respectively if their thermal conductivities are 5×10^{-4} and 9×10^{-1} C.G.S. units respectively.

21. A square glass window of side 6 m. and thickness 1 cm. is supported at the inner edge of a metal frame 6 cm. wide and 6 cm. thick. If the thermal conductivities of glass and metal are $2·5 \times 10^{-3}$ and $2·6 \times 10^{-1}$ C.G.S. units respectively, compare the contributions to the heat lost through the window and the frame.

22. A slab consists of two parallel layers of different materials 4·0 and 2·0 cm. thick and of thermal conductivities 0·54 and 0·36 C.G.S. units respectively. If the opposite faces of the slab are at 100° C. and 0° C., calculate the temperature at the surface dividing the two materials.

23. A pool of molten sulphur has a crust 10 cm. thick and is cooling by exposure to the air, which is at a mean temperature of 4° C. Given that the melting-point of sulphur is 444° C., that its latent heat of fusion is 9 cal./gm., and that its density is 2·00 gm./c.c., find its thermal conductivity if it takes 4 hours for the crust to increase to 20 cm. thick.

24. In a certain Bunsen's ice calorimeter the inner tube is a right circular cylinder with a flat end, the length being 6·0 cm. and the internal and external diameters 2·40 and 2·80 cm. respectively. When a current of air at 4° C. is passed steadily through the tube, the mercury is found to creep along the capillary tube of diameter 2 mm. at the rate of 2·70 cm. per min. Given that the density of the ice is 0·92 gm./c.c., find the thermal conductivity of the material of the inner tube. (16.)

25. In determining the thermal conductivity of a plate (area 75 sq. cm., thickness 2 mm.) of a poor conductor by Lees' method, the steady temperatures of the two sides of the conductor were 96° C. and 46° C. Find the thermal conductivity of the poor conductor, given that the mass of the metal disk radiating at 46° C. was 1000 gm., its specific heat 0·094, and its rate of cooling at 46° C. was 7·20° C./min.

26. A rubber tube of internal and external radii 0·90 and 1·10 cm. and of length 50 cm. is immersed in a calorimeter whose total water equivalent, including that of its contents, is 100 gm. If the temperature of the calorimeter rises from 15° C. to 35° C. in 38 sec. when a current of steam at 100° C. is blown through the rubber tube, find the thermal conductivity of the rubber.

27. Steam at 100° C. is blown into a cavity in a block of metal of an alloy that melts at 90° C. Given that the latent heat of fusion of the alloy is 5 cal./gm., compare the rates of increase of the relative amounts of molten metal and condensed water when melting is proceeding uniformly. (17.)

28. The brakes are suddenly applied to a train of mass 150 tons and the speed is thereby reduced from 60 to 40 m.p.h. Determine the amount of heat produced in calories. (20.)

29. Two equal lead bullets collide head-on. Show that if they stop and just reach their melting-point under the heat generated at the impact, their relative velocity must have been nearly 1800 ft./sec. The temperature of the bullets just before impact was 35° C. (14, 19, 20.)

30. The brakes are suddenly applied to a lorry of mass 2 tons and the vehicle skids. Determine the least speed at which the lorry was travelling if the rubber in contact with the road just begins to melt at the instant the lorry is reduced to rest. Effective mass of rubber in contact with road is 4 lb., and initial temperature of tyres is 10° C. (15, 18, 20.)

31. What is the least height from which a piece of lead must be dropped so that it shall just start to melt under the heat generated at the impact? Initial temperature of lead just before impact is 35° C. (14, 19, 20.)

32. Two cubes of ice, each of mass 50 lb., have two of their faces rubbed together by a machine working at 0·5 h.p. Determine how long it will take for the blocks to melt to half their size under the friction produced. (16, 20.)

33. Using Callendar's continuous flow method, it is found that in one experiment the thermometers register 15·00° C. and 25·00° C. respectively when the rate of flow of water is 36,000 gm./hour. To maintain, however, the second thermometer at 42·5° C. when water is supplied at a temperature of 32·5° C. (and electrical power is supplied at the same rate), the flow must be increased by 72 gm./hour. Compare the specific heat of water at 20° C. and 37·5° C.

34. A copper calorimeter of mass 200 gm. and specific heat 0·094 contains 100 gm. of a liquid immersed in which is a coil of wire carrying a current of 4 amp. under a potential difference of 4 volts. If

the temperature rises 10° C. in 140 sec., find the specific heat of the liquid, neglecting heat losses and the heat capacity of the wire. (20.)

35. In Ques. 34, the temperature is allowed to rise until the liquid boils, and it is then found that after 250 sec. the weight of the liquid has been reduced to 90 gm. Find the latent heat of vaporization of the liquid.

36. A narrow glass tube containing a column of mercury is sealed at both ends while the tube is horizontal and a volume of air is enclosed at each end, the volume at one end being twice that at the other. The barometric pressure is 76 cm. of mercury. On arranging the tube vertically the volumes of air at the two ends change to the ratio of three to one. Find the length of the enclosed mercury column.

37. In the process of the evacuation of a vessel by an ordinary air pump the pressure drops from an initial value of 76 cm. of mercury to 60 cm. after 10 strokes. How many strokes will be required to reduce the pressure to 10 cm.?

38. Into a vessel of volume V maintained at a temperature T three gases are passed. If the three gases had initial pressures, volumes and temperatures (p_1, V_1, T_1), (p_2, V_2, T_2), and (p_3, V_3, T_3) respectively, find the final pressure.

39. A flask containing 1000 c.c. of liquid air is placed under a closed vessel containing 1000 c.c. of gaseous air at a pressure of 1 atmosphere. If 1 c.c. of liquid air gives on evaporation 1000 c.c. of gaseous air at a pressure of 1 atmosphere at a temperature of −200° C., find at approximately what temperature the closed vessel will burst when all the liquid air has evaporated. The bursting pressure of the vessel is 3000 atmospheres.

40. Given that an explosion will occur in a room of volume 2000 c. ft. if a hydrogen content greater than 1 per cent by volume is present, determine whether it would be safe to light a pipe in the room if a leaky hydrogen cylinder of capacity 1 c. ft. standing in a box of ice and initially at a pressure of 100 atmospheres is observed to read 75 atmospheres. The room temperature is 15° C. and the barometric pressure 1 atmosphere.

41. Find the value of Joule's mechanical equivalent of heat from the following data: density of hydrogen at N.T.P. is 9.00×10^{-5} gm./c.c., its specific heat at constant volume is 2·40, and C_p/C_v is 1·40.

42. The space above the mercury in a barometer tube contains some air and saturated vapour, the pressure of the latter being 3·0 cm. of mercury. If the barometric pressure is 76 cm. of mercury and the barometer tube is reading 70 cm. of mercury, what will it read

when by depression of the tube the space above the mercury has been reduced to one-quarter of its original volume?

43. After collecting 500 c.c. of gas over water in a burette with a tap at the top, the tap is opened to an evacuated vessel and the total volume of the expanded gas becomes 1000 c.c. If the temperature is kept constant and the vapour remains saturated, find the final total pressure, given that the initial total pressure was 762 mm. of mercury and that the saturation vapour pressure of water at the temperature of the experiment was 17 mm. of mercury.

44. Using a Victor Meyer's vapour density apparatus, the weight of liquid used was 0·250 gm. and the displaced air, which was collected over water at 15° C., occupied a volume of 250 c.c. If the barometric pressure was 76 cm. of mercury and the saturated vapour pressure of water at 15° C. is 1·28 cm. of mercury, find the vapour density of the liquid at 0° C. and a pressure of 76 cm. of mercury.

45. A gram-molecule of helium at 20° C. is suddenly subjected to a pressure ten times its initial value. Find the final temperature momentarily attained. C_p/C_v for helium is 1·67.

46. Referring to Ques. 45, find the work done during the compression, given that the gas constant R for a gram-molecule is 2·0 cal.

47. Find the final temperature reached and the work done if a gram-molecule of a gas expands at constant pressure until its volume is doubled. Initial temperature of gas is 87° C.

48. In Ques. 47, find the work done if the expansion is isothermal.

49. Find the root mean square velocity of a hydrogen molecule at N.T.P., given that the density of hydrogen under these conditions is $9·00 \times 10^{-5}$ gm./c.c. (12.)

50. An observation of Tyndall showed that the heat radiated from a piece of platinum foil at 1200° C. was 11·7 times the amount radiated by the foil at 525° C. Is the observation in agreement with Stefan's law of radiation?

ANSWERS AND HINTS FOR SOLUTION

1. $C/100 = (F - 32)/180$; $2.1°$ F.

2. If combined length of iron rods is $(l_1 + l_2)$, then $(l_1 + l_2)a_1 = 3a_2$ for compensation; 4·8 ft.

3. $t_1 = 2\pi(l/g)^{\frac{1}{2}}$, $3599t_1/3600 = 2\pi\{l(1 - a\theta)/g\}^{\frac{1}{2}}$; 47° C.

4. If r_0 is common radius at lower temperature, considering the surface expansion, $\pi r_1^2 = \pi r_0^2(1 + 2a_1\theta)$, $\pi r_2^2 = \pi r_0^2(1 + 2a_2\theta)$; $-80°$ C.

5. Pull in dynes is $P = EAa\theta$, where E is Young's Modulus in dynes/sq. cm. and A is area of cross-section. Yes, 424 lb.

6. $S = S_0(1 + \beta\theta)$, also $S = l_\theta^2 = l_0^2(1 + a\theta)^2$; expanding and neglecting a^2, $\beta = 2a$. Similarly, $\gamma = 3a$.

7. Tension in rod on cooling is $P = EAa\theta$; tension due to centrifugal force would be $Mr\omega^2$, where ω is the angular velocity of rotation. Hence $\omega = (EAa\theta/Mr)^{\frac{1}{2}} = 283$ rad./sec.

8. Let m be mass of rod per unit length; element dx distant x from axis of rotation contributes centrifugal force $m . dx . x . \omega^2$. Total centrifugal force contributed by whole rod is therefore $m\omega^2 \int_0^r x\,dx = \frac{1}{4}M_r . r\omega^2$, where M_r is mass of whole rod. Hence effect in Ques. 7 is to increase M by $M_r/4$.

9. Distance d of apex below knife-edge is given by $d^2 = l_2^2 - l_1^2/4$ or $4d^2 = 4l_2^2 - l_1^2$. Differentiating to find change in d for change in l_1 and l_2, $8d . dd = 8l_2 . dl_2 - 2l_1 . dl_1$. Hence for $dd = 0$, $4l_2 . dl_2 = l_1 . dl_1$, that is, $4l_2 . l_2a_2 = l_1 . l_1a_1$; $l_1^2 : l_2^2 :: 4a_2 : a_1$.

10. Let height of ether from base at instant of escape be h; then for cylinder $\pi r^2 h = \pi r_0^2 . 10(1 + \gamma_1\theta)$; similarly for ether $\pi r^2 h = \pi r_0^2(9.9) (1 + \gamma_2\theta)$; 6·4° C.

11. $\gamma_l = (m_0 - m_t)/(m_t . t) + \gamma_g . m_0/m_t$; 5.31×10^{-4} per °C.

12. Since external pressure remains constant $\rho gh = \rho'gh'$, also $\rho = \rho'(1 + \gamma t)$; 75·86 cm.

13. Let length of short arm be $2l$; for equilibrium take moments about the bend. If w is the weight of shorter limb:
Case 1. $(w + 9w) . l \sin a_1 = 2w . 2l \cos a_1$.
Case 2. $w . l \sin a_2 + 9w(2l - l_0) \sin a_2 = 2w . 2l \cos a_2$, where l_0 is given by $l_t = 2l = 2l_0(1 + 3 \times 10^{-3} \times 100)$, or $l_0 = 10l/13$. Hence $\tan a_1 : \tan a_2 :: 157 : 130$.

14. 0·971 gm./c.c.; 3.93×10^{-4} per °C.

15. $(50s_1 + 50s_2)71.65 = (50s_2 + 50)13.35$; $(50s_1 + 50s_2)77.45 = (50s_2 + 100)7.55$; 0·11, 0·095.

16. Let W be water equivalent of second thermometer; when first thermometer reads $35 \cdot 00°$ C., second thermometer would have read $35 \cdot 05°$ C. Taking temperature differences on scale of second thermometer and equating heat gained by thermometer to heat lost by calorimeter and water:

$$W(33 \cdot 35 - 15) = (10 \times 0 \cdot 094 + 10)(35 \cdot 05 - 33 \cdot 35); \quad 1 \cdot 01 \text{ gm.}$$

17. $M_1 s_1 / M_2 s_2 = t_1 / t_2;$ $0 \cdot 94$.

18. $W c_v \theta = wL;$ $0 \cdot 21$.

19. $W c_p \{150 - (25 \cdot 4 + 15)/2\} = 100(25 \cdot 4 - 15);$ $0 \cdot 25$.

20. Apply relation $Q = -kA\, d\theta/dx$ to wood and wire respectively, where Q is quantity of heat conducted per sec. through area A by substance of thermal conductivity k, and temperature gradient $d\theta/dx$ is assumed linear; $50 : 9$.

21. As in Ques. 20; $1 \cdot 43 : 1$.

22. Let θ be temperature of interface; then if Q is quantity of heat flowing through unit area of slab per sec. for first layer, $Q = 0 \cdot 54(100 - \theta)/4 = 0 \cdot 36(\theta - 0)/2$ for second layer; $43°$ C. approx.

23. $Qt = -kA\, d\theta/dx \cdot t = mL = Ad\rho L;$ $4 \cdot 26 \times 10^{-4}$ cal. cm.$^{-1}$ sec.$^{-1}$ °C.$^{-1}$.

24. Volume creep in capillary is $\pi \times 10^{-2} \times 2 \cdot 70/60$ c.c./sec. If mass of ice melted per sec. is m, change in volume produced is $m(1/0 \cdot 92 - 1)$. Hence heat received per sec. $Q = mL = 0 \cdot 92 \times 80 \times \pi \times 10^{-2} \times 2 \cdot 70/0 \cdot 08 \times 60$. But $Q = -kA\, d\theta/dx = 4k(2\pi \times 1 \cdot 3 \times 6 + \pi \times 1 \cdot 3 \times 1 \cdot 3)/0 \cdot 2;$ $1 \cdot 2 \times 10^{-1}$ cal. cm.$^{-1}$ sec.$^{-1}$ °C.$^{-1}$.

25. $Q = -kA\, d\theta/dx = ms\, d\theta/dt;$ $6 \cdot 0 \times 10^{-4}$ cal. cm.$^{-1}$ sec.$^{-1}$ °C.$^{-1}$.

26. $k = (Q/t)/\{2\pi rl(T_1 - T)/(r_2 - r_1)\};$ $4 \cdot 5 \times 10^{-4}$ C.G.S. units.

27. $m_1 L_1 + m_1 \cdot 10 = m_2 L_2;$ $110 : 1$.

28. $\tfrac{1}{2} m(v_2{}^2 - v_1{}^2) = JH;$ $7 \cdot 3 \times 10^6$ cals.

29. Let vel. of each bullet be v. Then $2 \cdot \tfrac{1}{2} mv^2 = JH = J \cdot 2ms\theta$.

30. $\tfrac{1}{2} mv^2 = ws\theta J;$ $74 \cdot 6$ m.p.h.

31. $mgh = ms\theta J;$ $3 \cdot 83$ kilometres.

32. Rate of working $= 0 \cdot 5$ h.p. $= 373$ watts $= 3 \cdot 73 \times 10^9$ ergs/sec. Heat required is $50 \times 1000 \times 80/2 \cdot 2;$ $5 \cdot 7$ hours nearly.

33. $I^2 R = m_1 s_1 10 = m_2 s_2 10;$ $0 \cdot 998$.

34. $0 \cdot 35$.

35. 96 cal./gm.

36. Let x be length of mercury column; then if whole length of tube is $x + 3l$, applying Boyle's law, if p_1 and p_2 are pressures in volumes above and below mercury respectively, $p_1 \times 9l/4 = 76 \times 2l;$ $p_2 \times 3l/4 = 76 \times l;$ $x = p_2 - p_1 = 33\tfrac{7}{9}$ cm.

37. If volume of vessel is V and volume of cylinder of pump is v, pressure at end of first stroke is given by $p_1(V + v) = pV$, while at end of second stroke $p_2(V + v) = p_1 V = pV^2/(V + v)$, or pressure at end of nth stroke is $p_n = p\{V/(V + v)\}^n;$ 86 strokes.

38. $T(p_1V_1/T_1 + p_2V_2/T_2 + p_3V_3/T_3)/V$.

39. $-54°$ C. approx.

40. 1·3 per cent; no.

41. Use $c_p - c_v = R/J$ and $pV = RT$; $4·3 \times 10^7$ ergs/cal.

42. Apply Boyle's law; 61 cm.

43. 389·5 mm. of mercury.

44. $1·07 \times 10^{-3}$ gm./c.c.

45. $p^{(1-\gamma)/\gamma}$. $T = $ constant; $465°$ C.

46. Work done is $W = (p_2V_2 - p_1V_1)/(\gamma - 1) = R(T_2 - T_1)/(\gamma - 1)$; 1328 cal.

47. $447°$ C.; 720 cal.

48. Work done is $W = RT \log_e v_2/v_1$; 499 cal.

49. $V = (3p/\rho)^{\frac{1}{2}}$; $1·84 \times 10^5$ cm./sec.

50. Yes; $(1200 + 273)^4/(525 + 273)^4$ is 11·7 approx.

PART III

LIGHT

CHAPTER I

Fundamental Properties of Light

1. Introduction.

The sensation of light is a primary sense perception, and vision is of more importance to physical investigation than any of the other senses. In addition to the **visible spectrum,** scientific work has shown the existence of "invisible light", for example in the **ultra-violet** and **infra-red** regions. In this book we shall discuss mainly the laws of light (and deductions from them) in the visible region, although some space will be devoted to the other regions which may be examined by such instruments as the photographic plate and the thermocouple.

2. Beam, Pencil and Ray.

Observation of such common phenomena as sunlight breaking through an opening in the clouds or light streaming through an open doorway at night leads to the conception of a **beam** of light as a shaft

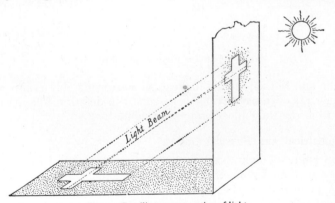

Fig. 1.—Rectilinear propagation of light

of illumination with a well-defined boundary as in fig. 1. If the source of light is very small, it is termed a **point-source.** A beam of light arising from a point-source S as in fig. 2 is usually referred to as a **pencil,** particularly if the angular divergence of the beam is small. In fact, the term beam is frequently restricted to mean a **parallel beam.** If the angular aperture of the pencil is extremely small, it is termed a **ray** of light. Theoretically a ray is conceived as a mathematical line, that is, an extension in one direction only, having no breadth or thickness, but such a phenomenon has no counterpart in

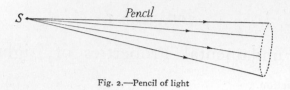

Fig. 2.—Pencil of light

the physical world. Indeed, if an attempt is made to limit a beam to such a mathematical ray, a remarkable phenomenon termed **diffraction** takes place. Thus, if the slit in fig. 3 is stopped down indefinitely, when the aperture becomes very small the light starts to spread out

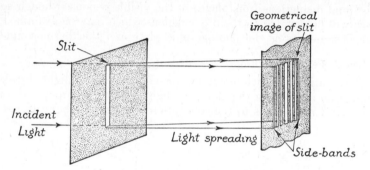

Fig. 3.—Passage of light through a narrow slit

to right and left of the slit instead of narrowing down into a finer and finer ray. This behaviour is discussed in detail in Chap. VII and arises from the wave-like character of light.

3. Geometrical and Physical Optics.

The study of light based upon the conceptions of beam, pencil and ray is termed **geometrical optics**. Phenomena such as diffraction or the photoelectric effect, involving the wave-theory or quantum theory of light, belong to the domain of **physical optics**. It is a general rule that if the objects or apertures which the light encounters are comparable in size with the wave-length of light, which is about 5×10^{-5} cm., geometrical optics becomes quite inapplicable. However, a great many optical phenomena and the working of most optical instruments are adequately explained on the principles of geometrical optics. The detailed and fuller explanation, however, requires the use of physical optics, and indeed the latter can explain all the phenomena dealt with by geometrical optics and many other phenomena which cannot be treated at all by geometrical optics. Unfortunately, the mathematical technique and physical conceptions necessary for treatment by physical optics are much more complicated than with geometrical optics, and therefore *in regions where the latter is adequate* treatment by geometrical optics is preferable.

4. Laws of Geometrical Optics.

The whole of geometrical optics is based on three general laws. These are:

(1) *Rectilinear propagation of light.*
(2) *Law of regular reflection.*
(3) *Law of regular refraction.*

We discuss laws (2) and (3) in detail in Chap. II and III, where we subdivide each of them into two laws. The first law given above simply states the observed fact that light travels in straight lines. The straight edges of a light beam afford crude evidence for this law.

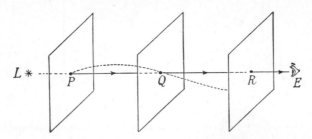

Fig. 4.—Rectilinear propagation of light

More scientific evidence is provided by some simple experiment such as that illustrated in fig. 4.

Three cards containing pinholes P, Q and R at equal heights from the bench are arranged vertically and a lamp L is placed in front of P. Observation with the eye at E shows that the lamp is visible only when P, Q and R are in the same straight line. Clearly, if light travelled in curved lines, it might be possible to displace one of the cards and still receive light at E if the ray would traverse a curved path such as that indicated by the dotted line in fig. 4. We must point out, however, that straight-line propagation occurs only if the medium through which the light is propagated is homogeneous. For example, if the medium between P and R consisted of material whose refractive index (see Chap. III) increased uniformly from P to R, an oblique ray from L would traverse a *curved* path between P and R. Indeed, in certain circumstances a ray of light through the earth's atmosphere is appreciably curved over large distances owing to the variation in density of the atmosphere with height (see Chap. X, Part I).

5. Pinhole Camera.

An interesting application of the rectilinear propagation of light is the pinhole camera. As shown in fig. 5, this consists of a light-tight box with a small pinhole in one side. Rays of light from some object such as AB proceed to the pinhole P and, continuing in straight lines, strike the far side of the box and give rise to a well-defined image of AB at B'A'. Actually B'A' consists of a large number of circular patches, the size of which depends on the size of the pinhole. The smaller the pinhole, within limits the sharper is the image B'A'.

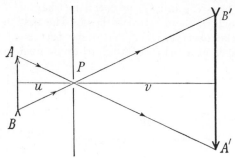

Fig. 5.—Pinhole camera

Owing to the failure of geometrical optics when the aperture becomes less than a fraction of a mm., the sharpness of the image cannot be improved indefinitely by reducing the size of the pinhole. We note that the image is *inverted* and that the linear magnification is given by v/u, where v and u are the distances of the image and object respectively from the pinhole. If a photographic plate is placed to receive the image, a permanent record may be obtained. Since good definition is produced only if the pinhole is small, the light intensity is very feeble and a long exposure is required. The pinhole camera is therefore not suitable for photographing moving objects. A slight modification of the pinhole camera forms the basis of similar instruments such as the **camera obscura** and the **camera lucida.**

6. Shadows.

The formation of shadows follows directly from the rectilinear propagation of light. As shown in fig. 6, no light rays can enter the region A'B', this region being defined by producing the straight lines SA and SB originating from the point-source at S, to cut the

receiving screen in A'B'. The shadow is clearly geometrically similar
to the object and the linear magnification is given by v/u, where v
and u are the distances of the shadow and the obstacle respectively
from the source.

If the source is of finite size, the shadow possesses a dense central

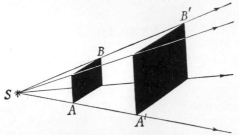

Fig. 6.—Formation of shadows

region, the **umbra,** surrounded by a less dense region, the **penumbra.**
No rays from any part of the source enter the umbra, but rays from
some parts of the source reach the penumbra. The general behaviour
is shown in fig. 7, where A'B' is the umbra and A"B" the penumbra.

Eclipses are due to the shadow of one celestial body falling across
another. An eclipse of the sun is due to the passage of the moon

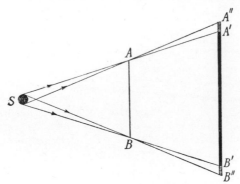

Fig. 7.—Umbra and penumbra

between the sun and the earth. Actually, the moon is of such a size
and at such a distance that the umbra which gives rise to a **total
eclipse** is only a very narrow band on the earth's surface. The penumbra
is, of course, wider and is responsible for the **partial eclipse** which is
visible over a wider area. A similar process leads to an eclipse of the
moon when the earth's shadow passes across the moon's surface owing
to the passage of the earth between the sun and the moon.

Very careful examination of the edges of shadows shows that some light does curve round behind the obstacle, in contradiction to the principles of geometrical optics. This phenomenon requires explanation in terms of physical optics such as that given in section 11, Chap. VII, on Diffraction at an Obstacle.

EXERCISES

1. Define the terms *beam*, *pencil* and *ray*, of light.

What are the conditions required for the treatment of a light problem according to the principles of geometrical optics?

2. Describe the pinhole camera. What are the height and breadth of the image of a rectangular poster 10 ft. high by 4 ft. wide, if the board is situated 30 ft. from the plate of a pinhole camera whose pinhole is 6 in. from the plate? [2 in. × 0·8 in.]

3. Explain the occurrence of eclipses.

A light source in the form of a disc of dia. 2 cm. is situated 20 cm. from a card of side 20 cm. Find the width of the umbra and penumbra formed on a screen at 20 cm. from the card, the whole system being coaxial with a line perpendicular to the plane of the source and passing through its centre. [38 cm.; 42 cm.]

CHAPTER II

Reflection

1. Laws of Regular Reflection.

These laws may be stated immediately as the reader will have no difficulty in understanding them from his ordinary everyday experience:

(a) *The incident ray, the normal to the tangent plane of the reflecting surface at the point of incidence, and the reflected ray all lie in the same plane.*

(b) *The angle of incidence equals the angle of reflection.*

The angles referred to in (b) are the angles between the rays and the normal.

One experimental proof of the second law consists in defining a ray by means of narrow obstacles such as pins in the manner shown in fig. 1. Viewed in the plane vertical mirror M down the line P_4, P_3, the pins P_2 and P_1 appear to be in a straight line P_4, P_3, P_2' and P_1', where P_2' and P_1' are the **images** of P_2 and P_1 in the plane mirror. Measurement of the angles of incidence and reflection shows that these are equal.

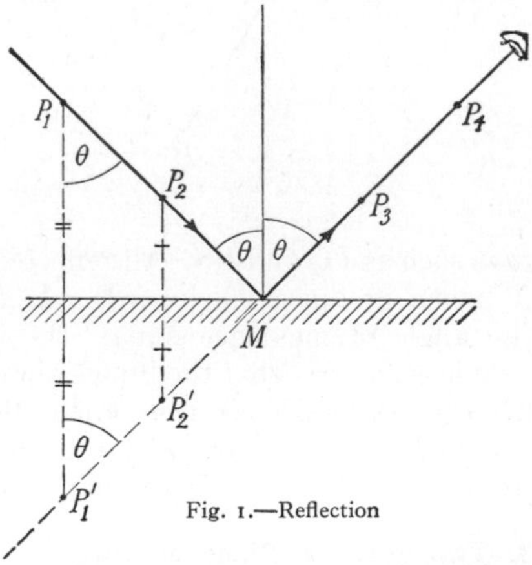

To demonstrate the validity of the first law, the ray defined by the pins P_1, P_2 may be replaced by a bright ray defined by slits. If the point of incidence on the mirror is viewed

Fig. 1.—Reflection

from different directions, the reflected ray will be observed only when incident ray, reflected ray and normal all lie in one common plane.

In practice it is impossible to obtain a surface which is mathematically plane and smooth. The truth of a surface is obtained by continual mechanical working of the surface and testing with an optical flat (see Chap. VII). Smoothness is produced by polishing.

Owing to the absence of perfect truth and polish, a certain amount of *random* or *diffuse reflection* accompanies all *regular* or *specular reflection*.

2. Images.

We define an image as a portion of space through which several of the rays arising from an object pass or appear to pass. If the rays actually pass through the image, the latter is said to be **real**; if the rays only appear to pass through the image, the latter is said to be **virtual**.

In fig. 2, A′B′ is the image of the arrow AB reflected in the plane mirror M; A′B′ arises from the continuation backwards of numerous

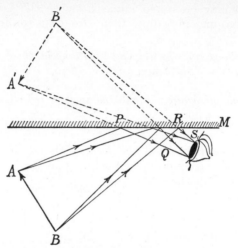

Fig. 2.—Image by reflection

rays such as PQ and RS. All reflected rays coming from A pass through A′ when produced backwards. It follows from the law stating that the angle of incidence equals the angle of reflection, together with simple geometry, that the image obtained in a plane mirror is (i) virtual, (ii) the same size as the object (unit magnification), (iii) laterally reversed, (iv) situated as far behind the mirror as the object is in front of it. The proofs are left as exercises to the reader.

3. Two or More Plane Mirrors.

If two or more plane mirrors are present, the total number of images observed depends on (i) the angle θ between the two mirrors, (ii) the position of the observer. The following construction, which is carried out in fig. 3 for the special case where $\theta = 60°$, illustrates a working rule based on the laws of reflection, for finding the number and position of the images formed by inclined mirrors.

A circle is drawn with its centre at the point of intersection O of the two mirrors and radius equal to the distance from this point to the object P. Let OP make angles α and β with the two mirrors ($\alpha + \beta = \theta$). Construction of images will show that they lie at points on the circle such that the angles subtended at O by the arcs between successive images are alternately 2α and 2β. Hence if $(n - 1)$ images are formed, taking account also of the object,

$$n(\alpha + \beta) = n\theta = 360°. \quad . \quad . \quad . \quad . \quad (2.1)$$

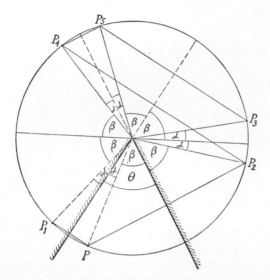

Fig. 3.—Multiple reflection

If the rays are carefully traced out, it will be found that images continue to be formed until the last images are formed behind the reflecting surfaces of both mirrors. If $360/\theta$ is integral, the final images formed in both mirrors coincide and the number of images viewed by an observer is independent of his position. If $360/\theta$ is not integral, these final images do not coincide and their appearance depends on the position of the observer, some portion of an image being usually observed.

For the special case where $\theta = 0$ and the mirrors are parallel, the number of images becomes infinite. Experimentally, a very large number of images is observed, but these rapidly become fainter owing to imperfection in the mirrors (diffuse reflection) and absorption of light in the material of the mirrors.

4. Rotating Plane Mirror.

Consideration of the geometry of fig. 4 shows that when the mirror M rotates through an angle α to the position M' the reflected ray turns through an angle 2α. Thus

$$\alpha = \phi - \theta, \quad \beta = \phi - \theta + \alpha, \quad \text{hence} \quad \beta = 2\alpha.$$

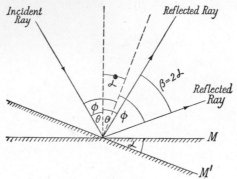

Fig. 4.—Rotating plane mirror

Such considerations are involved in the sextant, which is described under Optical Instruments in Chap. XI.

5. Reflection at Curved Surfaces.

A surface may be considered as consisting of an infinite number of infinitely small portions of the tangent planes to the surface. The reflection of light at curved surfaces is therefore completely determined by the laws for plane surfaces. In general we shall be con-

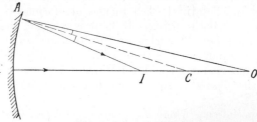

Fig. 5.—Spherical mirror

cerned with reflecting surfaces which are portions of cylinders or spheres. For spheres the normal to the surface is the radius, and the centre, or **centre of curvature,** is a point of fundamental importance. In fig. 5 we represent the centre of curvature of the spherical mirror by C; then a ray of light originating from the point O on the **principal axis** is reflected from a point A on the surface to cross the axis at I, where by the laws of reflection $\angle OAC = \angle CAI$. Now the ray arising from O which travels along the principal axis is reflected back again normally from the **pole** P of the mirror. Hence at least two of the rays arising from O come to-gether again at I, and geo-metrical construction will show that, if the **aperture** (twice PA) is small, all the *paraxial rays* (i.e. rays inclined at a small angle to the axis) reflected by the surface cross at a small region in the neighbourhood of I. This point is therefore termed the image of O in the mirror. If the aperture is large, the reflected rays will be found to cross over a con-siderable region and no well-

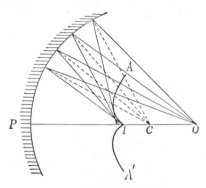

Fig. 6.—Caustic by reflection

defined image is formed of the object at O. The appearance is then as in fig. 6, and the vague image shown by the cusped curve is referred to as a **caustic curve**. In practice optical instruments are almost invariably constructed to have small aperture. In this con-dition certain useful algebraic laws may be derived connecting the size of the image, and its position with respect to the reflecting surface, with the size and position of the object.

6. Sign Conventions.

Before obtaining the algebraic relations desired we must make certain conventions concerning the sign to be attributed to the quan-tities considered. There are several systems of sign convention avail-able, and at present there is no unanimity among authorities as to which is the best. We adopt the following convention. Consider light incident from the right on to the reflecting surface; distances measured from that surface to the left are negative, those to the right are positive. For example, in fig. 5 the object distance PO is positive and the image distance PI is positive. This convention gives, as we shall see, a positive focal length to a concave mirror but a negative focal length to a convex lens, both of which are generally used as converging systems. Practising opticians usually prefer to refer to all converging systems as positive and diverging systems as negative. Care must therefore be taken in interpreting different work in geo-metrical optics, and the student is advised always to draw a rough sketch of the passage of the rays so that possible errors may be avoided.

11   (H 394)

7. Reflection at a Concave Spherical Surface.

From the geometry of the triangles CAO, IAO in fig. 7,

$$\left. \begin{array}{l} \beta = a + i, \\ \gamma = a + 2i. \\ a + \gamma = 2\beta. \end{array} \right\} \quad \cdots \cdots \cdots \quad (2.2)$$

Hence

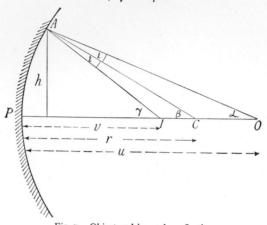

Fig. 7.—Object and image by reflection

Since the aperture is small, we may write approximately $a = h/u$, $\beta = h/r$ and $\gamma = h/v$, where u and v are the distances of object and image from the mirror, and r is its radius of curvature. (In fig. 7, v,

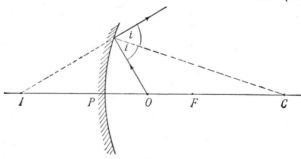

Fig. 8.—Virtual image

r, u are PI, PC, PO respectively.) Therefore, from the last of equations (2.2),

$$\frac{1}{v} + \frac{1}{u} = \frac{2}{r}. \quad \cdots \cdots \cdots \quad (2.3)$$

If $u = \infty$, $v = r/2$; hence a paraxial beam parallel to the axis is reflected to a single point on the axis midway between the centre of curvature and the pole of the mirror. This point is said to be the **focus** of the mirror, and the length PF is termed its **focal length** f. Equation (2.3) may therefore be written

$$\frac{1}{v} + \frac{1}{u} = \frac{1}{f}. \quad \cdot \cdot \cdot \cdot \cdot \cdot \quad (2.4)$$

If $u > f$, equation (2.4) shows that v is always positive, but if $u < f$, v becomes negative. Construction shows that the situation is now as represented in fig. 8. The image is a virtual one, formed by producing the reflected rays back on to the axis at I. The distance PI is now measured to the left, and hence is negative in agreement with our sign convention.

8. Object of Finite Extent.

The object at O has hitherto been considered as a point. We must now consider the image of an object of small but finite extension. Extension perpendicular to the axis is referred to as *lateral extension*, that along the axis is *longitudinal extension*. We shall concentrate on the effect of lateral extension. The general method of attack is graphical; various rays are considered to arise from the object and their path is traced before and after reflection from the mirror.

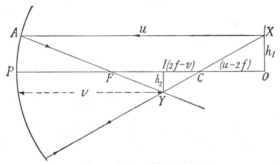

Fig. 9.—Image of finite object

Two simple rules for fixing the position of the image are available. These are:

(1) Trace a ray arising from the extremity of the object and passing through the centre of curvature of the mirror; this ray will return along its original path, since it meets the mirror normally.

(2) Trace a ray arising from the object and travelling parallel to the axis. After reflection this ray must pass through the focus.

The intersection of these two rays suffices to fix the size and position of the image.

Consideration of fig. 9 shows that an image IY is produced, similar to the object OX. Further, since the triangles COX, CIY are similar,

$$\frac{h_2}{h_1} = \frac{2f - v}{u - 2f} = \frac{v}{u} \quad \ldots \ldots \quad (2.5)$$

from equation (2.4).

The ratio (h_2/h_1) of the lateral extension of the image to that of the object is termed the **magnification** of the optical system. A positive magnification follows from our sign convention when the image is real and a negative magnification when it is virtual.

9. Reflection from a Convex Spherical Surface.

If the reflecting surface is convex to the object, the formation of an image occurs as in fig. 10. From the geometry we have

and

whence

$$\left.\begin{array}{l} 2i = \gamma + \alpha \\ i = \beta + \alpha, \\ 2\beta + \alpha = \gamma \end{array}\right\} \quad \ldots \ldots \quad (2.6)$$

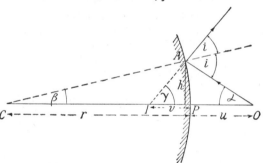

Fig. 10.—Reflection from convex surface

Since PC and PI are here measured to the left, r and v are negative, and $\alpha = h/u$, $\beta = -h/r$ and $\gamma = -h/v$; hence, from equations (2.6),

$$\frac{1}{v} + \frac{1}{u} = \frac{2}{r}. \quad \ldots \ldots \quad (2.7)$$

Again, if $u = \infty$, $v = f = 2/r$, and from our sign convention, since r is negative, f is negative, Equation (2.7) becomes

$$\frac{1}{v} + \frac{1}{u} = \frac{1}{f}, \quad \ldots \ldots \quad (2.8)$$

whence v is always negative. The image is therefore always virtual, and since v is always numerically less than u, the magnification is always less than unity. Note that equations (2.7), (2.8) are the same as (2.3), (2.4).

Construction shows that the images formed in a convex mirror are always upright, whereas those formed in a concave mirror are upright when the object is inside the focus but inverted when it is outside the focus. Further, the magnification in a concave mirror is less than unity when the object is outside the centre of curvature and greater than unity when it is inside this position. For the special case where $u = r$, reflection in a concave mirror gives $v = r$; hence the image is formed coincident with the object and the magnification is unity. The positions of object and image in an optical system are clearly interchangeable and are termed **conjugate points**. The point at which object and image coincide is termed a *self-conjugate point*.

10. Applications of Reflections at Curved Surfaces.

If an object is placed at the focus of a spherical concave mirror of small aperture, then either by construction or from equation (2.4) we see that $v = \infty$. This implies that the rays of light from the object

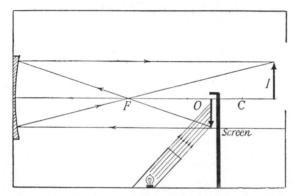

Fig. 11.—Pepper's ghost

will form a parallel beam after reflection in the mirror. The restriction to small aperture is often not practicable experimentally, as for example with motor-car headlights or the searchlight. For such problems a specially worked reflecting surface is required; this surface is parabolic since the parabola possesses the property that the normal at any point makes equal angles with a line parallel to the axis and one joining the point to the focus. Such a parabolic mirror is also used in wireless " beam " transmission, the transmitting aerial being placed at the focus.

" Shaving mirrors " are sometimes made in the form of concave mirrors of fairly large radius of curvature. Under these conditions the face of the shaver is generally situated inside the focus and a magnified, upright virtual image is observed. On the other hand, when it is required to compress a large field of view into a relatively small space a convex mirror is used. Common examples of this are the driving mirrors attached to automobiles. The famous **Pepper's ghost** is produced by placing the object O in an inverted position inside the centre of curvature but outside the focus of a concave mirror, as in fig. 11. To prevent aberrations the mirror must be of large aperture and consequently of large radius of curvature. It is placed at the end of a darkened room and a direct view of the object is prevented by screening. When the eye is close to the axis, a real image is observed at I which vanishes when the observer views the mirror from one side.

Curved mirrors often form part of more complicated apparatus; one important case is the construction of reflecting telescopes described in Chap. XI. Again, to avoid the absorption of ultra-violet and infra-red rays by glass, the lenses of some spectrometers are often replaced by mirrors, as mentioned in Chap. X.

EXERCISES

1. State the laws of reflection of light and describe how you would illustrate them experimentally.

2. Deduce the relation connecting the distance of the image from a spherical concave mirror, the distance of the object from the mirror, and the radius of curvature.

Find the radius of curvature of a mirror which gives a magnification of 2 for objects placed 20 cm. from the mirror. $\left[\dfrac{80}{3} \text{ cm.}\right]$

3. Why is the magnification produced by a convex spherical mirror always less than unity, whereas that due to a concave mirror may have any value? To what practical purposes are such mirrors put?

CHAPTER III

Refraction

1. Definition.

If a ray of light passes obliquely from one medium to another, then in general the direction of the ray is deviated at the junction of the media. This bending process is termed **refraction** and, as we shall see later in Chap. IX, is due to the change in the velocity of the light wave on passing from one medium to another.

2. Laws of Refraction.

As with reflection, there are two basic laws of refraction. These are:

(a) *The incident ray, the normal to the tangent plane of the refracting surface at the point of incidence, and the refracted ray all lie in the same plane.*

(b) *The ratio of the sine of the angle of incidence to the sine of the angle of refraction is constant for two given media, and is termed their mutual refractive index.*

The first law may be demonstrated as for reflection, that is, by trial, and observation that a coplanar refracted ray alone is formed. Of course, in practice, in the same way that a small percentage of *diffuse reflection* may accompany regular reflection, so a certain amount of *random deviation* sometimes accompanies normal refraction.

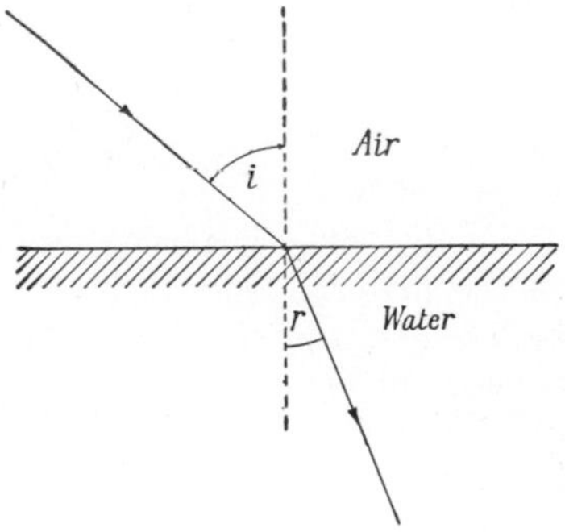

As shown in fig. 1, the ray in passing from air to water is refracted towards the normal. Water is, of course, hydrostatically denser than

Fig. 1.—Angles of incidence and refraction

air, and this idea of density has been transferred to optics, the optical density of a substance being defined as proportional to its refractive index. Thus, it is a general rule that *when rays pass from optically less dense to optically denser media, they are bent towards the normal.* Since

315

light rays are reversible, when rays pass from denser to less dense media they are refracted away from the normal. Materials which have large hydrostatic density do not necessarily have a high optical density. For example, carbon tetrachloride with density 1·6 has a refractive index of 1·46, whereas carbon bisulphide with a density of only 1·3 has a refractive index as high as 1·63. Optical density is correlated with many other optical phenomena; in particular the velocity of light in the medium is inversely proportional to its optical density.

The second law of refraction, usually stated in the form

$$\mu = \frac{\sin i}{\sin r}, \qquad \cdots \cdots \quad (3.1)$$

where μ represents the refractive index, may be proved in many ways, as the student will find by reference to a textbook of Practical Physics.

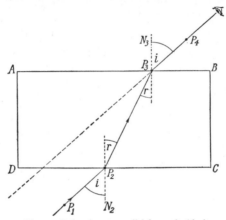

Fig. 2.—Refraction at parallel faces of a block

The value of μ is always understood to refer to refraction from air to the material under consideration. If the material is solid, it may be used in the form of parallel-sided slabs, prisms, or bodies with curved surfaces. All these variations provide a great many methods of finding the refractive index, and the simple method we give now is just to illustrate the idea and is by no means the best in practice.

As shown in fig. 2, let pins P_1, P_2 define a ray, incident upon a parallel-sided block of glass ABCD; the direction of the emergent ray appears to lie along the direction fixed by two more pins P_3, P_4. Construction of the normals N_2P_2, N_3P_3 and joining P_2P_3 allows the values of i and r to be measured, and hence a value of $\mu = \sin i/\sin r$ to be calculated. Repetition of the experiment with different values of i and r confirms the law that μ is constant.

This law was originally deduced by Snell in 1621. Although values of i and r had been tabulated by Ptolemy about A.D. 500, no simple connexion was deduced between the two angles until Snell's law was established. As we have indicated in Chap. I, practically the whole of geometrical optics consists in the elaboration of the laws of reflection and refraction with the aid of mathematical technique. Examples of this are given in the numerical examples set at the end of each chapter and at the end of this book, and consequently we shall not attempt to treat a great number of special instances in the general text. The best examples are those afforded by the construction of optical instruments, an account of which is given in Chap. XI. One simple but important point which emerges from fig. 2 is that a ray of light emerges parallel to its original direction, but suffers a lateral displacement, after oblique refraction through a parallel-sided block. Again, if several parallel layers of different materials are superposed, it may easily be shown that

$$\mu_{1,n} = \mu_{1,2} \times \mu_{2,3} \times \ldots \times \mu_{n-1,n}, \quad \ldots \quad (3.2)$$

where $\mu_{1,n}$ refers to the refractive index between materials 1 and n, $\mu_{1,2}$ to the refractive index between materials 1 and 2, and so on. Hence, if μ_1 and μ_2 be the refractive indices of two substances with respect to air, their mutual refractive index is μ_2/μ_1.

3. Apparent Depth.

If we consider the behaviour of rays of light passing from a spot P on the lower surface of a parallel-sided block, we observe that rays such as PA and PB in fig. 3, on emergence into the air, are refracted away from the normal. To an eye receiving the rays, these rays appear to arise from an object situated at P'. Consideration of the geometry shows that

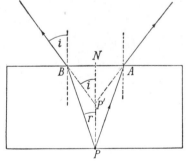

$$\frac{\sin i}{\sin r} = \frac{NB}{P'B} \Big/ \frac{NB}{PB} = \frac{PB}{P'B}.$$

Now, if the angles are small or observations are restricted to *small*

aperture, $\dfrac{PB}{P'B} = \dfrac{PN}{P'N}$. Also, since

Fig. 3.—Apparent depth

$\dfrac{\sin i}{\sin r} = \mu$, the real thickness of the block is greater than its apparent thickness according to the relation

$$PN = \mu P'N. \quad \ldots \ldots \quad (3.3)$$

This phenomenon affords a convenient method of finding refractive indices. For example, a spot on a flat piece of paper is focused by a vertical travelling microscope fitted with a vertical scale. On interposing a block of material of known thickness PN, it is found necessary to rack up the microscope a measured distance d, where clearly

$$d = PN - P'N.$$

Hence $P'N$ is calculated and the value of μ deduced.

In fig. 4 are drawn the refracted rays responsible for giving a stick the familiar bent appearance which it exhibits on partial immersion in water. Each portion of the immersed stick suffers apparent upward displacement proportional to its depth below the surface. Throughout problems of this nature, and in many other special phenomena,

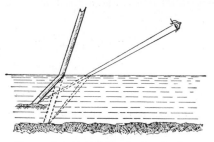

Fig. 4.—Apparent bending due to refraction

the student must bear in mind that simple mathematical treatments are possible only with restricted aperture. The apparent depth of a partially immersed stick varies with the direction of observation, and simple mathematical relations will exist only when the observation is restricted to a small cone around the vertical.

4. Total Internal Reflection and Critical Angle.

Consideration of Snell's law shows us that if light is passing from a denser to a less dense medium, there is a maximum value of r (the angle which the ray makes with the normal in the *denser* medium), since $\sin i$ cannot be greater than unity. The value of r for the condition $\sin i = 1$ and $i = 90°$ is usually denoted by C, and is termed the **critical angle.** From Snell's law,

$$\sin C = 1/\mu, \quad \dots \dots \quad (3.4)$$

which corresponds to a value of C of about 40° for ordinary crown glass. This mathematical consequence of Snell's law is accompanied by the physical phenomenon of **total internal reflection.** For angles of refraction greater than C, the light is specularly reflected at the interface between the two media. The general behaviour is shown

in fig. 5. The experimental measurement of the critical angle affords
a convenient method of determining the refractive index of substances.
A good example is the Pulfrich refractometer described in Chap. XI.

The existence of desert mirages is due to total internal reflection.
Light rays from above encounter layers of air which become less and

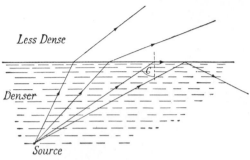

Less Dense

Denser

Source

Fig. 5.—Critical angle

less dense as the surface of the hot sand is approached. The ray of
light is therefore passing through a region of continuously diminish-
ing refractive index, and it is ultimately bent round as shown in
fig. 6. To an observer, the image of a cloud appears to be at ground
level; owing to the continuous fluctuation in refractive index due to

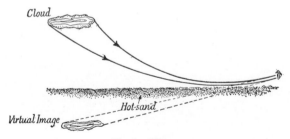

Cloud

Hot-sand

Virtual Image

Fig. 6.—Mirage

moving air currents of differing density, the illusion of rippling water
is easily produced.

5. Refraction through a Prism.

The standard method for finding the refractive indices of materials
is by refraction through a triangular prism under certain conditions.
Consider a ray of light PQ incident upon a triangular prism as shown
in fig. 7. Let the refracted ray be QR and the final emergent ray be
RS; the **refracting angle** of the prism is denoted by A. We denote
the angles of incidence and refraction at Q and R by (i, r) and (i', r')

respectively. The normals to the refracting surface at Q and R are represented by MQ and NR, and these when produced meet in O. Then, from the geometry, for the sum of the angles of the triangle BQR

$$A + (90 - r) + (90 - r') = 180°,$$

or
$$A = (r + r'). \qquad \ldots \ldots \quad (3.5)$$

Finally, from the triangle DQR, the **angle of deviation** of the ray PQ in its passage through the prism, which is also the exterior angle δ of the triangle DQR, is given by

$$\delta = (i - r) + (i' - r') = (i + i') - (r + r') \quad . \quad (3.6)$$

Hence, from (3.5) and (3.6),

$$i + i' = \delta + A. \qquad \ldots \ldots \ldots \quad (3.7)$$

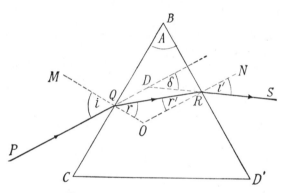

Fig. 7.—Unsymmetric Refraction through a prism

Now, by Snell's law,

$$\mu = \frac{\sin i}{\sin r} = \frac{\sin i'}{\sin r'}. \qquad \ldots \ldots \quad (3.8)$$

The case of particular importance is that in which δ is a minimum. We show later that this condition of **minimum deviation** occurs when the refraction is symmetrical, so that $i = i'$ and $r = r'$. Under these conditions, equations (3.5) and (3.7) reduce to

$$A = 2r, \qquad \ldots \ldots \ldots \quad (3.9)$$

and
$$\delta + A = 2i. \qquad \ldots \ldots \ldots \quad (3.10)$$

Hence
$$\mu = \frac{\sin i}{\sin r} = \frac{\sin\left(\dfrac{\delta + A}{2}\right)}{\sin \dfrac{A}{2}}. \qquad \ldots \ldots \quad (3.11)$$

This expression is exact and forms the basis of the spectrometer method for determining the refractive indices of materials, for which reference should be made to Chap. XI.

Prisms of small angle are used by opticians to correct muscular imbalance of the eye (see Chap. XI). If A is small, δ is small, and equation (3.11) becomes approximately

$$\mu = \frac{\delta + A}{A},$$

where we have written the angles in place of the sines.

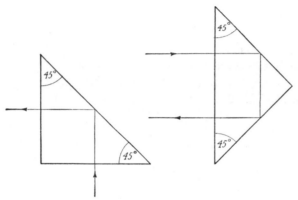

Fig. 8.—Totally reflecting prisms

The above expression is usually written

$$A(\mu - 1) = \delta, \quad \ldots \ldots \quad (3.12)$$

so that the angle of deviation produced by ordinary glass with refractive index about 1·5 is approximately half the refracting angle of the prism.

Prisms have many interesting uses in optical instruments, total internal reflection often playing an important part in the process. Since the critical angle for glass is less than 45°, right-angle prisms may be used to reflect light through 90° or 180° as shown in figs. 8(a) and 8(b).

To show that minimum deviation must occur when the rays are symmetrical and parallel to the base inside the prism, consider the ray PQRS in fig. 9, when QR is not parallel to the base. The corresponding ray P'Q'R'S' clearly suffers the same deviation, so that two rays P'Q' and SR incident from the right suffer the same deviation, and hence this deviation cannot be unique, that is, cannot have an extreme value such as constitutes a minimum. A unique value will occur only when these two rays coincide, that is, when PQ and RS are equally inclined to the prism and QR is parallel to the base.

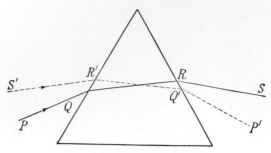

Fig. 9.—Equal deviations by prism

6. Refraction at Curved Surfaces.

Just as reflection at curved surfaces produces images, so does refraction. In fig. 10, let O be an object situated on the axis of the spherical refracting surface, concave to O, whose centre of curvature is at C. After refraction at A, the ray OA is bent towards the normal CA. This refracted ray, when produced backwards, cuts the principal

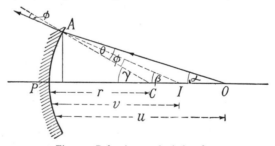

Fig. 10.—Refraction at spherical surface

axis at I. As for curved reflecting surfaces, if the aperture is small, construction of several rays gives a definite image of O situated at I. We require an algebraic relation connecting the object distance $PO = u$, with the image distance $PI = v$, the radius of curvature of the surface $PC = r$ and the refractive index μ. From the geometry

$$\gamma = \beta + \phi,$$
$$\beta = (\theta - \phi) + \alpha. \qquad \qquad \text{. (3.13)}$$

Also, $\sin\theta/\sin\phi = \mu$, $\gamma = h/r$, $\beta = h/v$ and $\alpha = h/u$.

We use, of course, the same convention regarding signs as in the previous work on reflection, namely, all distances measured to the

right from the refracting surface are positive, all those to the left are
negative. Since the aperture is to be small, θ and ϕ are small, and we
introduce the approximations $\sin \theta = \theta$ and $\sin \phi = \phi$, whence Snell's
law becomes $\theta = \mu\phi$. Substituting for θ in (3.13) and eliminating ϕ,
we obtain

$$\frac{\mu}{v} - \frac{1}{u} = \frac{(\mu - 1)}{r}. \quad \cdots \cdots \quad (3.14)$$

The algebraic relation for refraction at a convex surface is identical with (3.14) and is left as an exercise to the reader. [Hint: re-
member r, and possibly v, will be negative and proceed by analogy
with reflection at a convex surface.]

7. Thin Lenses.

A lens is defined as a portion of a refracting medium bounded
by two surfaces at least one of which is curved. If the lens is of appreciable thickness, the treatment is more complicated and we defer
it until the next chapter. For many purposes, however, the lens is

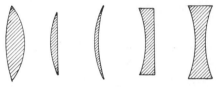

Fig. 11.—Lenses

sufficiently thin for approximate considerations to be valid. In fig.
11 are shown respectively examples of double-convex, plano-convex,
concavo-convex or meniscus, plano-concave, and double-concave
spherical lenses. Those which are thicker at the centre than at the
periphery are termed **converging** lenses, and those which are the reverse
are **diverging lenses.**

We require an algebraic relation connecting the distance u of an
object on the axis of the lens, with the distance v of the image, the
radii of curvature r_1, r_2 of the two surfaces, and the refractive index μ
of the material of the lens. Since the lens is thin, we neglect the deviation of the rays inside the lens and consider the deviation as occurring
at two surfaces almost coincident in position. The first refraction, by
equation (3.14), would produce an image at v', given by

$$\frac{\mu}{v'} - \frac{1}{u} = \frac{(\mu - 1)}{r_1}. \quad \cdots \cdots \quad (3.15)$$

This image distance v' is the *effective object distance* for the second
refraction; hence we put v' for u in the formula for refraction at the

second surface. We must also replace μ by $1/\mu$, since refraction is
now from denser to less dense medium. Hence we obtain

$$\frac{1/\mu}{v} - \frac{1}{v'} = \frac{(1/\mu - 1)}{r_2}, \quad \dots \quad (3.16)$$

and from equations (3.15) and (3.16) we obtain

$$\frac{1}{v} - \frac{1}{u} = (\mu - 1)\left(\frac{1}{r_1} - \frac{1}{r_2}\right). \quad \dots \quad (3.17)$$

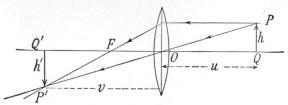

Fig. 12.—Path of the rays for a converging lens

We note that in the double-convex lens r_1 and r_2 are of opposite sign,
so that the right-hand side does not reduce to zero for an equi-convex
lens.

If $u = \infty$, $\dfrac{1}{v} = (\mu - 1)\left(\dfrac{1}{r_1} - \dfrac{1}{r_2}\right)$, which is constant for a given lens.

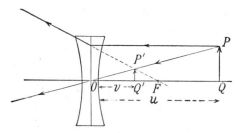

Fig. 13.—Path of the rays for a diverging lens

This expression is termed the **focal length** f of the lens, and hence

$$\frac{1}{v} - \frac{1}{u} = \frac{1}{f}. \quad \dots \dots \quad (3.18)$$

The focus is, as with reflection, the point at which all paraxial rays
parallel to the axis cross it after traversing the lens. The focal length is
negative for a converging and positive for a diverging lens on our
convention. The simple relation obtained in equation (3.18) allows us
to regard the action of a lens as a sudden refraction at a plane passing
through the centre of the lens, as shown in figs. 12 and 13. We

proceed to use the construction shown in these figures to determine the magnification of an object of finite size situated on the axis. The construction is based on the two facts:

(i) A ray arising from the object, and passing parallel to the axis, after refraction passes through the focus.

(ii) A ray passing through the centre (termed the **optical centre**) of the lens continues its path without deviation.

From the similar triangles PQO and P′Q′O in figs. 12 and 13, the *magnification*, or ratio of the height h' of the image to that of the object h, is

$$\frac{h'}{h} = \frac{v}{u}. \qquad \cdots \cdots \cdots \quad (3.19)$$

The magnification relation is therefore the same as for *reflection* at curved surfaces. With a diverging lens the image is always virtual, upright and diminished (cf. a *convex mirror*). With a converging lens the image is real, inverted and diminished for objects situated more than twice the focal length from the lens; real, inverted and magnified for objects situated between f and $2f$ from the lens; and virtual, upright and magnified for objects placed inside the focus. The last named constitutes the simple magnifying glass described on p. 410.

8. Two Thin Lenses in Contact.

The total focal length of two thin lenses in contact is calculated by considering the image formed by the first lens as the effective object for the second lens. Thus for a parallel incident beam, the first image is formed at the focus of the first lens. Hence the position of the final image, which by definition must lie at the focus of the combination, is given from (3.18), if f_1, f_2 are the focal lengths of the first and second lens, by

$$\frac{1}{F} - \frac{1}{f_1} = \frac{1}{f_2}.$$

Hence

$$\frac{1}{F} = \frac{1}{f_1} + \frac{1}{f_2}. \qquad \cdots \cdots \cdots \quad (3.20)$$

To avoid reciprocal relations, opticians normally use **powers** of lenses instead of focal lengths. The power of a lens in **diopters** is defined as the reciprocal of its focal length in metres. The total power of two or more lenses in contact is therefore by equation (3.20) the algebraic sum of the individual powers.

In the next chapter we deduce an expression for the effective focal length of combinations of lenses when they are not in contact. For two lenses, the algebraic expression is

$$\frac{1}{F} = \frac{1}{f_1} + \frac{1}{f_2} + \frac{d}{f_1 f_2}, \quad \ldots \ldots (3.21)$$

where d is the separation of the individual lenses. We may note, however, that at this stage this expression has no definite meaning for us, since we do not know from what point F is to be measured. Actually we have to define the *principal planes of a coaxial system* (opposite) before we can become clear on this point.

EXERCISES

1. State the laws of refraction and describe experiments which illustrate these laws.

2. Show that the floor of a swimming bath appears concave upwards to an observer from outside and that the ceiling of the swimming bath also appears concave upwards to an observer under water.

3. What is meant by the terms (a) *total internal reflection*, (b) *critical angle*? How do you explain the existence of desert mirages?

4. Show that the rays of light are parallel to the base inside a prism set for minimum deviation. If a ray is undergoing minimum deviation when incident upon a prism of refractive index 1·58 and vertical angle 45°, calculate the deviation produced. [29·4°.]

5. A sphere of glass of refractive index 1·50 has a small air-bubble 5 cm. from the surface. If the radius of the sphere is 15 cm., find the apparent position of the bubble when it is viewed through the glass at the point on the surface closest to the bubble. [3·75 cm. from sphere.]

6. Obtain an expression for the distance of the image from a lens in terms of the distance of the object from the lens, the radii of curvature of its faces and the refractive index of the material of the lens. Does an ordinary curved watch-glass behave as a lens?

7. The radii of curvature of the faces of a thin converging lens are 20 cm. and 40 cm., and the refractive index of the glass is 1·5. Find the focal length, (a) if the lens is double-convex, (b) if it is concavo-convex. [(a) $f = -26\frac{2}{3}$ cm.; (b) $f = -80$ cm.]

8. For each of the lenses of question 7, find the position and nature of the image, and the magnification, if the object in each case is 60 cm. from the lens. [(a) $v = -48$ cm., image real, magnification $\frac{4}{5}$; (b) $v = +240$ cm., image virtual, magnification 4.]

9. Define (a) the diopter, (b) the focus of a lens.

Deduce an expression for the combined focal length of two thin lenses in contact.

CHAPTER IV

Coaxial Optical Systems and Thick Lenses

*1. Fundamental Rules.

In view of the impossibility of defining a single effective plane at which refraction can be considered to take place when the lens is of appreciable thickness, or when the refracting system consists of a number of separate lenses, our approximate treatment for thin lenses must be modified for these cases. A complete discussion of the theory involved would carry us beyond the scope of this book, and we therefore content ourselves with the following rules, which are sufficient to solve most practical problems under consideration.

(1) The single effective refracting plane of a thin lens must be replaced by two refracting or **principal planes** with properties shown

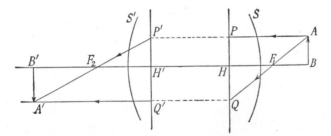

Fig. 1.—Principal planes and focal points

diagrammatically in fig. 1. These planes, represented by H, H', may lie completely inside, completely outside, or one inside and one outside the actual physical refracting surfaces, for example S, S', according to the nature of the lens system.

(2) The **focal points** and the **focal planes** at F_1 and F_2 are simply defined as the points or planes at which light initially parallel to the axis is focussed after traversing the system.

(3) The **nodal points** and **nodal planes**, which are the remaining two out of the **six cardinal points** or **planes** of an optical system, may best be understood by reference to fig. 2. It is found in practice that a certain ray RN gives rise to a parallel emergent ray N'R' after passage through the optical system. The points at which these conjugate,

parallel rays cross the principal axis are termed the nodal points, and the planes erected perpendicular to the axis at these points, the nodal planes.

(4) The construction for finding the position and size of an object AB in fig. 1, situated perpendicular to the axis, is as follows. Draw a ray AP parallel to the axis to meet the first principal plane H in P. Assume that the complete refraction occurs at the second principal plane at a point P′ where P′H′ = PH. (Owing to this equivalence property, the principal planes and points are sometimes termed the **unit-planes** or **points,** since the magnification is effectively unity for these points after the rays have traversed the optical system.) The emergent ray must therefore be represented by P′F$_2$, for we know that a ray parallel to the axis and incident from the right traverses the focus F$_2$ after refraction.

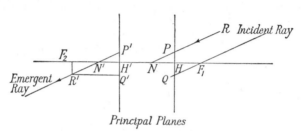

Fig. 2.—Nodal points (N and N′)

A similar complementary process is now carried out with the ray AF$_1$Q. This ray is assumed to experience all its refraction at the *first* principal plane. Since it has passed through the first focus it must emerge eventually parallel to the axis. By analogy with our previous construction this ray emerges from the second principal plane at Q′ where H′Q′ = HQ. The point of intersection of the rays P′F$_2$A′ and Q′A′ fixes the position of A′ and consequently the position and size of the image A′B′ of the object AB.

(5) The focal lengths of a system are defined as the distances HF$_1$, H′F$_2$ respectively. These two focal lengths are (numerically) the same only when the media in the **object space** and the **image space** are the same. Thus the focal lengths of a single curved refracting surface are different according as the object is situated in the denser or less dense medium. If, as is usually the case with lenses and lens combinations, both object and image are situated in air, the two focal lengths are numerically the same, but of opposite signs. Finally, for a thin lens, the two principal planes also coincide in a single principal plane.

* 2. Experimental Determination of Focal Length.

(i) **Newton's Method.**

To clarify our ideas we now proceed to develop a method for finding the focal length of a thick lens or lens combination. A parallel
beam of light is sent through the system from the right, and the point
where this crosses the axis can be found experimentally and fixes the
position of F_2. By repeating the process in the reverse direction the
position of F_1 is obtained. It is no use measuring the distance from
F_2 or F_1 to the physical refracting surfaces of the system in an en-
deavour to find the focal lengths, since the latter are defined as the distances to F_2 and F_1 from H' and H, the two principal points, the
position of neither of which is yet known. Our main problem is therefore to locate these planes, and we do this indirectly in the following
way, which is known as *Newton's method*. With reference to fig. 3, an

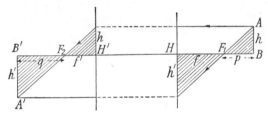

Fig. 3.—Newton's method for focal length

object such as a pin is erected at AB, the distance $F_1B = p$ being
measured. The image A'B' of AB is then located and the distance
$B'F_2 = q$ is measured. Let the heights of AB and A'B' be h and h'
respectively. Then from the similar triangles in fig. 3 (ignoring signs)

$$\frac{h'}{f} = \frac{h}{p} \qquad \cdots \cdots \cdots (4.1)$$

and

$$\frac{h}{f'} = \frac{h'}{q}, \qquad \cdots \cdots \cdots (4.2)$$

whence, eliminating h and h',

$$pq = ff'. \qquad \cdots \cdots \cdots (4.3)$$

When the object and image are both situated in the same medium,
$f = f'$, and therefore

$$f = \sqrt{pq}. \qquad \cdots \cdots \cdots (4.4)$$

(ii) Nodal Point or Goniometer Method.

From fig. 2, since RPN and P'N'R' are parallel and PH = P'H', NH = N'H'. Similarly since F_1Q is parallel to RPN and to P'N'R' and HQ = H'Q', $HF_1 = F_2N'$. But HF_1 is the first focal length f and F_2N' is the distance from the second focal point to the second nodal point. Consequently a determination of both the nodal and focal points allows the focal length to be determined without direct reference to and location of the principal planes. This fact is made use of in the goniometer method, a diagram of which is shown in fig. 4. A finely divided rule R is set up perpendicular to the principal axis of the system S whose focal length is required and the scale is viewed through a **goniometer**. The latter consists essentially of a convex lens L with a vertical wire W at its focus. The whole is fixed to a

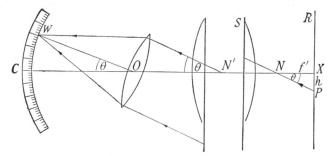

Fig. 4.—Goniometer method

horizontal board which rotates about a vertical axis situated underneath L. The angle of rotation θ of the central line WO with respect to the principal axis can be read directly from a circular scale C. Now a clear image of the rule R will be coincident with the wire at W only when a parallel beam is incident upon L, for W is the focus of L. Hence the rule R is moved to and fro along the principal axis until the position is achieved. Now for a parallel beam to emerge from the lens system S, R must be situated at its focus. Initially the goniometer is set along the principal axis of the whole system and a given mark X on the scale R is observed to be coincident with W. On rotating the goniometer through a known angle θ, some other mark P on the rule is observed to be coincident with W. Now the ray PN must be passing through the first nodal point at N, since it eventually gives rise to a ray parallel to itself. By the property of the nodal points XN = f', and since h and θ are both known, f' can be calculated. Reversing the optical system S and repeating the procedure allows the first focal length f to be determined.

(iii) **Method of Magnification.**

From the similar triangles ABF_1, QHF_1 in fig. 5, since $HB = u$, $HF_1 = f$, $H'B' = v$, and $H'F_2 = f'$, we have, ignoring signs,

$$\frac{h}{h'} = \frac{u-f}{f}. \qquad \ldots \ldots \text{(4.5)}$$

Similarly from the triangles $A'B'F_2$, $P'H'F_2$,

$$\frac{h}{h'} = \frac{f'}{v-f'} = \frac{f}{v-f}, \qquad \ldots \ldots \text{(4.6)}$$

if $f = f'$.

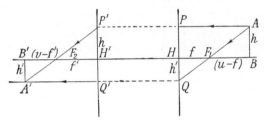

Fig. 5.—Method of magnification

If now the position of the object is changed so that u is increased by x, the position of the image will be changed by an amount y, and at the same time its magnitude will be altered to h''. As before,

$$\frac{h}{h''} = \frac{u+x-f}{f} \qquad \ldots \ldots \text{(4.7)}$$

and

$$\frac{h}{h''} = \frac{f}{v-y-f}. \qquad \ldots \ldots \text{(4.8)}$$

Since x and y are known and h, h' and h'' may be measured, these equations are more than sufficient to determine u, v and f absolutely.

The apparatus consists of an optical bench carrying a transparent scale, part of which furnishes the object of known size h. The size of the image resulting from the interposition of the optical system whose focal length is required is determined either with another scale in the image position or by observation of the image with a travelling microscope. This method is one of the most accurate for determining focal lengths and is useful in checking the uniformity of magnification across the entire field of the optical system examined.

If the algebraic signs of h, h', f, f', u and v are taken into account, fig. 5 gives, instead of (4.5) and (4.6),

$$-\frac{h}{h'} = \frac{u-f}{f}, \quad \cdots \quad (4.5)'$$

$$-\frac{h}{h'} = \frac{f'}{v-f''}. \quad \cdots \quad (4.6)'$$

Also $f = -f'$. Hence

$$\frac{u+f'}{-f'} = \frac{f'}{v-f''}$$

or

$$\frac{1}{v} - \frac{1}{u} = \frac{1}{f''}, \quad \cdots \quad (3.18)'$$

the fundamental equation, of which (3.18) is a particular case.

3. Two Separated Thin Lenses.

To deduce equation (3.21) for the combined focal length of two thin lenses separated a distance d we may make use of Newton's method summarized in equation (4.4). We first locate the foci on the

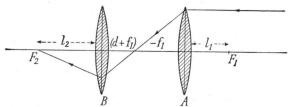

Fig. 6.—Principal focus for two thin lenses

two sides of the system, using a parallel incident beam. Referring to fig. 6, the distance $(-l_2)$ to F_2 from the second lens B is the image distance v for this lens for an object a distance $(d + f_1)$ from the lens. Hence, applying equation (3.18),

$$-\frac{1}{l_2} - \frac{1}{(d+f_1)} = \frac{1}{f_2}, \quad \cdots \quad (4.9)$$

for the arrangement shown in fig. 6. Therefore

$$l_2 = -\frac{f_2(d+f_1)}{(f_1+f_2+d)}. \quad \cdots \quad (4.10)$$

Similarly, for a parallel beam incident from the left, the distance of F_1 from the first lens A is

$$l_1 = -\frac{f_1(d+f_2)}{(f_1+f_2+d)}. \quad \cdots \quad (4.11)$$

Now, by Newton's method, an object placed at p from F_1 gives rise to an image q from F_2 where $pq = F^2$. Let the object be placed at the focus F' of the first lens: then the path of the rays is as in fig. 7, and the image is formed at the focus F'' of the second lens. Hence $p = (l_1 + f_1)$ and $q = (l_2 + f_2)$, and

$$pq = F^2 = (l_1 + f_1)(l_2 + f_2). \quad . \quad . \quad . \quad (4.12)$$

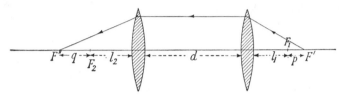

Fig. 7.—Two thin lenses

Substituting for l_1 and l_2 in equation (4.12) from equations (4.10) and (4.11), we obtain the desired formula

$$F^2 = \frac{f_1^2 f_2^2}{(f_1 + f_2 + d)^2} \quad . \quad . \quad . \quad . \quad (4.13)$$

or

$$\frac{1}{F} = \frac{1}{f_1} + \frac{1}{f_2} + \frac{d}{f_1 f_2}, \quad . \quad . \quad . \quad . \quad (4.14)$$

the sign of the square root being taken so as to agree with (3.20) when $d = 0$.

4. Approximate Methods for Determining Optical Constants.

We give below some rapid methods for estimating the focal lengths of spherical mirrors and thin lenses to an accuracy of one or two per cent. For thick lenses or coaxial systems, the more elaborate methods described in section 2 must be used.

(a) Concave Mirror.

The simplest method is to find the centre of curvature by means of some small object such as a pin. At the centre of curvature, the object and image coincide or are *self-conjugate*. The focal length is half the radius of curvature.

Otherwise, a parallel beam of light may be provided by placing a small source at the focus of a converging lens.

Fig. 8.—Determination of focus of concave mirror

This parallel beam, after reflection from a concave mirror, forms an image on a small screen at the focus of the mirror as shown in fig. 8.

(b) Converging Lens.

The simplest method of finding the focus is to note the position of the image of a distant light source. Since the distant light source will provide an almost parallel beam at the lens, the image is formed at the focus, and the distance from this point to the lens is the focal length.

A better method is to place a good plane mirror behind the lens. The object and image are then self-conjugate at the focus as shown

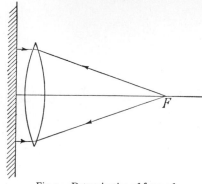

in fig. 9, for only when the light is incident normally on the mirror will the light be reflected back along its path.

For both concave mirrors and convex lenses, of course, the image of a bright light source may be located on a screen and the distances u and v measured, and equation (2.4) or (3.18) applied to determine the focal length f.

If a lens is of low power and consequently has an inconveniently long focal length, it may be placed in contact with a stronger converging lens of known focal length. The focal length of the combination is then found, say with a plane mirror, and then, by applying equation (3.20), since F and f_1 are known, f_2 may be calculated.

Fig. 9.—Determination of focus of converging lens

(c) Convex Mirror.

As a convex mirror does not form a real image, it is useless to attempt to receive the image of a small light source on a screen as

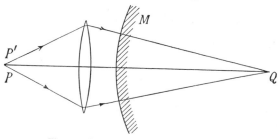

Fig. 10.—Centre of curvature of convex mirror

with a concave mirror. One satisfactory method for finding the radius of curvature of the mirror is illustrated in fig. 10. An image Q is formed of an object P by means of a converging lens in the usual way. The convex mirror M is then inserted between Q and the lens, and the position of M adjusted until the distance MQ is the radius of curvature of the mirror. This position is indicated by the formation of an image of P at P', coincident with P, for when Q is the centre of curvature, the light from P must be meeting M normally and will therefore be reflected back along its path to form an image at P', coincident with P.

(d) Diverging Lens.

The simplest method of finding the focal length of a concave lens is by contact combination with a considerably stronger converging lens of known focal length. A plane mirror may be used to locate the focus of the converging combination which results, and the focal length of the diverging lens calculated from equation (3.20).

The standard method used by opticians for finding the powers of lenses is to *neutralize* the given lens by trial and error by contact combination with a lens of opposite sign and known power, selected from a large bank of lenses termed a *trial case*. The pair of lenses is held in contact at about arm's length away, and a distant object is viewed through the combination. On gently rocking the combination the distant object will move across the field of view unless neutralization is perfect, whereupon the object will appear stationary, just as it would if a piece of plane window glass were moved across the field of view.

If the combination is converging, the image will move in a direction opposite to the direction of motion of the observer's arm, whereas if it is diverging, lens and image move across the field in the same direction.

(e) Radii of Curvature and Refractive Index.

If the radii of curvature and the refractive index of a lens are required, the following methods are convenient.

In a double concave lens each face will act as a (rather feebly reflecting) concave mirror. Consequently, the self-conjugate image of a bright source may be found just as for a concave mirror, first with one face and then with the other face of the lens. When r_1 and r_2 have thus been measured, f may be measured as under 4(d), and μ calculated from equations (3.17) and (3.18).

If the lens is double convex, each surface will act as a (rather feebly reflecting) convex mirror, and no real image will be formed by reflection. Actually, however, a self-conjugate image of a bright source is formed by the process shown in fig. 11. For some position of the source P, a ray PQ will be refracted into the lens along the direction QR where QR is perpendicular to the back face. Such a ray will therefore be reflected back again along RQ, and eventually be refracted back to form a self-conjugate image at P. Now, since RQ is perpendicular to the back face, it is part of a radius of curvature of the back face and RQ continued would cut the axis at C, the centre of curvature of the back face. This implies that if the lens were absent some light ray incident from the left would cut the axis at C, but owing to the introduction of the lens it cuts the axis at P. Hence light originating from P would diverge from C after passing through the lens, so that by (3.18), with f negative,

$$\frac{1}{OC} - \frac{1}{OP} = \frac{1}{f}.$$

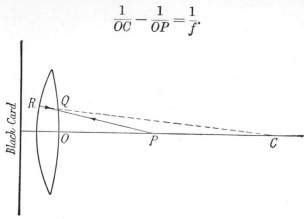

Fig. 11.—Radii of curvature and refractive index of lens

The focal length of the lens being measured in the usual way with the aid of a plane mirror, the above equation allows the determination of r_1. Reversal of the lens and repetition of the process enables r_2 to be determined. Finally, substitution of r_1, r_2, and f in equations (3.17) and (3.18) allows μ to be calculated. As the self-conjugate image at P is faint, the object at P must be brightly illuminated, and to avoid stray light a piece of black card is usually placed behind the lens. The whole process is termed *Boys' method*, and is used, for example, to find the radius of curvature of a lens used in the Newton's rings experiment described on p. 362.

* 5. Thick Lens.

We now proceed to work out approximate expressions for the focal length and the principal points of a thick lens, in terms of its thickness d, the radii r_1 and r_2 of its faces, and μ.

Consider a ray PQ incident parallel to the principal axis, as shown in fig. 12. By refraction at the first face AQ, whose radius of curvature is r_1, it is deflected into the line QR, which cuts the axis at X.

It is again refracted at R, where it emerges from the second face BR (radius r_2), as the line RF cutting PQ at E, and the axis at F, called the first principal focus. If EH is the perpendicular from E to the axis, H is the first principal point, by definition; also HF is the focal length f.

We now use equation (3.14), *adjusting it to this particular figure so that all lengths written down are positive.* We thus have

$$\frac{1}{AX} = \frac{\mu - 1}{\mu}\frac{1}{r_1}, \quad \cdots \cdots \quad (1)$$

and

$$\frac{1}{BF} - \frac{\mu}{BX} = \frac{\mu - 1}{r_2}. \quad \cdots \cdots \quad (2)$$

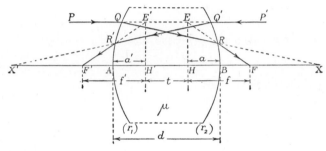

Fig. 12.—Thick lens

By similar triangles,

$$\frac{HF}{BF} = \frac{HE}{BR} = \frac{AQ}{BR} = \frac{AX}{BX}.$$

Hence

$$\frac{1}{f} = \frac{1}{AX}\frac{BX}{BF},$$

or, by multiplying by BX in (2),

$$\frac{1}{f} = \frac{1}{AX}\left(\mu + \frac{\mu - 1}{r_2} BX\right)$$

$$= \frac{1}{AX}\left\{\mu + \frac{\mu - 1}{r_2}(AX - AB)\right\}$$

$$= \frac{\mu}{AX} + \frac{\mu - 1}{r_2} - \frac{\mu - 1}{r_2}\frac{AB}{AX}.$$

Therefore, by (1), if $AB = d$,

$$\frac{1}{f} = (\mu - 1)\left(\frac{1}{r_1} + \frac{1}{r_2}\right) - \frac{d(\mu - 1)^2}{\mu r_1 r_2}. \quad \cdots \quad (4.16)$$

The distance $HB\ (=a)$ of the first principal plane HE from the physical refracting surface BR is given, from parallels, by

$$\frac{HB}{HF} = \frac{ER}{EF} = \frac{QR}{QX} = \frac{AB}{AX},$$

or
$$a = fd\frac{\mu - 1}{\mu r_1}. \quad \cdots \cdots \quad (4.17)$$

Similarly, on the other side of the system, if $F'H' = f'$, and $AH' = a'$, we get, from (4.16),

$$f' = f,$$

and, from (4.17),
$$a' = fd\frac{\mu - 1}{\mu r_2}. \quad \cdots \cdots \quad (4.18)$$

The distance t between the principal planes is given by

$$t = d - a - a', \quad \cdots \cdots \quad (4.19)$$

where a, a' are as given above.

Certain cases are of particular interest:

(i) If d is $\ll r_1$ or r_2, since we have $1/f = (\mu - 1)\left(\dfrac{1}{r_1} + \dfrac{1}{r_2}\right)$ approximately, the above equations become

$$a' = \frac{dr_1}{\mu(r_1 + r_2)}, \quad \cdots \cdots \quad (4.20)$$

$$a = \frac{dr_2}{\mu(r_1 + r_2)}, \quad \cdots \cdots \quad (4.21)$$

and
$$t = \frac{(\mu - 1)d}{\mu}. \quad \cdots \cdots \quad (4.22)$$

(ii) For crown glass, $\mu \simeq 1\cdot5$, so that the distance t between the principal planes of a thin lens is given by $t = \frac{1}{3}d$.

(iii) For an equiconvex or equiconcave lens $r_1 = r_2$ whence $a' = a = d/2\mu$.

(iv) For a plano-convex or plano-concave lens, $r_2 = \infty$, and hence $a' = 0$, that is, one principal plane coincides with the tangent plane to the curved refracting surface.

(v) If d is sufficiently large, although a lens is double convex it becomes a diverging instead of a converging lens.

EXERCISES

1. Explain carefully what is meant by the *cardinal points* of a coaxial system. Where are the cardinal points of a thin lens of focal length 10 cm. situated?

2. Describe Newton's method for finding the focal length of a converging lens system.

If an object and its real image are situated at 20 cm. and 5 cm. from the corresponding foci of a converging lens system, what is the focal length of the system? [10 cm.]

3. Enumerate methods for finding the focal length of a lens system and describe in detail the method that you prefer.

4. What is meant by the nodal points of a lens system? Describe an arrangement for finding the focal length of a lens system, based on the conception of nodal points.

5. Describe the method of magnification for finding the focal length of a lens system.

When an object is moved 10 cm. along the axis of an optical system, the real image moves through 20 cm. and at the same time the magnification changes from 4 to $\frac{1}{2}$. Find the focal length of the system. $\left[\dfrac{40}{7} \text{ cm.}\right]$

6. Deduce a general expression for the focal length of a thick lens.

Find the focal length of a meniscus lens of inner and outer radii 50 and 20 cm. if the lens is 4 cm. thick at the centre and the refractive index is 1·5. [63·8 cm.]

7. What is the distance between the principal planes in Question 6 and where do they lie? In § 5, take $r_1 = -50$, $r_2 = 20$, $d = 4$. Then HB = $a = 63\cdot8 \times 4 \times \frac{1}{3} \times (-\frac{1}{50}) = -1\cdot70$; AH′ = $a' = 63\cdot8 \times 4 \times \frac{1}{3} \times \frac{1}{20} = 4\cdot25$; H′H = $4 + 1\cdot70 - 4\cdot25 = 1\cdot45$.

8. Show that the principal planes of a fairly thin glass lens are situated a distance apart equal to about one-third of the thickness of the lens.

9. Find the thickness of an equiconvex lens of radius 5 cm. and of refractive index 1·5 if an incident parallel beam is to emerge parallel after refraction through the lens. [30 cm.]

CHAPTER V

* Defects of the Image in Optical Systems

The main defects of the images formed by optical systems are as follows: (1) astigmatism, (2) spherical aberration, (3) coma, (4) curvature of the field, (5) distortion, and (6) chromatic aberration. We shall treat the last of these in Chap. VI.

1. Astigmatism.

If examination is made of the image focused by the reflection of an oblique beam at a mirror or by the refraction of an oblique beam through a lens, it will be found that instead of a single image, two images occur separated by a certain distance termed the **astigmatic difference.** In particular, if the object is a small circular source, each

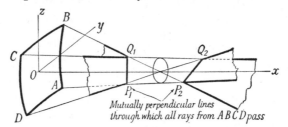

Fig. 1.—Focal lines, and circle of least confusion

image will be found to consist of a short line, and these lines will be perpendicular to each other. The explanation in terms of the wave theory of light discussed in Chap. IX is very simple. A spherical light wave emanates from the object, but since it traverses the optical system obliquely, different curvatures are impressed on the wave-front in two mutually perpendicular directions. Consequently two non-coincident images are formed, which are mutually perpendicular and neither of which is geometrically similar to the object. A blurred image occurs at some point between the two images, and this third image which, although less sharp, is more similar geometrically to the object than either of the other images, is termed the **circle of least confusion.** We represent the phenomenon diagrammatically in fig. 1. The collapsing wave-front (see p. 394) is represented by ABCD, where the curvature of AB equals that of DC, and that of AD equals that

340

of BC, but the curvatures in the two mutually perpendicular directions are different. The two images are formed at P_1Q_1 and P_2Q_2, and these two linear images resulting from an initially oblique, parallel beam are termed the **focal lines**. The circle of least confusion is shown between P_1Q_1 and P_2Q_2.

We shall now derive an expression for the astigmatic difference due to oblique reflection at a concave mirror. In fig. 2, C represents the centre of curvature of the mirror and PA and PB are two rays incident on the mirror at A and B. The reflected rays cross at a point P_1 off the axis and cross the axis at P_2 and P_3 respectively. If AB

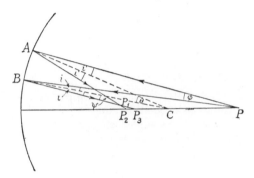

Fig. 2.—Astigmatic difference

is rotated about CP so as to form part of the zone of a sphere, then P_1 becomes a short circular arc which is approximately a short straight line and forms the primary focal line. The secondary focal line is P_2P_3. With the usual nomenclature $CB = r$, $PB = u$, $P_1B = v_1$, and $P_3B = v_2$. Let $\angle BCA = \theta$, $\angle BPA = \phi$, $\angle BP_1A = \psi$, $\angle PAC = \angle CAP_2 = i'$, and $\angle PBC = \angle CBP_1 = i$. Then we have

$$\left.\begin{array}{c} \phi + i' = \theta + i \\ \psi + i = \theta + i' \end{array}\right\} \quad \cdots \cdots \cdots (5.1)$$

Hence
$$\phi + \psi = 2\theta. \quad \cdots \cdots \cdots (5.2)$$

Also
$$\phi = \frac{AB \cdot \cos i'}{u}, \quad \cdots \cdots \cdots (5.3)$$

$$\psi = \frac{AB \cdot \cos i'}{v_1}, \quad \cdots \cdots \cdots (5.4)$$

$$\theta = \frac{AB}{r}. \quad \cdots \cdots \cdots (5.5)$$

Hence, since $i' = i$ nearly,

$$\frac{1}{u} + \frac{1}{v_1} = \frac{2}{r \cos i}. \quad \cdots \cdots \cdots (5.6)$$

(H 394)

To determine the position of P_2, we note

$$\triangle P_3 BC + \triangle CBP = \triangle P_3 BP, \quad \ldots \ldots (5.7)$$

that is,

$$\tfrac{1}{2} r v_2 \sin i + \tfrac{1}{2} r u \sin i = \tfrac{1}{2} u v_2 \sin 2i,$$

whence

$$\frac{1}{u} + \frac{1}{v_2} = \frac{2 \cos i}{r}. \quad \ldots \ldots (5.8)$$

Equations (5.6) and (5.8) determine the positions of the two focal lines. By subtraction we obtain

$$\frac{1}{v_1} - \frac{1}{v_2} = \frac{2}{r}\left(\frac{1}{\cos i} - \cos i\right), \quad \ldots \ldots (5.9)$$

or

$$\frac{v_2 - v_1}{v_2 v_1} = \frac{2}{r} \sin i \tan i. \quad \ldots \ldots (5.10)$$

Now $v_1 \sim v_2$ and $(v_2 - v_1)$ is the astigmatic difference. Hence, from equation (5.10), the astigmatic difference is proportional to $\sin i \tan i$.

The treatment for the astigmatism produced by lenses although very important in practice is too lengthy and laborious to be given here. It is important that the student should note that while many aberrations such as spherical aberration and coma result directly from the finite size of the aperture, astigmatism may occur with a very restricted aperture if the incidence is oblique. It may, however, be of larger magnitude if the aperture is large, since it increases with i according to equation (5.10).

2. Spherical Aberration.

If the aperture of an optical system is not small, then, although a beam may not be oblique and therefore no astigmatism be involved,

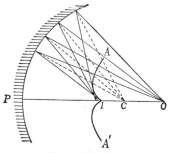

Fig. 3.—Caustic curve

the image is far from perfect. One type of error is termed spherical aberration, and the spherical aberration consequent on reflection at a concave mirror of large aperture is shown diagrammatically in fig. 3.

A point source at O gives rise to a series of intersecting rays, and the more or less well-defined images lie along a cusped curve AIA'. This curve is termed a **caustic curve.**

In general, as a result of spherical aberration, a point object situated on the axis of the system gives rise to an image of finite extent both along the axis and perpendicular to it. These phenomena are known as **longitudinal** and **lateral aberrations.** The most important use of a knowledge of aberrations is in connexion with lenses. As in the analogous problem of astigmatism the calculation is too lengthy to be given here, but no new principles are involved in its elucidation. One interesting result regarding spherical aberration is that minimum aberration is produced by a converging lens when $r_1 = -6r_2$. Hence the lens should be almost plano-convex and the convex side should be presented to the source The latter procedure is an example of a more general rule that to *reduce aberration to a minimum the refraction must be divided as evenly as possible between the refracting surfaces.*

3. Coma: Helmholtz's Sine Law.

It is found in practice that the image of a non-axial point source produced by a lens is often egg-shaped as shown in fig. 4. This image

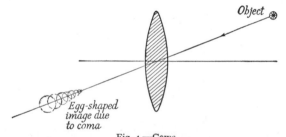

Fig. 4.—Coma

may be regarded as arising from the overlapping of a series of images formed by the central zone and a series of concentric zones of the lens. The central zone gives an approximate point image, the successive zones produce slightly displaced circular patches and the envelope of all these gives the observed image. Such behaviour is termed **coma,** and **Helmholtz's Sine Law** states: *For no coma, $\sin \theta / \sin \theta'$ = const., where θ and θ' are the angles made by conjugate rays with the common axis of the system.* To illustrate this law we consider refraction at a single surface as shown in fig. 5. From the diagram,

$$\frac{\sin i}{\sin \theta} = \frac{CP}{CA},$$

$$\frac{\sin r}{\sin \theta'} = \frac{CP'}{CA}.$$

Hence
$$\frac{CP \sin \theta}{\sin i} = \frac{CP' \sin \theta'}{\sin r}.$$

Now
$$\frac{\sin i}{\sin r} = \frac{\mu'}{\mu}.$$

Hence
$$\mu CP \sin \theta = \mu' CP' \sin \theta'.$$

Now the magnification y'/y is also given by CP'/CP: hence the general law becomes

$$\mu y \sin \theta = \mu' y' \sin \theta'. \quad \ldots \ldots \quad (5.11)$$

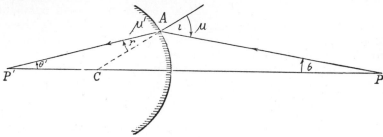

Fig. 5.—Helmholtz's sine law

Hence the linear magnification of the system is constant across a given object only if $\sin \theta / \sin \theta'$ is constant. Now, it is shown on p. 49 that for any optical system to be *free from distortion* $\tan \theta / \tan \theta'$ must be constant. This relation can only hold simultaneously with Helmholtz's sine law if θ and θ' are small. Hence coma and distortion cannot both be absent unless the aperture is restricted.

4. Curvature of the Field.

A further aberration arises from the impossibility of obtaining a flat image of a flat object, at least by using a single curved optical surface. In fig. 6 the centre of curvature of the concave reflecting surface is

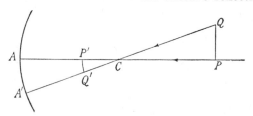

Fig. 6.—Curvature of the field

at C and the image of a point P on the object PQ is at P'. Now the image of Q will lie at some point Q' on QC, for the pairs of conjugate points (P, P'), (Q, Q') lie on the radii CA, CA'. But accurate construction shows that $CP/CP' \neq CQ/CQ'$, and hence $P'Q'$ is not perpendicular to the axis as in the object PQ. Curvature of the field results; it may be reduced to a minimum by the use of a complex system. Actually, for two lenses in contact, minimum curvature of the field occurs when $\mu_1 f_1 = -\mu_2 f_2$, where f_1 and f_2 are the focal lengths of the lenses and μ_1 and μ_2 their respective refractive indices. This expression should be compared with that for an achromatic combination of two lenses given on p. 351.

5. Distortion.

If a square is erected perpendicular to the axis of an optical system, and if the aperture is large the square exhibits the appearance shown

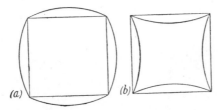

Fig. 7.—Barrel and pincushion effect

in figs. 7(a) and (b) according as the optical system is converging or diverging. The behaviour is termed the *barrel and pincushion effect*, and is an example of distortion.

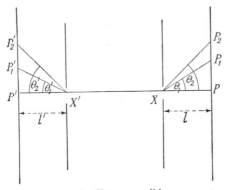

Fig. 8.—Tangent condition

We shall now show that for uniform lateral magnification, that is, freedom from distortion, the relation $\tan\theta / \tan\theta' = $ constant must be satisfied where θ and θ' are the angles made by conjugate rays with the common axis.

In fig. 8 let PP_1P_2 be a plane object and $P'P_1'P_2'$ its corresponding image. The points X and X′ in fig. 8 are termed the **entrance pupil** and the **exit pupil** of the optical system. These points have certain important properties, but for our purposes we can regard them loosely as restricted apertures imposed by the finite size of the lens on the entrance rays from the object and the exit rays to the image. Let $PX = l$ and $P'X' = l'$. Then we have

$$\frac{\tan\theta_1}{\tan\theta_1'} = \frac{PP_1}{l} \Big/ \frac{P'P_1'}{l'},$$

also

$$\frac{\tan\theta_2}{\tan\theta_2'} = \frac{PP_2}{l} \Big/ \frac{P'P_2'}{l'}.$$

Now for constant lateral magnification

$$\frac{PP_1}{P'P_1'} = \frac{PP_2}{P'P_2'},$$

and hence

$$\frac{\tan\theta_1}{\tan\theta_1'} = \frac{\tan\theta_2}{\tan\theta_2'} = \text{const.} \quad \ldots \quad (5.12)$$

If this tangent condition is obeyed for conjugate rays passing through X and X′, these points are said to be **orthoscopic**. Alternatively we may therefore say that *for no distortion the centres of perspective must be orthoscopic points.*

EXERCISES

1. Enumerate the defects of the image formed by optical systems. Which must be especially eliminated from (a) photographic objectives, (b) microscopic objectives?

2. Explain clearly what is meant by astigmatism. What is the astigmatic difference for rays incident at 30° to the radius of curvature of a concave mirror of radius 30 cm. if the object is 30 cm. from the centre of curvature. [8·56 cm.]

3. Where are the foci of a converging sphero-cylindrical lens of material of refractive index 1·5 if the sphere has a radius of 50 cm. and the cylinder a radius of −60 cm.? [100 cm.; 600/11 cm.]

4. Distinguish between spherical aberration and chromatic aberration. How is spherical aberration reduced to a minimum?

5. What is the condition for freedom from distortion in the image formed by an optical system? Show that simultaneous correction for distortion and for coma can be achieved only by stopping down the aperture of the lens.

6. Contrast the conditions necessary for the production of a flat image of a flat object if the image is also to be achromatic.

CHAPTER VI

Dispersion

1. Newton's Experiments.

The classical experiments on the dispersion of white light and the production of the visible spectrum are due to Newton. If a ray of white light is allowed to fall on a glass prism, then on emergence it is found to consist of several colours as shown in fig. 1.

All the colours show deviation from the initial direction of the white light in agreement with the laws of refraction, but the magnitude of the deviation depends on the quality of the light. Red is deviated the least, violet the most, and intermediate are orange, yellow, green, blue, and indigo. The refractive index of a medium

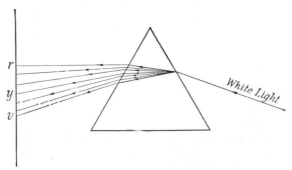

Fig. 1.—Dispersion by a prism

with respect to air depends therefore on the quality of the light. Unless otherwise indicated, *the* refractive index is the index corresponding approximately to the centre of the visible **spectrum,** namely, the yellow sodium D line (see p. 404). The separation of the different colours due to their different refractive indices is known as **dispersion.**

If a second prism identical with the first be inserted in the spectrum, with its refracting edge opposite in position to that of the first prism (e.g. below the prism instead of above it), white light is produced, as the separated colours and rays again coalesce. Finally, if with a small slit any one of the colours is selected and passed through a second prism it continues without further dispersion.

These facts led Newton to suggest that white light consists of super-posed light of different colours which may be separated by the process of dispersion. This view is still satisfactory as an elementary interpretation, although more subtle considerations make it likely that another, much more complicated view is nearer the truth.

Newton also introduced the method of **crossed prisms** which is illustrated in fig. 2. The spectrum which would have been vertical

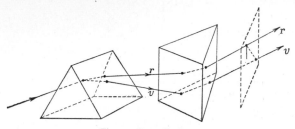

Fig. 2.—Crossed prisms

with one prism alone is then inclined as shown, the colours retaining the same order as before. Owing to the overlapping of the colours produced by the dispersion of neighbouring rays, the spectra obtained with the apparatus so far described present a rather blurred appearance. To eliminate this and obtain a pure spectrum on a screen, two convex lenses are included, in addition to the prism, source, slit, and screen, as shown in fig. 3. The source is placed at the focus of the first lens so as to yield a parallel beam incident on the prism. Such a process

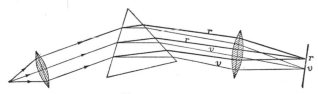

Fig. 3.—Collimation

is termed **collimation,** and the arrangement is referred to as a **collimator.** The screen is placed in the focal plane of the second lens and a pure spectrum is then obtained, for the following reasons. Since the rays of white light are parallel they are all incident on the prism at the same angle. Consequently rays of one colour, formed in the dispersion process, are all deviated through the same angle. Hence, for any one colour, the rays all emerge from the prism in a parallel beam, and therefore, after passage through the second lens, are focused in one position in the focal plane of the lens. The same process occurs with

all the other colours and a single pure spectrum is eventually obtained
on the screen.

2. Dispersive Power.

If instead of using a white light source, a coloured source such as
a yellow sodium flame is used, and the source is limited in extent by
a narrow slit, passage through a prism merely results in the formation
of a line of the same colour. This is an example of a line spectrum
discussed further in Chap. X. Different elements under thermal or
electrical excitation emit lines of different colour and may therefore
be used to map positions in a continuous spectrum. We discuss the
line spectrum in some detail in Chap. X, but for the present we are
concerned with its use in defining dispersive power. The **dispersive
power** of a material is defined by

$$\omega = \frac{\mu_b - \mu_r}{\mu_D - 1}, \qquad \dots \dots \quad (6.1)$$

where μ_b is its refractive index for the blue hydrogen line 4340 Ångström units (see Chap. VII), μ_r that for the red hydrogen line 6565
Ångström units, and μ_D that for the yellow sodium line 5893 Å. The
dispersive power therefore expresses the angular separation of the
extreme rays of the spectrum and takes also into account the mean
refractive index of the material. For a prism of small angle θ, the
angle of deviation is, by equation (3.12), given by

$$\delta = (\mu - 1)\theta.$$

Applying this expression to the red, blue, and yellow rays, we have

$$\delta_b = (\mu_b - 1)\theta, \qquad \dots \dots \quad (6.2)$$
$$\delta_r = (\mu_r - 1)\theta. \qquad \dots \dots \quad (6.3)$$

Hence the angular separation of the blue and the red rays is

$$\delta_b - \delta_r = (\mu_b - \mu_r)\theta. \qquad \dots \dots \dots \quad (6.4)$$

But
$$\delta_D = (\mu_D - 1)\theta. \qquad \dots \dots \dots \quad (6.5)$$

Hence
$$\delta_b - \delta_r = \frac{(\mu_b - \mu_r)}{\mu_D - 1} \delta_D = \omega \delta_D, \qquad \dots \dots \quad (6.6)$$

or the *angular separation is given by the product of the dispersive power
and the mean angle of deviation.*

3. Chromatism.

Since lenses may be regarded as prisms of varying angle, white light incident upon them is dispersed and each colour forms its own image at some position governed by the refractive index of the material of the lens for the colour concerned. Such behaviour is referred to as *chromatism of position.* In addition to this, the magnification resulting from a given position of the object is different for the different refractive indices, and even although chromatism of position may be corrected by certain devices, *chromatism of magnification* may still be present. The image then shows a multicoloured fringe with the colours in the order of the spectrum.

4. Achromatic Combination of Lenses.

It is possible by a suitable combination of lenses to produce an **achromatic effect.** Consider two lenses of different materials in contact. Applying the thin lens formula preceding equation (3.18) to the red, blue, and yellow rays respectively for the first lens, we have

$$\frac{1}{f_{1b}} = (\mu_b - 1)\left(\frac{1}{r_1} - \frac{1}{r_2}\right), \quad \ldots \ldots \quad (6.7)$$

$$\frac{1}{f_{1r}} = (\mu_r - 1)\left(\frac{1}{r_1} - \frac{1}{r_2}\right). \quad \ldots \ldots \quad (6.8)$$

Subtracting, $\quad \dfrac{1}{f_{1b}} - \dfrac{1}{f_{1r}} = (\mu_b - \mu_r)\left(\dfrac{1}{r_1} - \dfrac{1}{r_2}\right). \quad \ldots \quad (6.9)$

Now $\qquad\qquad \dfrac{1}{f_1} = (\mu - 1)\left(\dfrac{1}{r_1} - \dfrac{1}{r_2}\right), \quad \ldots \ldots \quad (6.10)$

where μ is the mean refractive index and f_1 the mean focal length; also

$$\omega_1 = \frac{(\mu_b - \mu_r)}{(\mu - 1)}. \quad \ldots \ldots \quad (6.11)$$

Hence $\qquad\qquad \dfrac{1}{f_{1b}} - \dfrac{1}{f_{1r}} = \dfrac{\omega_1}{f_1}. \quad \ldots \ldots \quad (6.12)$

Similarly for the second lens,

$$\frac{1}{f_{2b}} - \frac{1}{f_{2r}} = \frac{\omega_2}{f_2}. \quad \ldots \ldots \quad (6.13)$$

Adding equations (6.12) and (6.13), we obtain

$$\left(\frac{1}{f_{1b}} + \frac{1}{f_{2b}}\right) - \left(\frac{1}{f_{1r}} + \frac{1}{f_{2r}}\right) = \frac{\omega_1}{f_1} + \frac{\omega_2}{f_2}. \quad \ldots \quad (6.14)$$

Now if F_b and F_r represent the combined focal lengths for red and blue light, for achromatism of position $F_b = F_r$. But (p. 325)

$$\frac{1}{F_b} = \frac{1}{f_{1b}} + \frac{1}{f_{2b}}, \quad \cdots \cdots \quad (6.15)$$

and

$$\frac{1}{F_r} = \frac{1}{f_{1r}} + \frac{1}{f_{2r}}. \quad \cdots \cdots \quad (6.16)$$

The left-hand side of equation (6.14) must therefore be zero for achromatic conditions to prevail, and hence

$$\frac{\omega_1}{\omega_2} = \frac{-f_1}{f_2}. \quad \cdots \cdots \cdots \quad (6.17)$$

Since for ordinary dispersion ω is always positive the two lenses must be of opposite sign. It is usual also to make them with one radius of curvature in common.

Newton, misled by certain experiments, believed that ω_1 and ω_2 were always equal. From this it would follow that $1/f_1 + 1/f_2 = 0$, so that the combination of lenses, if achromatic, would act simply like a piece of glass with plane parallel sides.

In the above considerations the lens is only corrected for two colours. By the addition of a third lens its achromatism may be made nearly perfect and the arrangement is then termed **apochromatic.**

Achromatism may also be achieved by using two lenses of the *same* material situated a distance apart equal to the average of their two focal lengths. To prove this, if we differentiate equation (4.14), we obtain

$$\frac{\delta F}{F^2} = \frac{\delta f_1}{f_1{}^2} + \frac{\delta f_2}{f_2{}^2} + \frac{d}{f_1 f_2}\left(\frac{\delta f_1}{f_1} + \frac{\delta f_2}{f_2}\right). \quad \cdots \quad (6.18)$$

Now if δF, δf_1, and δf_2 represent the difference in focal length between red and blue rays due to chromatism, for an achromatic combination δF must be zero. Also if ω is the dispersive power of the material $\delta f_1 = f_1\omega$, as we see from equation (6.12), for this may be written

$$\frac{f_{1r} - f_{1b}}{f_{1b}\, f_{1r}} = \frac{\delta f_1}{f_1{}^2} = \frac{\omega_1}{f_1}. \quad \cdots \cdots \quad (6.19)$$

Hence equation (6.18) becomes

$$0 = \frac{\omega}{f_1} + \frac{\omega}{f_2} + 2\frac{d\omega}{f_1 f_2}, \quad \cdots \cdots \quad (6.20)$$

or

$$d = \frac{-(f_1 + f_2)}{2}. \quad \cdots \cdots \quad (6.21)$$

which makes d positive if f_1 and f_2 are both negative, that is, with converging lenses.

5. Achromatic Prisms.

For prisms of small angle we may derive a simple expression for the relation between the angles of the prisms and their dispersive powers when in achromatic combination. From equation (6.4), for the first prism

$$\delta_{1b} - \delta_{1r} = (\mu_{1b} - \mu_{1r})\theta_1. \quad \ldots \quad (6.22)$$

Similarly for the second prism

$$\delta_{2b} - \delta_{2r} = (\mu_{2b} - \mu_{2r})\theta_2. \quad \ldots \quad (6.23)$$

Adding (6.22) and (6.23), we have

$$(\delta_{1b} + \delta_{2b}) - (\delta_{1r} + \delta_{2r}) = (\mu_{1b} - \mu_{1r})\theta_1 + (\mu_{2b} - \mu_{2r})\theta_2. \quad (6.24)$$

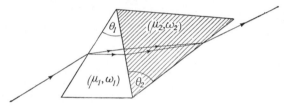

Fig. 4.—Deviation without dispersion

The total deviation Δ_b for the blue must equal the total deviation Δ_r for the red for achromatism. Hence, since $\Delta_b = \delta_{1b} + \delta_{2b}$ and $\Delta_r = \delta_{1r} + \delta_{2r}$, the L.H.S. of equation (6.24) vanishes, and we have

$$(\mu_{1b} - \mu_{1r})\theta_1 = - (\mu_{2b} - \mu_{2r})\theta_2. \quad \ldots \quad (6.25)$$

Since

$$\omega_1 = \frac{(\mu_{1b} - \mu_{1r})}{(\mu_1 - 1)}, \quad \ldots \quad (6.26)$$

and

$$\omega_2 = \frac{\mu_{2b} - \mu_{2r}}{(\mu_2 - 1)}, \quad \ldots \quad (6.27)$$

equation (6.25) may be written

$$\omega_1(\mu_1 - 1)\theta_1 = -\omega_2(\mu_2 - 1)\theta_2. \quad \ldots \quad (6.28)$$

Since θ_1 and θ_2 are seen to be of opposite sign, the angles of the prisms must be oppositely directed as shown in fig. 4. Although dispersion is eliminated (at least for two extreme colours of the spectrum), deviation, of course, still occurs so that we have obtained *deviation without dispersion* even with white light. The converse problem, *dispersion without deviation*, has an important practical use in the direct vision spectroscope described on p. 426.

* 6. The Rainbow.

A study of the formation of the rainbow affords a good illustration of the application of the principles of refraction and dispersion. The rainbow is produced by the action of white light traversing spherical

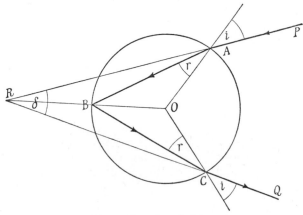

Fig. 5.—Formation of rainbow

raindrops, and the behaviour of the light rays is shown diagrammatically in fig. 5. A ray of white light PA is incident upon the drop at A, and after refraction is reflected from the back surface of the drop at B. It emerges from the drop along CQ after a further refraction in the front surface at C. The total deviation of the ray PA is represented by the supplement of the angle PRQ, and from the geometry we have

$$\angle PRQ = 2 \angle PRO = 2(\angle ABO - \angle RAB)$$

$$= 2\{r - (i - r)\} = 4r - 2i. \quad . \quad . \quad . \quad (6.29)$$

If the angle of incidence is plotted against the angle of deviation, a graph is obtained similar to that shown in fig. 6. We note that for a certain range of values of i, δ is practically constant. Hence near a certain value of i a large number of rays will be deviated through the same angle and an image will be formed at this angle of minimum deviation. To find the angle of minimum deviation we differentiate equation (6.29) with respect to i and equate to zero.

Hence
$$4\frac{dr}{di} - 2 = 0. \quad . \quad . \quad . \quad . \quad . \quad (6.30)$$

Now $\sin i = \mu \sin r$; hence

$$\cos i = \mu \cos r \frac{dr}{di}. \quad . \quad . \quad . \quad . \quad . \quad (6.31)$$

Eliminating dr/di from (6.30) and (6.31), we obtain

$$\cos i = \tfrac{1}{2}\mu \cos r. \quad \ldots \ldots \quad (6.32)$$

From this equation and Snell's law, substituting for r,

$$\cos i = \sqrt{\frac{\mu^2 - 1}{3}}. \quad \ldots \ldots \quad (6.33)$$

For water $\mu_r = 1 \cdot 329$ and $\mu_v = 1 \cdot 343$; substitution in (6.33) therefore gives $i = 59 \cdot 6°$ and $58 \cdot 8°$ and $r = 40 \cdot 5°$ and $39 \cdot 6°$ respectively for the red and violet rays. The angle subtended by the bow is the angle between the deviated red and violet rays and is therefore about 2°. The height of the bow in the heavens depends on the height of the sun above the horizon. Since $\delta_r \backsimeq 137°$ and $\delta_v \backsimeq 139°$, for a setting or rising sun the bow is formed about 40° above the horizontal. Clearly the red is on the outside, and the observer must have his back to the sun.

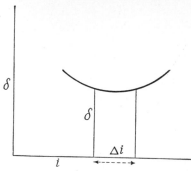

Fig. 6.—Deviation of ray passing through water drop

The rainbow considered above is termed the **primary bow.** In addition, secondary and tertiary bows are sometimes visible. These arise from multiple reflections of the light inside the drop.

EXERCISES

1. Describe an experimental arrangement for producing a pure spectrum. By what general methods may white light be split up into the spectral colours?

2. Distinguish between refractive power and dispersive power of a medium.

Derive the condition for an achromatic combination of two lenses in contact.

3. Deduce an expression for the focal length of a combination of two lenses situated a distance d apart. Hence find the condition for an achromatic combination of two lenses of the same material.

4. Explain, with reference to prisms, how it is possible to obtain deviation without dispersion and vice versa. Obtain a relation between the angles of two refracting prisms of small angle in terms of the dispersive powers and the mean refractive indices of the prisms.

5. Give the theory of the formation of the primary rainbow and show that the angle subtended by the width of the coloured band is about 2°.

CHAPTER VII

* Optical Interference and Diffraction

1. Optical Interference with Young's Parallel Slits.

If a source of light is placed behind a slit in front of which are two other parallel slits, the appearance of the illumination on the screen S, as shown in fig. 1, is quite contrary to what would be expected from the laws of geometrical optics. Instead of observing, as might be expected, two small slits of light surrounded by complete darkness, the whole field of view is crossed by regularly spaced light and dark bands in a direction parallel to the slits. To explain this phenomenon we are forced to assume that light does not always travel in straight lines. If we assume instead that light consists of a wave-motion, then we shall see that we arrive at a satisfactory quantitative

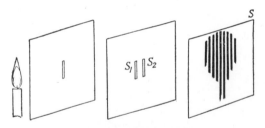

Fig. 1.—Interference fringes

as well as qualitative explanation of the phenomenon. We regard the two slits S_1 and S_2 as two **secondary sources** emitting cylindrical light waves, the wave-length being fixed for light of one particular colour. Now it is clear that the intermingling of the two emitted light waves may lead to two extremes of behaviour. For one extreme, at certain regions in space, crests from one source will coincide in position with troughs from the other source. Hence if the two waves are of equal intensity, the medium in which the light is propagated will remain undisturbed, and it will be as if no light is present. The two light waves are then said to **interfere** and the dark lines or **interference fringes** are said to be due to **destructive interference.** Conversely, at the other extreme, the bright bands are due to two crests or two troughs of the light waves coinciding and thus producing a large effect at the position under consideration. We discuss the general problem of interference in Part IV on Sound and Wave Motion.

We shall now derive a quantitative expression for the separation x of the fringes in terms of the wave-length λ of the light, the distance s between the two slits, and the distance b of the slits from the receiving screen. At the point O in fig. 2, since the distances S_1O, S_2O are equal, provided the light starts out simultaneously from S_1 and S_2 or is **in phase** at S_1 and S_2, it must arrive in phase at O. Hence a bright fringe will be formed at O. For the next adjacent bright fringe at P we must have the difference in the distances S_1P, S_2P equal to one whole wave-length. Hence

$$S_1P - S_2P = \lambda. \quad \ldots \ldots \ldots \quad (7.1)$$

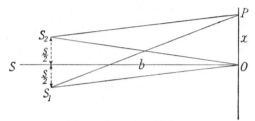

Fig. 2.—Separation of fringes

From the figure

$$S_1P = \left\{ b^2 + \left(x + \frac{s}{2} \right)^2 \right\}^{\frac{1}{2}},$$

$$S_2P = \left\{ b^2 + \left(x - \frac{s}{2} \right)^2 \right\}^{\frac{1}{2}}, \quad \ldots \ldots \quad (7.2)$$

so approximately

$$S_1P - S_2P = \frac{xs}{b}, \quad \ldots \ldots \quad (7.3)$$

and

$$x = \frac{b\lambda}{s}, \quad \ldots \ldots \ldots \quad (7.4)$$

which shows that the fringe separation is directly proportional to (i) the wave-length, (ii) the distance of the screen from the sources, and inversely proportional to the distance between the sources. The above expression holds for the first bright fringe from the centre; the general expression for the nth fringe is

$$x = \frac{nb\lambda}{s}. \quad \ldots \ldots \ldots \quad (7.5)$$

The number n is said to be the *order* of the fringe: at the centre O the fringe is said to be of *zero order*. A similar expression holds for the dark fringes except that the condition for their formation is that

$$S_1P - S_2P = (2n + 1)\frac{\lambda}{2}, \quad \ldots \ldots \quad (7.6)$$

where n is integral, that is, the *path-difference must be equal to an odd number of half wave-lengths*.

To avoid the introduction of very small numbers to denote the wave-length of light when measured in centimetres a unit is chosen called the Ångström, defined as equal to 10^{-8} cm.

The behaviour of systems of waves generally is discussed in Part IV on Sound and Wave Motion, and we shall therefore restrict our discussion here to just those aspects which are essential to gain an insight into optical phenomena.

2. Fresnel's Mirrors and Biprism.

For the production of a definite interference pattern certain important conditions must be fulfilled. For example, the two sources S_1 and S_2 must originate from the same source. Otherwise, local and

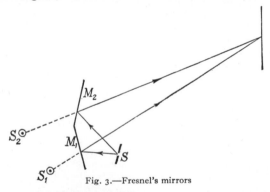

Fig. 3.—Fresnel's mirrors

separate variations in the emission of light from independent sources would lead to continually changing phase relations between the emitted wave-trains.

Any device which will produce two corresponding sources S_1 and S_2 may be suitable for producing optical interference. Two suitable devices introduced by Fresnel are his mirrors and his biprism.

In **Fresnel's mirrors,** two mirrors M_1, M_2, silvered on their front surfaces, are inclined at an angle of nearly 180°, and a slit S is placed as shown in fig. 3. The two images S_1 and S_2 then form the two secondary sources, and both register any fluctuations in S, and hence lead to a definite interference pattern. **Fresnel's biprism** consists of a glass prism with vertical angle nearly 180°. Two virtual images of the source S are then formed at S_1 and S_2 by refraction, as shown in fig. 4. The interference patterns produced by Fresnel's mirrors and biprism are identical with that produced by Young's slits, and the calculation of the separation of the fringes remains the same. The examination of the fringes is made with a low power travelling microscope; the purpose of the experiment is usually the calculation of the wavelength λ. In equation (7.4), to determine λ we require a knowledge of b, s, and x. The distance b is obtained by direct measurement with a scale; similarly x is found with the travelling microscope. Since $\lambda \sim 10^{-5}$ cm. and b is about a metre, unless s is small x is very small indeed. The reason for making the angles of the mirrors and biprism nearly 180° is to bring S_1 and S_2 close together, and thus keep s small and make x of reasonable magnitude. To measure s the usual method is to keep the slits and microscope fixed in position and to insert a

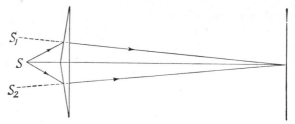

Fig. 4.—Fresnel's biprism

converging lens successively in two positions so as to form an image of s in the microscope. Then it may be shown that if s' and s'' are the sizes of these images as measured by the microscope,

$$s = (s' \, s'')^{\frac{1}{2}}.$$

4. Lloyd's Mirror.

In the Lloyd's mirror arrangement for producing interference fringes, one of the secondary sources S_1 is the source S itself, and the other S_2 is the image formed by reflection of S in a plane mirror. The effect is shown diagrammatically in fig. 5. A fringe system is formed similar to that produced by the Fresnel arrangements, but the central fringe is found to be dark instead of light. This odd result occurs for the symmetrical position O where the geometrical distances from the two sources are equal. Consequently some additional phenomenon is occurring, and it is found that the effect arises from the fact that when light is reflected at the boundary of a denser medium it suffers a phase change of π, that is, an effective wave-length change of $\lambda/2$. The same behaviour does not occur if the reflection is at the junction of a denser to a less dense medium (see Part IV).

Other differences in the two types of fringe system arise from the fact that, as shown in fig. 6, the sources, which are necessarily of finite width, are laterally reversed with Lloyd's mirror (fig. 6 (*a*)), whereas they are not reversed in the Fresnel experiment (fig. 6 (*b*)). Consequently

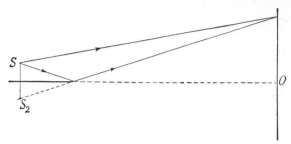

Fig. 5.—Lloyd's mirror

the centre of gravity of corresponding points on the two sources is midway between them for all points on the sources in the Lloyd's mirror arrangement, whereas with the Fresnel arrangement it is continually laterally displaced. Each pair of points, therefore, in the latter arrange-

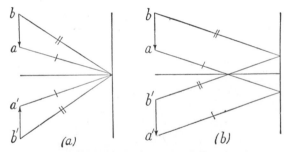

Fig. 6.—Sources in (*a*) Lloyd's mirror, (*b*) Fresnel's mirrors

ment give rise to their own fringe system with its centre slightly displaced from the neighbouring fringe system. Unless the slit is very narrow, which means low intensity of the fringes, the Fresnel system gives blurred indistinct fringes. The Lloyd's mirror fringes, on the contrary, are sharp for a considerable width of the slit.

5. Interference by thin Films.

Consider a thin film of thickness *e* with parallel sides as shown in fig. 7. An incident ray PQ is partially reflected along QX and partially refracted along QR. At R, partial reflection takes place along RT and partial refraction along RS. If a perpendicular TM is dropped from T on to the ray QX, we see that while the reflected part of PQ has traversed the short distance QM, the refracted portion which ultimately arrives at T has traversed the distance QRT. The latter will therefore suffer a phase retardation with respect to the former and interference effects will be produced. Owing to the phase change produced on reflection at a light-heavy boundary, the interference effect will give rise to maxima when the optical path-difference is an odd number of half wave-lengths and minima when it corresponds to a whole number of wave-lengths. Since light travels with a speed inversely proportional to the refractive index of the medium, the **optical path** is $\mu \times$ geometrical path. From the geometry of fig. 7, the path-difference is

$$QRT - QM = Q'RT - QM = Q'RT - NT = Q'N$$

$$= 2e \cos r, \quad \ldots \ldots \ldots \ldots \quad (7.7)$$

for NT is *optically* equal to QM.

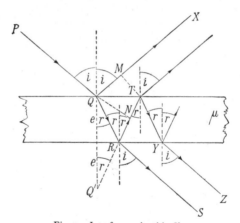

Fig. 7.—Interference by thin film

Hence the *optical path-difference* is

$$\Delta = 2\mu e \cos r, \quad \ldots \ldots \ldots \quad (7.8)$$

and for a *minimum*

$$\Delta = n\lambda = 2\mu e \cos r. \quad \ldots \ldots \quad (7.9)$$

For perpendicular incidence $i = r = 0$ and $\cos r = 1$: hence

$$n\lambda = 2\mu e. \quad \ldots \ldots \ldots \quad (7.10)$$

If the film is air, enclosed for example between two glass plates, $\mu = 1$ and

$$n\lambda = 2e. \quad \ldots \ldots \ldots \quad (7.11)$$

For light of a certain wave-length, therefore, observation from above would yield strong illumination, while for another wave-length, destructive interference would occur and blackness would result. If the film thickness is altered a series of maximum and minimum positions occurs, the thickness changing by $\lambda/2$ for each successive maximum or minimum.

If white light is used, then some wave-length is removed by destructive interference, and the field appears coloured with the complementary colour formed by the remainder of the spectrum. The colours of oil films on the road arise in this fashion; the film is usually of varying thickness and consequently different colours appear, complementary to that whose wave-length is destroyed for any given thickness.

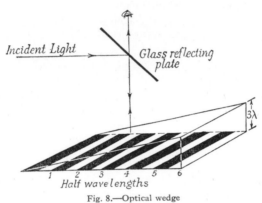

Fig. 8.—Optical wedge

Besides the interference between the reflected rays in fig. 7, interference also results in the transmitted beam between rays such as RS and YZ. The condition for interference in this case may be derived from the geometry of the figure as for the reflected beam, but an easier method is to note that the reflected and transmitted beams are *complementary*. Consequently, when a minimum is observed in the reflected beam, a maximum occurs in the transmitted beam. Such behaviour follows from the Conservation of Energy, for the incident light energy cannot have been destroyed.

If the sides of the film are not parallel the arrangement is said to constitute an **optical wedge**. In this case, for a wedge of small angle and perpendicular incidence, light of any one wave-length will produce straight line fringes parallel to the vertical angle of the wedge as shown in fig. 8. We may clearly define *an interference fringe as the locus of points for which the path-difference is the same*. With the optical wedge, all points have the same path-difference for straight lines drawn parallel to the angle of the wedge. Along dark fringes the relation

$$n\lambda = 2e$$

will hold where n is the order of the fringe. As we proceed from the thin end of the wedge we shall experience darkness until we reach the centre of the first bright fringe when

$$2e = \frac{\lambda}{2}. \quad \ldots \ldots \ldots \quad (7.12)$$

With white light, as with monochromatic light, the thin end of the wedge is dark, but from equation (7.12), on proceeding inwards we first meet a violet fringe, since the wave-length of the violet light is least. This is followed by other coloured fringes in the order of the spectrum. After a short distance, however, the field assumes a uniform grey appearance as bright fringes of one wave-length coincide in position with dark fringes of other waves, or as it is usually expressed, different orders of fringes of various colours are superimposed.

If the angle between the wedge is decreased the interference fringes are spaced farther and farther apart, as we have to proceed a greater distance along the wedge for an increase in thickness of one wave-length. It is upon this principle that the *optical flat* operates. This consists of a very true plane sheet of glass which is placed from time to time over a surface which is being ground flat. Interference occurs in the air film enclosed between the two surfaces, and as the surface becomes more and more true, the fringes becomes farther and farther apart until when there is only one fringe in the field a very high state of truth has been obtained.

6. Newton's Rings.

If a spherical lens of large radius of curvature is lying on a plane sheet of glass and the whole is illuminated with white light, a series of concentric coloured rings is seen in the neighbourhood of the point of contact of the lens and plate. The larger the radius of curvature of the lens, the larger the diameter of the rings. The rings are called *Newton's rings*; they arise from optical interference in the air film formed between lens and plate. The air film may be regarded as a wedge of continually varying angle. Since the locus of points where the path-difference is the same is, for perpendicular incidence, a circle in a horizontal plane with centre at the point of contact of lens and plate, circular interference fringes result. Referring to fig. 9, for some position where the film thickness is e, the condition for a minimum is

$$e = \frac{n\lambda}{2}. \quad \ldots \ldots \ldots \quad (7.13)$$

Now if R is the radius of curvature of the lens and a the radius of the circular fringe in question, by the properties of the circle

$$\frac{a^2}{2R} = e. \qquad \cdots \cdots \cdots \quad (7.14)$$

Hence, from (7.13) and (7.14),

$$a^2 = nR\lambda. \qquad \cdots \cdots \cdots \quad (7.15)$$

To find the wave-length of a specified monochromatic radiation, the radii of several rings are measured and a graph plotted of a^2 against n. If the point of contact of lens and plate is not perfectly clean, definite assessment of the order n of the fringe is difficult. It is therefore usual to use the expression

$$a_1{}^2 - a_n{}^2 = nR\lambda, \qquad \cdots \cdots \cdots \quad (7.16)$$

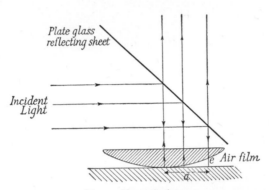

Fig. 9.—Newton's rings

where n is now the number of fringes between the radii r_1 and r_2. These radii or, rather, diameters are measured with a travelling microscope; the radius of curvature of the lens is found by Boys' method (see p. 336).

There are many applications of **interferometry** to the measurement of the wave-length of light or to the establishment of accurate standards of length. We make special reference to this in Chap. XI, where we describe Michelson's interferometer.

7. Position of Interference Fringes.

When we wish to examine interference fringes it is essential to know the position of the fringes. For example, since the fringes formed with a thin wedge film are situated close to the film a microscope is used for their examination. On the other hand, a telescope is used to observe the fringes formed by a parallel-sided film, since such fringes are formed at infinity. The position of the fringes depends on the angle of incidence of the light, whether the light is parallel, divergent or convergent, whether the source used is extended or a point source, and other factors. We give below a simple treatment which is of general use in estimating the position of interference fringes.

Consider the wedge-shaped film of angle a shown in fig. 10. The incident ray PQ gives rise to the reflected ray QR and the refracted ray QST which ultimately emerges along TU. Interference occurs between the rays QR and TU, and the position of the interference fringe is at V, the point of intersection of RQ and UT produced.

Let r be the mean distance of V from the small element of film $QT = l$, and suppose the film increases in thickness by δe as we pro-

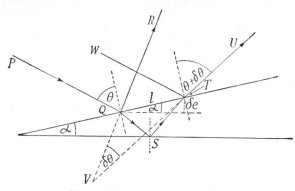

Fig. 10.—Position of interference fringes

gress from Q to T. Then if the angles of incidence of PQ and TU are θ and $(\theta + \delta\theta)$ respectively, $\angle QVS = \delta\theta$. We therefore have

$$l \tan a = la = \delta e,$$

and
$$r\delta\theta = l \cos \theta.$$

Now from equation (7.8), the path-difference Δ between the rays WT and PQST is

$$\Delta = 2e \cos \theta,$$

where e is the film thickness at T, and μ and r have been put equal to unity and θ approximately. Since by definition of a fringe $\delta \Delta = 0$, we have

$$0 = 2\delta e \cos \theta - 2e \sin \theta . \delta\theta,$$

whence
$$\delta e = e \tan \theta . \delta\theta.$$

Hence
$$r = \frac{e \sin \theta}{a}.$$

(i) For a wedge, a is finite, but for nearly normal incidence $\theta \to 0$ and $\sin\theta \to 0$, so $r \to 0$, and the fringes are formed close to the film.

(ii) For a parallel-sided film $a = 0$, so $r \to \infty$, and the fringes are formed at infinity.

* 8. The Banded Spectrum.

We have already shown how if white light is used in many interference experiments, except for a few coloured fringes, a general grey appearance is produced due to the coincidence of different orders of fringe systems of different wave-lengths. Suppose now that the slit of a spectrometer (see Chap. XI, p. 423) is placed in the field and a spectroscopic examination is made of the interference fringes. With a system such as Young's slits, a maximum occurs for all wave-lengths at the central symmetrical position. The spectroscope therefore shows the ordinary continuous spectrum when the slit coincides with the centre of the system. If the slit is then moved across the system a dark line or band appears in the violet end of the spectrum. This is the first minimum for the violet and occurs in a position where the path-difference is half a wave-length for violet light. As we continue to move the slit across the fringe system the dark band moves across the spectrum, but before it has disappeared out of the red end a second dark band has appeared in the violet, corresponding to the second minimum for violet light where the path-difference is now $3\lambda/2$. If we continue to move farther out we find that the bands move in faster from the violet end than they disappear at the red end of the spectrum. Consequently the bands become more numerous and closer together. By observations on these bands we can determine the order of the interference at any point in the interference pattern. Suppose the (unknown) path-difference at any point is δ. This must correspond to an odd number of half wave-lengths for any of the wave-lengths corresponding to a dark band in the spectrum. Suppose p is the number of fringes counted between any two known wave-lengths λ_1 and λ_2 (obtained, say, by the use of a *comparison spectrum* as described on p. 404). Then we have

$$\delta = (2n + 1)\frac{\lambda_1}{2} \quad . \quad . \quad . \quad . \quad . \quad . \quad . \quad (7.17)$$

$$= \{(2n + 1) + (2p + 2)\}\frac{\lambda_2}{2}. \quad . \quad . \quad . \quad (7.18)$$

Hence $\qquad (p + 1) = \dfrac{(2n + 1)(\lambda_1 - \lambda_2)}{2\lambda_2}. \quad . \quad . \quad . \quad . \quad (7.19)$

9. Diffraction at a Slit.

If, instead of having two slits as in Young's interference experiment, a single slit is used, the appearance on the screen is still not that to be expected from geometrical optics, that is, a simple geometrical image of the slit. If the slit is narrow and the source of illumination intense, the central geometrical image is observed to be flanked symmetrically on either side by faint images of the slit. The narrower the slit, the greater the separation of these images is observed to be, and the appearance on the screen is termed a **diffraction pattern.** The phenomenon arises from the wave properties of the light which emerges from the slit. Since the slit is necessarily of finite width, points on the emerging wave-front are at different distances from any

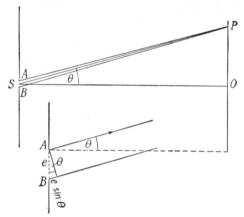

Fig. 11.—Diffraction at a slit

given point on the screen. Now if we assume with Huygens that we may regard each point on the wave-front (see p. 392) as a new secondary source, the effect at any point on the screen arises from the combined interference of all these secondary sources situated across the wave-front emerging from the slit. Thus, instead of having to consider the interference produced by two sources, as in Young's experiment, we have to consider the total interference effect of a large number of sources, and it is this process which gives rise to the diffraction pattern.

Let us consider the effect at P due to the diffraction at the slit S in fig. 11. The path-difference, for a parallel beam, from A and B is clearly $e \sin \theta$ where e is the width of the slit. We require the total effect of all the point sources between those with a maximum path-difference of $e \sin \theta$, or phase difference $(2\pi/\lambda) e \sin \theta$ (since a complete wave-length λ corresponds to a complete phase-angle 2π). If the

amplitudes of all secondary sources are regarded as equal, the total
effect at P is that of n equal vectors, where we consider the wave-
front as due to n secondary sources, the phase of each vector being
an equal amount in advance of the phase of its preceding vector.
Represented graphically, the vectors compound into a circular arc
as shown in fig. 12, where the angle 2α is the maximum phase difference, that is, $\alpha = (\pi/\lambda)e\sin\theta$. (Compare Part IV on Composition
of Simple Harmonic Motions.)

The resultant amplitude is clearly the chord BA. Now

$$\frac{\text{chord } BA}{\text{arc } BA} = \frac{2r\sin\alpha}{2r\alpha} = \frac{\sin\alpha}{\alpha}. \quad \ldots \quad (7.20)$$

The length of the arc represents sum of the amplitudes, or combined
amplitude, A, of the sources, and hence the resultant amplitude is

$$R = \frac{A\sin\alpha}{\alpha}. \quad \ldots \ldots \quad (7.21)$$

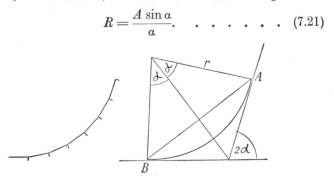

Fig. 12.—Composition of waves

We are particularly interested in the production of maxima and
minima, and therefore we examine the extreme conditions for R.
For $\alpha = 0$, $R = A$, and this corresponds to the central maximum.
For $\alpha = \pi$, 2π, &c., R is zero, and minima occur. Since $\alpha = \pi e\sin\theta/\lambda$,
the condition for minima is

$$e\sin\theta = n\lambda, \quad \ldots \ldots \quad (7.22)$$

or $$\sin\theta = \frac{n\lambda}{e}, \quad \ldots \ldots \quad (7.23)$$

The minima are therefore equidistant for small angles (for which
$\sin\theta = \theta$ nearly), and the angular separation is inversely proportional
to the width of the slit. To obtain the condition for maxima, we differentiate R with respect to α, and equate to zero. The condition is
that $\alpha = \tan\alpha$, and this is represented graphically in fig. 13. The
solutions are given by the points where the line $\alpha = \tan\alpha$ cuts the
curves. This occurs approximately at $\alpha = 0$, $3\pi/2$, $5\pi/2$, &c., and
hence the maxima lie approximately midway between the minima.

The relative intensities of the different order diffraction bands is given from (7.21) by R^2 since the intensity is proportional to the square of the amplitude (see Part IV). Hence $I \propto (\sin \alpha/\alpha)^2$, and the intensities are in the ratios

$$1 : \sin^2 \frac{(3\pi/2)}{(3\pi/2)^2} : \sin^2 \frac{(5\pi/2)}{(5\pi/2)^2}, \&c.,$$

or

$$1 : \frac{4}{9\pi^2} : \frac{4}{25\pi^2}, \&c.$$

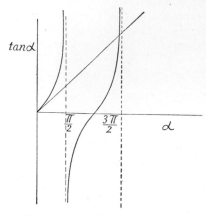

Fig. 13.—Graph for equation $\alpha = \tan \alpha$

The intensity of the diffraction bands therefore falls off extremely rapidly with the order of the band.

It is clear that diffraction effects must be present in the experiment with Young's slits, and careful examination shows the presence of diffraction bands in the field. These are usually much broader and more diffuse than interference fringes, and various devices such as the use of very fine slits in Young's experiments may reduce the diffraction effect very much, while leaving the interference effect relatively undisturbed.

10. Fresnel's Zones and the Zone Plate.

A most useful procedure in diffraction problems was introduced by Fresnel in the suggestion that plane wave-fronts could be divided into zones. Suppose we require the total effect at the point P in fig. 14

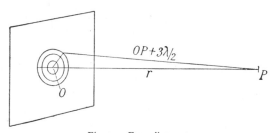

Fig. 14.—Fresnel's zones

due to a plane wave-front approaching from the left. Drop the perpendicular $PO = r$, and with P as centre, describe a series of circles on the wave-front such that the distances of any two adjacent circles from P differ by $\lambda/2$. The plane wave-front is thus divided into a number of circular zones, and the phase of the light arriving at P from any zone may be said to differ on the average by π from the phase of the light from either adjacent zone. The total intensity produced at P is due to the interference of the light arriving from all the zones.

We must first consider the effective intensity at a zone regarded as a source, and this is clearly proportional to the areas of the zones. But (see fig. 14) the area of the first zone (of radius a_1) is

$$\pi a_1{}^2 = \pi \left\{ \left(r + \frac{\lambda}{2} \right)^2 - r^2 \right\} = \pi r \lambda \quad . \quad . \quad . \quad (7.24)$$

approximately, since $\lambda \ll r$. Similarly, for the second zone, the area is given by

$$\pi a_2{}^2 - \pi a_1{}^2 = \pi \{ (r + \lambda)^2 - r^2 \} - \pi r \lambda = \pi r \lambda, \quad . \quad (7.25)$$

so that the *areas of all the zones are the same*. Since the direction of the zones gradually grows more oblique, each produces a slightly smaller

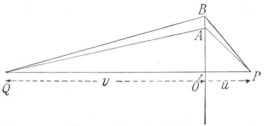

Fig. 15.—Action of zone plate

effect at P than the preceding zone. If this were not so, the total effect at P would clearly be either a maximum or zero according as the wave-front included an odd or an even number of zones. It may be shown that for an unrestricted wave-front the total effect eventually reduces to about half the effect of the central zone acting alone.

If all the alternate zones are blacked out, then a large effect will be produced at P, for all the clear zones now contribute effects differing in phase by 2π from each other and thus assist each other. Such an arrangement is realized experimentally in the zone plate. This often consists of a circular interference pattern (such as a Newton's rings system) photographed on to a transparent photographic plate. If the plate is mounted vertically on an optical bench and a source of light placed on one side, a series of images is formed on the other side. The zone plate thus behaves as a lens with several focal lengths. The action is produced as illustrated in fig. 15. Let OAB be the zone plate and A and B successive clear zones. Let the object be at P and suppose an image of P is observed at Q. Then the path length δ_1 via PBQ is

$$\delta_1 = PB + BQ = (OP^2 + OB^2)^{\frac{1}{2}} + (OQ^2 + OB^2)^{\frac{1}{2}}$$

$$= OP + OQ + \frac{OB^2}{2}\left(\frac{1}{OP} + \frac{1}{OQ}\right) \text{ approx.} \qquad (7.26)$$

Similarly, the path length δ_2 via PAB is

$$\delta_2 = OP + OQ + \frac{OA^2}{2}\left(\frac{1}{OP} + \frac{1}{OQ}\right). \qquad . \quad . \quad (7.27)$$

Now for an image at Q, constructive interference must occur, and

$$\delta_1 - \delta_2 = n\lambda = \left(\frac{1}{OP} + \frac{1}{OQ}\right)\tfrac{1}{2}(OB^2 - OA^2), \quad . \quad (7.28)$$

where n is integral. But by the property of the zone plate

$$(OB^2 - OA^2) = 2r\lambda.$$

Hence $\qquad\qquad\qquad \dfrac{1}{OP} + \dfrac{1}{OQ} = \dfrac{n}{r}. \quad . \quad . \quad . \quad . \quad . \quad (7.29)$

The formula is therefore identical with that of a lens [see equation (3.18)] except that there are n foci. The same law of magnification, $m = v/u$, is also obeyed.

11. Diffraction at an Obstacle.

If the shadow of a small circular obstacle is examined, it is to be expected from what has been said regarding diffraction that complete darkness will not occur in the confines of the geometrical shadow. In practice, light waves are diffracted round the obstacle and circular diffraction maxima and minima occur. We shall discuss in detail the **diffraction at a straight edge.** We shall also concentrate on *Fresnel* as opposed to *Fraunhofer diffraction.* The former may be defined as diffraction in which the source and screen are at finite distances from the obstacle. The wave-front is therefore spherical or cylindrical, and the phase is not constant even across the obstacle if the latter is plane. In Fraunhofer diffraction both source and screen are at an infinite distance from the diffracting system. This condition is realized in practice by using a parallel beam (plane wave-front) incident on the diffracting system, and collecting the diffracted parallel beam at the focus of a converging lens. Fraunhofer diffraction is therefore frequently met with in optical instruments where these conditions are common (see Chap. XI).

In fig. 16 let AB be the straight edge, and let the source of light be situated at S; we investigate the effect on the screen at P. The effect at P may be regarded as the sum of the effects of (a) the unobstructed half-wave lying above C, and (b) the portion of the wavefront CA. The former effect is constant for all points lying above O on the screen, and hence the effect at any of these points depends on whether the number of Fresnel zones contained in the portion CA is odd or even. If the number is odd the effect is a maximum, if even a minimum, and the final result is therefore that the geometrical edge of the shadow at O is flanked with a series of alternately light and dark diffraction bands.

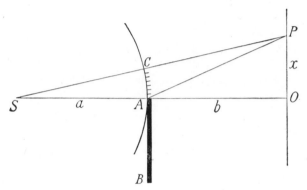

Fig. 16.—Diffraction at straight edge

To determine whether any given point P corresponds to a maximum or minimum we commence by noting that the number of zones in the wave-front is equal to the number of half wave-lengths in the difference $AP - CP$. From the geometry, if we represent OP by x and SA, AO by a and b respectively:

$$SP^2 = (a + b)^2 + x^2. \quad \cdots \cdots (7.30)$$

Hence $\qquad CP = SP - a = b + \dfrac{x^2}{2(a + b)} \text{ approx.} \quad \cdots (7.31)$

Similarly $\qquad AP = b + \dfrac{x^2}{2b}. \quad \cdots \cdots (7.32)$

Hence $\qquad AP - CP = \dfrac{x^2 a}{2b(a + b)}. \quad \cdots \cdots (7.33)$

For a minimum, $\qquad AP - CP = n\lambda. \quad \cdots \cdots (7.34)$

Hence $\qquad x^2 = \dfrac{2n\lambda b(a + b)}{a}. \quad \cdots \cdots (7.35)$

The diffraction bands are therefore not evenly spaced, x being proportional to $\sqrt{n}$.

Inside the edge of the geometrical shadow at O, we have the effect produced by the incomplete half wave-front, lying above A. As the effect depends essentially on the first zone only (see p. 369), and this

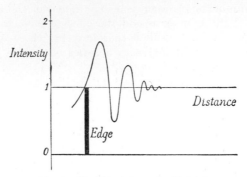

Fig. 17.—Straight edge: graph of intensity

becomes gradually and continuously smaller and more oblique, a gradual diminution in intensity is observed as we enter the geometrical shadow. The maximum intensity occurs at a short distance out from the edge of the geometrical shadow for the position when CA is the radius of the first zone. The intensity distribution is shown in fig. 17.

12. The Diffraction Grating.

The common diffraction grating consists of a large number of parallel grooves ruled on a transparent plate with great regularity of spacing. The whole may be treated as a series of equidistant slits, and consequently both interference and diffraction effects occur when light passes through the grating. Now, in general, the width of each individual groove is only slightly larger than the wave-lengths in the visible spectrum, and therefore, by equation (7.23), the first minimum for each slit is formed at very large values of θ, the inclination to the direct ray. Since observation is normally restricted to angles less than, say, 45°, all observations are made in the central maximum of the diffraction pattern. We can therefore neglect the diffraction effect and concentrate on the interference which occurs between light from the different slits. From this point of view, a better name for the arrangement would be an interference grating. If we consider a plane wave incident normally on the grating, then observation at some angle θ to the normal will give a maximum if two adjacent rays, as shown in fig. 18, differ in path by a whole number of wave-lengths.

Hence for a maximum

$$(e + f) \sin \theta = n\lambda, \quad \ldots \ldots \quad (7.36)$$

while for a minimum

$$\sin \theta = \frac{(n + \frac{1}{2})\lambda}{(e + f)}, \quad \ldots \ldots \quad (7.37)$$

where e is the width of a groove and f the width of a ridge of the grating.

Since the position of the first interference maximum is governed by the relation $\sin \theta \propto \lambda$, white light gives rise to a spectrum after passage through a diffraction grating. Gratings are often constructed

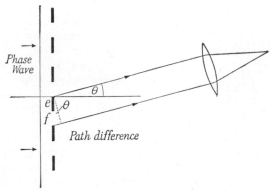

Fig. 18.—Diffraction grating

with about 5000 lines to the centimetre. Consequently the first diffraction maximum occurs at about 20° to the incident normal light for the visible spectrum. Since the number of rulings on a grating is known, $(e + f)$ is known, and hence measurement of θ allows the determination of λ.

For certain special purposes gratings are ruled on concave reflecting surfaces so that a focusing action is also obtained. Such a process is particularly useful in determining the wave-length of lines in the ultra-violet region where focusing lenses and a transmission grating absorb the radiation strongly.

Two very important characteristics of the grating are its **dispersive power** and its **resolving power**. The former is defined as the rate of change of angle of diffraction with wave-length, that is, $d\theta/d\lambda$. If there are m lines to the centimetre, $(e + f) = 1/m$, and hence, from (7.36), the dispersive power

$$\frac{d\theta}{d\lambda} = \frac{mn}{\cos \theta}. \quad \ldots \ldots \quad (7.38)$$

It is therefore proportional to the order of the spectrum and the closeness of the rulings. Since the angular spread of the visible spectrum formed by diffraction is small, $\cos\theta$ is approximately constant, and hence $d\theta \propto d\lambda$. A spectrum in which the displacement is proportional to the wave-length is termed a **normal spectrum.** The spectrum formed by dispersion in a glass prism is not normal, for the angular separation becomes progressively greater as we proceed towards the violet. The spectrum is therefore drawn out at the violet end and compressed at the red end. A third type of dispersion in which some colours even appear in incorrect order of wave-length is termed **anomalous dispersion,** and is discussed briefly in Chap. X.

13. Resolving Power of an Optical System.

If two wave-lengths λ and $(\lambda + d\lambda)$ are just separable as two distinct maxima (say as lines with a diffraction grating), they are said to be just resolved, and the resolving power of the arrangement is defined as $\lambda/d\lambda$. Good resolving power involves the production of sharp maxima as shown in fig. 19. Increased dispersive power, besides increasing the angular separation of the lines, also increases their width so that an increase of resolving power does not take place simultaneously.

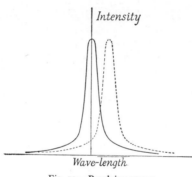

Fig. 19.—Resolving power

(i) The Grating.

To find an expression for the resolving power of a grating, let N be the total number of rulings included in the entire width of the grating. Then for a maximum for a wave-length $(\lambda + d\lambda)$, the path-difference for adjacent rays is given by

$$\delta = n(\lambda + d\lambda). \quad \ldots \ldots \quad (7.39)$$

Hence the path-difference for the extreme rays is

$$N\delta = nN(\lambda + d\lambda). \quad \ldots \ldots \quad (7.40)$$

The path-difference for the extreme maxima at wave-length λ is $nN\lambda$; and therefore the path-difference for the extreme minima may be taken to be $nN\lambda + \lambda$, corresponding to a difference of half a wave-length at each end of the grating.

Now it is found experimentally that for clear separation of two maxima, they must not lie closer together than the distance between adjacent maxima and minima for one of the wave-lengths concerned. Hence, if the lines λ and $\lambda + d\lambda$ are just resolved,

$$nN(\lambda + d\lambda) = (nN + 1)\lambda, \quad \ldots \ldots \text{(7.41)}$$

or

$$\frac{\lambda}{d\lambda} = nN. \quad \ldots \ldots \ldots \text{(7.42)}$$

The resolving power of a grating is therefore proportional to the total number of lines on the grating and to the order of the interference. Unfortunately, the intensities of the maxima decrease so rapidly with the order that the high resolving power cannot often be used to advantage. However, photographic recording over long periods is of assistance in this respect. The sodium D lines are easily resolved in the first order spectrum of an ordinary grating. This behaviour agrees with equation (7.42), for the resolving power required is $\sim 6000/6 = 1000$, and N is of the order of several thousand.

(ii) The Prism.

Suppose the plane wave-front AB, containing wave-lengths λ and $\lambda + d\lambda$ is incident on a prism in the position of minimum deviation as shown in fig. 20. After passage through the prism these wave-fronts are represented by CD and CD' inclined to each other at an

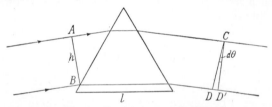

Fig. 20.—Resolving power of prism

angle $d\theta$. Let the length of the base of the prism be l and the width of the light beam be h. Then the maximum optical path-difference, which occurs for rays traversing the apex and base of the prism, is $l(\mu + d\mu) - l\mu = l\,d\mu$ where μ and $(\mu + d\mu)$ are the refractive indices for the wave-lengths $(\lambda + d\lambda)$ and λ. Now, from fig. 20, this optical path-difference is DD' $= h\,d\theta$. Hence

$$d\theta = \frac{l}{h}\,d\mu. \quad \ldots \ldots \text{(7.43)}$$

We now regard the passage of the light beam of width h through the prism as diffraction at a slit of width h. The angle $d\theta'$ between the first minimum and the central maximum is, from equation (7.23),

$$d\theta' = \frac{\lambda}{h}. \quad \ldots \ldots \text{(7.44)}$$

Now for resolution of the two wave-lengths λ and $\lambda + d\lambda$ the separation of the two maxima must be not less than the distance between adjacent maxima and minima for one of the wave-lengths. Hence from (7.43) and (7.44) the limit of resolution is reached when $d\theta = d\theta'$, and hence the resolving power R of the prism is given by

$$R = \frac{\lambda}{d\lambda} = l\frac{d\mu}{d\lambda}. \quad \ldots \quad (7.45)$$

For ordinary glass $d\mu/d\lambda \simeq 1000$ (neglecting sign), if λ is measured in centimetres, so that the *resolving power of a prism is approximately a thousand times the length of its base in centimetres.*

(iii) The Telescope.

The construction and mode of action of a telescope are discussed in Chap. XI. For the purpose of discussing the resolving power of a telescope we need simply consider that on entering the telescope the extent of a plane wave is limited by the size of the object glass, and hence we are dealing with *diffraction at a circular aperture.* Now each point on the object under observation sends light waves to the object glass and, if the diffraction patterns formed by the different light waves are such that the central maximum of one pattern lies closer to the central maximum of another than the separation of a maximum and minimum of one pattern alone, the image will be indefinite and may fail to reveal any likeness to the object. It is very important to realize that a great increase in magnifying power of the telescope is useless unless accompanied by increase in resolving power, for each diffraction pattern will simply be magnified and no further detail will be revealed. The process would be like attempting to increase the detail in a picture painted on an elastic sheet simply by stretching the sheet. The calculation of the resolving power for a circular aperture involves difficult integrations, so we shall consider the resolving power of a telescope with a rectangular aperture in front of the lens. Referring to fig. 11, and remembering our results for diffraction at a slit (which is a rectangular aperture of infinite extent in one direction), we see that the direction of the first minimum with respect to the central line is given by

$$\sin\theta = \frac{\lambda}{h}, \quad \ldots \quad (7.46)$$

or where θ is small,

$$\theta = \frac{\lambda}{h}, \quad \ldots \quad (7.47)$$

where h is the width of the aperture.

For a circular aperture, integration shows that the expression is the same as for a slit except for a factor 1·22, so we obtain

$$\theta = \frac{1 \cdot 22\lambda}{h}. \quad \ldots \ldots \ldots \quad (7.48)$$

Now θ is also the angle subtended by two adjacent points on the source if the central maximum due to one point is to fall on the first minimum produced by the other. Hence the angular separation of two points on an object subtended at the object glass must exceed $1 \cdot 22\lambda/h$ if the image of the two points is to be resolved into two distinct points. The angle subtended at the largest object glasses by any star is less than this, so the diameter and detail of a star can never be ascertained by simple observation through a telescope. However, Michelson has succeeded in measuring the diameter of several stars by an ingenious interference device described in Chap. XI. We discuss the resolving power of a microscope also in Chap. XI.

EXERCISES

1. Describe the production of interference fringes with the arrangement of two parallel slits. What is the effect of illuminating the slits with white light?

2. Compare and contrast the interference fringes obtained with Fresnel's mirrors and Lloyd's mirror. Determine the separation between two adjacent fringes if the distance between the two sources is 1 mm., the distance from the sources to the plane of observation is 2 m., and the wavelength of the light is 5×10^{-5} cm. [1 mm.]

3. Explain the coloured appearance of an oil film on the surface of a road. Why does a thick film not give the same appearance?

4. How would you determine the angle of a very thin wedge of transparent material? At what distance from the end of a wedge of angle 0·01 radian will the first bright interference band occur when the wedge is illuminated with light of wave-length 6×10^{-5} cm. for perpendicular incidence? [$1 \cdot 5 \times 10^{-3}$ cm.]

5. Give the theory of Newton's rings and describe how the wavelength of light may be measured from observations on the rings.

6. Describe the production of a banded spectrum. What is the order of interference at a point in the interference system formed by white light with two parallel slits if spectroscopic analysis shows that 19 fringes lie between two wave-lengths $5 \cdot 438 \times 10^{-5}$ cm., $4 \cdot 800 \times 10^{-5}$ cm.? [150.]

7. Distinguish between interference fringes and diffraction bands. In what way do the diffraction bands obtained with a slit differ from the interference fringes obtained with two parallel slits?

8. Give the theory of the diffraction of a plane wave at a slit. What is

the angle subtended at a slit 0·1 mm. wide by the line joining the central maximum to the fourth minimum if the wave-length of the light is 5·890 × 10⁻⁵ cm.?   [0·024 rad.]

9. Explain what is meant by *Fresnel zones*? Why is more light received at a point through an aperture containing one Fresnel zone than through a wider aperture containing six Fresnel zones?

10. Give the theory of the zone plate. What is the distance between the fourth and fifth images of an object at a distance of 50 cm. from a zone plate of constructional polar distance 100 cm.?   [$\frac{50}{3}$ cm.]

11. Show from first principles that the separation between the 16th and 9th dark bands is equal to that between the 9th and 4th dark bands, in the diffraction pattern formed by a straight-edged obstacle.

12. Give a brief account of the mode of working of an ordinary transmission diffraction grating at normal incidence. In what way may the spectrum formed by a diffraction grating be said to exhibit greater regularity than the spectrum formed by a glass prism when they are each submitted to white light?

13. Distinguish between the dispersive power and the resolving power of a diffraction grating. Why are large gratings and prisms necessary if high resolving power is to be obtained?

14. Write a short essay on the resolving power of optical instruments.

CHAPTER VIII

Double Refraction and Polarization

1. Double Refraction.

It was discovered by Bartholinus in 1669 that if a crystal of calcite was placed over a small object such as an ink spot on a piece of paper, then, on viewing the spot through the calcite, two images were generally observed instead of one. This phenomenon is termed **double refraction.** Observation of the spot from a certain direction yields only one image and the direction in the crystal for which this happens is termed its **optic axis.** The optic axis corresponds therefore to a certain direction, and not to a particular line as the name axis usually implies. If the crystal is rotated about a vertical axis on the horizontal sheet of paper, one image stays in its initial position but the other rotates round the fixed position of the first image. The stationary image, indeed, behaves exactly as the ordinary image observed through a glass block and is therefore termed the **ordinary image.** The other image is referred to as the **extraordinary image** and arises from **extraordinary rays.** Experimental investigation shows that the ordinary rays obey the ordinary laws of refraction stated on p. 315. On the other hand, the extraordinary rays obey neither of the laws of refraction, that is, the incident ray, the normal and the refracted ray do not in general all lie in one plane, nor is Snell's law obeyed.

If the angles of incidence and refraction are measured for the extraordinary rays it is found that the fraction $\sin i/\sin r$ varies regularly between two extreme values. One of these values coincides with the refractive index μ_0 of the ordinary ray and, indeed, applies to the case when the ordinary and extraordinary rays coincide, that is, the rays are passing in the direction of the optic axis. The other extreme value μ_e is termed the refractive index of the extraordinary ray and it may have a value greater or less than μ_0. In the former case the crystal is said to be positive and in the latter negative. Even a singly refracting material such as optical glass becomes doubly refracting if subject to large mechanical strain.

* 2. The Wave-front in Uniaxial Crystals.

We discuss the wave theory of light in more detail in Chap. IX. At the moment we are concerned with the proof that the ordinary wave-front is spherical and the extraordinary wave-front an ellipsoid of revolution touching the ordinary spherical wave-front at points of intersection with the common optic axis as shown in fig. 1.

To demonstrate conclusively that the ordinary wave-front is spherical, a prism is constructed of several small pieces of crystal

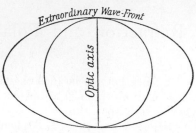

Fig. 1.—Wave-front in uniaxial crystals

cemented together with their axes in many different orientations. The extraordinary rays are bent in many different directions in their passage through the prism, since their bending depends upon the directions of the random optic axes. Consequently no clear extraordinary image of a slit (say) is observed. On the other hand, the

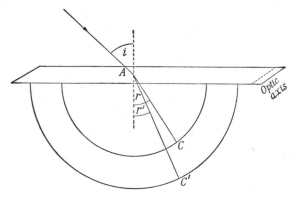

Fig. 2.—Optic axis perpendicular to plane of incidence

ordinary image is formed as for an ordinary glass prism, so the ordinary wave-front must be spherical.

To examine the nature of the extraordinary wave-front the method suggested by Huygens is usually followed. Two special cases are considered:

(i) *Refracting face parallel to the optic axis and the plane of incidence perpendicular to it.* The cross-sections of the ordinary and extraordinary wave-fronts under these conditions are semicircular as shown in fig. 2. The ordinary secondary wave spreading from A is represented by the semicircle with radius AC, and the extraordinary wave from A by the semicircle with radius AC'. Then $\mu_0 = \sin i/\sin r$ and $\mu_e = \sin i/\sin r'$, so the arrangement would allow the determination of μ_0 and μ_e. Experimentally a prism of crystal is taken with the optic axis parallel to the refracting edge; it is placed on the spectrometer in the usual way. Rays incident in the position of minimum deviation give rise to an ordinary and extraordinary image, and applying equation (3.11) the values of μ_0 and μ_e are obtained. It may be remarked that $\mu_0/\mu_e = \dfrac{AC'}{AC}$.

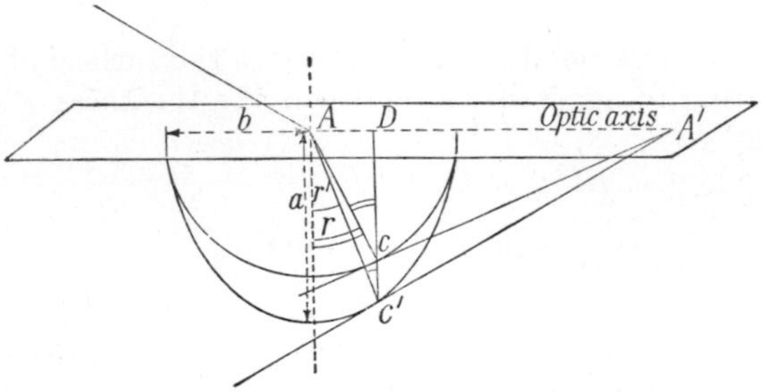

Fig. 3.—Optic axis parallel to plane of incidence

(ii) *Optic axis parallel to the surface of the crystal and also parallel to the plane of incidence.*

The appearance of the sections of the wave-fronts of the ordinary and extraordinary rays are now as shown in fig. 3. They consist of a semicircle and a semi-ellipse with common points of contact at the points of emergence of the optic axis. Now it may be shown from co-ordinate geometry that if tangents are drawn from a common external point A' to touch the circle and ellipse in C and C' respectively, C'C produced cuts AA' perpendicularly at D. Hence

$$\frac{\tan r}{\tan r'} = \frac{AD/CD}{AD/C'D} = \frac{C'D}{CD} = \frac{a}{b} = \frac{\mu_0}{\mu_e}, \quad \cdot \quad \cdot \quad \cdot \quad (8.1)$$

so that the ratio of the tangents of the angles of refraction for the ordinary and extraordinary rays should be equal to the ratio of the ordinary and extraordinary refractive indices. The value of μ_0/μ_e is known from experiment (i): hence we now proceed to measure r and r', to form the ratio $\tan r/\tan r'$, and thus see if the assumption of an ellipsoidal wave-front is correct. The experiment, which was carried out first by Malus, is as follows. Two horizontal intersecting scales AC, BC are engraved on a polished steel plate, and a thick plate of the crystal with optic axis parallel to the surface is laid over the scales. The images, which have the appearance shown in fig. 4, are viewed from above through a telescope mounted on a horizontal axis and attached to a circular scale in a vertical plane. The two images appear to intersect at some point h, and the axis of the telescope is

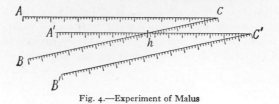

Fig. 4.—Experiment of Malus

directed towards this point so as to intersect the surface of the crystal at H. Referring to fig. 5, if we represent the thickness of the crystal by e, we have

$$ED = EP - DP$$

$$= e(\tan r' - \tan r). \quad . \quad . \quad . \quad . \quad . \quad (8.2)$$

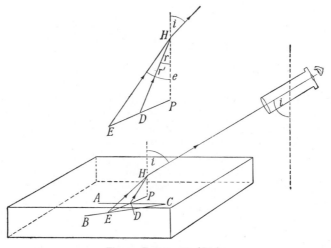

Fig. 5.—Experiment of Malus

Now ED is obtained by simple measurement on the scales, since the point h is known by direct observation. Also $\tan r$ may be calculated, for i is obtained by direct measurement of the position of the telescope on the vertical scale, μ_0 is known from previous experiments, and r is calculated from $\sin i = \mu_0 \sin r$. Hence from equation (8.2) $\tan r'$ may be determined. Forming the ratio $\tan r/\tan r'$, we have from equation (8.1) the ratio μ_0/μ_e. If the value thus obtained agrees with the ratio of μ_0/μ_e from experiment (i), then the ellipsoidal nature of the extraordinary wave-front may be considered to have been established.

3. Nicol's Prism and Polarization.

If a crystal of calcite is cut in half and a transparent layer of Canada balsam of refractive index 1·55 is used to cement the two halves together again, then under certain conditions one image only is transmitted through the prism. With the geometrical conditions as in fig. 6, the ordinary ray is entirely suppressed owing to the angle of incidence at the Canada balsam division being greater than the critical angle for the ordinary ray. On the other hand, the angle of incidence is below the critical angle for the extraordinary ray and the latter is therefore transmitted. Such an arrangement is termed a **Nicol prism,** or more usually, a **Nicol.**

If now light is transmitted through two Nicols situated any distance apart, a remarkable phenomenon is observed as they are rotated

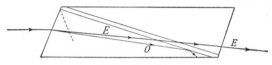

Fig. 6.—Nicol prism

with respect to each other about the common axis. For one position termed the position of **complete extinction** no light whatever is transmitted, although each crystal is individually transparent to the extraordinary ray. If the second Nicol is rotated in either direction through 90°, visibility is again restored to its maximum, which is not very different from that experienced when one Nicol alone is present. For intermediate orientations the field assumes an appearance of intermediate brightness. The phenomenon, which is said to be due to **polarization,** receives a ready explanation in terms of the wave theory of light if the waves are assumed to be transverse. We postulate (see Chap. IX) that ordinary light consists of transverse waves vibrating in a direction perpendicular to the direction of propagation but with all orientations. On passage into a doubly refracting medium, these waves are split into two groups, the ordinary and extraordinary waves. The vibrations in those groups are confined to two planes, mutually perpendicular to each other, and the light is now said to be **plane polarized.** The ordinary and extraordinary images are therefore formed by two polarized beams, and if, as in the Nicol prism, one beam is suppressed, a single beam of polarized light is obtained. Now the plane of polarization bears a definite relation to the optic axis, and if a second Nicol prism is orientated with respect to the first in a certain direction, the incident plane polarized beam is entirely suppressed. The two Nicols, in fact, behave like two slits as shown in fig. 7. Vibrations incident on the first slit are transmitted in a direction parallel to the slit and are thus plane polarized. If now the second slit (or Nicol) is parallel to the first the plane polarized beam is transmitted, but if it is perpendicular to it no vibrations can pass. Complete extinction results and the Nicols are said to be **crossed**. This interpretation of polarization is so simple and satisfying that it forms

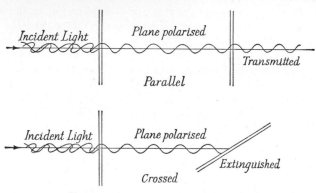

Fig. 7.—Action of parallel and crossed Nicols

extremely strong support for the transverse wave theory of light. The first Nicol is termed the **polarizer** and the second Nicol the **analyser.**

4. Polarization by Reflection, and Brewster's Law.

Polarization may be produced by reflection, refraction, diffraction, and by the action of electric and magnetic fields on light sources. An ordinary, homogeneous, singly refracting medium like glass is found to produce some polarization on light reflected by the glass. For a certain angle of incidence on a plane sheet of glass the polarization produced is a maximum, and if two glass plates are mounted so as to be capable of orientation at various angles in planes perpendicular to each other, they act as polarizer and analyser just as Nicol prisms do. The beam transmitted by the polarizer is likewise polarized, and by symmetry is polarized in a plane perpendicular to that of the reflected beam. When light is polarized by reflection, the plane of reflection is called the **plane of polarization,** and the light is said to be polarized in that plane. The polarization produced by reflection is not complete for any orientation, but it reaches a maximum when

$$\tan i = \mu, \quad \ldots \ldots \quad (8.3)$$

where i is the angle of incidence, called the **polarizing angle,** and μ is the refractive index. This relation is termed **Brewster's Law.** By measurement of Brewster's angle a value may be found for the refractive index of an opaque liquid such as ink. The simplest method now employed of obtaining a polarizer and an analyser is to make use of two sheets of *polaroid.* This is the trade name of a synthetic resin which has the property of polarizing by transmission.

* 5. Circularly and Elliptically Polarized Light.

If a beam of plane polarized light is passed more or less normally through a thin parallel-sided sheet of crystal as shown in fig. 8, then, in general, rotation of an analyser fails to produce complete extinction for any position, although some change in intensity may occur.

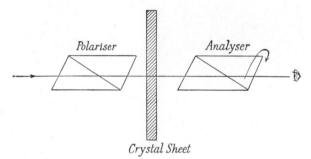

Fig. 8.—Passage of polarized light through a thin crystal

This behaviour is explained as follows. The plane vibrations of the incident plane polarized light are split into two sets of vibrations vibrating in planes at right angles, that is, the ordinary and extraordinary ray. If the crystal plate is thin these rays do not become appreciably separated laterally at the point of emergence of the rays from the crystal. Now since the refractive indices for the two rays are different, the velocities of the two rays through the crystal are different and they therefore emerge with a **phase difference.** The type of vibration which results from compounding the two vibrations will clearly depend on the amplitude of each vibration and the phase difference between them. In Part IV, on Wave Motion and Acoustics, we examine in detail the result of compounding two or more simple harmonic motions of different amplitude and phase. We therefore limit our account here to a very brief description of a qualitative nature. We propose to use the **pendulum analogy.**

Imagine a simple pendulum acted upon by two impulses mutually at right angles. Reference to fig. 9 will show that the oscillation of the pendulum will in general be elliptical, but in special circumstances this will reduce to circular or planar motion. The following instances may be considered:

(i) *Amplitudes equal or unequal; phase difference zero.*—As shown in fig. 10 (*a*) these would result in a linear diagonal movement and hence correspond to plane polarization.

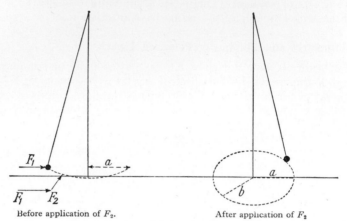

Before application of F_2.   After application of F_2

Fig. 9.—Simple pendulum acted on by two impulses

(ii) *Amplitudes equal and phase difference $\pi/2$.*—As shown in fig. 10 (*b*) this is equivalent to giving the pendulum a second impulse at right angles to its planar motion under the first impulse, just as it reaches the top of its swing. Since the amplitudes of the two vibrations are supposed equal, the bob will describe a circular arc; in the optical case this corresponds to **circular polarization.** Such behaviour will take place if the phase difference is any odd multiple of $\pi/2$.

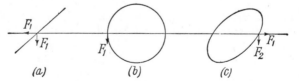

(*a*)   (*b*)   (*c*)

Fig. 10.—Plane, circular and elliptical polarization

(iii) *Amplitudes equal but phase difference not zero or multiple of $\pi/2$.*—In these circumstances the pendulum bob describes an ellipse of eccentricity varying with the phase difference, the general behaviour being as shown in fig. 10 (*c*). This clearly corresponds to **elliptical polarization.**

(iv) *Amplitudes unequal.*—In general this must result in elliptical polarization as experiments with the pendulum bob would show.

Observation by an analyser of light which was initially plane polarized and is then passed through a crystal plate therefore exhibits the following effects. As the analyser is rotated a fluctuation in intensity is observed. If the light is plane polarized, complete extinction occurs for a certain position of the analyser. If the light is circularly polarized no fluctuation in intensity occurs as the condition is symmetrical for all positions of the analyser. If the light is elliptically polarized, then, provided the eccentricity is sufficiently large, a minimum will occur when the minor axis of the ellipse is effective and a maximum when the major axis is fully operative.

The complete analysis of polarized light is beyond the scope of this book, but the type of difficulty which arises and calls for more elaborate methods of treatment is illustrated by the following example. If the analyser is rotated and fluctuations in intensity occur, then the reason may be *either* elliptical polarization or a mixture of ordinary unpolarized and some plane polarized light. Again, quantitative estimation of the amount of polarized light present in a mixture calls for more elaborate technique based on the interference of polarized light.

* 6. Interference with Polarized Light.

Consider now the appearance of a thin crystal wedge when illuminated by plane polarized light and viewed through a crossed analyser. The thickness of the wedge increases uniformly, and consequently the phase difference between ordinary and extraordinary rays increases regularly. Hence at regular distances along the sheet the light re-emerges plane polarized and will be extinguished by the analyser. The appearance will therefore be that of a number of equidistant light and dark bands, always assuming the incident light is monochromatic. Such a phenomenon affords a convenient method of estimating the thickness of a crystal wedge. The extreme tip will be dark since no phase change will occur, and the analyser will simply extinguish the plane polarized incident light. As we proceed along the wedge we arrive at the first bright band when the phase change between ordinary and extraordinary rays is π. The emergent light is then plane polarized in a plane at right angles to the original plane, and is therefore fully admitted by the analyser. On proceeding still further we encounter the next dark band at a position where the phase difference is 2π, and so on. The positions where the successive light and dark bands occur therefore correspond to a phase change of π or an increase in the thickness of the crystal of $\lambda/2$. Since the wavelength of the light is known, the thickness of the wedge can be estimated. Illumination of such a wedge by white light results in a chromatic appearance, for the violet waves will be the first to appear as we proceed from the thin end of the wedge with the analyser in the crossed position. A spectrum will then be observed; for a crystal plate of irregular thickness the field will assume a multicoloured patchwork appearance, the colours being complementary to those wave-lengths which are extinguished at the positions under consideration. Since a rock-slice of uniform thickness contains a large number of different minerals with different refractive indices and hence different optical thicknesses, the multicoloured appearance will be in evidence and is not necessarily an indication of varying physical thickness. Indeed, the method is used to assist in the determination of the nature of the minerals in a rock-slice.

If the analyser is rotated when observation is made on a crystal wedge illuminated by plane polarized monochromatic light, the light and dark bands change places. The explanation is simple and is left to the student. Similarly with white light and crystal plates, rotation of the analyser changes the intensity of colours but not the colours themselves at any given position.

The application of crystal plates to the analysis of polarized light may be illustrated by considering the examination of circularly polarized light. If the light is viewed simply through the analyser with no crystal plate interposed, rotation of the analyser produces no fluctuation in intensity and is thus unable to distinguish between circularly polarized and unpolarized light. Suppose now a **quarter-wave plate,** that is, a parallel-sided crystal plate, is introduced, of such a thickness that it produces a phase difference of $\pi/2$ between the ordinary and extraordinary rays. Then, if the incident light is circularly polarized, it will be converted into plane polarized light, since one of the components of the circular vibration is accelerated or retarded by $\pi/2$ with respect to the other. Viewed through the analyser, for a certain position the field will now be extinguished. On the other hand, had the incident light been unpolarized no fluctuation in intensity would result when the quarter-wave plate was inserted and the analyser was rotated.

Fig. 11.—Crystal and plane polarized converging light

If a crystal plate is illuminated by plane polarized **converging** light and then viewed through an analyser, the appearance depends on the direction in which the plate is cut with respect to the optic axis. Considering the special case where the optic axis is perpendicular to the surface of the crystal, then reference to fig. 11 shows that the loci of points at which equal phase differences are produced between the ordinary and extraordinary rays are circles about the common principal axis. Illumination with plane polarized white light therefore results in a series of **coloured rings,** each consisting of the complementary colour remaining when the phase difference for a given wave-length is such that the latter is extinguished. If mono-chromatic light is used the rings will be crossed by a light or dark cross according to the orientation of the analyser. To explain this we note that at the centre of the rings, since the light has passed along the optic axis, no phase difference is produced, and if the analyser is set for extinction a black spot will occur. Now, as we proceed outwards from the centre, one pair of directions mutually at right angles will correspond to the planes of the ordinary and extraordinary vibrations respectively. If we suppose that the plane of polarization of the incident light is parallel to one of these directions, the other direction transmits no vibrations at all and will therefore appear dark irrespective of the position of the analyser. In addition, the one beam which is transmitted will be extinguished if the analyser is in the crossed position.

Besides uniaxial crystals, **biaxial crystals** also exist possessing two optic axes, that is, two directions in the crystal for which no double refraction occurs. Biaxial crystals likewise give rise to curious patterns when viewed by polarized light with an analyser. The simple family of circles presented by a uniaxial crystal cut perpendicular to the optic axis is replaced by a family of lemniscates for a biaxial crystal cut perpendicular to the bisector of the angle between the two optic axes.

7. Rotation of the Plane of Polarization.

If a beam of polarized light is sent down the optic axis of a quartz crystal, which is uniaxial, then according to our considerations so far we should expect little effect to be produced. Observation with an analyser, however, would show that if it was arranged for extinction before the insertion of the quartz crystal, extinction was no longer present after the insertion of the crystal. This phenomenon is not due to any double refraction of the quartz crystal in the direction of its optic axis (such behaviour would contradict the definition of optic axis), but is due to **rotation of the plane of polarization.** Certain crystals, liquids, solutions, homogeneous substances, and electric and magnetic fields possess this property of rotating the plane of polarization of a plane polarized beam which is passed through them. In the study of organic chemistry, many substances are found which are similar in chemical and physical properties but which rotate polarized light in opposite directions. They are said to be dextro- and lævo-rotary forms of the given material, and the crystal structure of the pairs of substances is complementary. Quartz produces optical rotation along the direction of its optic axis, but none along a direction perpendicular to this.

The optical rotation produced by a solution is directly proportional to the concentration, and consequently the phenomenon provides an extremely useful method of determining the percentage of material present in a solution. Instruments designed for this purpose are termed **polarimeters**. The simplest type of polarimeter consists of a polarizer, a trough with transparent ends to contain the solution, and an analyser mounted on a circular scale. Standard solutions are taken and the apparatus is calibrated, a certain rotation of the analyser being required to produce extinction for a certain concentration of the solution. The **specific rotation** $[a]_D{}^t$ of a substance is defined as the quantity θ/ml, where θ is the rotation produced, l is the length of the solution in decimetres, and m is the concentration (the mass of dissolved substance per cubic centimetre). Of the symbols t and D, the former signifies that a particular temperature must be specified, while the latter indicates that light of the sodium D lines must be used. The simple polarimeter described here is not very accurate, special devices being employed to permit matching of illuminated fields rather than to require the judgment of the setting for complete extinction.

EXERCISES

1. What is meant by *double refraction*? In what ways do *ordinary* rays differ from *extraordinary* rays?

2. By what experiments may it be shown that the extraordinary wavefront in a uniaxial crystal is an ellipsoid of revolution?

3. Describe the construction and mode of operation of a Nicol prism both as a polarizer and analyser. What other methods are available for obtaining a plane polarized parallel beam of light?

4. Show that the angles of incidence and refraction are complementary when the maximum polarization is being obtained by reflection at a plane glass sheet.

5. Distinguish between plane, circularly, and elliptically polarized light. How would you show the existence of circularly polarized light in a mixture of ordinary light and circularly polarized light?

6. How may interference effects be produced with a crystal plate? What practical applications have been made of these phenomena?

7. Define the terms *optic axis, uniaxial crystal, biaxial crystal.* Give a general explanation of the coloured rings and dark brushes observed when crystal plates are viewed through an analyser and illuminated by convergent plane polarized light.

8. Describe experiments to illustrate the *rotation of the plane of polarization* and explain the action of a saccharimeter.

CHAPTER IX

The Emission and Wave Theories of Light

1. Introduction.

There are two known forms in which energy can be transferred from one place to another: (1) kinetic energy of energetic corpuscles or high-speed particles; (2) energy of wave-motion, which travels through the medium but is not conveyed by particles travelling from the source of energy itself. The simple and obvious properties of light, namely, rectilinear propagation, geometrical shadows, and regular reflection seemed overwhelmingly in favour of a corpuscular view, and this was adopted by Newton. On this view it was found difficult to account for simultaneous reflection and refraction, such as occurs at an unsilvered glass surface, where it became necessary to suppose that corpuscular "fits" existed directing one or other process at the critical moment. Such an artificial hypothesis might have received little consideration had an accurate method of measuring the velocity of light in different media been available, for the corpuscular hypothesis, contrary to experiment, requires the velocity of light to be greater in denser media.

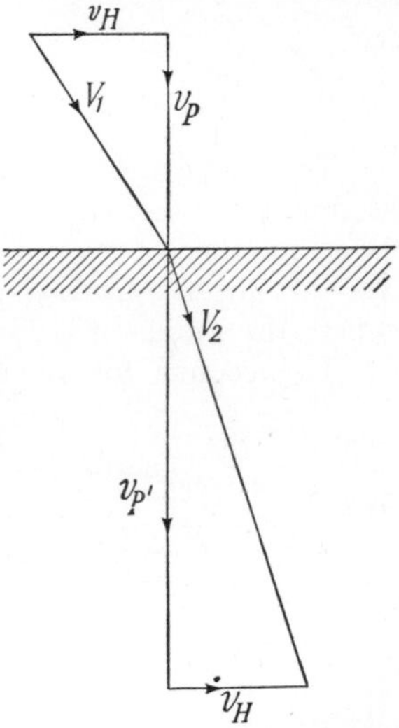

In fig. 1 we explain refraction on the corpuscular hypothesis by resolving the velocity V_1 of the incident corpuscle into two components, one parallel and one perpendicular to the refracting interface.

Fig. 1.—Refraction on corpuscular hypothesis

The former component is assumed to remain unchanged, while the latter is increased owing to the mutual attraction between the light corpuscle and the denser medium. As a result the ray is bent towards the normal in the manner found experimentally, while the total velocity of the light corpuscle is increased in the ratio $\mu : 1$ in the denser medium. Such a result is in disagreement with experiment.

Again, phenomena such as interference, diffraction, and polarization require many *ad hoc* assumptions and strained hypotheses before they can be made to fit into a corpuscular scheme. These last phenomena, as we have already seen, are readily explicable on a wave interpretation, and we must now show that the earlier simpler phenomena are likewise also explicable on the wave theory.

2. Huygens' Construction.

A conception of the utmost importance was introduced by Huygens. He suggested that *each small element of a wave-front might be treated as a new source of secondary waves and that the position of the whole wave-front at any subsequent time was given by the envelope of the secondary wavelets emitted by the secondary sources.*

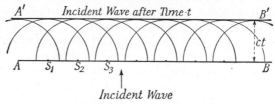

Fig. 2.—Propagation of plane wave

The propagation of a plane wave according to Huygens' principle is illustrated in fig. 2. The spherical wave-fronts spreading from a large number of secondary sources S_1, S_2, &c., situated on the plane wave-front AB, have a plane envelope at A'B' after a given time t, where the radius of each sphere is ct, c being the velocity of light.

To account for regular reflection, we consider the plane wave-

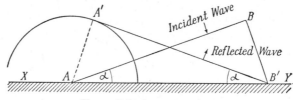

Fig. 3.—Reflection on wave theory

front AB incident on the plane reflecting surface XY as shown in fig. 3. Then with A as the centre of a secondary source, the position of the spherical wave spreading out from this point, at the time the wave from B strikes the reflecting surface at B', will be as shown, passing through A'. The complete reflected wave will be represented by the tangent from B' on to this hemisphere. The two waves AB and A'B' are clearly equally inclined to XY and thus we obtain regular reflection.

Simultaneous reflection and refraction is explained in a similar manner without further hypotheses. Clearly this explanation is a great improvement on the theory of corpuscular fits. The behaviour is shown in fig. 4, the reflected wave A'B' being formed exactly as in our previous example. To explain the bending of AA'' towards the normal, we must assume that the wave-front A''B' swings towards the denser medium. For this to occur AA'' must be less than BB', so the secondary wavelet emitted by A must have travelled a shorter

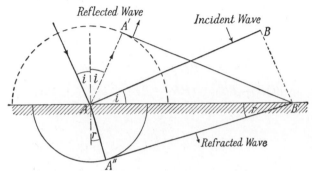

Fig. 4.—Reflection and refraction on wave theory

distance inside the denser medium than that travelled by the wavelet emitted at B and now arrived at B'. From the geometry the ratio of the velocity of light in air, V_a, to the velocity in the medium, V_m, is given by

$$\frac{V_a}{V_m} = \frac{BB'}{AA''} = \frac{AB' \sin i}{AB' \sin r} = \mu. \quad . \quad . \quad . \quad (9.1)$$

Hence the velocity of light in air should be μ times its velocity in the medium. This is in agreement with experiment and in opposition to the corpuscular theory of light.

3. Refraction at a thin Lens.

We can treat all our problems in Geometrical Optics, examined in Chap. I to VI, on the wave theory instead of using rays. However, such treatment, although strictly speaking more accurate, leads to no results of fresh interest unless interference and diffraction are involved, and, as the wave treatment is much more complicated, the method of rays still remains the standard.

To show how equation (3.17), p. 324, may be derived from the wave theory we take O in fig. 5 to be a source of light waves incident upon a converging lens and giving rise to an image at I.

Let ACB, ADB be arcs of circles with centres O and I and let the lens radii be r_2 and r_1 respectively.

Let $OR = u$, $IR = v$, and let V_a, V_g be the velocity of light in air and in the lens respectively. Then the time taken for light to travel from O to I via OAI must be the same as the time for it to travel via OQDCPI, otherwise the wavelets will not be in phase at I, and no distinct image of O will be formed. Hence, for equality of times,

$$\frac{OA + AI}{v_a} = \frac{OQ + PI}{v_a} + \frac{QP}{v_g}. \quad \ldots \ldots \quad (9.2)$$

Hence $$OA + AI = OQ + PI + \mu \cdot QP,$$

or $$OC + ID = OQ + PI + \mu \cdot QP. \quad \ldots \ldots \quad (9.3)$$

Hence $$(OC - OQ) + (ID - PI) = \mu QP,$$

i.e. $$QC + PD = \mu \cdot (QR + PR) \quad \ldots \ldots \quad (9.4)$$

or $$(QR + RC) + (PR + RD) = \mu(QR + PR). \ldots \quad (9.5)$$

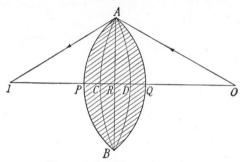

Fig. 5.—Action of lens on wave theory

Now by the properties of intersecting chords of circles, if $AR = h$,

$$h^2 = (2r_1 - QR)QR.$$

Hence, approximately,

$$QR = \frac{h^2}{2r_1}. \quad \ldots \ldots \ldots \quad (9.6)$$

Hence $$\frac{h^2}{2r_1} + \frac{h^2}{2u} + \frac{h^2}{2r_2} + \frac{h^2}{2v} = \frac{\mu h^2}{2}\left(\frac{1}{r_1} + \frac{1}{r_2}\right). \quad \ldots \quad (9.7)$$

or $$\frac{1}{v} + \frac{1}{u} = (\mu - 1)\left(\frac{1}{r_1} + \frac{1}{r_2}\right). \quad \ldots \ldots \quad (9.8)$$

Inserting the signs of u, v, r_1 and r_2, we have

$$\frac{1}{v} - \frac{1}{u} = (\mu - 1)\left(\frac{1}{r_1} - \frac{1}{r_2}\right), \quad \ldots \ldots \quad (9.9)$$

the standard thin lens formula deduced on p. 324.

4. Electromagnetic Theory of Light.

By the middle of the nineteenth century the phenomena of inter-ference and diffraction had received such a satisfactory qualitative and quantitative explanation on wave theory that the wave-like character of light was taken for granted. However, since the theory used the analogy with material waves, such as compression waves in rods and displacement waves in fluids, the need was felt for some definite medium in which the waves could be transmitted. Now light waves are readily transmitted across the natural vacuum which exists between celestial bodies or across the artificial vacua created in vessels in the laboratory. Scientists were therefore led to postulate the existence of some material, termed the **ether,** which was assumed to fill interstellar space and permeate all solid bodies, particularly transparent ones such as glass. By analogy with the properties of an elastic solid the rigidity of the ether was calculated, and various other physical characteristics were attributed to it.

The fact that these ideas had to be almost completely abandoned as a result of the Michelson-Morley experiment (described in Chap. XII), which paved the way for the theory of relativity, should not be allowed to undermine the student's faith in the value of the wave theory of light. All scientific theories are merely attempts to depict the workings of Nature, and we are fully justified in using simple theories to explain various physical phenomena, even though we realize that other theories, much more complicated mathematically, may be closer approximations to the " truth " about " reality ". Provided it is realized that the theory chosen has its limitations and that some deductions from it cannot be expected to agree with experiment, the student is not likely to be led astray.

As we shall see later, a complete dualism now exists between quantum theory (see Part II and Part V) and wave theory, and as yet these two conflicting views have not been replaced by a single unified theory. We are, therefore, at present in the pragmatic condition of using either theory, choosing in any particular case the one that best suits the experiments under discussion.

By the end of the nineteenth century the science of electricity had made tremendous strides, and the mathematical analysis of Max-well, and later the experiments of Hertz, showed that electromagnetic effects could be propagated across a vacuum in the same way as light waves. Among other facts which emerged, Maxwell showed that the velocity of propagation of these waves in a vacuum was identical with that of light. He was, therefore, led to postulate that light itself was an electromagnetic disturbance, only distinguishable from electro-magnetic " wireless " waves by the comparative shortness of the wave-length.   This interpretation, which is now accepted without question, is discussed more fully in Chap. X.

As further evidence we may cite the *Faraday effect* and the *Kerr electro-optic effect.* The former consists in the rotation of the plane of polarization of a plane polarized light beam traversing a transparent isotropic medium subjected to a transverse magnetic field.   In the

Fig. 6.—Electromagnetic wave

Kerr electro-optic effect a medium subjected to an intense electrical field becomes doubly refracting.   These experiments clearly indicate that there are factors present in the light beam which respond to both electric and magnetic phenomena.   As a result of much work along these lines it has been definitely established that for an enormous group of phenomena we may regard light as a transverse electro-magnetic wave with the electric and magnetic field intensities E and H mutually perpendicular to each other as shown in fig. 6.   An

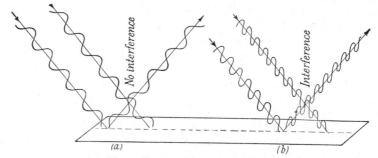

Fig. 7.—Test experiment on interference
(*a*) Incident and reflected vibrations mutually perpendicular.
(*b*) Incident and reflected vibrations parallel.

unpolarized beam is a beam in which the electric and magnetic fields are rotating rapidly around the direction of propagation of the beam. A plane polarized beam is one in which the planes of the electric and magnetic vectors are fixed.   Actually it may be shown that the magnetic displacement is *in* the plane of polarization and the electric displacement perpendicular to the plane of polarization.   The classical experiments of Wiener were carried out to demonstrate that the vibrations, on the elastic solid theory, took place in a direction perpendicular to the plane of polarization.   Since a photographic technique was used and the photographic effect is on modern electronic theory (see Part V) due to the action of the electric vector on the electrons in the photographic emulsion, this supports our statement that the electric displacement is perpendicular to the plane of polarization. The principles involved in Wiener's experiments are illustrated in fig. 7(a) and 7(b). Interference occurs between direct plane polarized waves and waves reflected from a metallic reflector. If the vibrations were *in* the plane of reflection no interference could occur between the two beams, for the displacement caused by the two groups of waves would clearly be in different planes. On the other hand, if the vibrations are perpendicular to the planes of incidence and reflection, direct and reflected waves can interfere. As interference *does* occur, the electric vibrations must be perpendicular to the plane of polarization.

5. The Photoelectric Effect and the Quantum Theory of Radiation.

At the close of the nineteenth century and in the years which have followed, many discoveries have been made which show that for certain phenomena light cannot be treated as an electromagnetic wave. The first clear evidence arose from the properties of heat radiation, and this has been discussed briefly in Part II. Other evidence is discussed in Part V, but we shall consider the evidence from the **photoelectric effect** at this stage, as it is particularly relevant to our discussion on the nature of light. We must assume some small knowledge of electronics on the part of the student, and it would be profitable to read the chapter on the subject in Part V before proceeding further with this section. By the year 1900 it had become apparent that some light radiations, particularly those towards the violet end of the spectrum, were capable of discharging negative electricity from a conductor subjected to the radiations. The classical experiments of Lenard showed conclusively that the **energy** of the emitted electrons was directly proportional to the **frequency** and was quite independent of the **intensity** of the incident light over an intensity range of a million to one. Such behaviour is in complete disagreement with the predictions of electromagnetic theory, for the energy of ejection of the electrons should depend on the strength of the electric field which acts upon them, and this electric field is directly dependent on the magnitude of the electric vector in the electromagnetic wave. On the other hand, the **number** of electrons emitted *was* proportional to the intensity of the incident radiation. In 1905, Einstein suggested his **law of the photoelectric effect**. He postulated that for many phenomena we must consider radiation to consist of small bundles of energy, termed **quanta** or **photons**. The energy in each photon was directly dependent on the frequency of the radiation; an increase in the intensity of radiation corresponded simply to an increase in the number of photons and not to any increase of energy present in any individual photon. Since each photon reacts with only *one* electron, an increase in intensity, that is, an increase in the number of photons, merely results in an increased number of emitted electrons. These ideas have been so successful as to leave no doubt of the correctness of this interpretation. For example, on the practical side, the **photoelectric cell** is one of the most widely used instruments in modern industry. As shown in fig. 8, a simple form of photoelectric cell consists of a layer of some metal, such as rubidium or cæsium, which is very sensitive to photoelectric effects, situated in an evacuated vessel. Illumina-

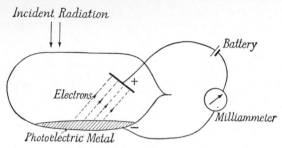

Fig. 8.—Photoelectric cell

tion results in the emission of **photoelectrons,** the electron current being registered by electrodes connected to some recording device such as a sensitive galvanometer. One of the best types of **photometer** (see Chap. XIII) depends on the photoelectric effect; for as we have already stated, the electron current is directly proportional to the intensity of the radiation over an enormous range.

While it is impossible at present to unify the wave and corpuscle aspects of radiation the following empirical rules are of great use:

(i) If in any experiment it is required to know the *distribution of intensity* of any radiation due to diffraction, interference and so on, the wave theory should be used.

(ii) If in any experiment any information is required concerning the *energy interchange* between radiation and matter as in the photoelectric effect or the emission of spectral lines, the quantum theory should be used.

EXERCISES

1. Write a short essay on the wave theory of light.

2. Explain what is meant by *Huygens' construction* for finding successive positions of a wave-front. Apply the construction to account for the laws of reflection and refraction.

3. Show that on the wave theory the ratio of the velocity of light in vacuo to its velocity in a material medium is equal to the refractive index of the medium. Why does the measured velocity ratio show a discrepancy which increases with the value of the ratio? (See Chap. XII, p. 439.)

4. Deduce the formula $\dfrac{1}{v} - \dfrac{1}{u} = (\mu - 1)\left(\dfrac{1}{r_1} - \dfrac{1}{r_2}\right)$ for refraction at a double convex lens from the principles of the wave theory.

5. On what grounds is light regarded as an electromagnetic wave? How has the photoelectric effect modified this conception?

6. Give an account of the photoelectric effect and its applications to practical measurement.

CHAPTER X

Spectra and Colour

1. Ultra-violet Radiations.

If a photographic plate is placed so as to receive the pure visible spectrum produced by a prism as described on p. 348, the general behaviour is as follows. Unless the plate has been specially sensitized and rendered panchromatic, little impression is produced at the red end of the spectrum. This is because red rays are comparatively inactive photographically. As we proceed to the violet end of the spectrum, however, the blackening of the plate becomes progressively more intense. Now this photographic action, far from stopping abruptly as we pass beyond the visible limit of the violet end of the spectrum, may actually increase in intensity. Radiations which are invisible to the eye but which are very effective photographically therefore exist beyond the limits of the violet end of the spectrum. These radiations are termed the ultra-violet or U-V radiations.

Although glass is transparent to visible light it nevertheless absorbs some regions of the U-V very strongly. Other substances, however, such as quartz are transparent to the U-V. A quartz prism should therefore replace the glass prism in **ultra-violet spectroscopy.** It is also necessary to use quartz lenses for the collimator and the camera, the latter being fitted with a photographic plate and replacing the telescope of the ordinary spectrometer. By experiments with mirrors and lenses we can demonstrate that U-V light obeys the ordinary laws of light, and such phenomena as Newton's rings may be demonstrated photographically. Regions very far in the U-V cannot be observed unless the whole spectrometer is situated in a vacuum, since even the air is a heavy absorber of U-V rays of very high frequency.

We have already described the photoelectric effect on p. 397, and it should now be mentioned that many conductors which do not emit electrons when subjected to visible light emit electrons copiously under U-V light. Actually, for all substances there is a well-defined frequency termed the **photoelectric threshold,** and this threshold generally lies well towards the violet if not in the ultra-violet region of the spectrum.

2. Infra-red Radiations.

Suppose an intense source of light such as a powerful arc is used and the radiations are passed through an ordinary spectrometer and allowed to fall on a sensitive thermopile (see Part II) connected to a galvanometer. Little effect is produced when the thermopile is in the U-V or violet part of the spectrum, but as it is moved towards the red end, the existence of heat radiations is made apparent. This thermal effect, far from stopping as we proceed beyond the red visible end of the spectrum, may actually increase, indicating the presence of invisible or **infra-red radiations.** Glass absorbs infra-red as well as ultra-violet radiations, and to obtain a large effect in the infra-red, prism and lenses of the spectrometer should be made of certain other materials, such as rock-salt.

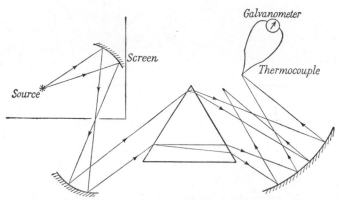

Fig. 1.—Apparatus for infra-red spectrum

On the other hand, in contrast with U-V light, air and even dense fog have little effect in absorbing I-R rays. This fact is of great practical importance since it allows photography through miles of fog where the penetrability of visible light is only a few feet. Of course, the photographic plate must be sensitized so as to respond to the I-R radiations. Infra-red radiations and heat radiations are identical and, as we have shown in Part II, radiant heat obeys the laws of light. To avoid the use of rock-salt lenses which are difficult to obtain, concave mirrors are usually used, as shown in fig. 1, to focus the radiations.

3. Fluorescence and Phosphorescence.

If certain salts such as calcium sulphide, and solutions such as quinine sulphate in water, are subjected to ultra-violet light they no longer remain colourless or inactive, but glow with a bluish or greenish light. Such behaviour is termed **fluorescence** if it stops immediately the U-V light is cut off, and **phosphorescence** if it continues for some time afterwards. The materials exposed have been excited by the U-V light to emit some radiation of longer wave-length, and if this emission is appreciably delayed the substance is phosphorescent. On the quantum theory the energy of the incident photons is directly proportional to their frequency, so the emission of visible radiations by substances exposed to U-V light results from a degradation in energy. The balance of energy is generally transformed into heat.

Stokes's law states that the fluorescent or phosphorescent radiation is always of longer wave-length than the exciting radiation. This is clearly the case when visible fluorescence is produced by U-V

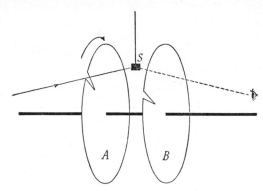

Fig. 2.—Becquerel's phosphoroscope

radiation. By using the resources of modern physics, and taking the fluorescent material in the gaseous form, it is now possible to obtain fluorescent lines of shorter wave-length than the incident radiation. Such contradiction of the Conservation of Energy is only apparent, as the energy gain in the radiation is derived from the kinetic energy of the gas molecules (see Part II, p. 246) in the fluorescent gas.

To distinguish between fluorescence and phosphorescence *Becquerel's phosphoroscope* was invented. As shown in fig. 2, two circular opaque discs A and B revolve about a common axis. An opening is pierced in each disc, that in A admitting light to excite the specimen S, and that in B allowing observation of S a short time after its illumination through A. The distance between an aperture in A and the corresponding aperture in B being known, the speed of revolution of the discs, substances may be accurately classified in the fluorescent or the phosphorescent group.

4. Types of Spectra.

Observation of light sources with a spectrometer shows the existence of several distinct types of spectra.

(a) Continuous Spectra.

The spectrum yielded by a white-hot solid is continuous, stretching from red to violet across the visible spectrum and continuing at the ends in the infra-red and ultra-violet regions respectively. The general explanation of a continuous spectrum is simple on molecular theory. As stated in the introduction to Part I, in the solid state the molecules have little room to move, and hence any vibrations of definite frequency which they might attempt to make are soon changed by collisions with the neighbouring molecules. Hence a large range of frequencies is present in the vibrating molecules, and this multiplicity of frequencies is exhibited also by the radiations emitted by the molecules in the solid state. In *general* appearance, the continuous spectrum is independent of the material of the light source provided it is solid.

(b) Band Spectra.

If examination is made of the flame spectra of burning organic compounds or of the spectra emitted by chemical compounds or even *molecules* (as opposed to atoms) *of elements,* stimulated by electrical discharge, the field is seen to be crossed by light and dark bands. These bands are usually rather ill-defined, a general fading off in intensity occurring at the edges of the bands. Sometimes, however, the edge on one of them is quite sharp and distinct. Peculiarities of this kind yield much information to experienced workers on the composition and condition of the light source. The band spectrum is thus not continuous but consists of groups of wave-lengths, the groups present being characteristic of the chemical compound present and dependent on the method and intensity of excitation. If a spectroscope of high resolving power (see p. 375) is used, the bands are found to consist of a great many fine lines very close together. The study of band spectra is a science in itself. Besides providing valuable information on the chemical condition of the source, it also forms our main supply of knowledge of the energy conditions of the molecules in a gaseous chemical compound. In fact, as mentioned in Part II, p. 220, measurement from band spectra, combined with much deduction using modern electrical theory, provides us with the most reliable values of the specific heats of gases at constant pressure and constant volume.

(c) Line Spectra.

The spectrum presented by atoms of elements subject to thermal or electrical excitation is one of sharp lines, sometimes confined to certain regions. For example, common salt (sodium chloride) when heated in a Bunsen flame yields two sharp yellow lines, the so-called D lines, very close together. These lines are characteristic of sodium and allow its presence in minute quantities to be detected. The student should notice that it is produced by the vaporized *gaseous* sodium atoms. If a large lump of sodium chloride is heated to white-heat, a continuous spectrum will, of course, be formed as with any other solid. Owing, however, to the ease with which the sodium chloride is evaporated, and dissociated (see Part V), the characteristic lines of the gas will be superposed with great intensity on the continuous spectrum. The characteristic line spectrum of chlorine must also be present, but this is not in the visible spectrum, so that effectively only the sodium lines are seen. With some elements such as iron, subjected to strong electrical excitation by passing an electric arc between two

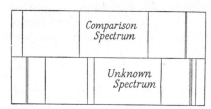

Fig. 3.—Use of comparison spectrum

iron rods, thousands of lines are visible in the spectrum. Thus line spectra vary enormously in appearance from element to element. A great number of these characteristic wave-lengths have been measured and tabulated, and the precise quantitative information they have yielded has been of the utmost importance in the development of the quantum theory. We discuss in some detail, in Part V, the quantum theory of the atomic hydrogen spectrum.

When the wave-lengths of several lines in some well-known spectrum have been measured with, say, a diffraction grating, these lines may be used to estimate the wave-length of other lines. For this purpose, a *comparison spectrum* of known wave-length is formed in the spectrometer alongside the spectrum whose wave-lengths are unknown, as shown in fig. 3. The unknown wave-lengths are then estimated by interpolation or extrapolation.

(d) Absorption Spectra.

Besides the **emission spectra** hitherto discussed there is another important class of spectra, termed **absorption spectra.** Suppose a solution of some substance such as *chlorophyll* (the essential constituent of the green colouring matter present in plant life) is interposed in the path of a continuous spectrum under observation on a screen. The continuous spectrum now becomes discontinuous owing to the presence of dark bands, the position of which is dependent on the nature of the substance interposed. These dark bands are termed the **absorption bands** of chlorophyll. If, instead of using a solution of chlorophyll, a strong sodium chloride flame is interposed, no absorption bands are observed, but two **dark lines** are observed. Further, these dark lines are in the exact position in the yellow, where the bright lines of sodium appear if a sodium source is used. The emission and absorption spectra of substances are therefore of identical wavelengths. Thus a powerful method is provided of examining the spectra of substances (such as, for example, chlorophyll) which cannot be conveniently caused to provide an emission spectrum.

One of the most characteristic properties of the **solar spectrum** is that while at first sight it appears to be continuous, closer examination shows it to be crossed by a large number of dark lines. These were first noted by Fraunhöfer and are termed *Fraunhöfer lines*. The obvious and accepted interpretation of these is that the central portion of the sun emits a continuous spectrum, but that this is surrounded by the vapours of certain elements and the dark Fraunhöfer lines are simply the characteristic *absorption lines* of these surrounding gaseous elements. The study of absorption spectra is extremely valuable in meteorology in showing the presence of various gases such as ozone as constituents of the atmosphere. Quantitative estimates may sometimes be made.

5. Spectroscopic Analysis.

The spectroscope clearly provides the chemist with a very powerful tool for examining the chemical constitution of the elements present in a light source or interposed between the light source and the spectroscope. Since the quantity of the element required to produce an emission or absorption line is extremely small, the spectroscope provides a most delicate means of chemical analysis. Indeed, by observation of the solar spectrum, Lockyer showed the existence of certain lines which had not been accounted for in the known lines of terrestrial elements. He attributed some of these lines to a new element in the sun which he termed **helium.** Some years later, the chemical element helium was discovered on the earth.

The discovery of some of the **rare earths** was similarly due to the observation of unidentified lines in the emission spectrum from certain minerals. Further, the rare earths are extremely difficult to separate chemically, but this can be accomplished by using spectroscopic analysis as a guide. Certain chemical operations are performed on the mixture known to contain the element in question, and the precipitate and the solution are then subjected to spectral analysis. Whichever spectrum shows increased intensity in the lines of the desired element, clearly corresponds to material containing most of the element. Proceeding in this way, purification is continued until a *spectroscopically pure* element is obtained; that is, no lines of any other element are visible when the final product is analysed spectro-

14   (H 394)

scopically. Such 100 per cent purification is extremely laborious, and for many purposes it is sufficient to attain a given percentage of spectroscopic purity.

Quantitative spectrum analysis has now reached a high degree of precision, but it requires the most carefully controlled conditions if it is to be reliable. The percentage of the given element present is gauged from the intensity of the lines produced, this intensity being determined from the measured photographic intensity of the lines obtained on a photographic plate. The general method is to use comparison plates containing spectral lines formed from sources whose composition is known. Not only must the two spectra be formed under as far as possible identical conditions, that is, arc spectra compared with arc spectra of the same current density, but the percentage of other elements present must be as nearly as possible the same.

6. Anomalous Dispersion.

We referred briefly in Chap. VII, p. 374, to the occurrence of continuous spectra in which the order of the colours is not that of continuously increasing or decreasing wave-length, the phenomenon being

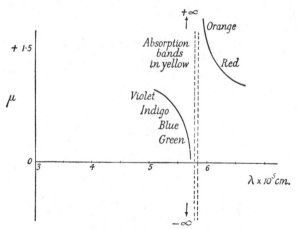

Fig. 4.—Refractive index for sodium " prism "

termed anomalous dispersion. Such a spectrum may be produced in the following way. The refracting glass prism is replaced by a " prism " of sodium vapour. The latter is constructed by heating sodium in a closed quartz vessel and producing a large density gradient between top and bottom by cooling the top vigorously while heating from beneath. The remainder of the apparatus is that of an ordinary spectrometer, and the slit is illuminated with white light. The spectrum obtained shows the colours in the following order from the *most* refrangible end: orange, red, violet, indigo, blue, green. Dark lines appear in the position of the yellow due to the formation of absorption spectra in this region, according to the principles discussed in section 4(*d*). In fact, the existence of anomalous dispersion is closely connected with the existence of absorption bands. This may best be illustrated by plotting a curve of the refractive index of the " prism " against the wave-length. Such a curve for sodium vapour is shown in fig. 4. The refractive index rises to $+ \infty$ on one side of the absorption band and falls towards $- \infty$ on the other side. The orange and the red refractive indices are observed to be higher than the violet refractive index, and hence the interchanged order of the colours with respect to those of a glass prism is explained. Indeed, the production of the colours in the order of wave-length by a glass prism is due to the fact that the glass prism contains no absorption bands in the visible spectrum. As we have mentioned in section 1, glass absorbs ultra-violet radiations, and hence the ultra-violet spectrum as given by a glass prism is anomalous in just the same way as the visible spectrum given by a sodium prism.

7. Colour.

The phenomenon of colour is largely a subjective one. It is, for example, confined to the visible spectrum. Again, colours are judged differently by different observers; the majority who are in agreement concerning a given colour term the minority who differ from them *colour blind*. Finally, while wave-length determines colour, the converse is not true. In a patch which appears red, therefore, there may not be present any wave-length corresponding to that of the red colour in an ordinary continuous spectrum.

Colour may be produced in at least five distinct ways: (*a*) selective absorption, (*b*) selective reflection, (*c*) interference, (*d*) diffraction, and (*e*) scattering. We have already described in Chap. VII how the destructive interference of one or more wave-lengths in white light leaves the remaining wave-lengths to constitute the complementary colour in the spectrum. The same explanation, of course, accounts for coloured diffraction bands.

As an example of the production of colour by scattering we shall consider the blue of the sky. The generally accepted explanation of the blue of the sky is that given by Lord Rayleigh, who showed that it followed on application of the electromagnetic theory of light to the scattering of light waves by small centres of scattering. We shall content ourselves with a simple treatment based on dimensional analysis (see Part I, Chap. V). We suppose that the incident light waves have a certain intensity, and that the amplitude s of the scattered waves depends on (i) the distance r of the point in question from the scattering obstacle, (ii) the volume v of the obstacle, (iii) the wave-length λ of the scattered radiation, (iv) the angle θ of scattering. Hence, if A is the incident amplitude, we have

$$s = kAr^\alpha v^\beta \lambda^\gamma f(\theta), \quad \ldots \ldots \quad (10.1)$$

where k may be some dimensionless constant and α, β, and γ represent various powers to which the corresponding quantities may be raised. Now it is well known that the intensity of scattered light of all wavelengths falls off inversely as the square of the distance. Hence the amplitude falls off inversely as the distance (see Part IV), so that $\alpha = -1$. Again, θ is dimensionless, so $f(\theta)$ may be included with the dimensionless constant k. Finally, experiment shows that the scattered amplitude is directly proportional to the volume v of the obstacle, so that $\beta = 1$. Equation (10.1) may therefore be written

$$\frac{s}{A} = kr^{-1}v\lambda^\gamma. \quad \ldots \ldots \quad (10.2)$$

Now the incident and scattered amplitudes have the same dimensions, so the L.H.S. of the equation is dimensionless. For the R.H.S. also to be dimensionless, putting in the dimensions of r, v, and λ

$$L^0 = L^{-1}L^3 . L^\gamma, \quad \ldots \ldots \quad (10.3)$$

so $\gamma = -2$.

Since the scattered amplitude is dependent on the inverse square of the wave-length, the scattered intensity is therefore proportional to λ^{-4}. Hence blue light is scattered to a much greater extent than red light. The colour of the sky arises from the diffuse scattering of white light from the sun, and hence its typical blue colour. To demonstrate the effect in the laboratory, a cloud of small particles such as tobacco smoke is placed in a rectangular glass box and illuminated with a beam of white light. Observation of the scattered light from a sideways direction shows the characteristic blue appearance. This fades away as the particles settle on the floor of the box under the action of gravity.

In practice, the colours of common bodies are due mainly to the first two processes, namely, selective absorption and reflection. The former is a volume effect and the latter a surface phenomenon. Thus a pigment appears red because the pigment absorbs the blue radiations from the white light incident upon it and reflects diffusely the remainder, that is, the red wave-lengths. Similarly, a sheet of blue glass appears blue by transmitted light owing to the fact that it transmits the blue wave-lengths but absorbs the red wave-lengths when white light is incident upon it. If a red object is viewed through a sheet of blue glass it appears black because the red wave-lengths, which are all that are reflected by the red object, are all absorbed by the blue glass and none is transmitted.

Experiments of Maxwell showed that all known colours may be matched by a mixture of correct proportions of three selected homogeneous radiations. These three are not uniquely determined though they reside in the red, green, and violet parts of the spectrum. They are termed the **primary colours.** Among Maxwell's apparatus are the *colour top* and the *colour-box.* The former consists of a disc which may be rotated rapidly by hand or by a motor. Different colours occupy varying sized sectors according to the disc chosen. Owing to the **persistence of vision,** the colours are superposed when the disc is rotated. Thus a white appearance is produced if the disc is covered with correct areas of the three primary colours. In a simple form of colour-box, a prism splits a beam of white light into the usual spectrum, and various colours from the latter pass through slits and are then superposed on a screen.

The colours due to *mixed pigments* arise in the following way. A blue pigment absorbs the red and yellow end of the spectrum, but besides reflecting blue strongly, reflects a certain amount of its adjacent colours green and violet. Similarly, a yellow pigment strongly reflects a certain amount of its adjacent colours green and orange. Consequently when the blue and yellow pigments are mixed, the common colour reflected is green, all the other colours being absorbed by one or other of the pigments. Thus the green colour, which was swamped previously by the intense blue and yellow reflections now becomes apparent and a green pigment is obtained.

EXERCISES

1. How may the existence of radiations beyond the limits of the visible spectrum be demonstrated? How would you find the wave-length of some given ultra-violet radiation?

2. Distinguish between *fluorescence* and *phosphorescence.* By what type of apparatus may the two phenomena be examined?

3. Into what groups may spectra be divided? Describe the general properties of any *one* of these groups, explaining how the spectrum selected is excited and examined.

4. Explain the principles underlying spectroscopic analysis. What are absorption spectra, and what particular advantages have they over emission spectra?

5. Give an account of anomalous dispersion.

6. Upon what evidence is colour regarded as a subjective phenomenon? Why do blue and yellow pigments produce a green pigment when mixed?

7. In what ways may colour be produced? Outline the theory of the blue colour of the sky.

CHAPTER XI

Optical Instruments

1. Introduction.

Now that we have discussed the phenomena of reflection, refraction, dispersion, interference, diffraction, polarization, and resolving power, we are in a position to enter into an elementary discussion on the construction and operation of optical instruments.

2. Magnifying-glass.

The simplest type of magnifying-glass is a single converging lens of short focal length. In fig. 1 is shown the construction on which the formation of the image is based. The image P'Q' is virtual and upright, and for maximum magnification the object is placed just inside the focus F. Now, according to the definition of magnification, namely, the ratio v/u, the magnification would appear to be a maximum when

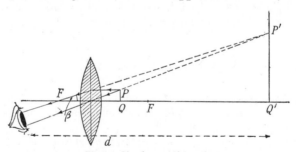

Fig. 1.—Simple magnifying-glass

$u = f$, for then, by equation (3.18), $v = \infty$. In practice, however, such a condition is excluded for several reasons. For example, owing to the finite aperture of the eye-pupil only a very small portion of the image could be observed at one time. Again, aberrations increase rapidly with the magnification.

Since the image is not then to be formed at infinity, we must consider carefully its optimum position. Reference to fig. 1 shows that for a **wide field** we require the angle β to be as large as possible. This could be attained by having the image P'Q' formed closer to the lens, but the human eye is incapable of observing a very close image without great eye-strain. It is this last factor which determines the posi-

410

tion of the image. The optimum distance from the image to the eye is termed the **distance of distinct vision,** and is taken to be 25 cm. In considering the magnifying-glass, therefore, v is fixed at some value d, the distance of distinct vision. Substituting $d = v$ in equation (3.18) and writing $m = d/u$ for the magnification, we obtain (making f positive)

$$m = 1 + d/f. \quad \cdots \cdots \quad (11.1)$$

Hence the magnification is, approximately, inversely proportional to the focal length. For strong magnification, therefore, the lens should be of as short a focal length as possible. A lens with small radii of curvature is therefore required, and consequently it is very thick. Ordinary thin lens formulæ will therefore give only approximate results. Again, aberrations increase rapidly with the power of the lens. (To obtain as wide a field as possible, reference to fig. 1 shows that the eye should be placed as close to the lens as is convenient.) In practice, the distortions become much too large for magnifications greater than 20 or 30. Compound lens systems must then be introduced in the form of some sort of microscope.

3. Spectacles.

We shall not discuss the structure of the human eye nor the subjects of optical response and colour vision, all of which are usually classified under the title of *physiological optics.* We are, however, concerned with the construction of spectacles, which may be considered as optical instruments designed to aid faulty vision. The

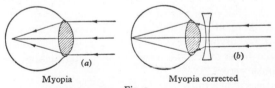

(a)

Myopia   Myopia corrected

Fig. 2

commonest defects of human sight which may be remedied with spectacles are **myopia, hypermetropia, presbyopia,** and **astigmatism.**

Myopia, or short-sightedness, is the inability to see distant objects clearly. The eye focuses objects at various distances by changing the radius of curvature and hence the focal length of the **crystalline lens.** This ability to change the focal length of the eye is termed **accommodation.** Owing to faulty construction of the eye, the myope is unable to accommodate the focal length to that required for the image of a distant object to be formed on the back of the eye or **retina.** The general behaviour is as shown in fig. 2(*a*). The converging power of the crystalline lens is too great and images are formed in front of the retina. The correction clearly consists in supporting a diverging lens of suitable power in front of the eye as shown in fig. 2(b), so as to compensate for the excessive convergence.

In **hypermetropia,** or long sight, the reverse conditions occur, the patient being unable to see near objects distinctly, although quite

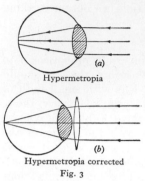

(a)
Hypermetropia

(b)
Hypermetropia corrected
Fig. 3

able to see at a distance. Again, owing to the faulty construction of the eye, accommodation is insufficient to change the focal length to the desired value, but in contrast with myopia, the converging power is now too weak, as shown in fig. 3(a). The correction clearly consists in using spectacles of converging lenses of suitable converging power as shown in fig. 3(b).

Presbyopia is the name given to hypermetropia which results from age and not from inherent faulty construction. After middle age a great many people whose eyesight has hitherto been normal are unable, owing to the insufficiency of natural secretions which keep the eye muscles supple, to accommodate sufficiently to see close objects. The remedy is the same as for hypermetropia.

Astigmatism has been discussed in detail in Chap V. An astigmatic eye, owing to different radii of curvature in different directions, is unable to form a point image of a point object; a blurred image is formed corresponding to the circle of least confusion. The correction consists in the use of a cylindrical lens of sufficient power to compensate for the lack of power of the eye in one plane. The axis of the cylindrical lens must be carefully aligned. Usually astigmatism is accompanied by myopia or hypermetropia, so the combined correction takes the form of a sphero-cylindrical lens of appropriate powers to correct both errors.

Squint arises from muscular imbalance of the eye, the muscles on the inside being stronger than those on the outside in an inward squint. The correction consists in incorporating a *prism effect* into the spectacles so that the eye is forced to turn inwards or outwards to receive the rays instead of looking straight ahead. The prism effect is obtained by the process of *decentring*, that is, the optical centre of the lens is displaced with respect to the geometrical centre so that the observer looks non-axially through the lens which acts as a combined lens and prism.

4. Astronomical Telescope.

To obtain a magnification in the size of a *distant* object with the aid of a single magnifying lens is clearly impossible, for $u > v$ and the image is therefore diminished. It is generally preferable to consider the **angular aperture** subtended by the image and object at the eye, that is, to represent the magnification by β/α (see fig. 4). In the astronomical telescope a real image $P'Q'$ of the object is formed at the focus of a converging lens termed the **object glass,** and this image is then examined with a second converging lens, termed the **eyepiece,**

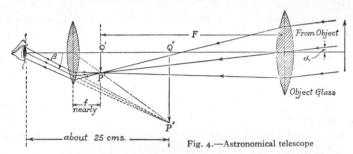

Fig. 4.—Astronomical telescope

which is used as a simple magnifying-glass. The first image will therefore be situated just inside the focus of the eyepiece, and the total distance between eyepiece and object glass will be approximately equal to the sum of the two focal lengths. The path of the rays is illustrated in fig. 4, in which $P'Q' = F\alpha = f\beta$.

The magnification is given by β/α, and from the figure this is given by F/f, where F is the focal length of the object glass and f that of the eyepiece. For maximum magnification, therefore, the object glass

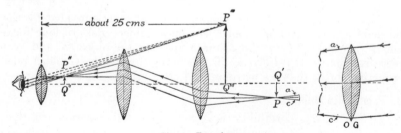

Fig. 5.—Erect image

should be of long focal length and the eyepiece of short focal length. We have discussed in the previous section the fact that practical considerations fix a lower limit to the focal length of the eyepiece. Increased magnification can therefore only be attained by increasing the focal length of the object glass. This procedure has the disadvantage of rendering the telescope unwieldy, but it is the practice which must be adopted if increased magnification is required. However, as important as magnification is resolving power—a point already discussed in Chap. VII. The resolving power is directly proportional to the diameter of the object glass, so that telescopes of high resolution and magnification must be wide as well as long. Practical difficulties in obtaining large glass lenses of homogeneous composition then arise, together with engineering problems of supporting these heavy lenses without undue mechanical strain. Incidentally, also, a strain which is not mechanically dangerous may cause the lens to become doubly refracting.

We note that the image observed in the astronomical telescope is inverted. If this inversion is undesirable it may be corrected by the use of an erecting eyepiece as shown in fig. 5. Such an arrangement is termed a **terrestrial telescope**.

5. Galilean Telescope.

If a diverging lens is used as an eyepiece of a converging lens, then an upright image may be observed as shown in fig. 6. Such an arrangement constitutes a *Galilean telescope*; the magnification is again given

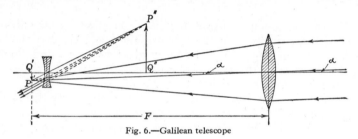

Fig. 6.—Galilean telescope

by F/f, and the limit to the magnification is again provided by the mechanical considerations contingent on an object glass of long focal length. Since, however, the distance apart of the objective and eyepiece is equal to the *difference* in the focal lengths, the Galilean telescope is shorter than its astronomical counterpart.

6. Prism Binoculars.

In binoculars, portability is a very essential criterion, so that field-glasses are sometimes constructed on the Galilean principles. On the other hand, the field of view obtained with a Galilean telescope is considerably less than with an astronomical telescope of the same power. By the use of prisms, however, the light may be sent backwards and forwards along a short tube so that the effective distance between objective and eyepiece may be made large enough to make use of the principles of the astronomical telescope. The diagram in fig. 7 shows immediately the mode of working of prism binoculars.

7. Reflecting Telescopes.

Owing to the existence of chromatism on refraction, many telescopes make use of the properties of concave mirrors. The action

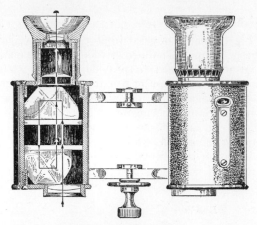

Fig. 7.—Prism binoculars

of a double concave (or Gregorian) telescope is shown in fig. 8, and of a concave-convex (or Cassegrainian) telescope in fig. 9. The former gives an upright image and the latter an inverted image, and they are

Fig. 8.—Gregorian reflecting telescope

therefore the counterparts of the Galilean and astronomical telescopes respectively.

The largest telescope in the world is in the Hale Observatory on

Fig. 9.—Cassegrainian reflecting telescope

Mount Palomar, California. It uses a 200-inch mirror, the casting, working, and mounting of which required some 17 years of labour. The second largest telescope (120 in.) is at the Lick Observatory, California, the third largest (102 in.) is in Russia, and the fourth largest is the Hooker telescope at Mount Wilson, California (100 in.).

8. The Sextant and the Periscope.

Two optical instruments of great importance in navigation are the sextant and the periscope. The former was perfected many years ago by Hadley, and was designed to provide sailors with a means of measuring the angular elevation of a star at a given time. Knowing this elevation, the navigator can calculate his latitude, with the help of data given in the Nautical Almanac. The principle of the sextant is shown in fig. 10. M_1 and M_2 are plane mirrors, M_1 being capable of rotation by rotating the arm A, while M_2 is fixed to the general framework. The observation is eventually made through the Galilean telescope T. An artificial horizon is usually used in the shape of a pool

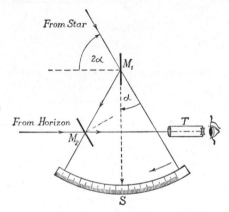

Fig. 10.— Sextant

of mercury. One half of M_2 is unsilvered, and the image of the star is viewed through this by direct reflection in the mercury. The two mirrors M_1 and M_2 are initially parallel, but M_1 is now rotated until the image of the star due to reflection in M_1 and M_2 coincides with the direct image. The altitude of the star is then given by half the angle between the two images, i.e. by the angle turned through by M_1, and this is read off the scale S. Fig. 10 illustrates an observation using the natural horizon.

The periscope also employs two plane mirrors, and its principle is simply to reflect rays into a more convenient position. Its chief use is with submarines when the main body of the craft is submerged and a small projection only is desirable. Besides the two mirrors, an *erecting prism* is usually incorporated in the instrument and a telescope used for magnification. Its mode of operation is shown in fig. 11.

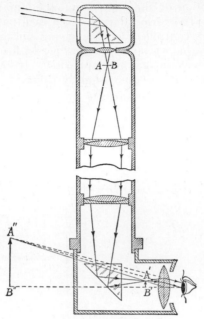

Fig. 11.—Periscope

9. The Optical Lantern and the Epidiascope.

The purpose of the optical lantern is to project an enlarged image of a slide on to a screen. The instrument (fig. 12) comprises a powerful light source A situated a short distance from a wide compound lens C,

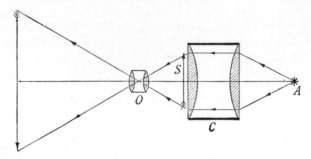

Fig. 12.—Optical lantern

termed the **condenser.** The function of the condenser is to furnish a beam of light of wide angle. A real image of the slide S is then formed on the screen by the achromatic compound objective O.

The **movie projector** is very similar, except that a restricted aperture occupies the position of the slide S and the film is run through at a constant rate. The period during which each picture is exposed is very short, and is controlled by a revolving shutter also close to S. Owing to the fact that visual impressions persist for longer than about $\frac{1}{10}$ sec., the successive images are superposed. If some image, such as that of a human arm, occupies slightly different positions on each

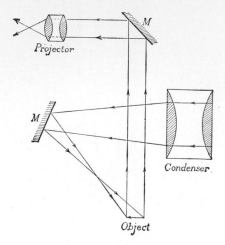

Fig. 13.—Epidiascope

image, the illusion will be produced of a continuous movement of the arm.

The **epidiascope** is a device for projecting images of an opaque object (as opposed to a transparent lantern slide) on to a screen. It simply uses the image of the object in a plane mirror, combined with suitable projection lenses as shown in fig. 13. The mirrors must be kept in a high state of polish if good intensity of illumination is to result.

10. Range-finder.

If the angle subtended by a known base line at a distant object is determined, simple trigonometry allows the distance of the object to be calculated. The range-finder is an optical device for measuring the subtended angle. As shown in fig. 14, rays of light from the object are inclined to each other at an angle θ and are incident on the mirrors M_1, M_2, each of which is inclined at 45° to the base line. Convex lenses L_1 and L_2 produce images at P and Q respectively, after suitable prismatic reflection. The separation of P and Q is a measure of the angular divergence of the rays incident on M_1 and M_2, and the instrument has initially been calibrated with objects at known distances.

Since the separation PQ is very small, observation is usually made
with a microscope. Also, instead of measuring the separation PQ, the

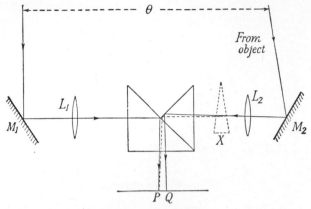

Fig. 14.—Range-finder

setting of an auxiliary prism X is adjusted until P and Q coincide.
The setting of X then gives the required angle.

11. The Microscope.

We indicated in section 2 that the maximum magnification obtainable by a single magnifying lens was about 20–30. The simplest
form of microscope consists of two converging lenses. There is therefore a superficial similarity between the simple microscope and the
astronomical telescope, but the purposes for which they are designed
are very different. With the telescope a magnified image of a distant
object was required; with the microscope a magnified image of an extremely small object situated quite close is commonly needed. With
the telescope, therefore, the incident rays are in the form of a narrow
pencil of small angular divergence, but with the microscope the angular
divergence is always large, as shown in fig. 15. In the simple microscope, the object is situated just *outside* the focus of the objective so
as to give a magnified real image. This image is formed just *inside*
the focus of the eyepiece, and a virtual magnified image obtained in
the usual way.

We have seen in section 2 that the magnification produced by a
lens is inversely proportional to its focal length, so the objective as
well as the eyepiece of a microscope must be of small focal length.
Now, owing to the proximity of the object, the angular divergence of
rays entering the microscope objective will be very large. Hence we

have the conditions for maximum aberration, namely, large aperture and short focal length. To overcome these difficulties special compound-objectives are required to be suited to the special conditions

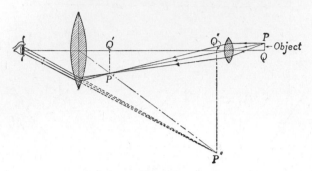

Fig. 15.—Simple microscope

prevailing. In fig. 16 is shown a typical objective containing ten component lenses, the combined focal length being only a few millimetres. The working of these lenses and their adjustment to relative positions which must not vary by a fraction of a millimetre is ob-

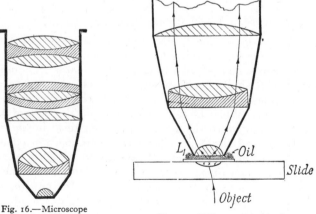

Fig. 16.—Microscope compound objective

Fig. 17.—Oil-immersion objective

viously a highly-skilled operation, and good objectives are very expensive. Even with the best lenses, when high magnification is desired, and consequently short focal length is imperative, the aperture must be stopped down to 1-2 mm. The quantity of light which now enters the objective is very small, and unless the object is strongly illuminated it is very difficult to see the image in the microscope. To increase the effective illumination an **oil-immersion objective** is commonly employed, the space between the first lens of the objective and the object being filled with oil of the same refractive index as the glass of the first lens of the objective. Consequently more highly inclined rays arising from the object at O, as shown in fig. 17, are not bent away from the normal and lost at the sides on leaving the coverslip, as they would be if no oil were present, but continue undeflected until they *emerge* from L_1.

For observing the image formed by the objective, two types of compound eyepiece are in common use. The **Ramsden eyepiece**, which is shown diagrammatically in fig. 18, consists of two equal plano-convex lenses with the curved surfaces facing each other. They are sometimes situated a distance apart equal to their focal length, as this arrangement, from equation (6.21), gives achromatic images.

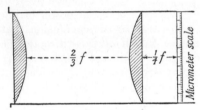

Fig. 18.—Ramsden eyepiece

Such an eyepiece has the disadvantage, however, that since the front or **field lens** lies at the principal focus of the back or **eye lens,** small dust particles or scratches on the former are greatly magnified by the latter. It is therefore usual to space the lenses by an amount equal to two-thirds of the focal length. This arrangement has the added advantage that the focal plane of the combination now lies (at $f/4$) in front of the field lens. The image formed by the objective may therefore be made to coincide with a graduated transparent scale, thereby allowing the size of the image to be determined directly.

The **Huygens eyepiece** is similarly compounded of two converging lenses, but they are frequently of the meniscus type, and the more curved faces are turned towards the object as shown in fig. 19. The focal length f_1 of the field lens is three times that of the eye lens, this arrangement giving minimum spherical aberration. The lenses are arranged for achromatism, that is, they are situated a distance apart equal to the mean of the sum of their focal lengths. As a result of this separation the focal plane of the combination lies between the two lenses, a distance $f_1/2$ behind the field lens. Consequently the arrangement has the disadvantage that an image formed by the objective, to coincide with a micrometer scale situated in the focal plane of the eyepiece, is eventually observed through both lenses of

the eyepiece, whereas the scale is observed through the eye lens only.
Although it is possible to achieve magnification of over 1000 with
the microscope, this is rarely done, as little is gained by increasing
magnification unless resolving power is also increased. In considering
the resolving power of a microscope we are usually concerned with

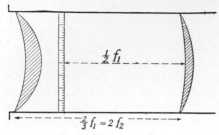

the problem of distinguishing
various points on the object
which are very close together.
If the object is a microscope
slide and is viewed by transmitted light, then the fine
structure which it is desired
to examine will act as a sort
of diffraction grating. The
classical work on the resolving
power of microscopes was car-

Fig. 19.—Huygens eyepiece

ried out by Abbe, who came to the conclusion that the image is like
the object in appearance only if *all* the diffracted pencils are collected
into the microscope to form the image. Such a criterion clearly requires
a prohibitively large aperture to the objective, but fortunately it is
often sufficient to collect only the direct light and the *first* diffracted

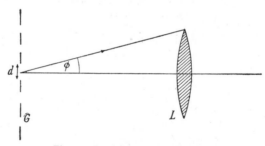

Fig. 20.—Resolving power of microscope

pencil. Suppose that in fig. 20 L represents the object glass and G is
a grating under observation, the width of a slit of the grating being d.
Then Abbe's analysis showed that for resolution $d = \lambda/2 \sin \phi$, where
ϕ is half the angle subtended by the lens at the slit. If an immersion
objective is used the effective wave-length of the light becomes λ/μ,
where μ is the refractive index, so the smallest resolvable separation
in the object is improved to

$$d = \frac{\lambda}{2\mu \sin \phi}. \quad \cdots \cdots \quad (11.2)$$

The quantity $\mu \sin \phi$ is termed the **numerical aperture** of an objective,
and practical considerations limit its maximum value to about 1·6.

Hence the minimum value of d which can be resolved is $d = \lambda/3 \cdot 2 =$ $1 \cdot 7 \times 10^{-5}$ cm. for the visible spectrum. Now the least angle which the normal human eye can separate is about $1 \cdot 5$ min.: at the distance of distinct vision, 25 cm., this corresponds to a slit width of $1 \cdot 1 \times 10^{-2}$ cm. Hence the magnification may be usefully increased to $1 \cdot 1 \times 10^{-2}/1 \cdot 7 \times 10^{-5} \simeq 650$, but beyond this the image will fail to be resolved.

It is clear from equation (11.2) that if the optical system is made of material which will transmit in the ultra-violet then the correspondingly small value of λ allows proportionately higher resolution. The image will then usually be recorded photographically, the wave-lengths involved being about half those near the centre of the visible spectrum. Much higher resolution is possible with the electron microscope discussed on p. 731.

12. The Spectrometer.

The essential parts of a spectrometer comprise the collimator, the refracting prism, and the telescope. The arrangement is shown diagrammatically in fig. 21. The collimator consists of two concentric

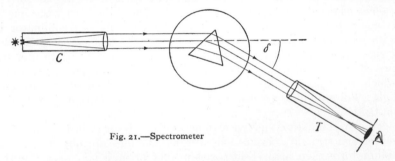

Fig. 21.—Spectrometer

metal tubes with an adjustable vertical slit at one end and a converging lens at the other. The distance between lens and slit is adjustable over a small range by means of a screw which racks one tube inside the other. The position usually required is with the slit at the focus of the lens so that light incident upon the slit is parallel on emerging from the collimator. The whole collimator C is carried on heavy bearings which may be rotated around a central axle. This axle is concentric with that supporting the prism table, the latter consisting essentially of a flat circular disk fitted with vernier and concentric circular scale. The telescope T is also mounted in heavy bearings and rotates about the common vertical axis. Verniers carried by telescope and collimator move over a horizontal circular scale and thus allow the angles between collimator axis and telescope axis to be determined.

As typical of the use of the spectrometer we shall describe the measurement of the refractive index of a glass prism by the method outlined in Chap. III. We required a beam of parallel light from the collimator, and there is usually a mark on the sliding tubes to indicate the " infinity " position. If this is not trustworthy there are two methods of procedure:

(i) The telescope is adjusted for infinity by focusing it on a distant object through the open window of the laboratory. The collimator and telescope are then rotated into the same straight line, and the collimator adjusted until a clear image is seen in the telescope. Since the latter has been previously adjusted for parallel light, the former must now be in correct adjustment.

(ii) Schuster's method may be used. We describe it now, although the student may find it necessary to reread the description after completing the remainder of this section. The slit is illuminated with monochromatic light and the prism is placed on its table and so rotated that the position of minimum deviation is passed. Suppose the collimator and telescope are out of adjustment and the image is blurred. The telescope is adjusted until a clear image is seen. The prism is now rotated, whereupon the image of the slit moves off but *returns again as the rotation is continued.* When it returns the image is again blurred, but to make it sharp this time the collimator is adjusted. The prism is then rotated back to its first position and the image again sharpened by adjusting the telescope. This to and fro process is continued until the image is sharp in both positions, under which conditions collimator and telescope are focused for parallel light. For a proof of this the student must consult some standard work on Optics.

When collimator and spectrometer have been adjusted they are set in one straight line and the vernier readings are observed. The collimator is then clamped in position. The prism is now placed on the central table and the telescope is rotated until an image of the slit is observed due to refraction through the prism. Prism table and telescope are then rotated so as to keep the image of the slit on the vertical cross wire in the telescope. Various adjustments of levelling screws may now require to be made on the prism table. We require the refracting edge of the prism to be vertical. If this is not so the image of the slit will not be vertical, and it will move across the field in a skew direction as the telescope is rotated. From time to time the rotation of the telescope is stopped and that of the prism is continued. Usually the image will continue to move across the field of the telescope, but ultimately a position is reached when further rotation of the prism table causes the image of the slit to move *back* across the field of the telescope. The position at which this motion just commences is the position of *minimum deviation,* and the telescope is now

clamped in position and the vernier is read. The angle through which
the telescope has been rotated is seen from fig. 21 to be the desired
angle of minimum deviation.

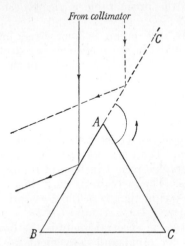

Fig. 22.—Measurement of angle of prism

From equation (3.11) we still require the angle A of the prism if
μ is to be determined. This angle is usually 60°, but it must be carefully measured with the spectrometer if an accurate value of μ is

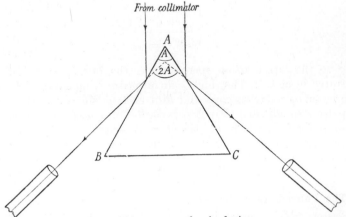

Fig. 23.—Measurement of angle of prism

required. To measure A, the image of the slit is observed in the telescope due to *reflection* at the prism surfaces AB and AC, as shown in
fig. 22. Two procedures are possible:

(i) The telescope is fixed in some position when the image is reflected into it by the face AB, and the *prism table* is then rotated until the image reflected from AC appears on the cross-wire. The angle turned through by the prism table is clearly the supplement of the prism angle.

(ii) Alternatively, the prism is kept fixed in position after the image has been observed in the telescope by reflection in the face AB. The telescope is now rotated until it picks up the image by reflection in the face AC. From fig. 23 the angle turned through by the telescope is twice the vertical angle of the prism.

13. The Direct Vision Spectroscope.

The ordinary spectroscope is identical with the spectrometer in general construction. The telescope may be replaced by a camera so as to give a photographic record instead of taking visual observations of the spectral lines. The instrument may thus be extended into the ultra-violet region, but in that case the glass prisms and lenses must be replaced by quartz.

For many purposes in spectral analysis the ordinary spectrometer is too cumbersome for rapid and convenient use. Recourse is then

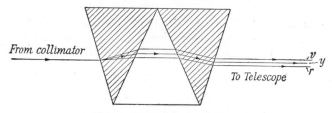

Fig. 24.—Direct vision spectroscope

made to the direct vision spectroscope, the principles of which are illustrated in fig. 24. The single central prism is replaced by a battery of three or more crown glass and flint glass prisms with their refracting powers so adjusted that the deviation of a *mean ray* (such as the yellow sodium line) is zero. Other wave-lengths will be deviated by different amounts owing to the different dispersive powers of the two groups of prisms, and consequently a spectrum will be formed on each side of the undeviated yellow line.

14. The Pulfrich Refractometer.

Besides the spectrometer method, refractive indices may be measured by special instruments termed **refractometers**. We select the Pulfrich refractometer, which is shown diagrammatically in fig. 25; its action depends on the existence of the critical angle. A vertical glass block PQ supports a cylindrical reservoir R which contains a liquid whose refractive index μ_2 is desired. When a horizontal beam of light illuminates the junction at Q, observation with a telescope from T shows a field with a well-defined edge. This edge clearly corresponds to such a ray as TSY, where the angle between YS and the vertical is the critical angle for glass and the liquid. From the diagram and application of Snell's law, we have

$$\mu_1 = \frac{\sin i}{\sin r}, \quad \ldots \ldots \ldots \ldots \quad (11.3)$$

and
$$\frac{\mu_1}{\mu_2} = 1/\cos r. \quad \ldots \ldots \ldots \quad (11.4)$$

Hence
$$\mu_2{}^2 = \mu_1{}^2 - \sin^2 i. \quad \ldots \ldots \ldots \quad (11.5)$$

The angle i is measured by rotating the observing telescope from the first position until it is normal to PQ.

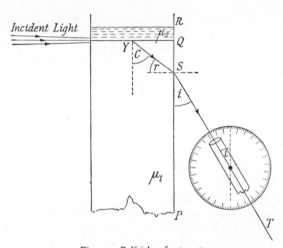

Fig. 25.—Pulfrich refractometer

15. Michelson's Interferometer.

We have described in sections 5 *et seq.*, Chap. VII, interference effects due to thin films. Based on these principles are certain important instruments termed **interferometers,** the main use of which is to determine accurately very small changes of length. Three important interferometers are the *Michelson interferometer*, the *Fabry-Perot interferometer*, and the *Lummer-Gehrcke plate*. We shall discuss the first of these in some detail; for an account of the last two reference must be made to some standard work on Optics.

The essential parts of the Michelson interferometer are shown diagrammatically in fig. 26. Two plane mirrors M_1 and M_2, silvered on their front surfaces, are situated perpendicular to each other, the latter being fixed while the former can be moved backwards and forwards along the normal to its surface by means of a very accurate screw fitted with a micrometer scale. Another mirror A is only lightly silvered on its back face, i.e. on the side remote from the source S. Light incident from S is partially reflected by A to M_1, and partially transmitted to M_2. Observation from O then shows two images, one due to the light reflected back from M_1 and then transmitted through

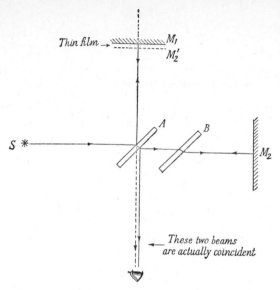

Fig. 26.—Michelson interferometer

A, the other reflected back from M_2 and then reflected from the back surface of A. Interference between these two beams will occur, the nature of which is best considered by regarding the effects as produced by the air film enclosed between M_1 and M_2', M_2' being the image of M_2 reflected in A. The transparent plate B is as nearly as possible identical with A; it is inserted to make the optical paths of the two beams as equal as possible. Thus the beam reflected from M_1 traverses the glass plate A three times, whereas, without B, the beam to M_2 would traverse a glass plate only once. The path-difference between the two beams at O is clearly equal to twice the thickness of the film M_1M_2'. The nature of the interference pattern is now easily deduced from our considerations of Chap. VII. If M_1 and M_2' are parallel and monochromatic light is used, destructive interference takes place and the field is dark when $2M_1M_2'$ is an odd number of half wave-lengths.

If M_1 and M_2 are not quite perpendicular to each other so that M_1 and M_2' are inclined to each other at a small angle, straight line fringes are formed as with a wedge-shaped film. With white light, coloured fringes are produced according to the principles of Chap. VII, and the appearance of the fringes is governed by whether the light source is extended, and the rays are converging, and so on.

As M_1 is screwed back the thickness of the film M_1 and M_2' is changed, and consequently, as M_1M_2' increases by $\lambda/2$, fringes move across the field and occupy the position previously held by adjacent fringes. If the wave-length of the light is known, a count of the number of fringes which move across a given point in the field allows the distance moved through by M_1 to be calculated to 10^{-5} cm. The **refractive index of gases** may easily be found with such an instrument by interposing an exhausted glass vessel into one of the beams. As the

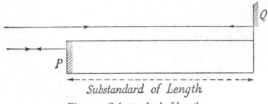

Substandard of Length

Fig. 27.—Sub-standard of length

gas is admitted into the vessel, the optical length of the container increases from l to μl, and $l(\mu - 1)$ is equal to $n\lambda/2$, when n is the number of fringes which move across a given point in the field. As might be expected, the refractive index of a gas is approximately proportional to the gas pressure, so that for gases there is a one-to-one correspondence between optical and physical density.

One of the most important applications of the Michelson interferometer is the expression of the standard metre (see Part I) in terms of a given light wave-length. As an enormous number of fringes would have to be counted if M_1 was moved back through a metre, a series of sub-standards were made of lengths 10 cm., 5 cm., and so on down to 0·05 cm. These had an appearance as shown in fig. 27, P and Q replacing the fixed mirror M_2 on the Michelson interferometer. The movable mirror M_1 had a total height equal to the sum of the heights of the mirrors P and Q. Fringes formed by reflection in P and Q could thus be compared simultaneously. The principle of the experiment was to adjust the distance PA (cf. fig. 26) so that the two distances PA and M_1A were initially equal. The mirror M_1 was then moved forward, fringes being counted, until $M_1A = AQ$. The distance moved through by M_1 was then equal to the sub-standard of length PQ. The smallest sub-standard needed the counting of over 1500 fringes. Special methods had to be adopted to estimate fractions of a fringe.

The sources of light used were the cadmium red, green, and blue lines. These lines are remarkable for their homogeneity, that is, they are as nearly monochromatic and definite as it is possible to get.

16. Michelson's Stellar Interferometer.

The nearest fixed star is too far away to be resolved by the most powerful telescope available. It was not until 1920 that Michelson succeeded in devising an interference method for estimating the angular diameter of a star. *Michelson's stellar interferometer* may be regarded as an ingenious modification of Young's parallel slits. The principle is illustrated in fig. 28. Consider the fringe system formed

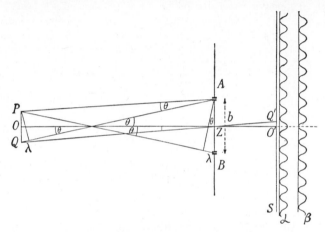

Fig. 28.—Principle of Michelson's stellar interferometer

on the screen S due to two parallel slits at A and B and light emitted from a point O on a source of finite extension PQ. A series of equidistant parallel fringes is observed, the centre of the fringe system lying at O′ on the normal from O, bisecting the line AB joining the slits. The intensity distribution will be as shown at a, a maximum occurring at the centre. If we now consider the point Q as the source, the centre of the fringe system which Q will produce is at Q′. Hence the intensity distribution of this fringe system is as shown at β. Now it may happen that the maxima of one system fall on the minima of the other, whereupon the interference system will vanish. The angle subtended by adjacent fringes O′Q′ at Z is clearly the angle subtended by half the star PQ, and since the former may be easily calculated, the latter is obtained. Actually, light will be emitted by a multitude of sources lying along PQ, and the net result is that the fringe system vanishes when the path-difference $QA - PA = PB - PA = n\lambda$ where n is integral. The *visibility of the fringes* therefore depends on the separation of the two slits. If they are close together $PB - PA < \lambda$, and the fringe system is easily seen. As A and B are moved apart the visibility decreases until it vanishes when $PB - PA = \lambda$. From the geometry of fig. 28, if θ is the angular diameter of the star

$$\theta = \frac{\lambda}{b}, \quad \ldots \ldots \ldots \quad (11.6)$$

where b is the first distance of separation of the slits for which the fringe system vanishes.

Now it will be remembered from Chap. VII, section 13 (iii), that the resolving power of a telescope is given by

$$\theta = \frac{\lambda}{h} \quad \ldots \ldots \ldots \quad (11.7)$$

(except for a numerical factor 1·22), where h is the diameter of the object glass. Now b in Michelson's interferometer can be made much larger than the diameter of the telescope objective, so the net result of Michelson's invention is to increase the resolving power available for stellar observation.

In practice, the two slits are replaced by plane mirrors mounted on a rigid girder. The distance b may thus be increased to many feet. Two other plane mirrors reflect the light into a telescope, and observations are made on the visibility of the fringes observed in the focal plane of the telescope. Examination of the giant star Betelgeux showed that the fringe system disappeared when the slit separation was 121 in., giving an angular diameter of 0·049 seconds of arc.

Another great advantage of the stellar interferometer is its independence of atmospheric conditions. With a telescope, local variations in the refractive index of the atmosphere are common over the wide area embraced by the large objective. Consequently the image sometimes adopts a curious indefinite appearance and is said to "boil". With the stellar interferometer, the mirrors acting as slits are so small that local variations in refractive index occur over the whole aperture of the mirror and merely cause the fringe system to move as a whole, and thus cause no change in its visibility.

EXERCISES

1. Explain, with diagrams, the working of a simple magnifying-glass and prove that the magnification is inversely proportional to the focal length of the lens.

2. To what structural defects is the human eye susceptible? Explain in detail how any *one* of these is corrected.

3. How are myopia and hypermetropia corrected? A slit (stenopaic slit) when held with its axis in a particular orientation assists the vision of a certain person. Explain this.

4. Explain, with diagrams, the mode of operation of an astronomical telescope. Upon what does its magnification depend, and why is unlimited magnification not necessarily advantageous?

5. Describe the action of a pair of prism binoculars. If the focal lengths of the objective and eyepiece of a pair of prism binoculars are 50 cm. and 2 cm. respectively, find the length of the binoculars if the light traverses this length three times. What is the magnification obtained? [16 cm.; 25.]

6. How have the properties of plane mirrors been turned to account in the sextant and the periscope?

7. Describe the mode of operation of an elementary form of microscope. How are the different forms of aberration reduced to a minimum in a good microscope?

8. Distinguish between the Huygens eyepiece and the Ramsden eyepiece. What particular advantage has the latter when a micrometer scale is used in the eyepiece?

9. Explain what limits the resolving power of a microscope, and show that the maximum useful magnification combined with resolution is about 700.

10. Give an account of the spectrometer and describe its use in determining the refractive index of a glass prism.

11. Describe some instrument for measuring refractive index which uses the phenomenon of total internal reflection.

12. Compare and contrast the ordinary spectroscope and the direct vision spectroscope.

13. Give an account of the Michelson interferometer. To what uses may it be put?

14. Explain carefully how the standard metre may be measured in terms of so many wave-lengths of light.

15. In what way may the angular diameter of stars be determined? Compare the properties of a giant telescope and a stellar interferometer for examining the characteristics of a star.

CHAPTER XII

Velocity of Light

1. Introduction.

The velocity of light is one of the most important constants in Physics. It is also the velocity of electromagnetic waves in vacuo, and—when measured in cm./sec.—the ratio between the units of electric charge on the electromagnetic and electrostatic system respectively (see Part V). Finally, it is independent of the frequency of the radiation, and it has the unique properties of (i) being independent of the velocity of the source or observer, (ii) being an upper limit of velocity with which energy can be transferred from one place to another. According to the experiments of Michelson, Pease, and Pearson in 1929, the velocity of light is 299,774 ± 2 Km. per sec.

2. Romer's Eclipse Method.

The velocity of light was first determined by Römer in 1675 from observations on the eclipses of the satellites of Jupiter. The principle of the method is illustrated in fig. 1. Suppose a time t_1 elapses between

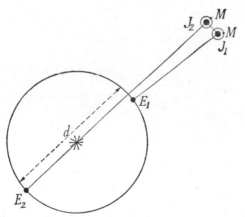

Fig. 1.—Eclipse method for velocity of light

a certain pair of eclipses (not consecutive), one observed when the earth and Jupiter are in conjunction as at E_1, and the other observed later when they are in opposition at E_2. If the actual period of eclipse is τ, and n intervals between eclipses occur while the earth goes from conjunction to opposition,

$$t_1 = n\tau + d/c, \quad \ldots \ldots \quad (12.1)$$

where d is the diameter of the earth's orbit round the sun and c is the velocity of light. Similarly, if t_2 is the observed time between eclipses when the earth moves from opposition to conjunction,

$$t_2 = n\tau - d/c, \quad \ldots \ldots \quad (12.2)$$

whence

$$c = \frac{2d}{t_1 - t_2}. \quad \ldots \ldots \quad (12.3)$$

As d is 186×10^6 miles and $(t_1 - t_2)$ is about 2000 sec., the velocity of light is about $1 \cdot 86 \times 10^5$ miles/sec., according to Römer's method.

3. Bradley's Aberration Method.

The principle of Bradley's aberration method is illustrated in fig. 2. Since a telescope fixed to the earth is moving with the earth's

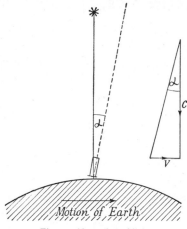

velocity, if the direction of motion is perpendicular to the direction of light from a star the telescope must be tilted through an angle α, given by

$$\tan \alpha = v/c, \quad . \quad (12.4)$$

where v is the velocity of the earth and c is the velocity of light. That is, if the image of a star which is directly overhead appears on the cross-wire of the telescope for a " still " earth, for a moving earth the telescope must be tilted through an angle α for the image still to remain on the cross-wire. The condition for a still earth is that

Fig. 2.—Aberration of light

obtaining when the earth is moving along and not across the direction of light from the star. Of course, as the earth moves across the terrestrial orbit the star appears to change its position owing to parallax, but the aberration effect is very many times larger. Moreover, the aberration is independent of the distance of the star under observation, so the two effects are easily separated.

4. Fizeau's Toothed-wheel Method.

In 1849, Fizeau measured the velocity of light by a purely terrestrial method, using the apparatus shown diagrammatically in fig. 3. Light from a source S is focused by a lens L_1 to a point P after reflection by a transparent glass sheet M_1. Perpendicular to the common axis, lenses L_2, L_3, L_4, and a plane mirror M_2 are erected as shown. Observation is made by the eye at E after reflection back from M_2 through the sheet M_1 and the lens L_4. A toothed wheel W is erected in such a position that light is alternately allowed to pass to P through a gap between teeth or is stopped by a tooth according to the orientation of W. The principle of the experiment is to rotate the wheel

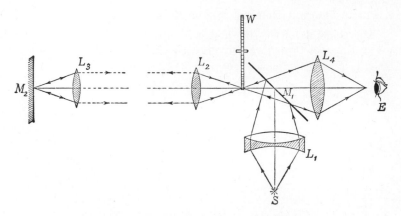

Fig. 3.—Fizeau's method for velocity of light

at gradually increasing speed until no light is visible at E. This implies that light is passing through a gap between teeth to the mirror M_2, but on reflection back from M_2 it is unable to pass on to E, since a tooth has now moved into the position previously occupied by the gap.

If the wheel has N teeth and revolves at n revs./sec., the time taken for one tooth to move to the position previously occupied by the neighbouring tooth is

$$\tau = \frac{1}{Nn}, \quad \cdots \quad \cdots \quad (12.5)$$

while the time for a tooth to move into a neighbouring gap is

$$\frac{\tau}{2} = \frac{1}{2Nn}. \quad \cdots \quad \cdots \quad (12.6)$$

This must also be the time for the light to travel from P to M_2 and back, and if the distance PM_2 is L,

$$\frac{\tau}{2} = \frac{2L}{c}. \quad \ldots \ldots \quad (12.7)$$

Hence $$c = 4LNn. \quad \ldots \ldots \quad (12.8)$$

Additional readings could be obtained by increasing the speed until the image reappeared, and then increasing the speed still more until a second eclipse occurred, and so on. Owing to the difficulty in determining exactly the condition of perfect eclipse, Fizeau's method is mainly of historical interest. Also, the distance L has to be several miles, and this is inconveniently large.

5. Fizeau-Foucault Rotating Mirror Method.

The principle of this method is illustrated in fig. 4. Light from a source S passes through a converging lens L and is brought to a focus

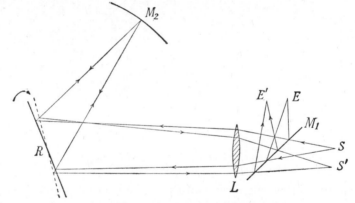

Fig. 4.—Fizeau-Foucault rotating mirror method

on the surface of a concave mirror M_2 after reflection at a plane mirror R. The mirror R is caused to rotate, and it has rotated through some small angle α when the light has returned from M_2. E, E' are the images, in the mirror M_1, of S and the reflected image S'.

Let τ be the time taken for the light to travel the distance from R to M_2 and back, and let r be the radius of curvature of M_2, then

$$\tau = \frac{2r}{c}. \quad \ldots \ldots \quad (12.9)$$

Referring now to fig. 5, consider the image of M_2 in R, formed at M_2'. A ray of light from S, passing through the optical centre of L, is brought to a focus with the other rays at some point X on the surface of M_2, represented by X′ in M_2′. When the mirror R is rotated through a, the image of X is formed at X″. Since the reflected ray turns through an angle $2a$ when the mirror rotates through a,

$$2a = \frac{X'X''}{r}. \qquad \ldots \ldots \quad (12.10)$$

Now if the mirror rotates at a speed of n revs./sec., the time taken to revolve through a is

$$\tau = \frac{a}{2\pi n}. \qquad \ldots \ldots \quad (12.11)$$

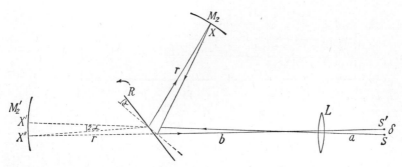

Fig. 5.—Principle of rotating mirror method

Hence, from (12.9) and (12.11),

$$a = \frac{4\pi n r}{c}, \qquad \ldots \ldots \quad (12.12)$$

and so, from (12.10) and (12.12),

$$X'X'' = \frac{8\pi n r^2}{c}. \qquad \ldots \ldots \quad (12.13)$$

Now, from the geometry of fig. 5,

$$X'X'' = \delta \cdot \frac{(b+r)}{a}. \qquad \ldots \ldots \quad (12.14)$$

Hence the displacement δ of the image is given by

$$\delta = \frac{8\pi n a r^2}{c(b+r)}. \qquad \ldots \ldots \quad (12.15)$$

In Foucault's experiments, r was about 20 m. and the displacement δ, which was measured with an eyepiece, was about 1 mm.

6. The Michelson, Pease, and Pearson Experiment.

Since the velocity of light as hitherto measured depends on the refractive index of the air traversed, Michelson, Pease, and Pearson have determined the velocity of light in an evacuated pipe one mile long. The method was essentially the rotating mirror method, but in the modified form introduced many years earlier by Newcomb and used with much success in several later measurements by Michelson.

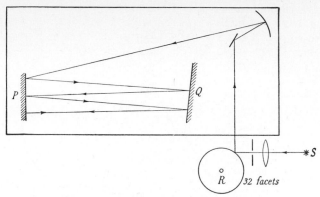

Fig. 6.—Method of Michelson, Pease, and Pearson

The modification now being described consisted in replacing the single plane mirror R by a rotating mirror with 32 facets. The time then taken for the light to traverse the double distance from R to M_2 must just equal the time required for one facet to replace the previous facet if the image is to remain undisturbed. Part of the optical system used is shown diagrammatically in fig. 6. The plane mirrors P and Q are slightly inclined to each other, their purpose being to reflect the light to and fro along the pipe and thus increase the effective path of the light from one to ten miles.

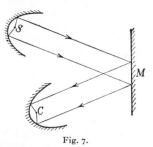

Fig. 7.

7. Bergstrand's Method.

A more recent method of measuring the velocity of light is that of Bergstrand. In fig. 7 light from a source S is focused into a parallel beam by a parabolic reflector and thence by a plane mirror M to a second parabolic reflector with a photoelectric cell C (see p. 728) at the focus. The intensity of S is varied rapidly at a frequency of about 8 megacycles per second by an electronic oscillator operating a Kerr cell. The latter consists of a liquid such as nitrobenzene placed between the

XII] THE MICHELSON-MORLEY EXPERIMENT 439

plates of a condenser; the light which traverses the cell is first polarized
by a polarizer and then extinguished with an analyser. On application
of the electric field the nitrobenzene becomes doubly refracting, thus
allowing some light to pass through the analyser; the whole arrangement comprises an electro-optical shutter of tremendous rapidity. The
same electronic oscillator also modulates the sensitivity of the photoelectric cell C. As the distance of M is changed, the signal strength
from the detector passes through a maximum when the time interval
for transmission from source to detector is equal to the delay time
between maximum intensity of the source and maximum sensitivity of
the detector. From these measurements and other methods based on
the assumption that light waves are electromagnetic waves, the velocity
of light is now determined as 299,793·0 ± 0·3 km. sec.

8. The Michelson-Morley Experiment.

It is well known from ordinary everyday experience that the relative velocity (see Part I) of two material bodies moving in the same
straight line is equal to the difference of the velocities, taken with
the proper algebraical signs. In the same way, the measured velocity
of sound (see Part IV) depends on the relative velocity of the source
and the observer. In 1881, Michelson and Morley examined the effect
of relative velocity on the measured velocity of light, using an indirect
method based on the Michelson interferometer (see previous chapter).
The principle consisted simply in rotating the arms of the interferometer so that different angles were presented to the moving light
source. In particular, if one arm is set along the direction of motion
of the light source, since the arms are mutually perpendicular, the
other arm must be at right angles to the direction of motion. Hence
the velocities along the two directions might be expected to be different, and the fringe system to be displaced with respect to the fringe
system formed with a stationary light source. Observation showed
no change in the fringe system for any orientation of the interferometer, and hence the velocity of light is a *natural invariant*. Such
behaviour has led to a completely new kinematics and dynamics to
replace the Newtonian system elaborated in Part I. In this system,
if u, v are the velocities of two bodies moving in the same straight
line, the velocity of the first relative to the second is

$$V = \frac{u - v}{1 - uv/c^2}. \quad . \quad . \quad . \quad (12.16)$$

For low velocities such as those of ordinary material bodies or of
sound, v and $u \ll c$, that is, $uv/c^2 \to 0$, so the formula reduces to the
ordinary Newtonian expression. At the other extreme, that is, at the
velocity of light $v = c$, the expression reduces to $V = c$, so that the
formula is consistent with the invariance of light velocity.

The new dynamics is termed **relativistic dynamics,** for the Michelson-Morley experiment had led to a general principle on which to base the new mechanics, termed the **Principle of Relativity.** Further discussion is beyond the scope of this book.

9. Velocity of Light in Matter.

By interposing transparent materials in the light beam the velocity of light may be determined in different media. The velocities found are less, as required by the wave theory of light discussed in Chap. IX, but they are not inversely proportional to the refractive index as the wave theory requires. This difficulty is easily solved, as it can be shown that the experiments measure the **group velocity,** whereas the refractive index involves the **wave velocity.** We discuss this problem in detail in Part IV on Sound and Wave Motion, but we may note here that the relation between the two is

$$G = W - \lambda \, dW/d\lambda, \quad \ldots \ldots \quad (12.17)$$

where G is the group velocity and W is the wave velocity. The expression indicates that if W depends on λ, G and W will not be equal, and G also may depend on λ, i.e. on the colour of the light. In fact, in the experiments on the velocity of light through matter, the final image is coloured when a white light source is used. The difference between group and wave velocity holds only in a dispersive medium; in vacuo the two velocities are equal, and all radiations are propagated with the invariant velocity c.

If the matter is in motion, as in a running water column, the net effect on the velocity of light traversing the column may be calculated according to the principles of Relativity. The results deduced are in complete agreement with experiment.

EXERCISES

1. Describe an accurate method for measuring the velocity of light. Why is this quantity of great significance in physics?

2. Compare and contrast the astronomical and terrestrial methods of measuring the velocity of light.

3. Give an account of some method of finding the velocity of light, involving the use of a rotating mirror.

4. Outline the Michelson-Morley experiment for examining the effect of the velocity of the source on the velocity of light emitted by a source. Of what special significance were the results obtained?

5. Distinguish between *group velocity* and *wave velocity*. Give examples from various branches of physics where these two quantities are involved.

CHAPTER XIII

Photometry

1. Introduction.

The subject of photometry deals with the intensity of light emitted by a source and the intensity of illumination falling on a given area. If judgment of intensity is made by eye the result is highly subjective. Apart from individual differences, energy in the red portion of the spectrum appears far less brilliant than the same amount of energy in the yellow. Again, owing to involuntary contraction of the eye-pupil and other physiological causes, a doubling of light intensity would appear to be a much smaller increase, a roughly logarithmic law being followed. For absolute determinations of intensity, therefore, indirect methods such as the photoelectric cell (see Chap. IX) must be used. Visual observation, however, is very satisfactory for *matching* intensities if a standard light source is available for comparison.

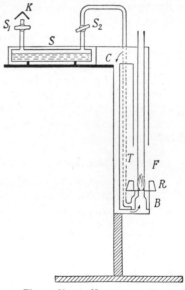

Fig. 1.—Vernon-Harcourt pentane standard

2. Light Standards.

The standard lamp is the **Vernon-Harcourt Pentane Standard,** a diagram of which is shown in fig. 1. A mixture of air and pentane vapour is drawn from the saturator S to the steatite burner B. The products of combustion pass up the flue F and warm the air which passes into the cooling chamber C. From this chamber the air descends at a constant rate via the tube T to the burner B. The percentage of air and pentane is strictly controlled by adjusting the stop-cocks S_1 and S_2 and a cone-valve K. Regular evaporation of the pentane is produced by heat conduction from the lamp itself along the frame supporting the saturator. The flame is adjusted to a definite height,

441

and an opening of definite size in the collar R allows a certain light intensity to escape.

Initially wax-candles were used as standards. The Vernon-Harcourt standard has an intensity about ten times that of the average wax-candle previously used. The term **candle-power** and **standard candle** have been retained, and the **international candle** is defined as *one-tenth the pentane standard*. For practical purposes, electrical filament standards are available, tested by the National Physical Laboratory.

3. Photometric Definitions.

(i) Luminous Flux.

The unit of luminous flux is the **lumen.** This is defined as the *amount of luminous energy falling per unit area per second on a sphere of unit radius from a point source of one candle-power situated at the centre of the sphere.* Hence the lumen is the luminous flux per second per unit solid angle from a point source of one candle-power.

(ii) Intensity of Illumination.

The intensity of illumination of a surface is defined as the amount of light (or luminous energy) falling normally per unit area per second. The unit is the **lux** which is the *illumination of a surface of area one square metre at a distance of one metre from a point standard-candle.* Another unit termed the *phot* is defined as one lumen per square centimetre, and is therefore equal to 10,000 lux. Full sunshine produces an intensity of about 10^5 lux, ordinary daylight outdoors about 5000 lux and indoors about 500 lux. Reading becomes uncomfortable if the intensity falls much below 20 lux. Full moonlight being only about $\frac{1}{5}$ lux is therefore much too feeble for continuous reading.

4. Inverse Square Law.

If we consider a point source S as in fig. 2, the luminous energy L emitted per unit time by the source travels outwards with the velocity of light and falls on spherical surfaces of increasing area as the light spreads farther and farther. If r_1 and r_2 are the radii of two such spheres, by definition of intensity of illumination, we have

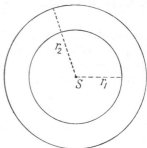

Fig. 2.—Inverse square law

$$I_1 = \frac{L}{4\pi r_1^2}, \qquad \qquad (13.1)$$

$$I_2 = \frac{L}{4\pi r_2^2}, \qquad \qquad (13.2)$$

where I_1 and I_2 are the intensities of illumination at the two spheres. Hence

$$\frac{I_1}{I_2} = \frac{r_2^2}{r_1^2}, \quad \ldots \ldots \ldots \quad (13.3)$$

or the *intensity of illumination falls off inversely as the square of the distance from the source.*

Consider now the intensity of illumination received by the eye observing a uniform glowing sphere as in fig. 3. If we take two small cones of equal solid angle $d\omega$ with their vertices at the eye, the luminous flux received will depend on (i) the areas dS_1, dS_2 of the sphere cut off by the base of the cones, (ii) the inclinations θ_1 and θ_2 of the mean

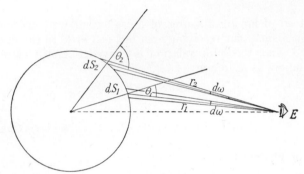

Fig. 3.—Lambert's Cosine Law

lines of the cones to the normals to the sphere, (iii) the distances r_1 and r_2 of the areas from the eye, (iv) the intrinsic intensity C of the source. Hence

$$I_1 = f(C, dS_1, \theta_1, r_1), \quad \ldots \ldots \quad (13.4)$$

where f is some function. Now C is constant, and from the inverse square law r_1 is involved as $1/r_1^2$; hence

$$I_1 = \frac{C}{r_1^2} f(dS_1, \theta_1). \quad \ldots \ldots \quad (13.5)$$

Similarly

$$I_1 = \frac{C}{r_2^2} f(dS_2, \theta_2). \quad \ldots \ldots \quad (13.6)$$

Now all parts of the sphere appear equally bright to the observer, that is, experimentally,

$$I_1 = I_2. \quad \ldots \ldots \ldots \quad (13.7)$$

Thus

$$\frac{f(dS_1, \theta_1)}{r_1^2} = \frac{f(dS_2, \theta_2)}{r_2^2}. \quad \ldots \ldots \quad (13.8)$$

But the two solid angles are both equal to $d\omega$, and by definition of these,

$$d\omega = \frac{dS_1 \cos \theta_1}{r_1{}^2} = \frac{dS_2 \cos \theta_2}{r_2{}^2}. \quad \ldots \quad (13.9)$$

Hence, comparing (13.8) and (13.9), the function f takes the form $dS \cos \theta$. The complete law for the intensity of illumination received at a point a distance r away from a small flat surface is therefore (if we take C equal to 1)

$$I = \frac{dS \cos \theta}{r^2}. \quad \ldots \ldots \quad (13.10)$$

The law of angular variation is sometimes termed **Lambert's Cosine Law.**

If instead of having a source of finite extent we consider a point source, but a small flat receiving area inclined at θ' to the line joining source and area, the same relation is obeyed. A still more general form of the law is therefore

$$I = \frac{dS\, dS' \cos \theta \cos \theta'}{r^2}, \quad \ldots \ldots \quad (13.11)$$

where dS, θ correspond to the source, dS', θ' to the receiving area.

5. Types of Photometer.

To measure the candle-power of a light source various types of **photometer** are available. They all depend essentially on comparing two intensities simultaneously and adjusting them until they are equal. This adjustment is usually carried out by varying the distances of the two sources, but an alternative method is to introduce a rotating sector in one light beam. Then, if the open portion of the sector has an angle a, the effective intensity is reduced to $a/2\pi$ of its value in the absence of the sector. By using a variable sector, light sources may be placed at any convenient *fixed* distances from the photometer, and intensities adjusted to equality by alteration of the aperture of the sector. We describe briefly the earlier simple types and then describe the more accurate Lummer-Brodhun and flicker photometers in some detail.

(i) Simple Types.

The *Rumford shadow photometer* is illustrated in fig. 4. It consists of a vertical solid obstacle such as a rod R standing in front of a white screen S. The two light sources to be compared are at L_1 and L_2, and two shadows R_1 and R_2 are cast on the screen. The distances of L_1 and L_2 from the screen are adjusted until the shadows R_1 and R_2, which are formed side by side (not so far apart as in fig. 4) are judged to be of equal density. If the distances are r_1 and r_2, then from the inverse square law

$$\frac{L_1}{L_2} = \frac{r_2{}^2}{r_1{}^2}.$$

Another value of r_1 is then taken and the new value of r_2 found; from several such readings a mean value of L_1/L_2 is obtained.

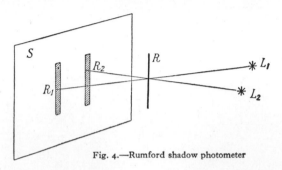

Fig. 4.—Rumford shadow photometer

The *Bunsen grease-spot photometer* is illustrated diagrammatically in fig. 5. It consists essentially of an opaque parchment screen with a grease-spot in the centre. The two light sources L_1 and L_2 are placed on opposite sides of the screen, and when the intensities of illumination on the two sides are equal the spot becomes invisible against the general parchment background. To prove this, let a be the fraction of light transmitted through the spot; neglect absorption so that a

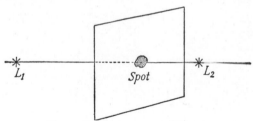

Fig. 5.—Bunsen grease-spot photometer

fraction $(1 - a)$ is diffusely reflected back from the spot. The spot is indistinguishable if the intensity reflected from the general background surrounding the spot is equal to that received from the spot itself. If I_1 and I_2 are the intensities of illumination on the two sides, considering the R.H.S. of fig. 5, the condition for the spot to vanish is that

$$I_2 = I_1 a + (1 - a)I_2, \quad \dots \dots \quad (13.12)$$

or
$$I_1 = I_2.$$

Since it is preferable to see both sides of the screen simultaneously, two plane mirrors are sometimes inclined symmetrically on each side of the screen, as shown in fig. 6. As with the Rumford photometer,

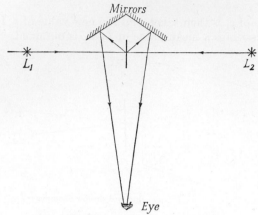

Fig. 6.—Grease-spot photometer with mirrors

a series of values of r_1 and r_2 is taken, and the mean value of L_1/L_2 calculated from (13.3).

Joly's paraffin-wax photometer consists of a cube of paraffin wax of side about 5 cm., which has been cut through symmetrically, a thin

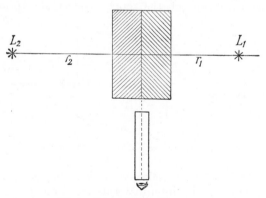

Fig. 7.—Joly's paraffin photometer

opaque metal sheet being inserted between the two halves, which are then gently warmed and replaced together. The two sources are placed on opposite sides of the cube as shown in fig. 7, and observation is made along a tube set at right angles to the block and directed towards the metal division. The paraffin wax is translucent, and it is possible to judge with considerable accuracy the condition when the intensities on the two sides of the sheet are equal. A series of values of r_1 and r_2 are taken, and the mean value of L_1/L_2 is calculated.

(ii) Lummer-Brodhun Photometer.

This photometer, which is capable of a high degree of accuracy, is shown in fig. 8. Light from the two sources to be compared is incident on opposite sides of a white screen S, and the diffusely reflected rays are reflected by the prisms M_1 and M_2 into the prism system P_1P_2, and thence to the observer who is supplied with a low power

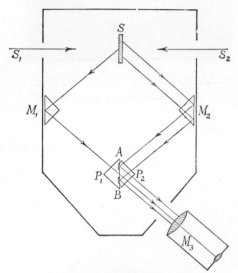

Fig. 8.—Lummer-Brodhun photometer

telescope M_3. The prism P_1, has a ring sandblasted in its hypotenuse face. The prism P_2, has the edges of its hypotenuse face slightly ground away. The two prisms make optical contact *within* the ring but not in the ring itself, nor beyond the ring. Consequently the light from M_2 is totally reflected by P_2 to M_3 *over the ring region itself*, but passes straight on through P_1 over the central area. On the other hand, the reverse happens with the light reflected from M_1, which passes through the central area to M_3, and not through the ring area itself. Consequently the field of view in the telescope appears as shown in fig. 9. The distances of the two sources from S are adjusted until the field is everywhere of uniform intensity, that is, until it is impossible to distinguish a central and a ring region. This condition will occur when the intensities reflected from M_1 and M_2 are equal, that is, when $L_1/L_2 = r_2^2/r_1^2$.

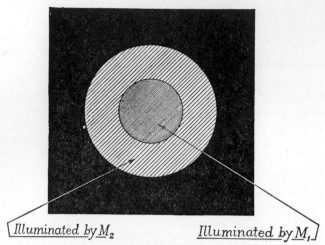

Illuminated by M_2 Illuminated by M_1

Fig. 9.—Lummer-Brodhun photometer

(iii) Flicker Photometer.

The principle of this instrument is extremely simple, and is illustrated in fig. 10. Light from the source L_1 illuminates a white fixed inclined screen A. Light from L_2 illuminates a white rotating screen S made of the same material as A and inclined at an equal angle to the line of vision ASE. One or more apertures in S may be opened so that the total effective aperture is 180°. On rotating S the observer sees the screens A and S illuminated alternately for equal intervals of

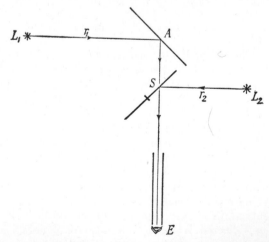

Fig. 10.—Flicker photometer

time. If the intensities of illumination are unequal a sensation of flicker is produced; when the intensities are made equal by adjusting the distances r_1 and r_2, the flicker disappears. Under these conditions $L_1/L_2 = r_2^2/r_1^2$. The flicker photometer has the great advantage that the flicker phenomenon disappears even when the light from L_1 and that from L_2 are of different colour, provided that the intensities are made equal. The other matching photometers we have described are clearly inadequate for comparing lights of different colours for, as already mentioned, illumination in the yellow appears much brighter to the eye than illumination of equal intensity in other parts of the spectrum.

(iv) Photoelectric-cell Method.

The number of electrons emitted (or the electric current produced) by a vacuum photoelectric cell such as that described on p. 728 is directly proportional to the intensity of the light falling upon it. Hence intensities of illumination may be directly compared if care is taken that the light shall always fall on equal areas of, and at the same angles to, the surface of the photoelectric emitter. Alternatively, a photoelectric cell which operates on the principle of the variation of electrical resistance with intensity of illumination may be used as in the selenium or lead sulphide cell (see p. 728). As the efficiency of the electrical response depends on the wavelength of the light, accurate comparisons can be made only for sources emitting the same spectral distribution.

6. Brightness of Optical Images.

We shall now discuss briefly the brightness of optical images, for although the full theoretical discussion is beyond the scope of this

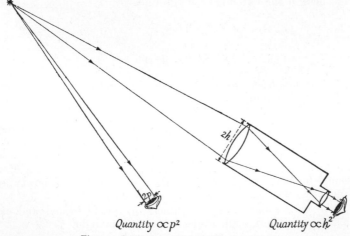

Quantity $\propto p^2$　　　　　　*Quantity* $\propto h^2$

Fig. 11.—Subjective brightness of point source

book, the subject is one of great practical importance. For example, it may be shown that the intensity of an image produced by a lens is directly proportional to the area of the lens and inversely proportional to the square of the focal length. Photographic objectives which are to be used for photographing feebly illuminated objects must therefore have as large an aperture and as short a focal length as possible. Reference to Chap. V shows that these are precisely the conditions under which aberrations are very large, so a compromise has to be effected between intensity of image and faithfulness of reproduction

Another interesting fact which emerges from theoretical considerations is that the **subjective brightness** (that is, the brightness as it appears to the human eye) of an *extended source* such as the sky is always less after passage through an optical instrument than that experienced by direct unaided vision. On the other hand, the subjective brightness of a *point source* is increased by the use of a telescope. This is easily intelligible from fig. 11, for, neglecting losses by absorption, diffuse reflection, and so on, all the light which falls on the objective of the telescope may ultimately be brought into the eye-pupil. Direct vision of the point source by the eye would receive only the amount of light incident on an area πp^2 where p is the radius of the eye-pupil. The subjective brightness of the point source is therefore increased by

$$h^2/p^2, \qquad \ldots \ldots \ldots \quad (13.13)$$

where h is the radius of the objective. It is owing to this fact that stars are visible through a telescope in broad daylight, for a large increase in brightness of the star is accompanied by a slight diminution in brightness of the extended background.

EXERCISES

1. Define the *lumen*, the *lux*, and the *phot*. What relation governs the intensity of the illumination received by a small flat surface from a small flat source?

2. Outline the principles underlying the photometric comparison of two light sources, and describe in detail some form of accurate photometer.

3. How may the intensities of two light sources of different colours be compared? A continuous spectrum, each component colour of which is of equal intensity, is observed by the eye. Does the intensity appear uniform across the entire spectrum?

4. Give an account of the brightness of optical images and explain why a star is visible through a telescope in full daylight.

EXAMPLES

1. Prove that the spot of a Bunsen grease-spot photometer will become indistinguishable from the background when the intensity of illumination is the same on both sides of the spot.

2. Find the wattage absorbed by a lamp of 2 candle-power per watt, if the illumination from it is balanced by that from a 30 c.p. standard, the distances of the lamp and the standard from the photometer screen being 20 cm. and 30 cm. respectively.

3. The illuminations from a fixed and from a movable source are balanced when the movable source is 25 cm. from a photometer screen. On interposing a transparent sheet of glass between the movable source and the screen it is found that the source must be moved 7 cm. nearer the screen for the balance of illumination to be maintained. What percentage of light does the glass sheet absorb?

4. If it takes 5 min. to toast a large piece of bread when the latter is placed 25 cm. from a very small source of radiant heat, find the time taken when the bread is placed 5 cm. from the source.

5. In Ques. 4, show that if a horizontal source of radiant heat is large and flat, the time required to toast a small piece of bread, lying at the bottom of a tin bowl in the shape of a truncated cone, is independent of the distance of bread from source for small distances.

6. All parts of the surface of a glowing sphere appear equally bright to an observer. Use this fact to prove that the intensity of radiation emitted by a surface is proportional to the cosine of the angle between the normal to the surface and the direction of emission.

7. If the fraction of incident radiation absorbed by a small thickness of material is proportional to that thickness, show that the intensity of the radiation I, after the incident radiation I_0 has traversed a distance d, is given by $I = I_0 \, exp^{-\mu d}$, where μ is a constant.

8. At what angle are two plane mirrors inclined to each other if an observer looking straight in front can see the top of his own head?

9. If two plane mirrors are inclined to each other at an angle $\theta°$, prove that if $360/\theta = n$, where n is an integer, there will be $(360/\theta - 1)$ images formed of an object placed between the two mirrors.

10. An observer at water level on board ship reflects, with a plane mirror, the light emitted from the top of a lighthouse, so that the illumination strikes the base of the lighthouse, the mirror being inclined at 80° to the horizontal. On steaming 200 ft. nearer to the lighthouse

it is found that the mirror must be turned through 5° for the light again to strike the base of the lighthouse. Find the height of the lighthouse and the distance of the ship from it in the second position.

11. An observer travels in a car on a long straight flat road leading to a large vertical plane mirror. The mirror and the road are inclined to each other at 60°. The observer, who is unaware of the mirror, sees what he thinks is his own road stretching out indefinitely and notes the light of an approaching car in the far distance. The light of the second car disappears when the first car is one mile from the mirror, owing to the second car having taken a cross-road which is the shortest possible distance to the first road. Both cars travel at the same speed and crash at the corner where the side road joins the first road. How far is this point from the mirror?

12. An object 2 cm. high is placed at distances of 15 cm., 8 cm., and 3 cm. from a spherical concave mirror of radius of curvature 10 cm. Find the position and size of the image, and state whether it is real or virtual, upright or inverted, for each case.

13. Obtain the answers for Ques. 12, but with the mirror convex instead of concave.

14. Show that for an object of small but appreciable thickness, placed perpendicularly on the axis of a spherical mirror or lens, the magnification in a direction parallel to the axis is equal to the square of the magnification perpendicular to the axis.

15. A parallel beam of light is incident on a concave mirror of radius of curvature 40 cm. in a direction parallel to the axis. If a convex mirror of 20 cm. radius of curvature is placed coaxially with the concave mirror and facing it at a distance of 15 cm., determine where the beam of light will form its first real image.

16. Determine the positions of the first two real images formed on the axis if the convex mirror is 25 cm. from the other in Ques. 15.

17. A square piece of card of side 1 cm. is placed symmetrically perpendicular to the axis of a concave cylindrical reflector of radius 10 cm. at a distance of 15 cm. from the reflector. Find the position and the area of the image formed in the reflector.

18. A concave spherical mirror of radius 10 m. and a concave cylindrical mirror of radius 10 cm. are set up coaxially and facing each other at a distance of 1520 cm. A square card of side 1 cm. is placed symmetrically on the axis, 20 cm. from the cylindrical mirror. The side of the card facing the spherical mirror is white, while that facing the cylindrical mirror is black. An observer looking into the cylindrical mirror sees a black image and a white image. Determine the position and size of each image.

19. Apply the data of Ques. 18 to find the positions and sizes of the black and white images seen by an observer in the spherical reflecting mirror.

20. At what distance from a convex mirror of aperture 10 cm. and focal length 30 cm. does the whole of the back of a van, assumed to be a square of side 3 m., become visible?

21. For a given liquid, the apparent depth as measured optically with a microscope is 3 cm., whereas the true depth is found to be 4 cm. What is the refractive index of the liquid?

22. Find the apparent positions of the first three images to be seen in a plane glass mirror (silvered on the back surface) of thickness 1 cm. and of material of refractive index 1·50, when a small object is placed 3 cm. from the front surface of the mirror. Which image is the brightest?

23. What is the apparent depth of a liquid 5 cm. deep, whose refractive index increases uniformly from a value 1·30 at the surface to a value 1·60 at the bottom?

24. Two immiscible liquids A and B, of depths 3 and 4 cm. respectively, lie one on top of the other. If the refractive index of the lower liquid B is 4/3, find the refractive index of the upper liquid if the apparent depth of the two liquids is 36/7 cm.

25. Show that the lateral displacement of a ray of light incident upon a parallel-sided block of refractive index μ and thickness t at an angle of incidence i is given by $t \cdot \sin i (1 - \cos i / \sqrt{\mu^2 - \sin^2 i})$.

26. An incandescent bulb is immersed at an unknown depth in a lake at a point 50 ft. from the shore. An observer whose eye is 5 ft. from the ground on the edge of the lake allows his gaze to travel slowly outwards from the shore and observes the first rays to emanate from the water at a point 20 ft. from the shore. If the refractive index of the water is 4/3, at what depth is the bulb immersed?

27. An observer places a pin 2 cm. in front of a thick block of glass of refractive index 1·50 and observes that a faint image of the pin is apparently coincident with a small air bubble in the glass. What is the actual distance of the bubble from the surface of the glass?

28. Show that the vertical angle of the cone of rays visible to a fish below water of refractive index 1·33 is about $97\frac{1}{2}°$, but that to an observer in a diving helmet containing air and fitted with a glass window, the cone widens out to a vertical angle of 180°.

29. Determine graphically or otherwise the angular deviation suffered by a parallel beam of light incident at an angle of incidence of 70° on one surface of an equilateral glass prism of refractive index 1·50, after passage through the prism.

30. Prove that the deviation suffered by a ray of light in traversing an isosceles prism is least when the light inside the prism travels parallel to the base.

31. What is the refractive index of the transparent liquid contained in a hollow equilateral glass prism if the angle of minimum deviation is 68°?

32. A triangular prism ABC having $\angle A = 90°$, $\angle B = 60°$, $\angle C = 30°$, and $c = 3$ cm., and $\mu = 1\cdot5$, has a ray of light incident normally to the face c at a point 1 cm. from A. Determine the point at which the refracted ray will leave the prism and the angle of deviation produced.

33. An observer finds the self-conjugate position of a pin as seen in a spherical concave mirror to be 20 cm. from the mirror. Find the new self-conjugate position when the mirror is covered with a thin film of liquid of refractive index $1\cdot55$.

34. A concave spherical mirror is placed at the bottom of a dish and the image of a pin is self-conjugate when placed 30 cm. from the mirror. Liquid is now poured into the dish to a depth of 2 cm. and the pin has to be moved 6 cm. nearer to the mirror again to be self-conjugate. What is the refractive index of the liquid?

35. A thin prism is immersed in a rectangular trough of liquid of known refractive index μ_1 and a ray of light is observed to be deviated through an angle D_1 on passage through the arrangement. If the angle of deviation with the prism in air is D_2, show that the angle A of the prism is given by $A = (D_2 - D_1)/(\mu_1 - 1)$. What is the refractive index of the material of the prism?

36. A ray of light is incident on a prism at grazing incidence and emerges after passage through the prism at an angle β to the surface. Show that the refractive index of the material of the prism is

$$\frac{(1 + 2\cos a \cos \beta + \cos^2 \beta)^{\frac{1}{2}}}{\sin a}$$

where a is the refracting angle of the prism.

37. A tetragonal prism is constructed so as to give a constant deviation of 90° to a ray entering one face and subsequently reflected at two other faces before emerging from the fourth face. An observer situated at a point A and placing the prism at a point B, observes a distant object C and finds that the image of C is again visible from A when the prism is moved to another point D. If the angle between AB and AD is 1° and the distances AD and BD are 10 ft. and 30 ft. respectively, find the position of the distant object.

38. Determine the angle between the base of a glass hemisphere of refractive index μ and the line joining the centre of the hemisphere

to the point on the spherical surface for which rays are first totally internally reflected at the base, if a parallel beam is incident on the curved surface of the hemisphere perpendicular to the base.

39. A horizontal parallel beam of light falls on a vertical glass hemisphere of refractive index 1·5. Neglecting absorption, diffuse reflection, and reflection from the front surface of the hemisphere, find the fraction of light transmitted through the hemisphere.

40. A flat surface is examined with a glass hemisphere used with the flat face down as a magnifying glass. If the eye is on the axis of symmetry, show that in order to view the entire surface beneath the hemisphere, the eye must not be more than $\mu^2 r/2(\mu^2 - 1)^{\frac{1}{2}}$ from the flat surface, where r is the radius of the hemisphere and μ is its refractive index.

41. In a preliminary test when constructing a direct vision spectroscope, a prism A of refracting angle α and mean refractive index μ_1 is to be cemented to an inverted prism B of mean refractive index μ_2. What must be the value of the vertical angle β of the second prism if a mean ray falling normally on the first prism is to emerge from the second prism parallel to its original direction?

42. Show that for rays near the axis and incident upon the plane surface of a plano-convex lens of radius r, the system behaves as a concave reflecting mirror of radius r/μ, if the curved surface of the lens is silvered and μ is the refractive index of the material of the lens.

43. What is the position and size of the image of a small obstacle 2 cm. high placed with its axis perpendicular to a radius of a glass sphere of radius 5 cm. and of material of refractive index 1·50? The object is 10 cm. from the centre of the sphere.

44. A thin glass tank of length 100 cm. has one end plane and the other end consists of a thin watch glass of radius of curvature 7 cm. If the tank is filled with liquid of refractive index 4/3, find the apparent position of and the size of the image of an object 2 cm. high placed in air 30 cm. from the curved end of the tank and viewed through the plane end.

45. Find the focal length of a thin concave lens if the image of an object formed by a thin convex lens of focal length 10 cm. moves from a distance of 30 cm. to a distance of 40 cm., from the convex lens when the concave lens is placed in contact with it.

46. Find the radius of curvature of the curved face of a plano-convex lens from the following data. On placing a plane mirror behind the lens the image of a pin is self-conjugate when the latter is placed 15 cm. from the lens. On replacing the mirror by a piece of black card placed behind the curved surface of the lens, a fainter image of the pin

is observed to be self-conjugate when the pin is moved 9·9 cm. nearer to the lens.

47. In Ques. 46 find the refractive index of the glass of the lens.

48. A cylindrical glass dish of diameter 20 cm. is filled with water ($\mu = 4/3$) and a pin is immersed vertically in the water 5 cm. from one edge of the dish. Find the apparent position of the pin to an observer who looks into the curved side of the dish from the opposite edge.

49. Two convex lenses of focal lengths 10 and 5 cm. are situated coaxially at a distance of 12 cm. Find the position and size of the image of a pin 2 cm. high placed vertically on the axis 12 cm. in front of the first lens, when viewed through the second lens.

50. A plano-concave lens of material of mean refractive index 1·6 is found just to neutralize the deviation of the mean ray through a double-convex lens of material of refractive index 1·5, when the two lenses are placed in contact. The curved face of the concave lens is of radius 30 cm. and fits one face of the convex lens exactly. Find the radius of curvature of the other face of the convex lens.

51. Prove that the minimum distance between object and real image as formed by a convex lens is four times the focal length of the lens.

52. Two fixed pin-points P and Q are situated a distance a apart. It is found that there are two positions for a convex lens between P and Q for which the pin-points are conjugate. If the distance between the two positions of the convex lens is b, show that the focal length of the lens is $(a^2 - b^2)/4a$.

53. A pin is placed 40 cm. from a convex lens of focal length 20 cm., and on placing a concave lens 10 cm. from the convex lens and on the image side of it, the image remains real but moves through 45 cm. Find the focal length of the concave lens.

54. A pin is placed 50 cm. from a convex lens of focal length 20 cm. Find the radius of curvature of the convex mirror which when placed 10 cm. from the lens gives an image self-conjugate with the pin.

55. Find the apparent volume of the image of a cube of side 1 cm. placed symmetrically on the axis of a cylindrical converging lens of focal length 25 cm., if the object is at a mean distance of 50 cm. from the lens.

56. Find the focal length of a concave lens if the self-conjugate image of a pin formed by reflection at the surface of a concave mirror of focal length 10 cm. moves to a position 30 cm. from the mirror when the concave lens is inserted 5 cm. from the mirror.

57. Two plano-concave lenses of glass of refractive index 1·50 have radii of curvature of 20 and 30 cm. respectively. They are placed in contact with the curved faces towards each other, and the space between them is filled with a liquid of refractive index 1·33. What is the focal length of the combination?

58. A small source of light is situated 20 cm. from a screen and a circular aperture is placed midway between source and screen. If a concave lens of focal length 10 cm. is placed in contact with and covering the aperture, compare the intensities of illumination on the screen before and after the lens has been interposed.

59. Two converging lenses each of focal length 3 cm. are situated 2 cm. apart. At what distance must an object be placed so that its image may be seen by a person whose least distance of distinct vision is 25 cm.?

60. Two converging lenses, one of focal length 2 cm. and the other of focal length 1 cm. are situated 10 cm. apart. At what distance from the first lens must an object be placed so that its image may be seen distinctly by a person whose least distance of distinct vision is 25 cm.?

61. A telescope consists of two convex lenses of focal lengths 100 and 5 cm., and it is used to view an object situated at 100 m. from the objective. If the final image is 25 cm. in front of the eye-lens, find (a) the distance apart of the two lenses, and (b) the magnification when the eye is close to the eye-lens.

62. An object is placed 20 cm. from the focus of a converging lens and the image is found to be 5 cm. from the focus. What is the focal length of the lens?

63. A thin double-convex lens of radii of curvature 15 and 20 cm. is of material of refractive index 1·52. The first surface is in contact with a liquid of refractive index 1·33, while the second surface is in contact with a liquid of refractive index 1·44. Find the position of the image of an object placed 500 cm. from the lens in the first liquid.

64. When a powerful parallel beam of light is passed through a thin double-convex lens, in addition to the normal image which is formed 102 cm. from the lens, a fainter second image is found 15 cm. from the lens. What is the refractive index of the material of the lens?

65. A thin convex lens is placed on a plane reflecting sheet and the self-conjugate image of a pin is formed 15 cm. from the lens. On filling the space between lens and plate with a liquid of refractive index 4/3, the self-conjugate point is found to be 24 cm. from the lens. Find the radius of curvature of the face of the lens in contact with the plate.

66. Two glass prisms A and B deviate blue rays through 15° and 20° and red rays through 10° and 15° respectively. Which prism has the greater dispersive power?

67. It is required to form an achromatic combination of two prisms of dispersive powers 0·043 and 0·061 (crown and flint glass) respectively. If the first prism has a vertical angle of 10° and a mean refractive index of 1·53, what must be the vertical angle of the second prism if its mean refractive index is 1·59?

68. What is the deviation of the mean ray in Ques. 67?

69. Five prisms, of crown and flint glass, are arranged to form a direct vision spectroscope. Using the data of Ques. 67, what must be the total vertical angles of the crown and flint prisms respectively, if the total dispersion is equal to that of a 15° flint glass prism?

70. It is required to form an achromatic objective of focal length 100 cm. from a double-convex lens of crown glass and a plano-concave lens of flint glass. Using the data of Ques. 67, find the radii of curvature of the convex lens.

71. Show that the angular separation of the red and violet bands in an ordinary rainbow is about 2°. The refractive indices of water for red and violet light may be taken as 1·329 and 1·343 respectively.

72. A converging lens is made of material of dispersive power 0·028, and is of mean focal length 20 cm. What is the separation between the red and blue foci?

73. Observation of the eclipse of the moons of Jupiter by that planet shows that a time T_1 elapses between an eclipse observed when Jupiter and the earth are in conjunction and that observed when they are next in opposition, whereas a further time T_2 elapses before the next eclipse when the two planets are again in conjunction. If the radius of the earth's orbit round the sun is 93 million miles and the velocity of light is 3×10^{10} cm./sec., find $(T_1 - T_2)$.

74. In Fizeau's method for determining the velocity of light, the disappearance of the image occurs when the angular velocity of rotation of the wheel is 177 radians/sec., and again when the angular velocity is 295 radians/sec. If the number of teeth in the wheel is 800 and the total effective distance traversed by the light is 20 Km., find the velocity of light.

75. In a simple Foucault apparatus for determining the velocity of light, the distance between the plane revolving mirror and the concave reflector was 1 Km., the distance from revolving mirror to telescope being 20 m. If the frequency of rotation of the revolving mirror is 512 per sec., find the displacement of the image, taking the velocity of light as 3×10^{10} cm./sec.

ANSWERS AND HINTS FOR SOLUTION

1. Let fraction transmitted by spot be T and neglect absorption. For spot to disappear, intensities from area surrounding spot and from spot itself must be equal. If intensities on two sides are I_1 and I_2, from area surrounding spot on one side amount reflected is I_1; amount from spot on this side is $I_1(1 - T) + I_2T$; hence $I_1 = I_1(1 - T) + I_2T$ or $I_1 = I_2$.

2. Candle-power of lamp is $30 \times 20^2/30^2 = 40/3$; hence wattage is $20/3$.

3. Let intensity due to fixed source be I; then if candle-power of movable source is L, $I = L/25^2$. After interposition of glass, effective candle-power of movable source is reduced to L' given by $I = L'/18^2$; hence $L'/L = (18/25)^2$, and percentage of light absorbed is 48 per cent approx.

4. Time $\propto 1/$intensity; hence $t = 5 \times 60/25 = 12$ sec.

5. Total radiation received $\propto$ area of source$/d^2$; effective area of source is limited by edges of conical bowl and is approximately proportional to d^2; hence total radiation received is independent of d.

6. Consider radiation contained in two elementary cones of same solid angle $d\omega$, the vertex of the cones being at the eye and the bases cutting the sphere. Then if the axis of one cone lies along the line joining the eye to the centre of the sphere and the axis of the other lies at an angle θ to this, the areas cut off on the surface of the sphere will be as 1 to $1/\cos\theta$. Hence, since total intensities are observed to be the same, intensity of radiation must fall off as $\cos\theta$.

7. $-dI/I = \mu dx$, hence $\int_{I_0}^{I} dI/I = \int_{0}^{d} -\mu dx$ or $\log_e I - \log_e I_0 = -\mu d$ or $I = I_0 \, exp^{-\mu d}$.

8. Imagine one mirror rotated to position of the other; angle reflected ray turns through is twice angle mirror turns through. But ray is to be turned through $270°$; hence mirror is to be turned through $135°$ or mirrors are inclined at $45°$ to each other.

9. Draw a circle with centre at the point of intersection O of the two mirrors and radius equal to the distance from this point to the object P. Let OP make angles α and β with the two mirrors. Construction of images will show that they lie at points on the circle such that the angles subtended at O by the arcs between successive images are alternately 2α and 2β. Hence if $(n - 1)$ images are formed, taking account also of the object, $2n(\alpha + \beta) = n\theta = 360°$ or $(n - 1) = 360°/\theta - 1$.

10. The angles between the rays from the lighthouse to the mirror and the horizontal in the two positions are $20°$ and $30°$ respectively. Representing the height of the lighthouse by h and the distance by d, $h/d = \tan 30°$ and $h/(200 + d) = \tan 20°$. $h = 197 \cdot 0$ ft. and $d = 341 \cdot 1$ ft.

460   ANSWERS AND HINTS FOR SOLUTION

11. Since cars travel at same speed, each must be initially at same distance x from corner. From geometry $x/(1 - x) = \tan 60°$; 644·2 yd.

12. Apply $1/v + 1/u = 2/r$; (a) $v = 7·5$ cm., $h = 1$ cm., real, inverted; (b) $v = 40/3$ cm., $h = 10/3$ cm., real, inverted; (c) $v = -7·5$ cm., $h = 5$ cm., virtual, upright.

13. Images are all virtual and upright; (a) $v = -15/4$ cm., $h = 1/2$ cm.; (b) $v = -40/13$ cm., $h = 10/13$ cm.; (c) $v = -15/8$ cm., $h = 5/4$ cm.

14. Calling the thickness of the object du, the longitudinal magnification may be expressed as dv/du. Since $1/v + 1/u = 1/f$, differentiating and remembering f is constant, $dv/du = \pm(v/u)^2 =$ square of lateral magnification.

15. After reflection at concave mirror, light would pass to the focus at $40/2 = 20$ cm. from this mirror. Image would therefore be formed $(-20 + 15) = -5$ cm. from convex mirror. Hence first real image is formed at point given by $1/v - 1/5 = -1/10$ or $v = 10$ cm. from convex mirror.

16. Apply $1/v + 1/u = 2/r$; *1st real image* I_1 formed at focus of concave mirror $= 40/2 = 20$ cm. from concave mirror. Virtual image I_2 formed at $(1/v + 1/5 = -1/10)$ or $85/3$ cm. from concave mirror. I_3 virtual at 68 cm. I_4 virtual at $(1/v - 1/43 = -1/10) = 13$ cm. approx. from convex or 38 cm. from concave. I_5 virtual at 42·2 cm. from concave. Continuing in this way, I_6, I_7 are at 49 and 34 cm. from the concave mirror, I_8 is 65 cm. *behind* the concave mirror, and the *second real image* is I_9 formed at 15·3 cm. from the concave mirror.

17. Applying $1/v + 1/u = 2/r$, $v = 7·5$ cm.; magnification in one direction is $v/u = 1/2$ and in the other direction is unity; hence new area is $1/2$ cm.^{2}.

18. Apply $1/v + 1/u = 2/r$ to concave cylinder, black image is $20/3$ cm. from cylinder and of area $1 \times 1/3 = 1/3$ cm.^{2}. For white image in concave sphere $v = 750$ cm. and area is $1/2 \times 1/2$ cm.^{2}. This image is at so large a distance from the concave cylinder, compared with the radius of curvature of the latter that the white image formed in the latter will be almost at the focus, that is 5 cm. from the mirror and will have the appearance of a white line $1/2$ cm. long, parallel to the axis of the cylinder, the breadth of the line being only $1/154$ cm.

19. From the previous solution, the white image seen in the concave sphere is 750 cm. from the mirror and of area $\frac{1}{2} \times \frac{1}{2}$ cm.^{2}. The black image is that due to a rectangle of sides $1 \times 1/3$ cm.^{2} placed $4540/3$ cm. from sphere; 747 cm. and of size approx. $1/2 \times 1/6$ cm.^{2}.

20. Since the head of the observer must be a considerable distance from the mirror in order not to block the field of view, the effective size of the van is that of a square which just fits into the circular mirror of radius 5 cm., that is a square of side $5\sqrt{2}$ cm. Hence magnification $= v/u = 5\sqrt{2}/300 = \sqrt{2}/60$. Hence $u = 12·75$ metres.

21. $\mu = d_1/d_2 = 4/3$.

22. First image is due to reflection at front surface, 3 cm. behind front surface. Second image is formed by refraction at front face, reflection at silvered face, and refraction again at the front face. Owing to thickness of glass silvered face is effectively at distance $1/1\cdot5$ cm. from front face. Hence second image is apparently at $3\frac{2}{3} + 2/3 = 4\frac{1}{3}$ cm. from front face. For third image, effective position of reflecting surface is $4/3$ cm. behind front surface; $5\frac{2}{3}$ cm.

23. Let $\mu_x = a + bx$ where a and b are constants given by $\mu = 1\cdot30 = a$ when $x = 0$ and $\mu = 1\cdot60 = 1\cdot30 + b\cdot5$ when $x = 5$. Hence $b = 0\cdot06$. Apparent thickness of slice of thickness dx at depth x is dx/μ_x, hence total apparent thickness is $d = \int_0^{\cdot5} \dfrac{dx}{1\cdot30 + 0\cdot06x} = 3\cdot46$ cm.

24. Apparent thickness of top liquid is $3/\mu$ and of lower liquid is $4 \times 3/4 = 3$: hence total apparent thickness is $3 + 3/\mu = 36/7$; $7/5$.

25. Referring to fig. 1, $d = t \sec a . \sin(i - a)$; also $\sin i = \mu \sin a$.

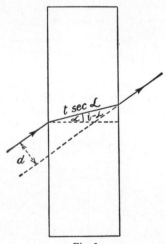

Fig. 1

26. If angles of incidence and refraction of ray are i and r, depth $d = 30 \cot r$; also $\sin i/\sin r = 4/3$ and $\tan i = 20/5$; $28\cdot3$ ft.

27. $d \times 2/3 = 2$; 3 cm. deep.

28. Vertical angle is $2 \sin^{-1}1/1\cdot33$.

29. If i, i', r and r' are the angles of incidence and refraction respectively, $\sin 70°/\sin r = 1\cdot50$, $r = 40\cdot3°$, $r' = 19\cdot7°$; $\sin i'/\sin 19\cdot7° = 1\cdot50$, so $i' = 30\cdot4°$. $D = (i - r) + (i' - r') = 40\cdot4°$.

30. Since $D = (i + i') - (r + r')$ and $(r + r') =$ vertical angle of prism $=$ constant, then for D to be a minimum, $dD = di + di' = 0$, and $dr + dr' = 0$. Now $\sin i = \mu \sin r$ and $\sin i' = \mu \sin r'$, so differentiating, $\cos i . di = \mu \cos r . dr$ and $\cos i' . di' = \mu \cos r' . dr'$. Dividing and squaring

$\cos^2 i/\cos^2 i' = \cos^2 r/\cos^2 r'$ or $(1 - \mu^2 \sin^2 r)/(1 - \mu^2 \sin^2 r') = \cos^2 r/\cos^2 r'$, or $\cos^2 r' - \cos^2 r = \mu^2(\cos^2 r' - \cos^2 r)$. Hence $r = r'$ and $i = i'$.

31. $\mu = \sin\{(A + D)/2\}/\sin(A/2) = 1\cdot8$.

32. Along face b at $(2\sqrt{3} + 1/\sqrt{3})$ from A; deviation is $60 - (48\cdot6 - 30) = 41\cdot4°$.

33. $h = 20/1\cdot55 = 12\cdot9$ cm.

34. $\mu = (30 - 2)/(30 - 6 - 2) = 14/11$.

35. Effect is that of two liquid prisms of total vertical angle A, opposing glass prism of vertical angle A. Since for thin prisms, $D = (\mu - 1)A$, total deviation D_1 for immersed prism is $D_1 = (\mu_2 - \mu_1)A$; also $D_2 = (\mu_2 - 1)A$ or $\mu_2 = (D_2 + A)/A$.

36. $\mu = \cos\beta/\sin r'$, where r' is angle of refraction for light leaving prism; also $\sin r = 1/\mu$ and $(r + r') = a$.

37. In triangles ABC, ADC, $\angle$B and $\angle$D are both $90°$, and lie on a circle with AC as diameter. Calling $\angle$ABD $= \beta$, $10/\sin\beta = 30/\sin 1°$ or $\beta = 20'$; also $30/\sin 1° = $ CD $= 1715$ ft.

38. If a is the angle of incidence on hemisphere, then $90° - a$ is required angle; calling angle of refraction β and critical angle C, $\sin a/\sin\beta = \mu$, $a = (C + \beta)$ and $\sin C = 1/\mu$.

39. Total effective area presented by hemisphere is πr^2, where r is radius of hemisphere; effective area for transmission is $\pi r^2 \sin^2 a$ from Ques. 38; hence fraction is $\sin^2 a = [\mu^2 + 2(\mu^2 - 1)^{\frac12} + 1]/\mu^4 - 2\mu^2 + 5 = 0\cdot986$.

40. From fig. 2, $d = r/\sin 2C$, where $\sin C = 1/\mu$.

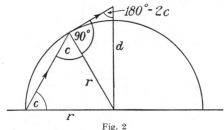

Fig. 2

41. From geometry $\beta = (r + r')$; $\sin a/\sin r = \mu_2/\mu_1$ and $\sin(\beta - a)/\sin r' = \mu_2$.

42. System behaves as concave mirror and two convex lenses in contact (since light traverses lens twice); hence if f is equivalent focal length, $1/f = 1/f_1 + 1/f_2 = 2/r + 2(\mu - 1)/r = 2\mu/r$ and equivalent mirror would have a radius $2f = r/\mu$.

43. Apply $\mu/v - 1/u = (\mu - 1)/r$; after first refraction $v = 15$ cm.; after second refraction $v = 25$ cm. from opposite side of sphere; size of image is 6 cm.

44. Apply $\mu/v - 1/u = (\mu - 1)/r$; $v = -93^1/_3$ cm.; hence apparent depth $= 20/3 \times 3/4 = 5$ cm. in liquid from plane end; size is $6^2/_9$ cm.

45. Apply $1/v - 1/u = 1/f$ to find $u = 15$ cm. for convex lens alone; also $1/v - 1/u = 1/F$, where F is total focal length and is given by $1/F = 1/f_1 + 1/f_2$; 120 cm.

46. $f = 15$ cm.; in second position, centre of curvature is conjugate point with point 5·1 cm. from lens. Hence $1/r - 1/5\cdot1 = -1/15$; 7·7 cm.

47. Apply $1/f = (\mu - 1)(1/r_1 - 1/r_2)$; 1·51.

48. $1/v - \mu/u = (1 - \mu)/r$; 18 cm. across dish from observer.

49. Position of first image is -60 cm.; hence for final image $1/v + 1/48 = -1/5$; $-4\cdot53$ cm. behind second lens.

50. Apply $1/f = (\mu - 1)(1/r_1 - 1/r_2)$; for concave lens $1/f = 0\cdot6/30$ or $f = 50$ cm.; hence for convex lens $1/50 = 0\cdot5(1/30 + 1/r)$; 150 cm.

51. $1/v - 1/u = -1/f$ for a convex lens; hence $(v + u) = u(2f - u)/(f - u)$; this is a minimum when $u = 2f$, and resubstitution gives $v = 2f$; hence $(v + u) = 4f$.

52. Two positions will be symmetrical; in first position object and image distances are u and $(a - u)$, and from symmetry $u = (a - b)/2$ and hence $v = (a + b)/2$, so $-2/(a + b) - 2/(a - b) = -1/f$ or $f = (a^2 - b^2)/4a$.

53. $1/30 - 1/75 = 1/f$; 50 cm.

54. Convex mirror must be placed at radius of curvature from image formed by convex lens alone. Latter image is formed at 100/3 cm. from lens; $r = 23^1/_3$ cm.

55. $v = -50$ cm.; hence magnification in both lateral directions is unity and longitudinal magnification is also unity; same size as object.

56. Centre of curvature and final position of image are conjugate points of lens, hence $1/15 - 1/25 = 1/f$; 37·5 cm.

57. $1/F = 1/f_1 + 1f_2 + 1/f_3 = (1\cdot5 - 1)/20 + (1\cdot5 - 1)/30 - (1\cdot33 - 1)(1/20 + 1/30)$; 70·6 cm.

58. If area of aperture is a, by similar cones area of screen initially illuminated is $a . 20^2/10^2 = 4a$. After interposition of lens, light proceeds as if from point $v = 5$ cm. from lens. Hence new area illuminated is $a . 15^2/5^2 = 9a$, so intensity ratio is 9/4.

59. Distance of image formed by first lens from second lens is given by $1/25 - 1/u = -1/3$ or $u = 2^{19}/_{28}$ cm. Hence image is 19/28 cm. in front of first lens and object distance to give this image is given by $28/19 - 1/u = -1/3$ or $u = 57/103$ cm.

60. Proceed as in previous question; 2·57 cm.

61. Reverse procedure of preceding questions; 105·2 cm.; if magnification produced by object-glass and by eye-lens are m_1 and m_2, $m_1 = 1/99$, $m_2 = 25/4\cdot2$, and $m = m_1 m_2 = 0\cdot06$.

62. Rearranging $1/v - 1/u = 1/f$, $u/v = (u - f)/f$ and $v/u = (v + f)/f$; hence $f^2 = (u - f)(f + v)$; 10 cm.

63. Apply $\mu_2/v - \mu_1/u = (\mu_2 - \mu_1)/r$; 103 cm. from lens in second liquid.

64. The second image is a secondary focus due to rays which have been twice reflected inside the lens before coming to a focus. If primary and secondary focal lengths are f_1 and f_2, it may be shown that $\mu = 1 + 2f_2/(f_1 - 3f_2)$; 1·53.

65. Effect is that of a converging lens and a diverging liquid lens in contact. $-1/24 = -1/15 + 1/f$ or $f = 40$ cm. for liquid lens. Hence $1/40 = 1/3r_1$; $13^1/_3$ cm.

66. Dispersive power is defined as $(\mu_2 - \mu_1)/(\bar{\mu} - 1)$ where μ_2 and μ_1 are extreme refractive indices and $\bar{\mu}$ is the mean refractive index. The differences $(\mu - 1)$ are approximately proportional to the angles of deviation; since $(15 - 10)/12·5 > (20 - 15)/17·5$, first prism has greater dispersive power.

67. Since for a thin prism $D = (\mu - 1)A$, applying this relation to the extreme rays for each prism, the separation which is to be neutralized is $(D_1 - D_2) = (\mu_1 - \mu_2)A = (\mu_1 - \mu_2)(\bar{\mu} - 1)A/(\bar{\mu} - 1) = \omega(\bar{\mu} - 1)A = \omega'(\bar{\mu}' - 1)A'$; 6·3°.

68. $\bar{D} = (\mu - 1)A$; 1·6°.

69. Dispersion produced by 15° flint prism is $0·061 \times 0·59 \times 15 = 0·54$. Hence $0·061 \times 0·59 \times A' - 0·043 \times 0·53A = 0·54$; also for no deviation $0·53A = 0·59A'$; $A = 56·6°$, $A' = 50·9°$.

70. $1/F = 1/f_1 + 1/f_2$; $\omega_1/f_1 = -\omega_2/f_2$, hence $f_1 = -29·5$ cm., and $f_2 = 41·9$ cm., $1/f_1 = (\mu_1 - 1)(1/r_1 - 1/r_2)$, and $1/f_2 = (\mu_2 - 1)/r_1$; $-24·7$ cm., 42·6 cm.

71. The deviation produced by refraction into a raindrop, reflection at the back of the drop and refraction again out of the front of the drop is $D = 4r - 2i$; hence for a stationary value $dr/di = \frac{1}{2}$. Now $\sin i/\sin r = \mu$, so $\cos i = (\mu \cos r)/2 = \{(\mu^2 - 1)/3\}^{\frac{1}{2}}$. Hence $D_1 - D_2 = 42·8 - 40·8 = 2°$.

72. $1/f_1 = (\mu_1 - 1)(1/r_1 - 1/r_2)$; hence $(f_2 - f_1) = f_1 f_2(\mu_1 - \mu_2)(\bar{\mu} - 1)(1/r_1 - 1/r_2)/(\bar{\mu} - 1) = f^2\omega/f = f\omega$; 0·56 cm.

73. If the actual period of eclipse is τ and n eclipses occur while the earth goes from conjunction to opposition, $T_1 = n\tau + d/c$ where d is the diameter of the earth's orbit round the sun and c is the velocity of light. Similarly $T_2 = n\tau - d/c$; hence $(T_1 - T_2) = 2d/c = 997·7$ sec.

74. If total effective distance is d, angular velocity of rotation is ω, the order of the disappearance is n, the velocity of light is c, and the number of the teeth is N, equating times $d/c = (2n - 1)2\pi/2N\omega$. Hence $295/(2n + 1) = 177/(2n - 1)$ or $n = 2$ and $c = 3 \times 10^{10}$ cm./sec.

75. If deviation is δ, $\delta = 8\pi nab/c$ where n is the number of revolutions of the mirror per sec., c is the velocity of light, and a and b are the distances from the revolving mirror to the telescope and the concave mirror respectively; 85·8 cm.

PART IV

WAVE-MOTION AND SOUND

CHAPTER I

Fundamental Properties of Wave-motion

1. Introduction.

Everyday experience provides us with many illustrations of the term **wave**. For example, besides the familiar sea-waves, the general term includes crime waves, waves of bombers, and so on, the underlying conception being some singularity (i) which changes its magnitude more or less regularly with time at a fixed place, (ii) whose maximum and minimum values at a fixed time vary from place to place in a more or less regular manner.

2. Types of Waves.

In Physical Science, there are two well-known types of waves. The first of these is the **pulse,** in which a singularity which has been created in a very short space of time then travels throughout a medium. A pulse is produced, for example, by earth-movements such as sudden faulting, creating an earthquake of short duration.

The other type is the **regular train of waves,** which implies the regular creation of a succession of pulses over a considerable period of time. Thus, if a floating cork is pushed up and down regularly on the surface of a tank of water, a regular train of waves will be propagated over the surface of the water.

The nature of the singularity propagated by the pulse or wave-train may be a **displacement,** as in the above examples, but it may also take the form of **density fluctuation,** as in the case of waves through gases, or **variations of electric and magnetic force** as in electromagnetic waves (see Part III, p. 396). The medium through which the waves are propagated must possess elasticity and inertia or corresponding properties. It is in this sense that the **ether** is required in order to explain the propagation of electromagnetic waves in vacuo.

Waves may be further divided according to the nature and direction of motion of the elements of the medium transmitting the wave. Thus, if the wave consists of oscillations to and fro along the direction of propagation of the wave, it is said to be a **longitudinal wave.** Such a wave is propagated through a gas subject to regular compressions and rarefactions, and, in fact, constitutes a **sound-wave.** The wave

467

transmitted by a stretched string when it is plucked consists in a lateral displacement of the elements of the string and therefore constitutes a **transverse wave**. If a metal bar is gripped firmly at one end and then twisted at the other, when the twisting couple is removed the elements of the rod will execute small circular arcs about the axis of the rod, which is then said to transmit **torsional waves**.

3. Analytical Expression for Wave-motion.

We shall now show that a regular train of waves travelling to the right along the x-axis with a velocity v is represented analytically by the expression

$$y = f(vt - x), \quad \ldots \ldots \ldots (1.1)$$

where f is some function of x and t, and y is the magnitude of the condition which is changing. Suppose at some point $(x + x_1)$ and some subsequent time $(t + \tau)$, y has the same value as in (1.1), then

$$y = f\{v(t + \tau) - (x + x_1)\}. \quad \ldots \ldots (1.2)$$

Thus y will remain unchanged provided

$$v = \frac{x_1}{\tau}. \quad \ldots \ldots \ldots (1.3)$$

We may clearly regard the singularity of magnitude y at (x, t) as having been conveyed to $(x + x_1)$ at time $(t + \tau)$, that is of having traversed the distance x_1 in the time τ. Hence v in equation (1.3)

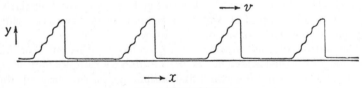

Fig. 1.—Wave Motion

represents the velocity of the wave. Similarly, $y = f(vt + x)$ represents a wave travelling to the left along the x-axis with velocity v. The quantity expressed in equation (1.1) may be quite general and asymmetrical as shown in fig. 1, but it would still constitute a wave-motion.

4. Simple Harmonic Waves.

The most important type of wave is the simple harmonic wave in which the periodic change follows the symmetrical sine or cosine law as shown in fig. 2. Now y is to have a maximum positive value a

(i) at regular intervals of time if we fix x, (ii) at regular intervals of x if we fix t. Also, from fig. 2, as we proceed along the wave, for each *positive* maximum of y we encounter *two* zero values, one corresponding to y increasing and the other to y decreasing. The equation for a sine wave must therefore be of the form

$$y = a \sin 2\pi\left(\frac{t}{\tau} - \frac{x}{\lambda}\right), \quad \ldots \ldots \text{(1.4)}$$

where, (i) if we put $x = 0$, y passes through zero for y increasing at regular intervals of time τ, and (ii) if we put $t = 0$, y passes through zero for y increasing at regular intervals of distance λ. The quantities τ and λ are termed respectively the **period** and the **wave-length** of the

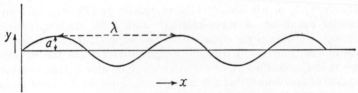

Fig. 2.—Simple Harmonic Wave

wave-motion. As shown in fig. 2, *the wave-length is defined as the distance between successive crests or successive troughs, or between alternate maxima of the wave-motion.* Further, if we write (1.4) in the form

$$y = a \sin \frac{2\pi}{\lambda}\left(\lambda\frac{t}{\tau} - x\right), \quad \ldots \ldots \text{(1.5)}$$

and compare the coefficient of t with that in equation (1.1), we see that the velocity v of propagation of the wave is given by

$$v = \frac{\lambda}{\tau}. \quad \ldots \ldots \ldots \text{(1.6)}$$

The reciprocal of the period τ is termed the **frequency** ν of the wave-motion, and hence (1.6) may be written

$$v = \nu\lambda. \quad \ldots \ldots \ldots \text{(1.7)}$$

This simple equation connecting wave-length, frequency and velocity of propagation is of fundamental importance in wave-motion.

If we write (1.5) in the form

$$y = a \sin \frac{2\pi}{\lambda}(vt - x). \quad \ldots \ldots \text{(1.8)}$$

and differentiate (1.8) twice with respect to x, we shall again obtain

16   (H 394)

the sine term on the right-hand side, and substituting from (1.8) the expression becomes

$$\frac{\partial^2 y}{\partial x^2} = -\frac{4\pi^2}{\lambda^2} y. \quad \cdots \cdots \quad (1.9)$$

Similarly, if we differentiate (1.8) twice with respect to t, we obtain

$$\frac{\partial^2 y}{\partial t^2} = -\frac{4\pi^2}{\lambda^2} v^2 y. \quad \cdots \cdots \quad (1.10)$$

Hence, from (1.10) and (1.11),

$$\frac{\partial^2 y}{\partial t^2} = v^2 \frac{\partial^2 y}{\partial x^2}. \quad \cdots \cdots \quad (1.11)$$

Equations (1.9), (1.10) and (1.11)—especially (1.11)—are said to be **differential equations of wave-motion**; and if in studying physical phenomena we obtain an equation of the type (1.11), we know that a wave-motion must be involved. Equation (1.11) has the important feature that the coefficient of the derivative on the R.H.S. represents the square of the velocity of the wave, so that we do not need to solve the equation to obtain the velocity of propagation.

The coefficient a in (1.4), (1.5) or (1.8) is called the **amplitude** of the wave.

Note that if instead of (1.8) we take

$$y = a \sin\frac{2\pi}{\lambda}(vt - x) + b \sin\frac{2\pi}{\lambda}(vt + x),$$

we shall again get (1.11), which may thus represent a combination of two waves travelling in opposite directions along Ox with velocity v.

5. Superposition of Wave-trains.

If we have present more than one train of waves, the total displacement of the medium is obtained by superposing the displacements which would be caused by each wave-train acting alone. The final result will, of course, depend upon whether the vibrations of the wave-trains are in the same or in different planes. If the planes are the same, the waves **interfere** with each other. We have already discussed this process of interference in the case of light waves in Chap. VII, Part III. If two wave-trains of the same wave-length and amplitude, and vibrating in the same plane, are **in phase**—that is, if two wave-crests, two wave-troughs or two corresponding points on the wave-surface, arrive at a given place simultaneously—the displacement of the medium is twice that which would occur with one wave-train acting alone. Conversely, if the wave-trains are completely out of phase—that is, if a wave-crest from one wave-train arrives simultaneously with a wave-trough from another—the two displacements of the medium would be equal and opposite, and the total effect would be zero displacement, which is said to be due to **destructive interference.**

If the vibrations in the wave-train are confined to one plane, they are said to be **plane polarized** (Chap. VIII, Part III), and destructive interference can occur between two plane polarized waves only if they are polarized in the same plane. Otherwise the displacement of the medium will be the resultant displacement due to two impulses inclined at some angle to each other. This displacement may be *linear*, *circular* or *elliptical*. In Chap. VIII, Part III, we have pursued in some detail the analogy of a vibrating pendulum bob subject to impressed forces, with plane, circularly and elliptically polarized light.

Finally, if the waves are longitudinal, that is, if the displacement is along the direction of propagation, as in sound, then destructive interference can occur between two or more wave-trains only if they are propagated along the same line. An important type of interference occurs when two waves are propagated along the same line, but in opposite directions; this accounts for the stationary nodes and antinodes in organ pipes (see § 6).

6. Progressive and Stationary Waves.

The waves we have considered so far have been **progressive waves,** that is, waves spreading outwards continuously from some source so that small portions of the medium oscillate up and down (transverse waves) or to and fro (longitudinal waves) as the waves pass by. Now if the medium is limited, say by the waves meeting a rigid barrier, **reflected waves** are produced which interfere with the oncoming waves. The effect of the interference is remarkable in that the progressive nature of the waves vanishes. At certain regular distances from the reflecting barrier the medium is perpetually at rest: these points are termed **nodes.** There are also other regularly spaced points, termed **antinodes,** at which the amplitudes have maximum, though fluctuating, values.

Since the portion of medium immediately in contact with the rigid barrier must be at rest, the amplitudes produced by the incident and reflected waves at that point must be equal and opposite. *Reflection of waves at a denser or more rigid medium therefore results in a change of phase of π with respect to the incident wave.*

The formation of a **stationary** or **standing wave** is shown in fig. 3. The incident wave represented by the thin line travels from left to right. It meets the rigid barrier on the right and gives rise to a reflected wave represented by the dotted line travelling from right to left. The total displacement of the medium or the standing wave which results from the interference of the incident and reflected waves, is shown by the heavy line. The points N_1, N_2, N_3, &c. (the nodes) are observed to be perpetually at rest; whereas points midway between these (the antinodes) undergo the maximum displacement.

It is important to note that the wave-length is *twice* the distance between consecutive nodes.

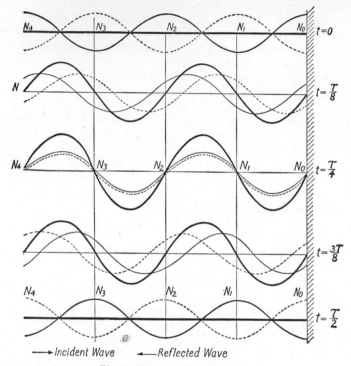

Fig. 3.—Stationary or Standing Wave

On the other hand, if the progressive wave passes from a denser to a less dense medium, the displacement of the latter under an incident compression is greater than the average displacement of the former. At the boundary, therefore, the denser medium moves into the less dense for a short distance, and hence a rarefaction is created in the denser medium close to the boundary. This results in a reflected wave of rarefaction. Since the boundary is free to move, the boundary becomes an antinode and the waves are reflected without change of phase.

The analytical examination of stationary waves produced by reflection without change of phase is as follows. The total displacement y of the medium at any point x from some arbitrary origin O is the sum of the two displacements y_1 and y_2 produced by the incident and reflected waves respectively. Hence

$$y = y_1 + y_2 = a \sin\frac{2\pi}{\lambda}(vt - x) + a \sin\frac{2\pi}{\lambda}(vt + x)$$

$$= 2a \sin\frac{2\pi}{\lambda}vt \,.\, \cos\frac{2\pi}{\lambda}x.$$

This equation shows that *for all values of t*, at distances given by $x = (2n + 1)\frac{\lambda}{4}$, where n is integral, the displacement y is zero. These points clearly represent the nodes of the stationary wave system and the distance between successive nodes is half a wave-length.

7. Sound Waves.

The phenomenon of sound is directly perceptible to the senses. Unlike light, heat and electromagnetic and gravitational effects,

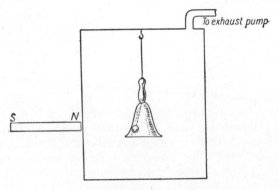

Fig. 4.—Bell in a Vacuum

sound is not transmitted across a vacuum. This may be proved by a simple experiment as shown in fig. 4. A bronze bell with a steel clapper is suspended by a fine thread inside a vessel connected to an exhaust pump. The clapper is operated by a magnet brought up outside the vessel. As the air is withdrawn the sound of the bell becomes progressively fainter until, when the vacuum is very high, the faint sound heard is that transmitted through the suspension fibre alone. Liquids and solids transmit sound even better than gases, but since, under ordinary conditions, sound reaches the ears through the air, we shall concentrate initially on the propagation of waves through gases.

The source of sound consists of some mechanically vibrating

system such as a vibrating strip shown in fig. 5a. As the strip moves up, air which is in contact with the strip on its upper surface is compressed. This **compression** causes a local rise in pressure which compresses in turn the air immediately above it. So the process continues, with the result that a compression pulse C spreads through the air as shown in fig. 5b. As the strip moves downwards, a slight vacuum or **rarefaction** is created in the wake of the moving strip. Consequently air moves from neighbouring points to occupy this vacuum, and therefore a rarefaction pulse R spreads through the medium following the

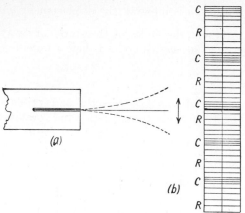

Fig. 5a and 5b.—Compression and Rarefaction

preceding compression pulse. Succeeding vibrations of the strip create a series of compressions and rarefactions following each other in regular succession. Such a series constitutes a **sound wave.** It is detected by the ear, which possesses a delicate membrane which is set vibrating by the successive compressions and rarefactions which constitute the sound wave. If the frequency of the vibrations is too high or too low, they are undetectable by the ear, and the analogy is complete in this respect with the limited range of the visible spectrum (Part III).

EXERCISES

1. Show that the expression $y = f(vt - x)$ represents a wave-motion. What form does this expression take for waves of simple harmonic type?

2. Define the terms *wave-length* and *frequency* as applied to wave-motion, and deduce a relation connecting these quantities with the velocity of propagation of the waves.

3. Explain fully the physical significance of an equation of the type

$$\frac{\partial^2 y}{\partial t^2} = v^2 \frac{\partial^2 y}{\partial x^2}.$$

4. Distinguish between progressive and stationary waves, illustrating the formation of the latter with the aid of a diagram.

CHAPTER II

Velocity of Sound

1. Velocity of Waves in a Material Medium.

We proceed to calculate an expression for the velocity of waves in a material medium. Consider a wave propagated along the x-axis. Let the displacements of the medium at sections x and $(x + \delta x)$ be a and $\left(a + \dfrac{\partial a}{\partial x}\delta x\right)$, respectively, as illustrated in fig. 1. If the mean

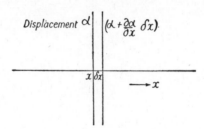

Fig. 1.—Displacement at Adjacent Sections

strain in the element is s, the change in the displacement as we proceed from one section to the other is, by the principles of Chap. VIII, Part I,

$$s\,\delta x = \frac{\partial a}{\partial x}\,\delta x,$$

so that
$$s = \frac{\partial a}{\partial x}. \quad\quad \cdots \cdots \quad (2.1)$$

Let the stresses at the two sections be P and $\left(P + \dfrac{\partial P}{\partial x}\delta x\right)$. Then the average stress is $\frac{1}{2}\left(P + P + \dfrac{\partial P}{\partial x}\delta x\right) = P$ to the first order of small quantities. Hence, if the modulus of elasticity is E,

$$P = Es,$$

and
$$\frac{\partial P}{\partial x} = E\frac{\partial s}{\partial x}. \quad\quad \cdots \cdots \quad (2.2)$$

476

Hence, differentiating equation (2.1) and substituting in (2.2),

$$\frac{\partial P}{\partial x} = E \frac{\partial^2 a}{\partial x^2}. \qquad \ldots \ldots \quad (2.3)$$

Now the net force per unit area causing an acceleration $\partial^2 a / \partial t^2$ is $\left(P + \frac{\partial P}{\partial x} \delta x\right) - P = \frac{\partial P}{\partial x} \delta x.$ Hence, by Newton's second law of motion, if ρ is the density of the medium,

$$\frac{\partial P}{\partial x} \delta x = \rho \, \delta x \frac{\partial^2 a}{\partial t^2}. \qquad \ldots \ldots \quad (2.4)$$

From equations (2.3) and (2.4) we therefore have

$$\frac{\partial^2 a}{\partial t^2} = \frac{E}{\rho} \frac{\partial^2 a}{\partial x^2}. \qquad \ldots \ldots \quad (2.5)$$

Comparison of equations (2.5) and (1.11) shows that (2.5) represents a wave of velocity

$$V = \sqrt{\frac{E}{\rho}}, \qquad \ldots \ldots \quad (2.6)$$

so the velocity of propagation of the wave is given for any medium by the square root of the quotient of its elasticity by its density.

2. Velocity of Sound in a Gas.

To calculate the velocity of sound in a gas we require an expression for the elasticity E of the gas. Now the wave spreads in all directions from the source, and consequently compressions and rarefactions also occur in all directions. Reference to Chap. VIII, Part I, will show that we are therefore concerned with the **bulk modulus of elasticity.** This is defined by

$$E = \frac{\text{stress}}{\text{strain}} = \frac{\text{force per unit area}}{\text{change in volume per unit volume}}. \quad (2.7)$$

Now, if the pressure changes by δp, the stress is δp. Owing to this stress a volume v is *decreased* by δv. Hence

$$E = -\frac{\delta p}{\delta v / v}. \qquad \ldots \ldots \quad (2.8)$$

Now, as we have seen in Part II, the pressure and volume relations of a gas are governed by the laws $pv = \text{constant}$ or $pv^\gamma = \text{constant}$, where γ is the ratio of the specific heats of a gas at constant pressure and constant volume respectively. The former corresponds to an isothermal expansion or compression and the latter to an adiabatic change. Hence we have for the two cases, by differentiation,

$$p \cdot \delta v + v \cdot \delta p = 0,$$

or

$$\frac{\delta p}{\delta v / v} = -p; \quad \ldots \ldots \quad (2.9)$$

and

$$\gamma p \cdot \delta v \cdot v^{\gamma - 1} + v^{\gamma} \cdot \delta p = 0,$$

or

$$\frac{\delta p}{\delta v / v} = -\gamma p. \quad \ldots \ldots \quad (2.10)$$

The elasticity E is therefore equal to p or γp according as the change is isothermal or adiabatic. Now the changes in compression and rarefaction are very rapid at *audible frequencies*, so that the phenomenon of sound is governed by adiabatic considerations. Hence, for sound waves in air, equation (2.6) becomes

$$V = \sqrt{\frac{\gamma p}{\rho}}. \quad \ldots \ldots \ldots \quad (2.11)$$

Since the density of a gas is directly proportional to its pressure, it follows from equation (2.11) that the velocity of sound in a gas is independent of the pressure. On the other hand, if, as is usually the case, the gas is free to expand, p/ρ varies as the absolute temperature T. Hence, the velocity of sound in a gas is proportional to $T^{\frac{1}{2}}$.

Although it is usually sufficient to regard a gas as a continuous medium as regards sound propagation, application of the molecular hypothesis is particularly instructive. For example, the propagation of a compression wave by the vibrating strip described in § 7, Chap. I, takes place as follows. Molecules of the gas with the gas-kinetic velocity appropriate to their temperature (Part II, Heat) have their velocity raised when they rebound from the approaching strip. These molecules which constitute a compression, collide with others, and in consequence the small gain in velocity is transmitted from layer to layer of the molecules. We should therefore expect the velocity of sound to be transmitted with the gas-kinetic velocity of the molecules, or more correctly, since only a fraction of the molecules make head-on collisions, with about two-thirds of this velocity (Chap. XI, Part II, Heat). This deduction is in good agreement with experiment and, moreover, explains the variation of the velocity of sound with temperature, for the gas-kinetic velocity of the molecules is proportional to the square root of the absolute temperature. A similar process takes place in the propagation of a rarefaction, but the average gas-kinetic velocity of the molecules is reduced instead of being augmented.

Common observation shows that the order of notes in a musical tune remains unaltered when the tune is heard over varying distances, indicating that the velocity of sound is independent of the frequency. Such behaviour is consistent with the molecular hypothesis. On the other hand, if the intensity of the source is very large, the number of molecules affected by the source and the displacement and velocity acquired by them is large enough for an appreciable amount of energy to be transmitted by the fraction of molecules which undergo head-on collision. This fraction will transmit a greater velocity than the average, and consequently sound from an intense source will travel faster than from one of medium or feeble intensity.

3. Measurement of the Velocity of Sound.

Some of the methods available for measuring the velocity of sound will now be tabulated.

Method	Application
(i) Free air explosion.	Free air.
(ii) Tube methods.	Air or gases in tubes.
(iii) Hydrophone methods.	Liquids.
(iv) Stationary wave methods.	Solids, liquids and gases.

Examples of the last group are Hebb's experiment, manometric flames, strings, organ pipes, Kundt's tube, &c.

Methods (ii) and (iv) involve the use of the equation $V = \nu\lambda$. We shall discuss the first three methods and Hebb's experiment here. Determinations by other arrangements, which are often the most convenient, will be considered in the appropriate chapters.

(i) *Free Air Explosion Method.*

Owing to its low value of about 1000 ft./sec., the velocity of sound (unlike that of light) may easily be determined by direct measurement of the time taken for the sound to traverse a given distance. One of the earliest determinations was that of the French Academy in the middle of the eighteenth century. Two stations about 30 Km. apart were chosen, and the time interval which elapsed between seeing the flash and recording the sound of cannons exploded at the stations was observed. By measuring the velocity in two opposing directions, the effect of wind-velocity was eliminated. The chief inaccuracy arises from the *personal equation,* that is the lag in response between visual and aural observation and muscular contraction to operate the stop-clocks. In modern technique, where the reception is by microphone (Chap. VIII) and the recording is automatic, the small personal equation of the apparatus may usually be neglected. It can be eliminated altogether if the velocity is measured over several distances, for the personal equation of the apparatus remains constant. Of the experiments which have been made we shall describe that of Regnault. The recording apparatus is shown diagrammatically in fig. 2. The wire W is broken by a gun fired at one station. The style S is therefore released by the electromagnet E, and consequently a short horizontal mark is made on the drum D, which is rotating at a known constant speed. When the sound wave arrived at the microphone M, the membrane moved back and again completed the electrical circuit. Consequently the electromagnet pulled the style to the right, making another horizontal mark on the revolving drum. Since the distance between the source of sound and the microphone was known, and the time interval could be calculated from the speed of revolution of the drum and the distance between the two marks upon it, the velocity of sound could be obtained. The main inaccuracies are: (i) if large distances are taken to give large time intervals, uncertain corrections are involved for wind, temperature and humidity; (ii) if very intense sounds are used, the velocity varies with the intensity.

(ii) *Tube Method.*

To avoid uncertainties due to wind velocity, temperature and humidity, the velocity of sound has been determined in tubes by methods essentially similar to those used in the free-air experiments.

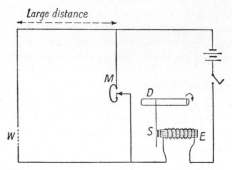

Fig. 2.—Regnault's Apparatus for Velocity of Sound

For example, Regnault measured the velocity of sound by the apparatus shown in fig. 2 in the Paris underground water mains. The velocity of sound varies both with the intensity and frequency of the source, and with the diameter of the tube. To obtain the free-air velocity from tube measurements a correction term must be added which varies inversely as the tube diameter and inversely as the square root of the frequency.

(iii) *Velocity of Sound in Liquids.*

The velocity of sound in water was first determined by Colladon and Sturm in 1836, using a bell immersed in Lake Geneva. At the instant the bell was struck, a flash of gunpowder was produced, and the interval between the observation of the flash and the arrival of the sound at the receiving station was noted. The receiving instrument was a simple form of **hydrophone,** consisting of an ear-trumpet closed by a stretched membrane and inserted in the water.

In a modern determination of the velocity of sound in sea-water, a wireless operator on board ship explodes a submerged charge of gun-cotton and simultaneously transmits a radio-signal to the receiving station. The time which elapses between the arrival of the radio-signal (the transmission of which may be considered practically instantaneous) and the detection of the sound wave by a submerged microphone is measured together with the distance between the two stations. An approximate relation connecting the velocity of sound in sea-water with temperature is $V = (4756 + 14t)$ ft./sec., where t is in °C.

(iv) *Hebb's Arrangement.*

Of the methods involving a knowledge of the frequency ν of a source and requiring a measurement of wave-length λ with subsequent

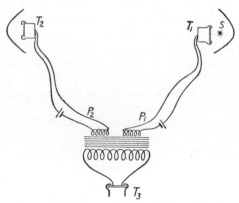

Fig. 3.—Hebb's Arrangement for Velocity of Sound

use of the relation $V = \nu\lambda$, we shall consider only Hebb's arrangement at this stage. Methods involving vibrating strings, organ pipes, Kundt's tube, &c., will be discussed later in the appropriate chapters. In Hebb's experiment, made in 1905, an apparatus was used as shown in fig. 3. Two parabolic mirrors (Part III, Chap. II) were situated facing each other, the source of sound S being placed at one focus and a telephone receiver T_2 at the other. A second telephone receiver T_1 is fixed a short distance from the source, while T_2 together with its appropriate mirror may be moved measured distances up to 100 ft. along the common axis. The receivers are connected to independent primaries P_1 and P_2 (Part V) of a transformer with a common secondary which is connected to a third telephone receiver T_3. As the telephone receiver T_2 and the mirror are moved away from T_1, a series of positions at regular intervals of half a wave-length will be obtained for which the electrical impulses set up in T_3 will be a maximum or a minimum according as the impulses to P_1 and P_2 assist or oppose each other. The average distance between many such positions was found, and since the whole measurement took place indoors, there was no wind correction required.

The source of sound was a tube closed at one end with air blown across the open end. The pitch was adjusted to be equal to that of a standard fork to one part in 5000. The mean temperature could also be ascertained accurately by means of suitably placed thermometers. A final value of $3 \cdot 315 \times 10^4$ cm./sec. at $0°$ C. was obtained for the velocity of sound.

EXERCISES

1. Derive an expression for the velocity of waves in a material medium of density ρ and modulus of elasticity E.

2. Outline the interpretation of the propagation of sound waves in terms of the kinetic theory of gases. Deduce the variation of sound velocity with temperature and pressure.

3. Contrast the methods available for determining the velocity of sound in air, describing in detail one method with which you are familiar.

4. How may the velocity of sound in liquids be determined?

Calculate the velocity of propagation of sound waves through water if the bulk modulus of the latter is 2×10^{10} dynes/cm.^{2}. [$\sqrt{2} \times 10^5$ cm./sec.]

CHAPTER III

Propagation of Sound through Gases

1. Introduction.

The propagation of sound through media is subject to laws very similar to those of other types of wave-motion. For example, as for light, reflection at a plane surface is such that the angle of incidence equals the angle of reflection. Refraction and interference also occur with sound waves, and experiments to illustrate these properties are described below.

2. Reflection of Sound Waves.

To demonstrate that the angle of incidence equals the angle of reflection, with sound waves, an apparatus may be used as shown in fig. 1. Any convenient source of sound, such as a ticking watch, is

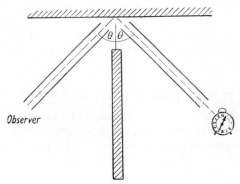

Fig. 1.—Reflection of Sound

placed opposite a vertical wall or cardboard screen, and the incident sound ray is canalized by the use of a cylindrical cardboard tube. It is then found that maximum intensity is observed when a second cylindrical tube is arranged as shown in the figure, that is, with the angle of incidence equal to the angle of reflection. If greater precision is required than aural estimation can give, either a manometric flame (Chap. V) or a microphone is used. The latter may be connected to an electrical circuit, and the position noted for which the electrical impulses are a maximum. We discuss the reflection of sound further in connexion with Acoustics in Chap. VIII.

3. Refraction of Sound Waves.

Refraction of light takes place (as discussed in Part III) when a change occurs in the optical density of the medium in which the light is propagated. If the change in density is gradual the ray of light is bent into a smooth curve; if the change is sudden the straight ray of light undergoes a sharp bend. The behaviour of sound is similar. To illustrate the refraction of sound an acoustical lens may be constructed of a balloon containing some gas of density different from that of air. If the gas chosen is denser than air, for example carbon dioxide, the lens is converging, and by setting up an apparatus as in fig. 2, a focal length of the lens may be derived just as in the optical case. The laws governing the position of sound object and sound

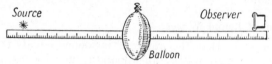

Fig. 2.—Refraction of Sound

image are identical with those of optical lenses, but with sound the sharpness of the image is not nearly so well defined. The reason for this is discussed in the next section. To produce a diverging lens, the balloon must be filled with some gas, such as hydrogen, which is lighter than air.

4. Propagation of Sound Waves.

If solid objects of variable extension are interposed between the source of sound and the observer, the intensity observed is diminished but it is not in general reduced to zero. The lower the pitch of the sound, that is, the longer the wave-length, the less effective the screen becomes. In view of our discussion in Part III of the diffraction of light around obstacles into the region of the geometrical shadow behind them, it is clear that the bending of the sound waves round the screen is an example of diffraction. From the general rule that diffraction is large when the linear dimensions of the obstacle are comparable with or smaller than the wave-length of the wave-motion, it follows that, in the case of sound waves, enormous obstacles such as mountains will be required to produce sound shadows of any appreciable extent. Similarly, it is only through large apertures such as valleys and mountain passes that sound is propagated in straight lines.

5. Effect of Motion of the Medium.

If there is relative motion of different parts of the medium through which sound is passing, both the intensity and the frequency of the sound noted by the observer are affected. We discuss the effect on frequency in § 6. The effect on intensity is due to refraction. Consider a plane sound wave proceeding across the earth's surface from left to right as shown in fig. 3. If there is a wind blowing from left to right, then, owing to viscosity (Part I) the layers of air will be travelling progressively more slowly as we descend from higher altitudes to the earth's surface. Consequently the elements of the plane wave-front in the higher altitudes will gain on the elements at lower altitudes, and the net effect will be to swing the wave-front down towards the observer, who therefore notes an increased intensity. If the wind is blowing against the direction from which the sound is coming, the intensity is correspondingly diminished, for the upper

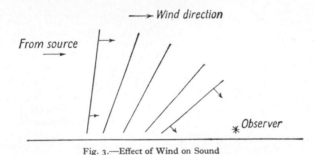

Fig. 3.—Effect of Wind on Sound

parts of the plane wave are subject to a greater retardation of velocity than the lower parts, and consequently the plane wave is swung upwards away from the observer at a steeper and steeper angle as the wave proceeds.

6. Doppler Effect.

Common observation on the pitch of the steam whistle of a locomotive or of the horn of an automobile shows that while the note may be of a particular frequency with respect to an observer travelling with the moving vehicle, its pitch is raised or lowered with respect to a stationary observer according as the vehicle is approaching or receding from the observer. This is termed the *Doppler* or *Doppler-Fizeau effect.* It is found that the change in frequency does not depend simply on the relative velocity of source and observer, but that it is different according as the source or the observer is moving with respect to the medium transmitting the waves.

(i) *Stationary Observer, Moving Source.*

Let V, λ and ν represent the velocity of sound, the wave-length and the frequency respectively for an observer travelling with the source.   Then if the latter is travelling with a velocity v towards a stationary observer, the sound waves emitted by the source will be as shown in fig. 4.   Each successive sound wave, emitted at regular intervals according to the frequency of the note, is closer to the preceding wave than it would be for a stationary source owing to the movement of the source.   Consequently the apparent wave-length of the sound is λ_1, where

$$\frac{\lambda_1}{\lambda} = \frac{V - v}{V}. \quad \cdots \cdots \cdots \quad (3.1)$$

Now
$$V = \nu\lambda, \quad \cdots \cdots \cdots \cdots \quad (3.2)$$

and
$$V = \nu_1\lambda_1. \quad \cdots \cdots \cdots \cdots \quad (3.3)$$

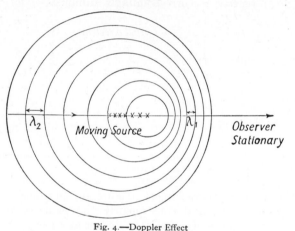

Fig. 4.—Doppler Effect

Hence, from equations (3.1), (3.2) and (3.3),

$$\nu_1 = \frac{\nu V}{(V - v)}. \quad \cdots \cdots \cdots \quad (3.4)$$

Inspection of fig. 4 shows that if the source is travelling away from the stationary observer, the apparent wave-length λ_2 is increased in the ratio

$$\frac{\lambda_2}{\lambda} = \frac{V + v}{V}; \quad \cdots \cdots \cdots \quad (3.5)$$

and consequently the apparent frequency ν_2 is given by

$$\nu_2 = \frac{\nu V}{V + v}. \quad \cdots \cdots \cdots \quad (3.6)$$

(ii) *Moving Observer, Stationary Source.*

With a stationary source the wave-length of the sound is uniform in all directions, but the observer encounters more waves in unit time if he is proceeding towards the source and fewer if he is receding from the source. The effect observed is therefore a direct change in frequency. Representing the velocity of the observer in the direction of propagation by v', and using the same notation as before,

$$\frac{\nu_1}{\nu} = \frac{V + v'}{V},$$

or
$$\nu_1 = \nu\frac{V + v'}{V}. \quad \cdots \cdots \cdots \quad (3.7)$$

If, in addition, there is a wind velocity w in the direction of propagation, this must be added algebraically to V, both in (3.6) and in (3.7), so that (3.7), for example, becomes:

$$\nu_1 = \nu\frac{V + w + v'}{V + w}. \quad \cdots \cdots \quad (3.8)$$

The Doppler effect applies to all types of wave-motion, but in terrestrial experiments the velocity of light is so much larger than that of source and observer that an apparent change in optical frequency is generally undetectable. With celestial bodies, however, the effect may be appreciable; in fact, the apparent change in spectral frequency provides a most powerful method in astrophysics for determining the relative velocities of celestial bodies. Doppler originally suggested that stars travelling away from the observer would appear red and those travelling towards the observer blue, since the former should give rise to an apparent decrease in frequency and the latter to an increase. Fizeau, however, pointed out that since stars emitted radiations of all frequencies extending into the infra-red and ultra-violet regions, the general appearance will be independent of the motion of the star, since wave-lengths in hitherto invisible regions of the spectrum will simply move into vacated positions in the visible spectrum according to the movement of the star. He showed, however, that if comparison spectra (Part III) were used, that is, if the spectrum of the star is formed side by side with the spectrum from some terrestrial source, individual wave-lengths of particular elements *will* show relative displacement dependent on the velocity of the star.

As examples of the applications of the Doppler-Fizeau principle we shall consider the determination of the velocity of rotation of the sun, and the elucidation of the nature of Saturn's rings. With regard to the former it is found that on examining the edges of the sun's disk with a spectroscope a change in wave-length of the radiation emitted by specific elements is observed according as the eastern or western limb is viewed. In one case the emitting particles are moving away from and in the other towards the observer. With regard to Saturn's rings, it was for long a subject of controversy whether the rings were solid or composed of numerous small particles. From elementary dynamics (Part I), if the former hypothesis were true, the velocity of the outer edge of the rings would be greater than that of the inner edge. On the contrary, with the latter hypothesis, to balance the increased gravitational attraction, the nearer particles would have to rotate with a velocity greater than that of the outer particles. Since the change in wave-length observed is greater with the inner than with the outer edge, it is concluded that the rings are composed of swarms of individual particles.

7. Vibrating Columns of Gas.

Consider the simple experiment shown in fig. 5, in which a vibrating tuning-fork is held close to the open end of a cylindrical tube closed by a water seal at the other end. Waves propagated down the tube

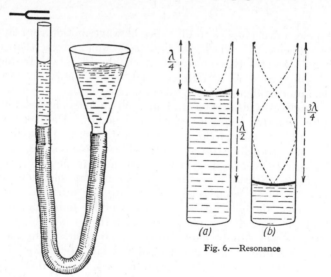

Fig. 5.—Vibratory Column of Air

Fig. 6.—Resonance

will be reflected from the closed end by the principles discussed in Chap. I, § 6, and stationary waves may be produced, owing to the interference of the incident and reflected wave-trains. From physical considerations, the air must be at rest at the closed end although it may vibrate at the open end. The condition that a stationary wave of appreciable intensity shall be set up is therefore that the closed end shall be a node and the open end an antinode. If the length of the tube is gradually increased, reference to fig. 6a shows that this

condition will first occur when the length of the tube is one-quarter
of a wave-length. When this condition is attained, the **natural
frequency** of the tube is said to be equal to the **applied frequency** of
the fork. The condition is then said to be one of **resonance,** a subject
we discuss in further detail in Chap. IV, § 8. If the frequency of the
fork is ν, and the velocity of sound in the
gas is V, then we should expect

$$V = \nu\lambda = \nu \cdot 4l_1, \quad . \quad . \quad (3.9)$$

where l_1 is the length of tube for which
resonance first occurs. We have already
stated in Chap. I, § 3, that the propagation
of waves in tubes is somewhat different from
that in free air, that is, in unbounded media,
and that a correction is required which depends on the radius of the tube. Writing
this correction generally as $f(r)$, we have

$$V = \nu\lambda = \nu \cdot 4\{l_1 + f(r)\}. \quad (3.10)$$

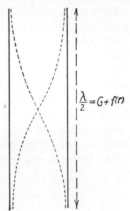

$$\frac{\lambda}{2} = G + f(r)$$

Fig. 7 — Resonance with
Tube Open at both Ends

Detailed calculation and experiment have
shown that $f(r)$ is approximately equal to
$3 \cdot 2r$, but as the correction is found to be to
some extent personal to the tube and to the
nature of the reflecting surfaces at the ends, it is usual to increase
the length of the tube until resonance again occurs. Bearing in
mind that the closed end must remain a node and the open end an
antinode, we see from fig. 6b that resonance occurs again when

$$\frac{3\lambda}{4} = l_2 + f(r). \quad . \quad . \quad . \quad . \quad . \quad (3.11)$$

Eliminating $f(r)$ from (3.10) and (3.11), we find

$$\lambda = 2(l_2 - l_1). \quad . \quad . \quad . \quad . \quad . \quad (3.12)$$

With a tube open at *both* ends, a similar state of resonance occurs,
except that both ends are free to vibrate and will therefore be antinodes. From fig. 7, therefore, resonance first occurs when

$$\frac{\lambda}{2} = l_1 + f(r);$$

and similarly, resonance next occurs when there are two nodes, so
that

$$\lambda = l_2 + f(r).$$

Hence, for an open tube as well as a closed tube,

$$\lambda = 2(l_2 - l_1).$$

8. Kundt's Tube.

A device which enables the frequency of a high note to be measured, and which at the same time exhibits the vibrations in a gas column, is *Kundt's tube*. As shown in fig. 8, it consists of a cylindrical glass tube about a metre long, placed horizontally and fitted with a loose sliding plug at one end. The other end is fitted with a fixed plug which is attached to a long horizontal glass rod gripped at its centre point. Lycopodium powder is sprinkled uniformly along the base of the tube and the glass rod is then stroked smartly horizontally with a wet cloth. A note of high frequency is emitted, and if the two plugs in the glass tube are just the correct distance apart for standing waves to be produced in the vibrating gas column, the lycopodium powder will be vibrated away from the antinodes and collect in equally spaced ridges at the nodes. By varying the distance between the plugs good resonance may be established, and the distance between consecutive nodes is then the half wave-length of the

λ

Fig. 8.—Kundt's Tube

note in air or whatever gas is filling the tube. By jacketing the tube with different temperature baths the variation of the velocity of sound with temperature may be examined. By using notes of known frequency, the velocity may be calculated absolutely from the measured wave-length. Subsequent application of equation (2.11) then gives the value of γ; indeed, Kundt's tube provides one of the best experimental methods of determining the ratio of the specific heats of a gas.

Conversely, if the velocity of sound in the gas is known, the frequency ν in the rod, which is the same as that in the gas, may be calculated from the measured wave-length in the gas. Now by analogy with the vibrations of a gas column in an open tube, a rod gripped in the centre also has antinodes at each end and a node in the middle. Hence the length of the rod is $\frac{1}{2}\lambda'$, where λ' is the wave-length of the sound *in the rod*. Hence the velocity V' of the sound *in the rod* is

$$V' = \nu\lambda',$$

and Kundt's tube therefore affords a method of finding the velocity of sound in solids. Finally, since longitudinal stroking gives rise to longitudinal vibrations in the rod the elasticity modulus involved in equation (2.6), $V' = (E'/\rho)^{\frac{1}{2}}$, will be *Young's modulus*, so a dynamical method of measuring Young's modulus (Part I) is provided if the density ρ of the material of the rod is separately determined.

EXERCISES

1. Why are the laws of reflection and refraction capable of less accurate test with sound than with light? Describe experiments which illustrate your answer.

2. What effects has motion of the medium on (a) the intensity, (b) the apparent frequency, of sound waves propagated through the medium?

3. Write a brief essay on the Doppler-Fizeau effect, giving illustrations from different branches of physics.

4. Describe the measurement of the velocity of sound with a resonance tube, explaining clearly how discrepancies arising from tube diameter and end correction are overcome.

5. How may the velocity of sound be conveniently measured at different temperatures? What other connexions exist between the phenomena of sound and heat?

6. Describe an experiment to compare the wave-lengths of a note of given frequency when the note is transmitted through a solid and through a gas. If the velocity of sound through a solid is ten times that through a gas, compare the wave-lengths of a given note transmitted successively through solid and gas. [10 : 1.]

CHAPTER IV

Vibration of Solid Bodies

1. Introduction.

We have already seen in our discussion of Kundt's tube how the longitudinal vibrations in a rod may be examined. Other possible forms of oscillation are transverse and torsional. The analytical discussion of the latter is beyond the scope of this book, but the former are capable of simpler treatment and are of particular importance as they form the basis of notes emitted by tuning-forks and by stretched strings.

2. Transverse Vibrations of a Stretched String.

Let a string, stretched along the axis of x under tension F, be slightly disturbed. Consider the motion of an element (fig. 1) which in the disturbed state lies at time t_1 between the points (x, y) and $(x + dx, y + dy)$.

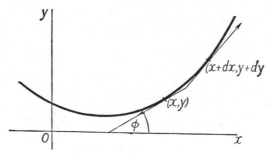

Fig. 1.—Transverse Vibrations of a Stretched String

At the end x, the component tension parallel to the axis of y is $F \sin \phi$, which, since ϕ is small, is nearly equal to $F \tan \phi$, i.e. $F \dfrac{\partial y}{\partial x}$; at the other end the corresponding component is

$$F \frac{\partial y}{\partial x} + F \frac{\partial}{\partial x} \left(\frac{\partial y}{\partial x} \right) dx.$$

The force parallel to Oy on the element is the difference of these two expressions, i.e. $F\dfrac{\partial^2 y}{\partial x^2}dx$; this must be equal to the mass-acceleration $m\,dx\,\dfrac{\partial^2 y}{\partial t^2}$, where m is the mass per unit length. Hence

$$\frac{\partial^2 y}{\partial t^2} = \frac{F}{m}\frac{\partial^2 y}{\partial x^2}. \quad \ldots \ldots \quad (4.1)$$

Like equations (1.11) and (2.5), this equation represents a wave, or waves, travelling along the axis of x in either direction with velocity V, where

$$V = \sqrt{\frac{F}{m}}. \quad \ldots \ldots \ldots \quad (4.2)$$

Suppose now that the string is fixed at two points at distance l apart. Since a node must occur at each fixed end, the **fundamental** frequency ν_1 is given by

$$\nu_1\lambda_1 = \nu_1 \,.\, 2l = V = \sqrt{\frac{F}{m}}$$

or

$$\nu_1 = \frac{1}{2l}\sqrt{\frac{F}{m}}. \quad \ldots \ldots \ldots \quad (4.3)$$

Another mode of vibration is clearly possible in which two antinodes are present in the vibrating string, and the distance between the end-nodes is a complete wave-length (cf. Chap. I, § 6). Hence a second frequency ν_2 is present, given by

$$\nu_2 = 2\nu_1 = \frac{1}{l}\sqrt{\frac{F}{m}}.$$

When such a string is vibrating, any number of these possible frequencies may be present simultaneously, in various relative intensities. The higher frequencies ν_2, ν_3, &c., given by

$$\nu_n = n\nu_1,$$

where n is integral, are termed the **overtones** or **harmonics** of a vibrating system. They are present to some extent in the vibrating columns of gas discussed in the previous chapter and, indeed, in all vibrating systems. The stretched string arrangement described above is termed a **sonometer** or **monochord**. The fundamental frequency of a sonometer is, as just shown, proportional to the square root of the tension, and inversely proportional to the length and to the square root of the mass per unit length or *linear density*.

3. Transverse Vibrations of Rods.

If a rod is gripped at one end and is free at the other, on the general principles hitherto discussed the fundamental mode of vibration will be such that a node occurs at the fixed end and the adjacent antinode at the free end. Consequently the wave-length excited is four times the length of the rod. Various modes of vibration are illustrated in fig. 2; these are observed to be quite analogous to those of a closed tube containing a gas column. We should note, however, that the latter executes only longitudinal vibrations, whereas the former may execute longitudinal, transverse or torsional oscillations. In the longitudinal vibrations the effective elasticity modulus was Young's

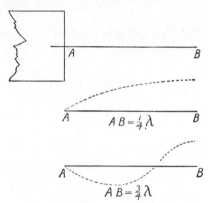

Fig. 2.—Transverse Vibrations of Rod Fixed at one End

modulus. In the transverse vibrations the effective modulus is also Young's modulus, as the vibrations involve a stretching and a compression of filaments of the bar. The problem is identical with that of the vibrating cantilever discussed in Part I, p. 88.

If the rod is free at both ends, then when it is sounding its fundamental it has an antinode at each end and a node at the centre. Should the rod be bent round until the two ends are parallel and close together, we arrive at the condition of the **standard tuning-fork** as shown in fig. 3. The tuning-fork has the unique property that overtones are damped by internal friction extremely rapidly, so that after it has been sounding for a short time it emits the fundamental tone with remarkable purity. This behaviour may be contrasted with that of a violin string which owes the piercing character of its note to the prominence of high harmonics. The factors governing the frequency of vibration of a tuning-fork may be ascertained by dimensional analysis (Chap. V, Part I). The time of oscillation will depend on the following quantities: (i) linear dimensions l of the fork of dimension L, (ii) Young's modulus q of the material of dimensions $ML^{-1}T^{-2}$, and (iii) density ρ of the material of dimensions ML^{-3}. Hence, expressing the relation as a power formula in the usual way, we have

$$t = kl^{\alpha}q^{\beta}\rho^{\gamma},$$

where k is a dimensionless constant and α, β and γ are the required powers. Writing this in dimensional form,

$$T = L^{\alpha}M^{\beta}T^{-2\beta}L^{-\beta}M^{\gamma}L^{-3\gamma},$$

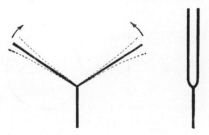

Fig. 3.—Standard Tuning Fork

and hence, equating the indices on each side of the equation.

$$\left. \begin{array}{r} \beta + \gamma = 0 \\ -2\beta = 1 \\ \alpha - \beta - 3\gamma = 0 \end{array} \right\} \quad \ldots \ldots \quad (4.4)$$

Solving (4.4), we obtain

$$t = klq^{-\frac{1}{2}}\rho^{\frac{1}{2}}; \quad \ldots \ldots \ldots \quad (4.5)$$

so the frequency $\nu = 1/t$ of tuning-forks of similar shape is proportional to the square root of Young's modulus, inversely proportional to the square root of the density and inversely proportional to the linear dimensions.

4. Vibrations of Plates: Chladni's Figures.

Just as wires and rods possess nodal points when stationary waves are present, so two-dimensional bodies such as plates give rise to nodal lines when set in vibration. Examples of the nodal lines exhibited by square and circular plates are shown in fig. 4. To exhibit these nodes experimentally the plates may be screwed to a vertical rod at their centre, sprinkled with sand and then bowed at one edge. If the plates are free at all points except at the centre a comparatively simple figure will be registered for the nodal lines as indicated by the ridges of sand. By stopping the plate with the finger at one or more points around the edge or on the surface of the plate, a variety of forms of vibration is obtained. These figures are termed Chladni's figures, and they are capable of mathematical investigation, which is, however, beyond the scope of this book. The possible modes of vibrations of

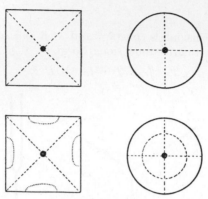

Fig. 4.—Chladni's Figures

plates are important in practice, since most types of microphones employ diaphragms of this form.

5. Quartz Oscillator.

We refer in Part V to a phenomenon termed the **piezoelectric effect.** This is the name given to the electrical behaviour of certain crystals when subjected to pressure. If a plate of quartz is cut with its length l parallel to the optic axis (Part III) and one of the electric axes in the direction d as in fig. 5, then such a crystal is found to develop positive and negative charges on its two opposite faces when subjected to pressure. If the crystal undergoes a tension instead of a compression the signs of the electric charges are reversed. The quartz plate also exhibits the **inverse piezoelectric effect,** that is, if metal plates are placed in contact with the crystal plate, then the application of a potential difference between the plates results in a compression or extension of the crystal. If the applied potential is alternating (Part V), the quartz plate undergoes regular contractions and expansions and becomes a quartz oscillator undergoing elastic vibrations.

Now, just as with the stretched string and other systems, if the frequency of the applied oscillation is equal to the natural frequency of the system, resonance occurs and a large amplitude of vibration is produced. The opposite surfaces of the crystal will be antinodes and a single node will occur at the centre for the fundamental vibration. Consequently the wave-length of the resonant vibration is $\lambda = 2d$, where d is the thickness of the crystal. If v is the velocity of propagation of longitudinal waves in the crystal and ν is the frequency of vibration, then

$$\nu = \frac{v}{\lambda} = \frac{v}{2d}.$$

Owing to the excellent elastic qualities of quartz, a given plate exhibits the same natural frequency over a long period of time. The frequency of such a plate is much above **audio-frequency,** that is

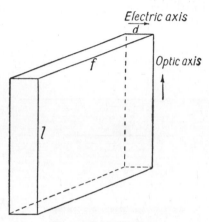

Fig. 5.—Quartz Oscillator

the range of frequency detectable by ear. In fact, the main function of quartz oscillators is to stabilize the frequency of the electrical oscillations from a wireless transmitter, that is in the region of **radio-frequency.**

6. Supersonic Waves.

The region of sound waves of shorter wave-length than can be detected by ear is termed the **supersonic region,** and supersonic waves possess certain remarkable properties. The type of apparatus used in these investigations is shown in fig. 6. A quartz oscillator is lying close to the bottom of a vessel containing oil, and the two plates of the oscillator are connected to an A.C. supply of 50,000 volts and of frequency 300,000 cycles per second. If a flat glass plate P is inserted in the oil parallel to the oscillator, it is found that for certain regular positions P and P_1 the plate experiences an upward thrust sufficient to support a considerable weight. These positions are the nodes of the supersonic standing waves set up in the region between the oscillator and the plate P. The reason why the force exists at the nodes and not at the antinodes is that the sustaining force in the fluid is due to the *difference* of pressure between adjacent parts, and the *rate of* *change* of pressure in the fluid is greatest near the nodes and not near the antinodes.

The high-frequency vibrations which supersonic waves stimulate in bodies with which they come in contact cause intimate mixing between very small particles of matter, and may even instigate or accelerate molecular reactions. Hence, oil and water emulsion may be produced by the passage of supersonic waves through a coarse mixture of the two components. Crystallization is similarly accelerated in the presence of high-frequency vibrations, and nitrogen iodide may be readily exploded.

If a thermometer is inserted into a fluid subjected to supersonic waves, the temperature which it registers will probably be slightly

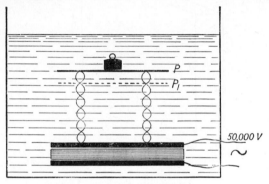

Fig. 6.—Supersonic Standing Waves

above room temperature. Should, however, the bulb of the thermometer be grasped in the hand while it is still immersed in the fluid, it will rapidly become too hot to hold owing to the friction between bulb and fingers produced by the high-frequency vibrations.

Owing to the much shorter wave-length of supersonic waves, the shadows of objects are far more definite than with ordinary sound waves. Consequently, high-frequency waves are of considerable use in locating accurately the position of submerged rocks, submarines, &c.

7. Vibrations of Three-dimensional Solids.

We have so far concentrated on the vibrations and the waves transmitted in one or two dimensions of space. The vibrations of a three-dimensional object such as a bell or gong are very complicated, and in general many possible modes of vibration are excited simultaneously. In fig. 7 are shown some of the nodal planes present in a vibrating sphere.

The transmission of waves through a sphere is the special problem of **seismic waves,** that is, those which travel through the earth accompanying natural or artificial earthquakes.   Both longitudinal and transverse waves are present, the former constituting the first or *primary waves* which are detected by the *seismograph* at any receiving station.   The type of record or *seismogram* obtained is shown in fig. 8.

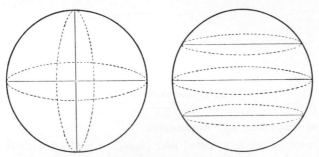

Fig. 7.—Nodal Planes in Vibrating Sphere

The *secondary waves* are transverse; finally, the *main shock* arrives with the *long waves,* which consist of a mixture of transverse and longitudinal waves.   By observation of the times of arrival of any groups of waves at different stations, combined with knowledge of the velocity of the waves, the region of origin or **focus** of the earthquake may be located.   In this way maps of unstable regions of the earth's interior have been drawn, and areas liable to serious earthquakes are

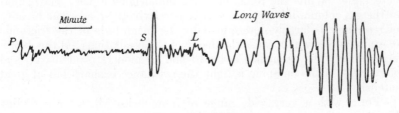

Fig. 8.—Seismic Waves

now fairly well determined.   One region lies in the Pacific Ocean close to Japan, and another in the Eastern Mediterranean.

Artificial seismic waves are used in **geophysical prospecting,** that is, in determining the positions of deposits of ores, salt or oil.   As an example of the application of seismic methods, the location of salt domes (associated with which are oil deposits) will be described.   Waves are created by the explosion of dynamite at some point S (fig. 9).   The times of arrival of the waves which travel through the earth to recording stations at points A, B, C, D, &c., are recorded.   Then, if the distances SA, SB, &c., are known, the velocity of the waves is easily derived. Should the waves encounter material of different density from that of the surrounding earth, an anomalous velocity will be observed. By repeating the experiment two or three times with varying positions of S, the intersection of the directions giving anomalous velocities locates the salt dome with considerable precision.

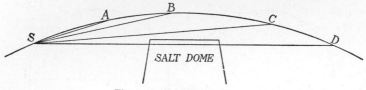

Fig. 9.—Artificial Seismic Waves

8. Forced Vibrations and Resonance.

If a tuning-fork is sounded and placed in contact with the board of a sonometer which has been tuned to the same frequency as the fork, the sonometer wire is set into violent vibration which persists for some time after the tuning-fork is removed. Such behaviour, of which we have already had several examples, is said to be due to **resonance**. If the frequency of the fork is not quite equal to that of the sonometer wire, the latter will still respond but the vibration which is set up in the string is only a small fraction of its previous magnitude. If the frequencies of the fork differ considerably from the natural frequency of the wire, the oscillations set up in the latter will probably be undetectable. While the resonance of a monochord is very sharp, that of the gas column in a resonance tube is relatively broad. The breadth of resonance is largely determined by the magnitude of the frictional damping forces which cause the decay of the oscillations. If the damping is heavy the resonance is broad and of moderate intensity; and conversely, if the damping is light the resonance is sharp but of great intensity.

Forks with a very wide range of frequencies will set a sounding board in vibration. Such vibrations are termed **forced vibrations,** since none of them is a true resonance. A system which responds to any frequency is termed *aperiodic*. When a system is set into forced vibration, the resonant natural frequency of the system is temporarily set up, but this **transient vibration** is quickly damped out by the frictional forces, leaving only the forced vibrations. We discuss important applications of these phenomena in alternating-current theory in Part V (Electricity and Magnetism).

EXERCISES

1. Deduce an expression for the velocity of transmission of a transverse wave along a stretched string. How does the frequency of the note emitted depend upon (i) the tension, (ii) the length and (iii) the diameter for strings of the same material?

2. Describe briefly how the longitudinal and transverse vibrations of rods may be examined. Why is Young's modulus of elasticity involved in both types of oscillation?

3. Explain the importance of a tuning-fork as a source of pure sound, and deduce by the method of dimensions an expression for the time of oscillation of a fork in terms of the length of the prongs and Young's modulus and the density of the material of which the fork is made.

4. Describe briefly the production of Chladni's figures. What are the essential properties of a good microphone diaphragm?

5. Write a short essay on the production and properties of supersonic waves.

6. What are seismic waves, and for what purpose are artificial seismic waves employed?

7. Discuss the phenomenon of resonance, illustrating your answer with examples from different branches of physics.

CHAPTER V

The Production and Detection
of Sound Waves

1. Introduction.

The production and detection of sound waves is now undoubtedly most conveniently carried out by the use of the electrical microphone. In fact, so closely are sound and electrical oscillations connected in practice that the student is strongly advised to read and to refer constantly to the relevant chapter in Part V, before proceeding with this chapter. We have already discussed in some detail the use of (a) the sonometer, (b) the closed and open tube (organ pipes), (c) the vibrating rod or tuning-fork, and (d) the quartz oscillator, as sources of sound.

2. Electrically-maintained Tuning-fork.

In order that the vibrations of a tuning-fork shall not die away a few seconds after excitation of the fork, they must be maintained by coupling the fork with some external energy supply. In fig. 1 is

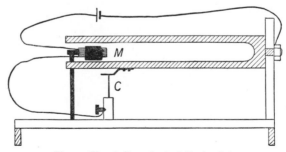

Fig. 1.—Electrically-maintained Tuning-fork

shown an arrangement suitable for maintaining the vibrations of a standard fork electrically. An electromagnet M is supported between the prongs of the fork, the latter being of steel, or bearing steel blocks facing the electromagnet. The electrical circuit is completed via the contact " make and break " C fixed to one prong of the vibrating fork. Vibrations are started by hand and are then maintained by the

502

regular impulses exerted by the electromagnet on the regular intervals of the " make ".

3. The Siren.

A common form of siren, shown in fig. 2, consists of a cylindrical tube opening at one end into a pipe through which air is forced, and fitted at the other end with two disks. Each disk contains a regular row of holes around its periphery, but whereas one disk is a fixture,

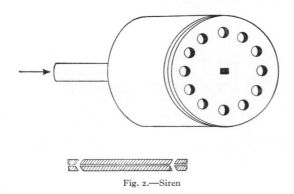

Fig. 2.—Siren

the other is free to rotate about a common axis passing perpendicularly through the centre of the disks. Owing to the inclination of the direction of the holes due to oblique boring, the air pressure causes the movable disk to rotate and hence a regular series of compressions escapes from the arrangement each time the apertures in the movable disk come squarely opposite those in the fixed disk. The frequency with which the compressions escape is the frequency of the note emitted, and hence the latter is directly governed by the speed of rotation of the disk.

4. Electrical Microphone.

The most convenient instrument for the production and detection of sound waves is the electrical microphone. It consists, in general, as shown in fig. 3, of a thin circular steel disk or diaphragm D, gripped at its periphery and subject to forced vibrations due to electromagnetic impulses from the electromagnet M. By altering the frequency of the applied electric oscillations, the frequency of the note of the vibrating diaphragm is changed, and thus a source of sound over a wide range of frequency is provided. As a detector, the reverse process is employed, the sound waves causing the diaphragm to vibrate and thus setting up electromagnetic impulses in the electrical circuit. These impulses are either recorded directly or, if of feeble intensity, are amplified by means of a thermionic valve amplifier, and recorded by a vacuum junction and milliammeter.

Owing to the non-uniformity of distribution of the magnetic field interaction of the electromagnet with the wide steel diaphragm, considerable distortion of the quality of the applied vibrations is in

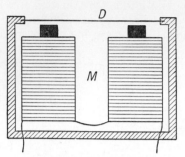

Fig. 3.—Electrical Microphone

evidence in the electrical impulses recorded. It is therefore preferable to use a **moving coil** of small linear dimensions in place of the steel diaphragm, as shown in fig. 4. In this instrument, a non-magnetic (say aluminium) diaphragm m_0 communicates its mechanical vibrations to a small moving coil which is situated in the magnetic field of a fixed magnetizing coil, the latter being excited by a steady

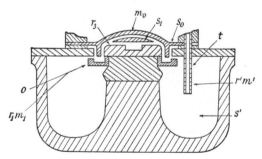

Fig. 4.—Moving-coil Microphone

external current. The electrical impulses superposed on the steady current may then be amplified as before. If the instrument is to be used as a source of sound, electrical impulses are fed to the moving coil, the varying magnetic field of which interacts with the fixed magnetic field of the electromagnet to produce vibrations of the coil which are in turn communicated to the diaphragm m_0.

Instead of electromagnetic interactions, electrostatic interactions may be used as in the condenser microphone. These have so far not proved so satisfactory as the magnetic type owing to the large voltages required to produce appreciable electrostatic forces.

In all types of microphone, the natural frequency of vibration of the coil and diaphragm must be much higher than the impressed frequencies if distortion is not to be produced by resonance.

5. Helmholtz's Resonators.

To detect aurally the presence of any given frequency in a mixture of frequencies in a complex sound, Helmholtz introduced the use of resonators of the type shown in fig. 5. These consist of large vessels

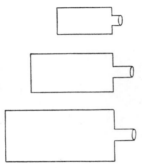

Fig. 5.—Helmholtz's Resonators

with narrow necks which resonate loudly at their natural frequency, but give very little response at all other frequencies. The disadvantages of uniform cylindrical tubes or organ pipes as resonators lies in their possessing a very poor sharpness of resonance.

6. Manometric Flames.

In a burning jet of coal-gas, the gas flows out of the orifice in the burner along certain stream-lines of flow. If the gas pressure and the shape of the orifice are adjusted to certain critical values, just as with a viscous liquid (Chap. XII, Part I), the flow becomes unstable and changes from stream-line flow to turbulent motion. The presence of sound waves in the neighbourhood of the flame is sometimes sufficient to affect the appearance of the flame appreciably when the latter is in critical adjustment. In fig. 6 is shown Rayleigh's *manometric* or *sensitive flame*. The upper part of a bunsen burner is fitted with a horizontal cylindrical metal vessel which is covered with a thin membrane at one end and closed at the other. Variations in pressure due to the presence of sound waves then cause violent movements of the flame if the latter is adjusted to sensitivity. The effect is most marked when the frequency of the sound waves is high.

If the variations in the appearance of the flame are very rapid they may not be detectable by unaided vision. A rotating mirror device as shown in fig. 7 is then sometimes used. If no variations in

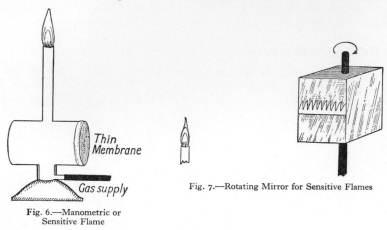

Fig. 7.—Rotating Mirror for Sensitive Flames

Fig. 6.—Manometric or Sensitive Flame

the flame occur, the appearance in the mirror is that of a continuous band of light, whereas when variations take place the image acquires a serrated appearance.

EXERCISES

1. Describe the construction and mode of operation of an electrically-maintained tuning-fork. How could you find the frequency of such a fork absolutely?

2. What is a manometric flame, and how could such a flame be used to detect the presence of standing waves in the region between a high-pitched source and a neighbouring vertical wall?

3. Define the terms *fundamental* and *harmonic*. How may the existence of various harmonics in the notes emitted by musical instruments be demonstrated?

CHAPTER VI

Measurement of Frequency

1. Introduction.

Probably the most accurate method for finding the frequency of sound waves is to convert them into electrical waves of the same frequency by means of a microphone, and then determine the frequency of these impulses with a cathode ray oscillograph (Part V). We shall describe here other older methods; we may also note that if the velocity of sound is known, then a measurement of the wavelength by Kundt's tube or some similar arrangement allows the frequency to be calculated.

2. The Siren.

This instrument has been described in Chap. V. If the number of holes around the periphery of the rotating disk is N, and the number of revolutions per second is n, the frequency of the sound emitted is nN. The number of revolutions in a given time is measured directly by gearing the axle of the rotating disk to a revolution counter. The speed of revolution of the siren is adjusted until the given sound and that emitted by the siren are judged to be of the same frequency.

3. Falling Plate Method.

The falling plate method for finding the frequency of (say) a tuning-fork is of interest mainly as a laboratory exercise. The tuning-fork is mounted horizontally and has a fine bristle attached by wax to one prong. The bristle is in contact with a vertical plate of smoked glass, and the wavy trace made by the bristle as the plate falls vertically under gravity is subsequently examined. The acceleration due to gravity must be accurately known; the calculation is then identical with that already given in Part I, p. 56, on the determination of g with Atwood's machine, the desired frequency ν being given by $1/\tau$. The corrected frequency of the fork free from the weight of wax and bristle is found by the method of beats (§ 6).

4. Stroboscopic Method.

This is a convenient and accurate method of determining the frequency of a tuning-fork. The stroboscope consists of an opaque

disk perforated with holes at regular intervals around its periphery
and maintained in uniform rotation by coupling to an electric motor.
Two light metal plates perforated with small slits are attached to the
prongs of the fork, as shown in fig. 1, in such a manner that when the
prongs are at rest the two slits are opposite each other and permit
observation of the stroboscopic disk mounted behind the fork. If the
fork is set vibrating and the stroboscopic disk is set rotating, then
observation of the disk through the fork shows that, in general, movement of the holes in the disk can be detected. As, however, the stroboscopic disk is accelerated the movement of the disk appears to become

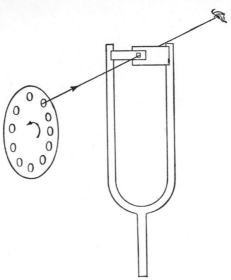

Fig. 1.—Stroboscopic Method for Frequency

slower and slower until ultimately, when the speed is just correct, the
hole viewed through the slits appears to be stationary. This effect is
produced by the movement of an adjacent hole in the disk into the
exact position previously occupied by its neighbour during the interval
represented by one-half of a complete vibration of the tuning-fork,
for the prongs are in the normal position of rest *twice* in each complete vibration of the fork. If there are N holes in the disk and the
latter makes n revs. per second, the time τ_0 taken for one hole to
occupy the position previously occupied by its neighbour is given by

$$\tau_0 = 1/Nn,$$

and since the frequency ν of the fork is equal to $1/2\tau_0$,

$$\nu = \tfrac{1}{2}Nn. \qquad \ldots \ldots \ldots \quad (6.1)$$

As in Fizeau's toothed wheel method for finding the velocity of light (Part III), an apparent stationary appearance of the holes will occur when the speed of rotation is any whole number of times the speed for which the holes first appear stationary. The frequency of the fork unloaded with slit apparatus must be determined by the method of beats.

5. The Phonic Wheel.

If the mechanical vibrations of a tuning-fork are converted into electrical impulses, for example by causing the fork to operate a make and break electrical circuit, the frequency of such impulses can be determined very accurately with the phonic wheel. This consists of an iron wheel carrying teeth on its periphery as shown in fig. 2, and rotating between the poles of an electromagnet. The latter is excited

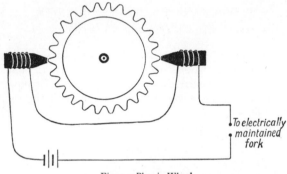

To electrically
maintained
fork

Fig. 2.—Phonic Wheel

by the impulses from the fork, and the wheel is then set rotating by an air blast or some similar device. When the rate of passage of the teeth just corresponds to the frequency of the applied impulses, the rotations are maintained indefinitely. If there are N teeth and the wheel makes n revs./sec., the frequency of the exciting impulses is Nn.

6. Beats.

The methods hitherto described enable absolute determinations of frequency to be made. If a source of known frequency is available, there are several methods of determining slightly different frequencies, and we shall discuss these methods in the remaining sections of this chapter.

If two tuning-forks of the same numerical frequency are sounded and one of them is slightly loaded with, for example, a piece of wax and a bristle as in § 3, then a marked pulsation in the intensity of sound is heard in the neighbourhood. The frequency of one of the forks has been slightly reduced by the loading, and the fluctuations in sound intensity, or **beats,** arise from the superposition of two neighbouring frequencies. As will be shown, the number of beats per second is equal to the difference in the two frequencies, and as this difference is easily determined by direct counting over a convenient period, the frequency of any fork may readily be determined if another fork of neighbouring and known frequency is available.

To show analytically the relation between the beat frequency and that of the two components, let the two wave trains have the same amplitude and commence in phase. Then if the individual displacements of the waves at any point x and time t are y_1 and y_2, and the frequencies are ν_1 and ν_2, the total displacement is

$$y = y_1 + y_2 = a \sin 2\pi\nu_1(t - x/v) + a \sin 2\pi\nu_2(t - x/v)$$
$$= 2a \sin \pi(t - x/v)(\nu_1 + \nu_2) . \cos \pi(t - x/v)(\nu_1 - \nu_2)$$
$$= 2a \cos \pi(t - x/v)(\nu_1 - \nu_2) . \sin 2\pi\nu(t - x/v), \quad . \quad (6.2)$$

where we have put $(\nu_1 + \nu_2) = 2\nu$. Now $\nu \sim \nu_1 \sim \nu_2$ since the frequencies of the two vibrations are not very different. The last equation may therefore be regarded as a wave-motion of frequency ν, but with a varying amplitude given by the first half of the expression on the R.H.S. This amplitude goes through successive maxima (or minima) at regular intervals of time τ, such that

$$1/\tau = \nu_1 - \nu_2; \quad . \quad . \quad . \quad . \quad (6.3)$$

that is, if β is the beat frequency,

$$\beta = 1/\tau = \nu_1 - \nu_2. \quad . \quad . \quad . \quad . \quad (6.4)$$

The production of beats is shown graphically in fig. 3a and 3b, where two S.H. waves of equal amplitude and in phase, but of 5 vibs./sec. and 4 vibs./sec. respectively, are drawn for a period of 4 sec. Fig. 3c shows the total displacement of the medium due to the two waves. There is observed to be an envelope wave whose maximum displacement is twice as large as that of the two component waves but whose frequency is equal to the difference of the two frequencies. This envelope wave clearly constitutes the beat wave.

If waves of several different frequencies, phases and amplitudes are present, the resultant wave may have a complicated form such as that shown in Chap. I, fig. 1. These considerations may be reversed, so that a complicated wave form may be considered to consist of a certain number of S.H.M.s compounded together. Such a conception is embodied formally in **Fourier's theorem,** which states that *any* *anharmonic wave-form may be analysed into a finite or infinite number of component harmonic waves, the frequencies of which are integral multiples of a fundamental frequency.* The process of **harmonic analysis** may be effected mathematically, but it is often very laborious, and machines termed **harmonic analysers** have been invented for the purpose.

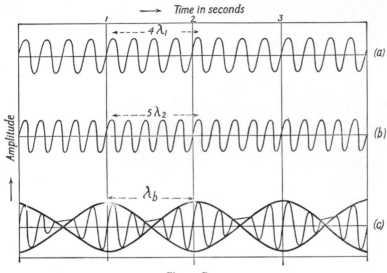

Fig. 3.—Beats

*7. Group Velocity and Phase Velocity.

The beat-wave is a particular example of the wave-group or wave-packet. Sound waves are propagated with a velocity which is independent of the frequency. Consequently the velocity of the wave-group is equal to the velocity of the component waves. With other forms of wave-motion, however (Part III, p. 347), the velocity of propagation in a dispersive medium is a function of the frequency. We shall now derive a general expression connecting wave velocity and group velocity.

Let two groups of waves of wave-lengths λ and $(\lambda + \delta\lambda)$ be travelling along the common x-axis with velocities V and $V + \delta V$ respectively. In fig. 4 the position of maximum disturbance at C will move to B when the crest A of the longer wave has moved forward to the crest B of the shorter wave. Let the period of time required for this to occur be τ. Then the distance

$$AB = \delta\lambda = \delta V \cdot \tau. \quad \ldots \ldots \quad (6.5)$$

During this interval the train of wave-length λ has travelled a distance $V\tau$, so the centre of the group has moved forward a distance

$$\Delta = V\tau - \lambda$$

$$= \tau\Big(V - \lambda\frac{dV}{d\lambda}\Big), \quad \cdots \cdots \quad (6.6)$$

from equation (6.5).

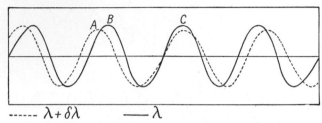

$$------ \ \lambda + \delta\lambda \qquad ----\ \lambda$$

Fig. 4.—Group Velocity

But the group velocity U is defined by $U = \Delta/\tau$. Hence

$$U = V - \lambda\frac{dV}{d\lambda}. \quad \cdots \cdots \quad (6.7)$$

The group velocity is therefore smaller or larger than the wave or phase velocity according as the velocity of the waves increases or decreases with wave-length. In a non-dispersive medium the group velocity and the wave velocity are identical.

8. Lissajous Figures.

We have mentioned many times the effect of compounding two S.H.M.s of equal amplitude and frequency but of differing phase. If the two vibrations are collinear, interference takes place. If the vibrations are perpendicular to each other, the resultant vibration is in a straight line, a circle or an ellipse according to the particular value of the phase difference. If the frequencies differ from each other, then the resultant vibration may be very complicated. The curve representing it is termed a **Lissajous figure.**

The subject may be examined graphically by a device illustrated in fig. 5. If we assume that the amplitudes a_1, a_2 and the periods $2\pi/\omega_1$, $2\pi/\omega_2$ are different, and that there is also a phase difference a, the two displacements mutually at right angles may be represented by the equations

$$x = a_1 \cos\omega_1 t, \quad y = a_2 \cos(\omega_2 t + a).$$

Fig. 5 represents the example

$$x = 5\cos 6t, \quad y = 4\cos\left(5t - \frac{\pi}{2}\right) = 4\sin 5t.$$

Take a rectangle ABCD with sides $AB = 2a = 10$, and $BC = 2b = 8$ parallel to the axes. On AD and AB describe semicircles, and divide their arcs into 6 and 5 equal parts respectively. Through the points of division draw parallels to the axes as shown. The point of intersection of two corresponding lines is then a point on the curve. The points E, F, G, H correspond to values of t equal to 0, $\pi/30$, $2\pi/30$, $3\pi/30$; and so on. At D and A the velocity is zero, and the motion is reversed.

To demonstrate Lissajous figures experimentally, perhaps the most striking method is to use the cathode ray tube (Part V), in which

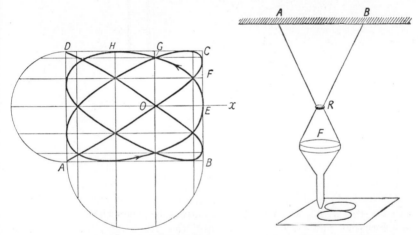

Fig. 5.—Construction of a Lissajous Figure   Fig. 6.—Blackburn's Pendulum

two alternating potentials are applied to the pairs of x-plates and y-plates of the tube. Mechanically, the appearance of Lissajous figures may be shown by *Blackburn's pendulum* or *two tuning-forks*. In the former arrangement, shown diagrammatically in fig. 6, a funnel F contains fine sand and is suspended from a horizontal beam by a non-vertical symmetrical bifilar suspension. The two strings pass through a small ring R, and the net effect is that the motion of F is that imparted by two S.H.M.s, that of the strings RA, RB and that of the strings RF. These two vibrations are made to occur mutually at right angles, and their relative frequencies are varied by adjusting the position of the ring R. The pattern traced out by the sand as it falls on a horizontal board beneath F then gives the appropriate Lissajous figure.

To exhibit Lissajous figures with two tuning-forks, the forks are set up so that their prongs vibrate in directions mutually at right angles (fig. 7). The prongs are fitted with small mirrors, so that a beam of light is reflected first from one fork and then the other on to a screen. The method may be used to determine the frequency of the one fork in terms of another in the following way. Varying curves are observed to be traced out on the screen, but at some instant when the phase difference is $\pi/2$ the curve is observed to be a *closed figure*. When the slower fork has again made one complete oscillation less than the

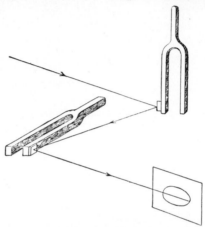

Fig. 7.—Two Tuning-Forks

other, the phase difference will again be $\pi/2$, and the closed figure will return. If t is the time which elapses between these two events, one fork has made $\nu_1 t$ vibrations and the other $\nu_2 t$ vibrations. The frequency of the second fork is given by

$$\nu_2 = \frac{\nu_1 t \pm 1}{t}.$$

The sign may be determined by observing the change in pattern when a small additional load is placed on one or other of the forks.

9. Musical Scale.

If the frequency of a given note c is twice that of another note C, the former is said to be an octave above the latter. In the **diatonic scale** six other notes are introduced between the fundamental, or

keynote, C and its octave *c* such that the frequency ratios to that of
the keynote are given by the accompanying table.

	C	D	E	F	G	A	B	C
Ratio of frequency	1	$\frac{9}{8}$	$\frac{5}{4}$	$\frac{4}{3}$	$\frac{3}{2}$	$\frac{5}{3}$	$\frac{15}{8}$	2
Interval - - -		$\frac{9}{8}$	$\frac{10}{9}$	$\frac{16}{15}$	$\frac{9}{8}$	$\frac{10}{9}$	$\frac{9}{8}$	$\frac{16}{15}$

The ratios of the frequencies of adjacent notes are termed the *intervals*.

The choice of these particular intervals has arisen from experience
that these notes when sounded simultaneously produce the maximum
concord not only between their fundamentals but also between their
harmonics. In particular it is found that the sound is especially con-
cordant when notes having frequencies in the ratio 4 : 5 : 6 are sounded
simultaneously. Reference to the table shows that the notes (C, E,
G), (G, B, *d*), and (F, A, *c*) have their frequencies in the ratio 4 : 5 : 6,
and these chords are termed *harmonic triads*. These particular chords
are usually designated as the *tonic, the dominant*, and the *subdominant*
triads.

Further reference to the table shows that the intervals on the
diatonic scale are either $\frac{9}{8}, \frac{10}{9}$ or $\frac{16}{15}$. The first two intervals, although
not exactly equal, are termed *tones*, and the last, a *semi-tone*. As the
interval between all notes but (E–F), (B–C) are too large for musical
requirements, additional notes are inserted such that the notes are
raised or lowered by an interval of 25/24. The raised note is termed
a sharp (♯) and the lowered note a flat (♭).

Simple calculation will show that if we proceed strictly according
to the above principles a musical instrument would require an enormous keyboard since each keynote will give rise to its own scale. To
avoid this the *scale of equal temperament* is often used. This is defined
to contain eleven notes between the extreme notes of the octave,
such that the interval between each adjacent note is $2^{\frac{1}{12}}$. This
chromatic scale does not give rise to harmonic triads with their frequencies in exactly the desired ratio of 4 : 5 : 6, so a small amount of
discord is inevitably present in fixed-note instruments.

EXERCISES

1. Describe the stroboscopic method of finding the frequency of a given tuning-fork. By what alternative method could the result be checked?

2. Explain carefully the production of beat notes, illustrating your answer by diagrams. Two forks A and B produce beats when sounded simultaneously, and the number of beats steadily increases as A is loaded with increasing amounts of wax. Which fork has the lower frequency?

3. Show analytically that the beat frequency is equal to the frequency difference of two sources. Give examples of beats occurring in different branches of physics.

4. State Fourier's theorem, and explain how a bank of Helmholtz resonators might be used to examine the components and to build up the wave-form of a given sound.

5. Distinguish between wave velocity and group velocity, and derive an expression connecting these two quantities. Of what experimental significance is the difference?

6. Describe experiments to illustrate the production of Lissajous figures and construct the Lissajous figure resulting from two S.H.M.s whose amplitudes and frequencies are in the ratio $1 : 3$ and $1 : 2$ respectively, and which start initially $\pi/2$ out of phase.

7. Write a short essay on musical scales.

8. A circular saw with 100 teeth in contact with a wooden strip emits a note which is two octaves above middle c (256 vibs./sec.). Find the number of revolutions made by the saw in one minute. [614.]

CHAPTER VII

Intensity of Sound

1. Introduction.

Since sound consists in variations in pressure or displacement of the medium conveying the sound, one general method of estimating sound intensity is to determine the amplitude of the variations caused by the sound wave. Alternatively, since energy is travelling outwards from the source of sound, the small steady radiation pressure which results may be measured.

The intensity of sound falls off inversely as the square of the distance from a point source. This is to be expected theoretically according to the reasoning given in Part III, p. 442.

2. Units of Sound Intensity.

On the C.G.S. system, absolute sound intensity is measured in ergs per sec. per cm.², since it represents the rate of flow of energy across unit area. For many purposes, however, the fractional decrease or increase in sound intensity is required. The human ear does not estimate a sound of twice the energy flux of a given standard as having twice the loudness. In fact, a logarithmic increase in intensity is the physiological response. In accordance with this behaviour a change to sound intensity P_2 above or below an arbitrary sound intensity P_1 is said to be a change of N *bels*, where

$$N = \log_{10}\frac{P_2}{P_1}. \quad \cdots \cdots \quad (7.1)$$

The bel is a large unit, and therefore one-tenth of the bel, the **decibel,** is more commonly used.

Unfortunately the aural response to sound intensity depends also on the frequency. Loudness is therefore expressed in terms of the loudness of a standard reference tone of 1000 cycles/sec. The loudness of the standard tone is that which produces an energy flux of 10^{-15} watts/cm.². On this basis, the loudness of any sound in **phons** is numerically equal to the sound intensity in decibels of an equally loud 1000 cycles/sec. pure note.

3. Refractometer Measurements of Intensity.

Toepler and Boltzmann introduced the use of a refractometer for estimating the changes in density occurring at the node of an air column subject to stationary waves. In principle the method is illustrated in fig. 1. Light from a source S traverses two air columns A and B, one of which is undisturbed, the other being subject to stationary sound vibrations.

The light beam through the sounding tube is arranged to pass in the neighbourhood of one of the nodes, since density fluctuations are greatest at these points. The interference fringes formed by light traversing the two paths (Part III) oscillate with an amplitude which

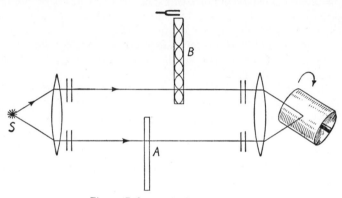

Fig. 1.—Refractometer for Sound Intensity

may be measured directly on photographic paper carried by a revolving drum. The method is not very sensitive, appreciable fluctuations in the fringe position occurring only for relatively large sound intensities.

4. Rayleigh Disk.

For absolute measurements of sound intensity the Rayleigh disk is usually used. This consists of a thin disk of mica, a few millimetres in diameter, suspended by a torsion fibre in the path of the sound but at an angle to its direction of propagation. The disk tends to turn with its flat face across the direction of propagation of the sound, and the torque produced is obtained directly from the reflection of a ray of light from the disk.

VII]   MEASUREMENT BY MICROPHONE   519

5. Measurement by Microphone.

The vibrations set up when the sound impinges on a diaphragm afford the most convenient method of estimating sound intensity. The movement of the diaphragm may be determined by mechanical, optical or electrical means. The last of these is now almost universally used, and a great many types of electrical microphone are available. Examples have already been described in Chap. V.

Microphones are calibrated against the Rayleigh disk.

EXERCISES

1. Define the *decibel* and the *phon*.
How may the absolute intensity of a sound be determined?

2. Compare the methods available for estimating sound intensities. Why is direct aural observation unsatisfactory?

3. How have optical interference methods been used (*a*) to photograph sound waves, (*b*) to estimate sound intensity?

CHAPTER VIII

Acoustics

1. Introduction.

There are many important applications of sound such as the gramophone, electrical pick-ups and so on, but these depend for their action upon invention rather than science. Their successful operation depends on technological improvements, and really new principles are very rarely involved. On the other hand, the construction of public buildings for the optimum sound efficiency, which is usually termed architectural acoustics, involves many points of interest concerning the absorption, reflection and interference of sound waves. The main points to be considered are: (i) loudness, (ii) reverberation period, (iii) focussing, (iv) echelon effects, (v) exclusion of extraneous noise (a) air borne, (b) structural, (vi) avoidance of resonance, and we shall now discuss these in order.

2. Loudness.

For the direct hearing of unassisted speech the audience may not be much larger than about 1000. Some improvement may be obtained with sounding boards situated near the speaker and directed towards the audience, but unless these are large they have little value. The use of low ceilings is an advantage, and the avoidance of alcoves is desirable. Electrical amplifying equipment is now in common use, the loud speakers being placed some distance above the speaker's head. Owing to the selective effect of amplifiers the amplification is limited by the tendency to give undue prominence to the tones of lower frequency.

3. Reverberation.

The most serious source of difficulty met with in the construction of public buildings is confusion due to reverberation. This is the name given to prolonged reflection of the sound to and fro between the boundaries of the auditorium. If the reflected sound does not die away below the limit of audibility in a short space of time, successive utterances become hopelessly confused. The standard *reverberation time* of a room is defined as the time required for the intensity of a previously sustained note to fall to 10^{-6} of its value when the note is cut off. The classical work of Sabine showed that the reverberation time of a room was given by an expression of the type

$$t = \frac{kV}{aS}, \qquad \ldots \ldots \quad (8.1)$$

where V is the volume, aS the total absorbing power of the room, and k is a constant. The quantity aS is defined by

$$aS = \sum_{1}^{n} a_j S_j, \qquad \ldots \ldots \quad (8.2)$$

where S_j is any given surface area exposed to the sound and a_j is the absorption coefficient of that surface, defined as the ratio of the energy absorbed to the energy incident upon the surface. As practically none of the sound is reflected by an open window, the absorption coefficient of the latter is unity. Compared with this, brick and marble have absorption coefficients as small as 10^{-2}. Much better absorption is shown by fibre-board panelling, heavy curtains with folds, slag wool, &c., whose absorption coefficients are between 0·5 and 1.

The optimum reverberation times are 1–2 sec. for speech and 0·5–1 sec. for music. Smaller reverberation times, while increasing the clarity of the sound, either lend too little support to the voice or diminish the brilliance of the music, giving it a " dead " effect. If a room has not yet been constructed, Sabine's formula in equation (8.1) may be used to relate the volume of the room and its absorptive powers for different materials so as to produce the optimum reverberation time for the purpose for which the room is required. For a hall already in existence the volume is fixed, and hence the only effective method of changing the reverberation time is the introduction of different areas of materials of differing absorptive powers. It is of interest to note that the absorption coefficient of the average audience is nearly unity, so that the reverberation time may differ considerably according to the size of the audience.

4. Focussing.

The existence of concave, cylindrical or spherical surfaces in the walls or roof of an auditorium can give rise to undesirable focussing effects if the surfaces are several feet in diameter. For example, with the arrangement illustrated in fig. 1, an observer at O will experience a loud intensity since he will receive the sound both directly from the source S and by focussing from the dome. Moreover, owing to the path difference in the two routes the sounds arrive out of phase and considerable confusion results.

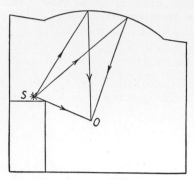

Fig. 1.—Focussing Effect

5. Echelon Effect.

If a short sharp sound is made in front of a regular flight of stairs or railings as shown in fig. 2, a musical note is often observed. This note arises from the regular train of reflected sounds each one of which

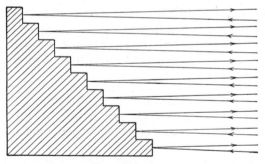

Fig. 2.—Echelon Effect

would individually consist of a simple echo of the original sound. If these echoes follow each other at the observer with a frequency in the audible range, a note of that frequency will be observed. Should such an effect be undesirable, the regular spacing of objects which give rise to sound reflection must be avoided.

6. Exclusion of Extraneous Noise.

Air-borne noise is reduced by using double or triple windows or doors, each with separate frames. It is clear that air-borne noise cannot be completely eliminated if ventilation is to occur. It may, however, be much reduced by using felt baffles in the ventilator duct. Simple lining of the duct with felt may often reduce the sound intensity by 1 decibel per foot. Maximum permissible speeds of fans and air circulation must also be observed.

Structure-borne noise, such as that due to machinery, is reduced by breaking the continuity of the solid conducting path by interposing layers of cork or felt-like material. Hot-water pipes and similar systems must be acoustically insulated from the main structure of the building.

7. Avoidance of Resonance.

It is very undesirable that resonance should occur for any note of audio-frequency, otherwise the observed intensity of the note may be quite other than that intended. The resonant frequency of a large room with the source in a smaller attached volume is approximately inversely proportional to the square root of the volume of the room. In halls of ordinary size the resonant frequency is well below the lower limit of audibility, but it may be observed in the lowest notes emitted by some organs where the sound pulsations build up to large magnitudes when they are felt rather than heard.

EXERCISES

1. Explain what is meant by *time of reverberation*. Upon what does it depend and how is it adjusted to its optimum value?

2. Write a short essay on architectural acoustics.

FOR ADDITIONAL READING

Modern Acoustics, A. H. Davis (Bell).

Acoustics, A. Wood (Blackie).

EXAMPLES

1. Given that the velocity of sound in hydrogen at N.T.P. is $1\cdot26 \times 10^5$ cm./sec., find the ratio of the specific heats of hydrogen at constant pressure and constant volume, if its density is 9×10^{-5} gm./c.c.

2. Find the barometric pressure on a day when the velocity of sound in air is $3\cdot40 \times 10^4$ cm./sec., and the density of air is $1\cdot22 \times 10^{-3}$ gm./c.c. The ratio of the specific heat of air at constant pressure to its value at constant volume may be taken to be $1\cdot41$.

3. Determine the change in volume in 1 litre of water when the pressure is increased from 1 to 2 atmospheres, given that the velocity of sound in the water is $1\cdot40 \times 10^5$ cm./sec.

4. If the velocity of sound in air changes from $3\cdot30 \times 10^4$ cm./sec. to $3\cdot35 \times 10^4$ cm./sec. on the admission of aqueous vapour, determine the percentage of vapour present if the ratio of the densities of air and aqueous vapour under the conditions of the experiment is $1\cdot6 : 1$.

5. Find the velocity of a car with respect to a stationary observer if the latter observes a drop in pitch of 100 vibrations/sec. when the car passes him. The car emits a note with a frequency of 1000 vib./sec. and the velocity of sound is 1142 ft./sec.

6. A car is proceeding along a straight road at a uniform speed of 60 m.p.h. and emitting a note with a frequency of 200 vib./sec. An observer approaches the first road by a straight side-road at a speed of 30 m.p.h. Given that the side-road is at right angles to the first road, determine the apparent pitch of the note observed at the instant when the line joining the two cars is at 45° to the two roads.

7. Using the data of Ques. 6, determine the apparent pitch of the note if the observer experiences a head-wind blowing at a speed of 15 m.p.h. at an angle of 15° to the side-road.

8. On examining the edges of the sun's disk with a spectroscope, a change in wave-length is observed according as the eastern or western limb is viewed. If the ratio of the mean wave-length to the change in wave-length is 75,000 and the velocity of light is 3×10^{10} cm./sec., determine the linear velocity of a point on the sun's equator due to the rotation of the sun.

9. A closed brass pipe emits a note of frequency 512 at 0° C. If

the coefficient of linear expansion of brass is $1·87 \times 10^{-5}$ per °C., determine the pitch of the note at 20° C.

10. The third overtone of a closed organ pipe is found to be in unison with the first overtone of an open pipe. Find the ratio of the lengths of the pipes.

11. Resonance is found to occur first when the closed end of a given tube is 20 cm., and next when it is 63 cm., from the open end of the tube. Determine the end-correction of the tube.

12. A closed organ pipe is suddenly opened and it is observed that the second overtone of the closed pipe differs by 200 vib./sec. from the first overtone of the open pipe. What is the fundamental frequency of the closed pipe?

13. A closed pipe and an open pipe are sounding simultaneously and producing 5 beats/sec. If the open pipe is 30 cm. long and the velocity of sound is taken as $3·30 \times 10^4$ cm./sec., find by how much the length of the closed pipe must be changed to bring the two pipes into unison.

14. A given steel wire of density 7·7 gm./c.c. fractures when the tension is greater than $9·68 \times 10^7$ dynes. If the wire snaps when 100 cm. of the wire are emitting a note with a frequency of 1000 vib./sec., determine the diameter of the wire, assumed uniform, at the instant of fracture.

15. A wire 75 cm. long and of mass 1 gm. is making 256 vib./sec. under a tension supplied by a brass weight hanging vertically. On immersing the weight in water the vibrating length of the wire has to be shortened by 4·45 cm. to regain its original pitch. What is the density of brass?

16. In Melde's experiment, a fine string is attached at one end to a tuning-fork while the other end supports a weight of 200 gm. When the fork is caused to vibrate, the string shows 5 vibrating loops. Determine the weight required for the string to vibrate with 2 loops.

17. A rod is clamped at the centre and attached to a Kundt's tube containing air. The distance from the first to the tenth node when the rod is stroked longitudinally is 135 cm. If the velocity of sound in air is $3·30 \times 10^4$ cm./sec., find the frequency of the note emitted by the rod.

18. If the rod in Ques. 17 is 100 cm. long and is made of material of density 8·0 gm./c.c., determine Young's modulus for the material.

19. The disk of a siren is rotating at a speed of 1500 rev./min. and the note emitted is observed to give 60 beats/min. with a given tuning-fork. On decreasing the speed of the siren to 1495 rev./min. the number of beats/min. is reduced to 40. If the siren contains 20 holes around the disk, find the frequency of the tuning-fork.

20. A stroboscopic disk is revolving at the rate of 40 rev./sec. The disk contains 20 holes and when viewed through a vibrating tuning-fork in its rest position the holes appear to move back at the rate of 1 hole every 3 sec. What is the frequency of the fork?

21. Show that the amplitude of the disturbance due to a stationary source emitting sound waves is inversely proportional to the distance from the source.

22. A source of sound is placed in front of a flat wall and it is found that a manometric flame shows maximum disturbance when it is placed 12 in. or 18 in. from the wall. Determine the frequency of the note emitted by the source if the velocity of sound is taken as 1100 ft./sec.

23. It is found that when a sharp tap is made in front of a regular flight of stairs whose depth of tread is 1 ft., a regular note is heard which is in unison with a tuning-fork sounding 550 vib./sec. What is the velocity of sound according to this result?

24. Two notes have frequencies 256 and 864. Determine the frequencies of two intermediate notes such that equal intervals occur between successive notes.

25. A vertical smoked plate falls vertically under gravity, and the traces formed by transverse vibrations of a fork show 10 complete vibrations in each of two consecutive lengths which differ by 1·497 cm. What is the frequency of the fork?

ANSWERS AND HINTS FOR SOLUTION

1. $V = (\gamma p/\rho)^{\frac{1}{2}}$ or $\gamma = V^2\rho/p$; 1·41.

2. Apply preceding relation; 10^6 dynes/cm.^{2}.

3. $V = (E/\rho)^{\frac{1}{2}}$ where E is bulk modulus of elasticity; also by definition $E = \Delta p/(\Delta v/v)$, where Δp is increase in pressure and $\Delta v/v$ corresponding fractional change in volume; 0·05 c.c.

4. If density of mixture is ρ', and density of air alone is ρ, then if the volume fraction of water vapour is x, $\rho' = (1 - x)\rho + x\rho/1\cdot6 = \rho(1 - 0\cdot375x)$. Since $V^2 = E/\rho$, $V^2/V_1{}^2 = \rho'/\rho$ or $(3\cdot30/3\cdot35)^2 = (1 - 0\cdot375x)$; 7·9 per cent.

5. Change in pitch is $n'' - n' = nV/(V - v) - nV/(V + v) = 2nvV/(V^2 - v^2)$, where V is the velocity of sound and v is velocity of car; 57·1 ft./sec.

6. Apparent pitch for stationary observer in position of second car is $n' = nV/(V - v')$ where v' is component of velocity along 45° direction; hence for moving observer

$$n'' = n'(V + v'')/V = n(V + v'')/(V - v');$$

$v'' = 22\sqrt{2}$ ft./sec., $v' = 44\sqrt{2}$ ft./sec.; 217·2 vib./sec.

7. If wind velocity in direction from source to observer is w, then $n'' = n(V + w + v'')/(V + w - v')$ where $w = 11\sqrt{3}$ ft./sec.; 216·8 vib./sec.

8. If change in frequency is Δn and change in wave-length is $\Delta\lambda$, since $V = n\lambda$, $\Delta n/n = -\Delta\lambda/\lambda$. Also $\Delta n = 2nv/V$ where v is the linear velocity and V is the velocity of light; 2 kilometres/sec.

9. Neglecting end correction, since length of pipe is one quarter of a wave-length, $512 \times 4l_0 = V_0$ and $n \times 4l_1 = V_1$; also $l_1 = l_0(1 + at)$ and $V_1 = V_0(1 + \gamma t)^{\frac{1}{2}}$, where a is co-efficient of linear expansion of brass and $\gamma = 1/273$; 530·5.

10. Frequencies of harmonics are in the ratio $1 : 3 : 5 : 7$ for a closed pipe, and $1 : 2 : 3 : 4$ for an open pipe; $7n = 2n'$, also $n = V/4l$ and $n' = V/2l'$; hence $l' : l = 4 : 7$.

11. If end correction is $f(r)$, $\lambda/4 = l_1 + f(r)$ and $3\lambda/4 = l_2 + f(r)$; hence $\lambda = 86$ cm. and $f(r) = 1\cdot5$ cm.

12. If n is fundamental of closed pipe and n' that of open pipe, $n' = 2n$; also $5n = 2n' + 200$; 200.

13. Length of consonant resonance pipe would be $30/2 = 15$ cm. If frequencies are n' and n for open and closed pipes respectively, $n' = V/\lambda' = 3\cdot30 \times 10^4/60 = 550$. Hence n is 550 ± 5, and since $\lambda = 4l$, pipe must be lengthened or shortened by 0·14 cm.

14. $n = (T/m)^{\frac{1}{2}}/2l$, where n is frequency, m is mass of unit length of the wire, l its length and T is the tension; also $m = \pi d^2 \rho/4$ where ρ is density and d is the diameter of the wire; 0·2 mm.

15. If volume of weight is V, acceleration due to gravity is g, and density of brass is ρ, $n = (V\rho g \times 75/1)^{\frac{1}{2}}/2 \times 75 = \{Vg(\rho - 1) \times 75/1\}^{\frac{1}{2}}/2 \times 70·55$; 8·7 gr./c.c.

16. If length of string is l, effective length when 5 loops are present is $l/5$ for substitution in $n = (T/m)^{\frac{1}{2}}/2l$; hence, since n remains constant, $n = 5(200/m)^{\frac{1}{2}}/2l = 2(T/m)^{\frac{1}{2}}/2l$; 1250 gm.

17. Wave-length of vibration in air is $2 \times 135/9 = 30$ cm., so frequency $n = 3·3 \times 10^4/30 = 1100$ vib./sec.

18. Wave-length of disturbance in rod is 2×100, and hence velocity in rod is 200×1100 cm./sec. Now $V = (E/\rho)^{\frac{1}{2}}$ where E is Young's modulus and ρ is the density; $3·872 \times 10^{11}$ dynes/cm.².

19. Initial frequency of siren is $1500 \times 20/60 = 500$; frequency of fork is 500 ± 1; final frequency of siren is $1495 \times 20/60 = 498·3$; frequency of fork is $498·3 \pm 0·6$; 499 vib./sec.

20. If θ is angle subtended by arc between consecutive holes at centre of disk, $\theta = 2\pi/20 = \pi/10$. If n is frequency of fork, since holes are visible twice in every complete vibration, time between successive views is $1/2n$. In this time next hole just fails to occupy position of previous hole by amount a. Hence, since disk makes 40 rev./sec., $(\pi/10 - a) = 40 \times 2\pi/2n$; but in 3 sec., complete coincidence is again observed, hence $a \times 6n = \pi/10$; $400\frac{1}{6}$ vib./sec.

21. Consider two spherical shells of radius r_1 and r_2 with source as centre; then sound energy which passes through first shell of area $4\pi r_1^2$ ultimately passes through second shell of area $4\pi r_2^2$. Hence energy per unit area in the two cases is as r_1^2/r_2^2, and thus intensity falls off as $1/r^2$. Since amplitude varies as (energy)$^{\frac{1}{2}}$ amplitude falls off as $1/r$.

22. $\lambda = 2(18 - 12) = 12$ in.; hence $n = V/\lambda = 1100$ vib./sec.

23. Echoes from successive steps reach observer at intervals of $2/v$ sec.; 1100 ft./sec.

24. Since interval is defined as ratio of adjacent frequencies, if unknown frequencies are a and β and interval is t, $a/256 = \beta/a = 864/\beta = t$, hence $t = 1·5$, $a = 384$ and $\beta = 576$.

25. If first length is d_1 and second length is d_2, times taken to cover d_1 and d_2 are the same t, and if initial velocity of plate is u, $d_1 = ut + \frac{1}{2}gt^2$, hence $t^2 = (d_2 - d_1)/g$ or $t = 1/25·6$; 256 vib./sec.

PART V

ELECTRICITY AND MAGNETISM

CHAPTER I

Introductory

Unlike many physical phenomena, electric and magnetic forces are not directly detectable by the senses. Further, according to modern ideas the branches of physics classified under the title of Electricity and Magnetism are on a different footing from those branches already discussed in Vols. I–IV. In problems involving General Physics, Heat, Sound, and to a lesser extent Light, the majority of the experimental results are adequately explained in terms of mechanics and the molecular theory of matter, together with the mathematical aid afforded by thermodynamics. With electric and magnetic phenomena, however, the molecular theory is of little assistance, the simplest experiment requiring interpretation on the modern view in terms of particles smaller than atoms. Of these sub-atomic particles, the electron plays at present the dominant role. It is true that electricity and magnetism achieved tremendous advances during the hundred years prior to the discovery of the electron, yet to attempt to interpret those advances to-day without constant reference to the electron theory would be analogous to an attempt to account for chemical phenomena in terms of phlogiston theory. In fact, just as the student was urged to interpret phenomena in other branches of physics in terms of the molecular theory, so all phenomena in electricity and magnetism should be referred to electron theory. From the point of view of a student approaching the subject for the first time, there is, however, a great difference between the two theories. The molecular theory was familiar as a philosophical speculation for two thousand years before chemical experiment demanded its adoption. The electron theory was a product of several years of patient experiment but had no philosophical history of comparable duration. Consequently, while molecular theory is comparatively easily appreciated, a considerable knowledge of electric and magnetic phenomena is required before the need for the electron theory, as opposed to other possible explanations, is realized. The student will therefore be in a much better position to understand why electric and magnetic phenomena are interpreted in terms of the electron after having arrived at the end rather than the beginning of this book. Provisionally, then, the student is asked to accept the following tenets of the electron theory. Electricity, like matter on the molecular theory, does not exist in any arbitrary amount but only in discrete amounts. These discrete amounts are whole number multiples of a definite amount of electricity, termed the electronic charge. That is, any quantity of electricity consists of one or more electrons, each electron being pictured in the first instance as a small ball of electric charge. Electrons at rest produce only electrical and not magnetic effects.

An electric current consists simply in the movement of electrons. Magnetic effects which accompany electric currents therefore arise only when electrons move and are a direct result of electrons in motion.

Now the electron theory has turned out to be of far greater significance than just a useful idea to explain electric and magnetic phenomena. The atoms and molecules of molecular theory have been shown themselves to consist of electric charges and therefore of electrons. Consequently, electron theory is much more fundamental than atomic theory. In fact, *all* physical phenomena are now explicable in terms of electron theory. However, as indicated in the Introduction to Vol. I, such a fundamental analysis is often unnecessary, the atomic theory giving sufficient explanation of the phenomenon without recourse to electron theory. For example, nothing is to be gained by interpreting sound waves in terms of electron theory. On the other hand, anomalous dispersion (see Vol. III, Light, p. 406) requires the electron theory if it is to be satisfactorily explained.

CHAPTER II

Elementary Electrostatics

1. Introduction.

The fact that amber which had been rubbed with cloth acquired the property of attracting light bodies such as dust and chaff, was known to the ancients. Such a body is said to have acquired an **electric charge.** The properties of electrified bodies with the charge at rest is the domain of **electrostatics.** If the charge is in motion it is said to constitute an **electric current.** An electric current is always accompanied by a **magnetic field** in the neighbourhood of the current. Since a static charge is unaccompanied by a magnetic field, problems in electrostatics are physically simpler than in electromagnetics and we therefore commence our study of electricity with electrostatics.

2. Negative and Positive Electricity.

If an ebonite rod which has been electrified by friction with cat's fur is suspended in a light stirrup supported by a torsionless fibre of unspun silk as shown in fig. 1, it is found that another similarly elec-

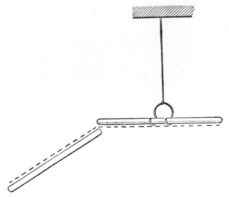

Fig. 1. — Repulsion of Electrified Ebonite Rods

trified ebonite rod exerts a repulsion on the former rod when the two are brought into proximity. Similarly, two glass rods electrified by friction with flannel will also exhibit a mutual repulsion. Should,

18   (H 394)

however, the electrified glass rod be presented to the electrified ebonite rod an attraction takes place. These simple experiments show:

(1) There are at least two kinds of electricity;

(2) Bodies charged with the same kind of electricity repel each other, while those charged with different kinds attract each other.

All subsequent experiments have shown that only these two kinds of electricity exist. The electricity acquired by the ebonite rod when rubbed with cat's fur is *arbitrarily* termed **negative electricity,** while that acquired by the glass rod when rubbed with flannel is termed **positive electricity.** The first law of electrostatics is therefore: **Like charges repel, and unlike charges attract each other.**

3. Production of Electricity by Friction.

Consider the simple experiment illustrated in fig. 2. An ebonite rod is fitted with a close-fitting cap of cat's fur and electricity is generated by rotating the cap. On removing the cap and presenting the rod to an electroscope (see section 5) the leaves diverge. If the cap

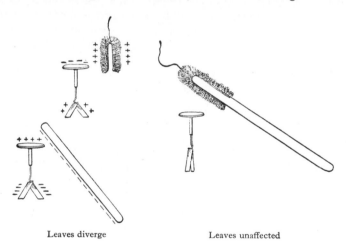

Leaves diverge   Leaves unaffected

Fig. 2. — Equal and Opposite Charges.

alone is presented the leaves again diverge. If, however, the unseparated but excited cap and rod are simultaneously presented to the electroscope, no divergence results. This clearly indicates that the charges generated are equal and opposite.

These results receive a ready explanation on the electrical theory of matter which is developed more fully in Chap. XX. *Ordinary, uncharged matter consists of equal quantities of positive and negative electricity.* Some of the negative electricity, which consists of electrons, has the property of being fairly easily transferred from one body to another. Simple mechanical friction is sufficient to effect this transfer. Consequently the body which gains the electrons acquires an excess negative charge, while the body which loses them acquires a net positive charge equal in magnitude to the negative charge which it has lost. With ebonite and cat's fur, friction transfers the electrons to the ebonite, while with glass and flannel they are transferred from glass to flannel.

On the modern view, therefore, electricity is not "generated" but merely *separated*. Paradoxically a body is said to " acquire " a positive charge when in fact it has lost the corresponding number of electrons.

4. Conductors and Insulators.

If a metal rod which is held in the hand is subjected to friction, then simple experiments will fail to detect any electrification of the rod, although the cat's fur will show some charge. Should, however, the metal be attached to a piece of ebonite or glass and should it be held by the non-metal, it will become electrified by friction in the usual manner. If the metal is touched with a succession of substances held in the hand it will be found that touching produces little result with some substances, such as glass and ebonite, whereas metals or water produce immediate discharge. Materials like dry wood occupy an intermediate position and cause a slow discharge. Substances are accordingly classified as **conductors, insulators** and **semi-conductors** of electricity. A thin film of moisture will completely ruin the insulating properties of the best insulator. Ordinary glass, being hygroscopic, is therefore very unsuitable for insulation in experiments on static electricity.

With a conductor the charge spreads itself out to the boundary of the conductor, for the individual electrons which constitute the charge, being all of one sign, exert a continual mutual repulsion. Consequently, if a charged conductor is touched by another conductor the charge will continue to spread until it again reaches the boundary of the new conductor. Clearly since the new conductor, say the hand, is normally connected through the rest of the body to the earth, the charge will spread itself to the boundaries of the planet and consequently a negligible fraction will remain on the initially charged conductor.

5. Gold-leaf Electroscope.

The gold-leaf electroscope, a diagram of which (single-leaf type) is shown in fig. 3, is of great value in demonstrating the laws of electrostatics and in measuring quantities such as charge, potential and capacity. It consists essentially of a vertical brass rod to the lower end of which are gummed one or two small strips of very thin gold leaf. The brass rod is insulated from the cubical tin container by an insulating sulphur plug. Charge is communicated to the leaves from a brass disk attached to the top of the brass rod. Owing to the mutual repulsion the leaves diverge at their lower end, and observation of the magnitude of the divergence as registered on a graduated scale allows an estimate of the charge to be made. For accurate work the movement of the image of the leaves over a micrometer scale in the eyepiece

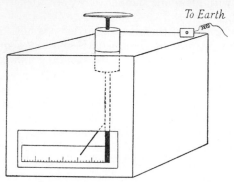

Fig. 3. — Gold-leaf Electroscope

of a microscope is registered. The tin container should be connected to earth throughout the measurements so as to ensure that it is at a definite potential (see section 10).

6. Electrostatic Induction.

If a charged body is brought up to the disk of an electroscope, the leaves of the latter diverge before any charge has been communicated to the leaves by actual contact of the charged body with the disk. This divergence is normally temporary and disappears when the charged rod is removed from the neighbourhood. Such behaviour is due to **electrostatic induction.** When the charged rod, which we shall suppose to be negatively charged, is brought close to the conducting system of disk, support and leaves, some of the electrons in the disk are repelled to the leaves which constitute the boundary farthest removed from the exciting rod. Consequently an excess negative charge is temporarily present on the leaves and the latter diverge. When the exciting rod is removed, the electrons redistribute themselves uniformly, and since the system initially contained equal quantities of positive and negative electricity at all points, it resumes that condition and the leaves collapse.

Suppose, however, that while the leaves are still under the influence of the electrostatic induction, the disk is touched with the finger. The electrons which previously were unable to travel farther from the exciting rod than the leaves, are now able to get to earth. Consequently the temporary excess of electrons travels away from the

leaves and the latter collapse. If now the finger is removed and finally
the exciting rod is removed, the leaf system will be left with a net
positive charge, for the electrons which have escaped will be unable to
return to the system. The remaining electrons distribute themselves
as evenly as possible among the positive charges, but the net effect is
that a *positive* charge has been produced by *electrostatic induction* from
the *negatively-charged* exciting rod. The student will notice that it is
always the electrons which move and never the positive residues, in
which the main mass of the atom resides. Such immobility of the
positive part of the atom is confined to solids. In electrical conduction
through fluids both positive and negative charges are in motion.

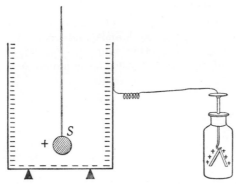

Fig. 4. — Electrostatic Induction

There is complete analogy between the equal and opposite charges
produced by friction in that the *maximum* charge which can be communicated by induction is equal and opposite to the inducing charge.
To demonstrate this experimentally an apparatus such as that shown
in fig. 4 is used. A charged metal sphere S is suspended by an insulating
thread of unspun silk in an insulated metal container connected by a
metallic wire to an electroscope. Once the sphere is well inside the
container, but not in contact with it, the divergence of the electroscope
leaves remains constant. The container is then touched momentarily
with the finger and the sphere is removed. The divergence now shown
by the leaves gives the value of the permanent induced charge. If the
sphere is then again introduced and allowed to come into contact with
the container the whole charge disappears on both leaves and sphere,
showing that the induced charge is equal and opposite to the inducing
charge. This neutralization may not appear quite complete in practice,
since there is no perfect insulator, and the leak of electricity which is
continually taking place from all charged bodies may occur at different
rates from the sphere and the other system respectively. By conducting

the experiment skilfully and rapidly, however, the proposition may be proved to within a few per cent.

It follows that the attraction between uncharged bodies and charged bodies is due to induction. Under the inducing action of the charged body, like charges in the other body are repelled (more or less effectively) to the far end, and an excess of charges of opposite sign are situated close to the charged body. The attraction between the unlike charges exceeds the repulsion between the like charges owing to the greater proximity of the former; and if the particles are light, the electrostatic forces are sufficient to overcome the force of gravity and to lift the particles.

7. Distribution of Charge.

In fig. 5 are shown a number of conducting bodies of different shapes supported on insulating stands and charged with electricity either by contact or by induction from an ebonite rod. To examine the distribution of the charge over the conductors a **proof plane** is

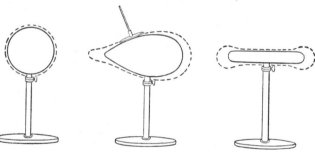

Fig. 5. — Distribution of Charge

used. This consists of a small brass disk attached to an insulating handle; it is placed in contact with the conductor at various points and then presented at a standard distance to an uncharged gold-leaf electroscope. For the charged sphere it is found on sampling that the distribution is uniform over the surface. If the sphere is hollow it may easily be shown that **no charge resides inside the conductor.** This is to be expected, since the various parts of the charge exert a mutual repulsion and consequently are urged to the farthest boundaries of the conductor.

The cylindrical conductor with hemispherical ends will be found to have a greater **surface density** of charge at the ends and least where the curvature is least. This is shown still more strikingly with the pear-shaped conductor where the surface density on the tip is very large. Now the air, although a moderately good insulator for small surface densities, becomes less good for large ones, and consequently points and sharp edges must be avoided on conductors which are required to retain electrostatic charges.

8. Unit Charge.

In order to provide a measure of the quantity of electricity on a conductor, the unit charge requires definition.   This is assumed to be a quantity of electricity which is concentrated on a conducting sphere of extremely small dimensions, so that for most practical problems the charge may be considered to be concentrated in a point at the centre of the sphere. **The magnitude of the electrostatic unit charge is such that it will repel an equal like charge at a distance of 1 cm. with a force of 1 dyne.** If any charge is designated by $\pm\,q$ it is implied that it contains q unit charges of positive or negative electricity, and that it would repel a unit charge of the same sign placed at a distance of 1 cm. with a force of q dynes. Such a direct measurement of the magnitude of a charge is most unsuitable in practice; actual methods depend on a much fuller development of electrostatic theory.

9. Electric Field and Lines of Force.

Electrical forces, like light, are propagated freely across a vacuum. Consequently **action at a distance** occurs, that is, mechanical movements may be produced by electrical forces which have no apparent

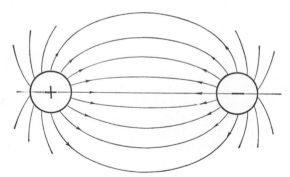

Fig. 6. — Lines of Force: Attraction

means of connexion with the body moved. To " explain " such behaviour, that is, to enable a mechanical picture to be constructed of the process by which the electrical forces work, Faraday stressed the conception of lines and tubes of force. He supposed that there emanate from all electrical charges myriads of lines of force, visualized as stretched strings. With two equal charges of opposite sign these lines of force stretch from one charge to the other in the manner shown in fig. 6. Under the elastic tension in the lines the charges are drawn together. Repulsion was explained as due to lateral repulsion between neighbouring lines of force, and the repulsion between two like charges is assumed to take place as illustrated in fig. 7. This concept has been of great value in providing a mechanical picture of the production of electromagnetic waves (see Chap. XVI).

The region of electric force around any charge or group of charges is referred to as an **electric field.** An electric field may be considered to consist of myriads of lines of force. Now the *direction* of the field at any point is the direction in which a unit charge is urged when it is placed at that point. Hence **a line of force may be defined as an imaginary line drawn in the electric field showing the direction of the electric force at all points on the line.** As so defined there are clearly an infinite

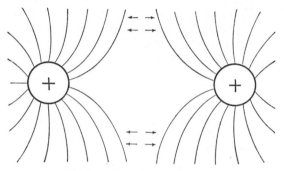

Fig. 7. — Lines of Force: Repulsion

number of lines of force in an electric field. For reasons we shall discuss later, it is often convenient to consider a **tube of force** rather than a line of force. This is simply a volume of space bounded by and containing a large number of lines of force. In section 11 we show that there are 4π tubes of force arising from a unit charge.

The lines of force arising from a conductor must cut the conductor at right angles or **orthogonally,** since otherwise the force would have a component parallel to the surface of the conductor and the charge would move across the surface and would no longer be static.

10. Inverse Square Law.

The force of attraction or repulsion between two electric charges varies inversely as the square of the distance between the charges and is directly proportional to the product of the two charges. The validity of this law was early demonstrated with the torsion balance by Coulomb. The principle of the experiment was similar to that used by Boys for determining the gravitational constant in Chap. VI, Part I. Owing to the leakage of the charges, however, the accuracy is very poor and the experiment is only of historical interest. The accepted test of the law is an indirect one based on the experimer tal fact that there is no electrical force inside a closed conductor. The fact can be shown to be consistent only with the inverse square law, but here we will be content to prove the converse, viz. that if the inverse square law be assumed, then the experimental fact follows.

Consider a conducting sphere charged with a uniform surface density of electrification σ as shown in fig. 8. Then the effect on a unit charge placed at any arbitrary point inside the sphere is due to the action of all the elements of charge situated over the surface of the sphere. Consider the elements of surface cut off by the cones of

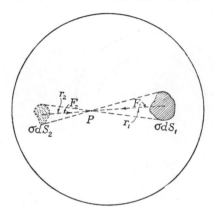

Fig. 8. — The Inverse Square Law

small solid angle with vertices at P. If the force is proportional to r^{-2}, where r is the distance from the element of charge, then according to fig. 8 the charge experiences two opposite directed repulsions F_1 and F_2, where

$$F_1 = \frac{\sigma\,dS_1}{r_1{}^2}$$

and
$$F_2 = \frac{\sigma\,dS_2}{r_2{}^2}, \quad \cdots \cdots \cdots (2.1)$$

where dS_1 and dS_2 are the areas cut off by the cones of approximate altitudes r_1 and r_2.

Now by the geometrical properties of similar cones

$$\frac{dS_1}{dS_2} = \left(\frac{r_1}{r_2}\right)^2, \quad \cdots \cdots \cdots (2.2)$$

and hence from (2.1) and (2.2),

$$F_1 = F_2.$$

Since the whole space within the sphere can be divided into pairs of cones such as these considered, with vertex at P, it follows that there is no resultant force on the charge at P.

The experiment was first carried out accurately by Cavendish, and repeated in an improved form by Maxwell, who used an apparatus as in fig. 9. A certain charge was communicated to the inner conducting sphere A, and this was registered on an electroscope. The two spheres A and B were then momentarily connected, and it was found that although the electroscope registered a deflection when it was connected to B, it failed to register any electrical force when connected to any part of A although the latter was surrounded with a sphere of electrical charge. Using spheres of different radii for A, it is easily

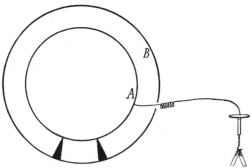

Fig. 9. — Experiment of Cavendish and Maxwell

shown that there is no electrical force at any point inside a closed charged conductor. The success of the test depends, of course, upon using only a small aperture in B through which to insert the test wire. Expressed mathematically, therefore, the inverse square law may be written

$$F = \frac{q_1 q_2}{d^2}, \quad \cdots \cdots \quad (2.3)$$

where q_1, q_2 are the two charges, *regarded as points*, and d is the distance between them.

If the space between and around the point charges is other than air, or more strictly, other than a vacuum, the force is found experimentally to be reduced. This reduction is characteristic for a given material which is termed a **dielectric,** and the **dielectric constant** k must be introduced in the force equation, thus:

$$F = \frac{q_1 q_2}{k d^2}. \quad \cdots \cdots \quad (2.4)$$

Further discussion of dielectric constants is given in Chaps. III and IV.

11. Electrostatic Potential.

In dynamics the concept of energy is of great value in solving problems, as an alternative method to working from first principles with force concepts. Similarly, in electrostatic problems it is convenient to deal with the electrical potential energy (or electrical potential as it is briefly called) in the field due to an electric charge. A unit charge, of the same sign as the fixed charge q in fig. 10, has a potential (energy) at a point P, a distance r from q, equal to the kinetic energy which the unit charge would derive in being repelled from r to infinity. This kinetic energy is clearly equal to the work done in the reverse process of forcing the unit charge from an infinite distance up to the point r against the mutual repulsion.

While mathematically the potential falls to zero only at an infinite distance from the charge, in practice, any body which is connected to earth is considered to be at zero potential. In the majority of instances

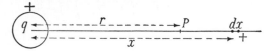

Fig. 10. — Potential due to Point Charge

the earth acts as a perfect sink of charge and consequently reduces all charged bodies placed in communication with it to its own zero potential.

To calculate the potential at r, we note that the element of potential dV gained when the unit charge is moved from x to $(x - dx)$ from q is

$$dV = \text{force} \times \text{distance} = F_x(-dx), \quad . . \quad (2.5)$$

$$= \frac{q}{x^2}(-dx). \quad . . . . \quad (2.6)$$

The potential at r (in electrostatic units) is therefore

$$V_r = \int_\infty^r \frac{q}{x^2}(-dx) = \left[\frac{q}{x}\right]_\infty^r$$

$$= \frac{q}{r}. \quad . . . . \quad (2.7)$$

The **potential therefore varies inversely as the distance from a point charge.** The surfaces of equal potential will therefore be spheres, and since the lines of force from an isolated point charge are radial the appearance will be as in fig. 11. This diagram is an example of a general principle that the **lines of force cut the equipotential surfaces orthogonally.** The conducting surface of a charged conductor is therefore an equipotential surface. This deduction also follows from physical reasoning, since if different potentials occurred throughout the same conductor, charge would flow from regions of high to regions of low potential, just as water flows from high to low level (compare equation (2.5)).

Equation (2.5) may be written

$$F_x = -\frac{\partial V}{\partial x}. \quad \ldots \ldots \ldots \quad (2.8)$$

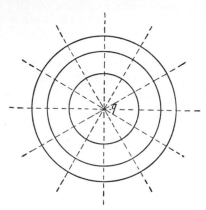

Fig. 11. — Field round Point Charge

When the potential is known, it is often very convenient to derive the forces on systems in any direction by partial differentiation of the potential with respect to that direction.

12. Gauss's Theorem.

In much the same way that potential is a useful tool derived mathematically from the law of force, so Gauss's theorem is a convenient alternative statement of the force law, of great value in mathematical problems in electrostatics. Consider the point charge q in fig. 12 to be enclosed by a surface of arbitrary shape. If the mean electrostatic force component normal to any small area dS is F, the **normal induction** through that surface element is defined as $F \cdot dS$. Gauss's theorem states that the **total normal induction through any surface completely enclosing a charge is ($4\pi \times$ charge enclosed), while through any surface enclosing no charge it is zero.**

To prove this, consider the contribution to the T.N.I. made by the elementary cone shown in fig. 13. This is

$$\Delta \mathrm{T.N.I.} = F_1 \cos\theta_1 \, dS_1. \quad \ldots \ldots \quad (2.9)$$

Now from solid geometry, the elementary solid angle $d\omega$ is defined by

$$d\omega = \frac{dS_1 \cos \theta_1}{r_1^2}. \quad \cdots \cdots (2.10)$$

Hence

$$\Delta \text{T.N.I.} = F_1 \, d\omega r_1^2. \quad \cdots \cdots (2.11)$$

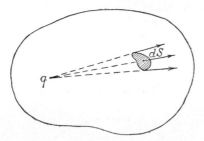

Fig. 12. — Induction through a Surface

But, from the inverse square law,

$$F_1 = \frac{q}{r_1^2}. \quad \cdots \cdots (2.12)$$

Hence from (2.11) and (2.12)

$$\Delta \text{T.N.I.} = q \, d\omega.$$

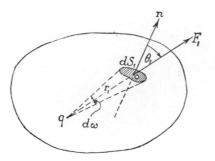

Fig. 13. — Gauss's Theorem

The total normal induction is therefore the product of the whole solid angle subtended by the enclosing surface at the charge, multiplied by the charge itself. Hence

$$\text{T.N.I.} = 4\pi q. \quad \cdots \cdots (2.13)$$

If the charge is situated outside the closed surface, the total normal induction is zero, for the angle between the outward normal and the force may be either acute or obtuse, and the contributions to the T.N.I. from any elementary cone, with vertex at q, are alternately positive and negative, but of the same numerical value.

As an example of Gauss's theorem, we shall deduce that for points *outside* a charged sphere the forces are equal to those which would be produced by a point charge equal to the charge on the sphere and situated at its centre. Consider a point P situated a distance x from the centre of a sphere S of radius r and charge q, as shown in fig. 14. Then to determine the force at P, construct an imaginary sphere of radius x passing through P and concentric with S. The total normal induction through the outer sphere is

$$\text{T.N.I.} = F \cdot 4\pi x^2.$$

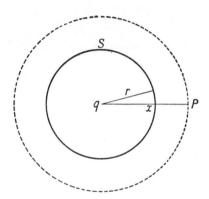

Fig. 14. — Force due to Charged Sphere

Now by Gauss's theorem,

$$\text{T.N.I.} = 4\pi q.$$

Hence
$$F = \frac{q}{x^2},$$

or the charge produces a force at P equal to that which would be produced if the charge q were concentrated at the centre of the sphere.

EXERCISES

1. Describe experiments which show that equal and opposite quantities of electricity may be produced by (a) friction, (b) induction.

2. Explain what factors govern the distribution of electricity over the surface of conductors. How is the corona discharge caused and how is it reduced?

3. Define (a) unit charge, (b) strength of an electric field. Quote examples illustrating the use of the conception of lines and tubes of force in understanding electrical phenomena.

4. Upon what evidence is it assumed that the law of force between two electrical charges varies inversely as the square of their distance apart?

5. Define electrical potential at a point and calculate the potential at a point a distance r from a point charge q. Of what value is the potential concept in electrical theory?

6. State and prove Gauss's theorem as applied to electrostatic forces and use the theorem to show that for points external to a charged sphere the forces exerted are the same as would be produced if all the charge were concentrated at the centre of the sphere.

7. Show that if a line of force starts from a charge e_1, in a direction making an angle α with a straight line joining e_1 to a second charge e_2 (of opposite sign), this line of force meets e_2 at an angle β given by

$$e_1 \sin^2 \frac{\alpha}{2} = e_2 \sin^2 \frac{\beta}{2}.$$

[Consider the induction through cones of semi-vertical angles α and β at the two charges.]

CHAPTER III

Electrostatics

1. Capacity.

The potential of a charged sphere of radius r and charge q is q/r, from equation (2.7), and hence the ratio

$$\frac{\text{charge}}{\text{potential}} = r = \text{constant.} \quad \ldots \ldots \quad (3.1)$$

This relation, that the potential is directly proportional to the charge for a given conductor, holds quite generally, and the ratio is defined as the **capacity** of the conductor. Since then

$$C = \frac{Q}{V}, \quad \ldots \ldots \ldots \quad (3.2)$$

by putting $V = 1$ we may define the capacity alternatively as **the charge required to raise the potential of the conductor by unit amount.** The capacity of a sphere (in electrostatic units) is, from (3.1), equal to its radius and is therefore measured in centimetres on the C.G.S. system of units. The capacity of any system of given form is proportional to the first power of its linear dimensions.

2. Condensers.

It is usual to reserve the term electrical condenser for a system composed of two charged surfaces one of which is charged and insulated, while the other, which is earthed, acquires by induction an equal and opposite charge. For example, two parallel plates or two concentric spheres might constitute a condenser. The capacity of a condenser, as opposed to that of an isolated conductor, will depend on the proximity of the insulated and earthed plates of the condenser as well as upon their linear dimensions. We calculate below the capacities of various systems of practical importance.

The method is to calculate the potential V due to a charge Q on the condenser, and then form the ratio Q/V, which is by definition the capacity.

(i) *Two Concentric Spheres, Inner Sphere Insulated, Outer Sphere
   Earthed.*

The charge $+Q$ on the inner insulated sphere induces an equal and
opposite charge $-Q$ on the inside of the outer sphere as shown in
fig. 1.   The outer sphere, being earth connected, is at zero potential;
we wish to calculate the potential of the inner sphere due to the two
charges $+Q$ and $-Q$.   The potential due to the inner sphere itself is
equal to the potential at its centre, i.e.

$$V_1 = \frac{Q}{a}, \qquad \cdots \cdots \cdots \quad (3.3)$$

for the potential at all points *inside* a closed conductor is the same and
equal to that at the surface of the conductor.   This follows from the
experimental fact that there is no force anywhere inside a closed conductor (Chap. II, section 10), for by equation (2.8) the force is equal

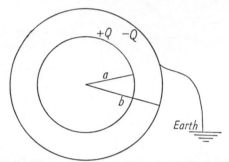

Fig. 1. — Capacity of Spherical Shell (Outer Sphere Earthed)

to the rate of change of potential with distance and since the force is
zero there can be no change in potential.   By the same argument, the
potential of the inner sphere due to the charge $-Q$ on the outer sphere
is therefore the same as the potential of the outer sphere due to its
own charge, that is

$$V_2 = \frac{-Q}{b}. \qquad \cdots \cdots \cdots \quad (3.4)$$

The total potential of the inner sphere is

$$V = V_1 + V_2 = Q\left(\frac{1}{a} - \frac{1}{b}\right), \qquad \cdots \cdots \quad (3.5)$$

and the capacity of the system is therefore

$$C = \frac{Q}{V} = \frac{ab}{(b-a)}. \qquad \cdots \cdots \cdots \quad (3.6)$$

The capacity is inversely proportional to the distance between the
conductors composing the spherical condenser.

(ii) *Two Concentric Spheres, Inner Sphere Earthed, Outer Sphere Insulated.*

In the previous example, all the lines of force which arose from the central charged sphere cut the outer sphere, and hence the induced charge was equal and opposite to the inducing charge. With the outer sphere insulated and the inner sphere earthed, however, only some of the lines of force proceed inwards to the inner sphere, a large number going outwards to the walls as shown in fig. 2. The induced charge $-q$ is therefore only a fraction of the inducing charge $+Q$, and before we can calculate the potential V of the outer sphere

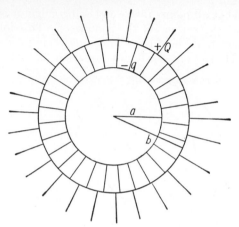

Fig. 2. — Capacity of Spherical Shell (Inner Sphere Earthed)

we require to calculate q in terms of Q. This is accomplished by considering that under the influence of the two charges, the potential of the inner sphere is zero. Hence, from the previous example,

$$0 = -\frac{q}{a} + \frac{Q}{b},$$

or
$$q = Q\frac{a}{b}. \quad \cdots \cdots \cdots \quad (3.7)$$

The potential of the outer sphere is therefore

$$V = \frac{Q}{b} - \frac{q}{b}$$

$$= Q\frac{(b-a)}{b^2};$$

and
$$C = \frac{Q}{V} = \frac{b^2}{(b-a)}. \quad \cdots \cdots \quad (3.8)$$

(iii) *Parallel Plate Condenser.*

If a spherical condenser is imagined to expand indefinitely until its radius becomes very large compared with the separation of the two conductors, it will approach the case of a parallel plate condenser of infinite extent. Hence, putting $b = a$ in the numerator but not in the denominator of (3.6) and (3.8), we have

$$C = \frac{a^2}{t}, \quad \ldots \ldots \ldots \quad (3.9)$$

where $t = (b - a)$.

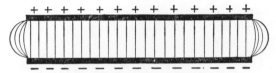

Fig. 3. — Parallel Plate Condenser

Since the area of the surface of the sphere is $4\pi a^2 = S$, equation (3.9) becomes $C = S/4\pi t$. The capacity for a finite area A is therefore

$$C = \frac{A}{4\pi t}, \quad \ldots \ldots \ldots \quad (3.10)$$

which is the required formula for the capacity of a parallel plate condenser, where A is the area of either plate, and t is the distance between them. As shown in fig. 3, the lines of force will be perpendicular to the plates in the central regions but will curve at the edges owing to the attraction of the walls of the room. The formula is in error in so far as it neglects this edge effect, but the correction is small if the ratios of plate length and breadth to plate separation is kept large.

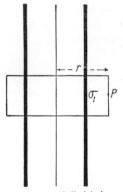

Fig. 4. — Cylindrical Condenser

*(iv) *Cylindrical Condenser.*

The case of two concentric cylinders is of great practical importance since cables and lines generally occur in this form. We first require to calculate the potential at any point a distance r from the common axis of the two cylinders. As in fig. 4, let the charge *per unit length* of the cylinder be σ_1. Then the force at a point P is found by constructing a concentric cylindrical surface through P and applying Gauss's theorem. If the force at P is F, the total normal induction

$$\text{T.N.I.} = F \times (2\pi r \times 1) = 4\pi\sigma_1.$$

Hence

$$F = \frac{2\sigma_1}{r}. \quad \ldots \ldots \ldots \quad (3.11)$$

The force due to a charged cylinder of infinite length therefore falls off inversely as the distance from the axis of the cylinder. With a cylinder of finite length the lines of force are no longer perpendicular to the axis of the cylinder and an error is involved as with the parallel plate condenser of finite extent. This error is again small if the distance r from the cylinder is small compared with its length.

The difference in potential between any two points r_1 and r_2 from the axis of the cylinder is calculated by the method of Chap. II, section 11. We therefore have

$$(V_{r_1} - V_{r_2}) = \int_{r_2}^{r_1} F_r(-dr) = -\int_{r_2}^{r_1} \frac{2\sigma_1}{r}\, dr$$

$$= 2\sigma_1 \log_e \frac{r_2}{r_1}. \quad \ldots \ldots \ldots \quad (3.12)$$

Hence, the capacity of a length l of a cylindrical condenser is given by

$$C = \frac{\sigma_1}{V} = \frac{l}{2 \log_e (b/a)}. \quad \ldots \ldots \quad (3.13)$$

2. Electric Force between Two Charged Plates.

The lines of force are parallel (fig. 3). By applying Gauss's Theorem (p. 15) to a cylinder with ends perpendicular to these lines, we find that the force is everywhere of the same magnitude. If we represent the force by F, the work done in taking a unit charge from one plate to the other is

$$V = Ft, \quad \ldots \ldots \ldots \ldots \quad (3.14)$$

and this work is by definition equal to the potential difference V between the two plates. Now since

$$V = \frac{Q}{C},$$

we have, by (3.10),

$$V = (A\sigma)\frac{4\pi t}{A}, \quad \ldots \ldots \quad (3.15)$$

$$= 4\pi\sigma t,$$

where σ is the surface density of charge *per unit area* of the plates. (Compare σ_1 in (3.11).) Hence from (3.14) and (3.15)

$$F = 4\pi\sigma. \quad \ldots \ldots \ldots \quad (3.16)$$

Each plate contributes symmetrically to the total force and hence **the force close to a single charged plate is**

$$F = 2\pi\sigma. \qquad \ldots \ldots \quad (3.17)$$

3. Mechanical Force of Attraction between Two Flat Condenser Plates.

The following device enables us to calculate the mechanical force of attraction between two condenser plates. Imagine a unit charge to be situated in a small hole in one condenser plate as shown in fig. 5. Then the force on this charge arises entirely from the other plate, since this alone gives rise to lines of force passing through the hole. Hence the force on the charge is

$$F = 2\pi\sigma \times 1.$$

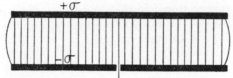

Fig. 5. — Attraction between two Condenser Plates

If the hole is replaced by an element of surface dA with charge density σ, the force becomes

$$F = 2\pi\sigma^2 dA,$$

and hence the total force of attraction between the plates is

$$F = 2\pi\sigma^2 A. \qquad \ldots \ldots \quad (3.18)$$

4. Energy Stored in a Charged Condenser.

The energy stored in a charged condenser is equal to the work done in the process of forcing the charge on to the plates against the repul-

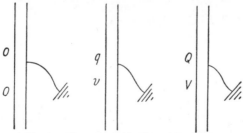

Fig. 6. — Energy stored in Charged Condenser

sion of the charge which has already been communicated. In fig. 6 we illustrate three conditions: (*a*) when the charge and potential are zero; (b) some intermediate stage in the process when the charge and potential are q and v respectively; and (c) the fully charged state, with final values Q and V. The element of work done in communicating a further charge dq when the existing potential is v is

$$dW = v\,dq;$$

for by definition, the potential v is the work done in bringing **unit** charge to the system, and hence the work done in bringing an element of charge dq is vdq. The total work done in raising the charge from 0 to Q is therefore

$$W = \int_0^Q v\,dq, \quad \ldots \ldots \ldots \text{(3.19)}$$

and this is the energy stored in the condenser. Since v varies with q, equation (3.19) cannot be integrated directly, but the capacity C of the system is constant throughout and

$$C = \frac{q}{v}. \quad \ldots \ldots \ldots \text{(3.20)}$$

Substituting for v from (3.20) in (3.19) we therefore have

$$W = \int_0^Q \frac{q}{C}\,dq$$

$$= \tfrac{1}{2}\frac{Q^2}{C}. \quad \ldots \ldots \ldots \text{(3.21)}$$

Since $C = Q/V$, equation (3.21) may alternatively be expressed in the forms:

$$W = \tfrac{1}{2}QV = \tfrac{1}{2}CV^2. \quad \ldots \ldots \text{(3.22)}$$

5. Capacities in Parallel and in Series.

The total capacity of two condensers connected in parallel is equal to the sum of their separate capacities. Connexion in parallel implies that the earthed plates have a common connexion and the insulated plates another common connexion as shown in fig. 7. Since the effect is simply to enlarge the areas of the insulated and earthed plates respectively, the proposition is obvious physically. Mathematically we have, with reference to fig. 7,

$$Q = Q_1 + Q_2 = VC, \quad \ldots \ldots \text{(3.23)}$$

where C is the final total capacity.

Again,

$$Q_1 = VC_1,$$
$$Q_2 = VC_2,$$

whence, by addition and use of (3.23),

$$C = C_1 + C_2. \quad \ldots \ldots \quad (3.24)$$

The reasoning clearly applies to any number of condensers.

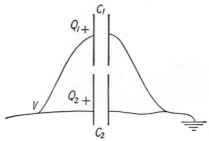

Fig. 7. — Capacities in Parallel

In fig. 8 two condensers are connected in series. In series connexion only one plate is earthed and the potentials of the other plates increase each time we pass across a condenser. The two insulated middle plates are connected, and are therefore at the same potential. Since they are initially uncharged, the total charge on them is zero. The charges facing each other on the interior faces of the plates of the condensers all have the values $\pm Q$ (fig. 8). (There may in addition be a charge

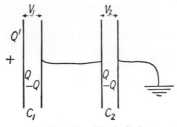

Fig. 8. — Capacities in Series

Q' on the outer surface of the left-hand plate.) Then, if the potential drops are as shown in fig. 8,

$$V_1 = \frac{Q}{C_1},$$

$$V_2 = \frac{Q}{C_2},$$

so that the total fall in potential is

$$V = V_1 + V_2 = Q\left(\frac{1}{C_1} + \frac{1}{C_2}\right). \quad \cdots \quad (3.25)$$

Now the total capacity of the system is defined by

$$C = \frac{Q}{V}. \quad \cdots \cdots \cdots \quad (3.26)$$

Hence from (3.25) and (3.26)

$$\frac{1}{C} = \frac{1}{C_1} + \frac{1}{C_2}. \quad \cdots \cdots \quad (3.27)$$

6. Effect of Dielectrics.

The preceding calculations have been based on Gauss's thorem, that is upon a mathematical formulation of the inverse square law. We have already stated in Chap. II, section 10, that should the charges be embedded in material of dielectric constant k, the force is reduced, being inversely proportional to k. Since the force is the rate of charge of potential with distance, the potential is likewise reduced and the potential at a distance r from a point charge q in an infinite dielectric of dielectric constant k is

$$V = \frac{q}{kr}. \quad \cdots \cdots \cdots \quad (3.28)$$

Now the capacity is by definition the ratio of the charge to the potential, and since the former is independent of the dielectric, the capacity must be directly proportional to the dielectric constant. Should therefore the space between the plates of a condenser be completely filled with dielectric, the capacity becomes k times its previous value. In fact the most convenient method of defining the *dielectric constant is that it is the ratio of the capacities of a condenser when the space separating the plates is filled with the dielectric and when it is a vacuum, respectively.*

If the insulated plate is removed with insulating tongs from a charged condenser filled with dielectric, then it will be found that only a fraction of the charge is removed with the plate. If the plate is now replaced, the charge it acquires on contact with the dielectric will be almost equal to the original charge. This experiment shows that the charge is absorbed by the dielectric somewhat as a sponge absorbs water. The penetration is small, as is shown by the fact that it is readily given back to the plate when it is replaced. Dielectrics differ considerably amongst themselves in this property of absorption, which is a function of the molecular structure of the material. The phenomenon is associated with the electrical hysteresis (see Chap. XV) of the specimen.

In terms of the electron theory a good insulator is a material in which the electrons move with extreme difficulty. The negative charges on the condenser plate do, however, move a *short* distance into the dielectric, and similarly the electrons in the dielectric move a *short* distance out of the material towards the positive plate. This general drift extends throughout the entire dielectric, which consequently develops charges of opposite sign on its two surfaces and is said to be in a state of *electrical strain*. The commonly used dielectrics such as mica and ebonite have dielectric constants lying between 1 and 10. These substances are insulators, but conductors also have dielectric properties. Indeed, water has the abnormally high value of 80 for its dielectric constant. The measurement of dielectric constants is described in the next chapter.

EXERCISES

1. Define the term " capacity of a conductor ".
Regarding the earth as a sphere of radius $2 \times 10^9/\pi$ cm., show that its electrical capacity is about 700 microfarads. (1 microfarad $= 9 \times 10^5$ electrostatic units.)

2. Distinguish between the electrical force in the region between two flat condenser plates and the mechanical force of attraction between the plates, and show that the ratio of these two magnitudes is $2/\sigma A$, where A is the area of one of the plates and σ is the surface density of charge.

3. Obtain an expression for the electrical energy stored in a charged condenser of any type. Deduce the same result for the special case of a spherical conductor by the principle of virtual work.

4. Show that when two equal condensers are connected in parallel the system has four times the capacity of that obtained when the condensers are connected in series.

5. Explain fully the meaning of the term " dielectric constant " of a material. Upon what factors does the value of the dielectric constant depend?

CHAPTER IV

Electrostatic Measurements

1. Introduction.

For measuring small charges and potentials the gold-leaf electroscope is very suitable, as the charged system may be made extremely small and therefore of small capacity. However, for many purposes a more robust instrument is required, and electrometers and electrostatic voltmeters satisfy this requirement.

*2. Quadrant Electrometer.

The quadrant electrometer, as shown in fig. 1, consists of a flat cylindrical brass pillbox B divided into four separate quadrants. Between the top and bottom of the quadrants is a light paddle C of

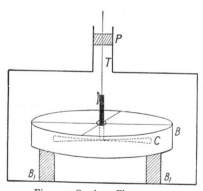

Fig. 1. — Quadrant Electrometer

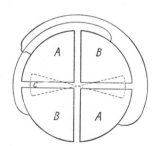

Fig. 2. — Quadrant Electrometer:
Connections

aluminium suspended by a delicate torsion fibre T of phosphor bronze. The latter is insulated from the rest of the instrument by an amber plug P, and the brass quadrants likewise are supported on amber blocks B_1. Opposite pairs of quadrants are connected as shown in fig. 2, and the paddle may either be completely insulated from them or may be connected with either pair of quadrants as required.

When the quadrants and paddle acquire electric charges, electrostatic forces are set up which rotate the paddle until an equal and

558

opposite torque is introduced by the suspension. The deflection is magnified by reflection of light from a mirror attached rigidly to the paddle.

Let V_A, V_B and V_C be the potentials of the two pairs of quadrants and paddle respectively, and suppose the paddle twists through an angle θ so that it passes towards the quadrants A and away from B. The capacity of the A-C system is increased and that of the B-C system is decreased by an amount $P\theta$, where P is a constant. Then the change in electrical potential energy of the system is, from (3.22),

$$W_E = \tfrac{1}{2}P\theta(V_1{}^2 - V_2{}^2)$$
$$= \tfrac{1}{2}P\theta\{(V_C - V_B)^2 - (V_C - V_A)^2\}$$
$$= P\theta(V_A - V_B)\left(V_C - \frac{V_A + V_B}{2}\right), \quad \text{. . (4.1)}$$

where $V_1 = (V_C - V_B)$ and $V_2 = (V_C - V_A)$.

The gain in potential energy of the suspension is

$$W_G = \int_0^\theta G\theta \cdot d\theta = \tfrac{1}{2}G\theta^2, \quad \text{. . . . (4.2)}$$

where G is the couple required to produce unit angle of twist. Now the sources of supply to which the quadrants and paddle are connected will have supplied energy at *constant* potentials V_A, V_B and V_C respectively. Consequently in equation (3.19) the integration may be effected directly with v constant and will give

$$W = QV = CV^2 = Q^2/C, \quad \text{. . . . (4.3)}$$

which is *twice* the value obtained when the charged conductors are not connected to steady sources of potential. This energy derived from the source will therefore be equal to the sum of (4.1) and (4.2) and will actually be numerically equal to twice (4.1). We therefore have

$$W = W_G + W_E,$$

that is,

$$2P\theta(V_A - V_B)\left(V_C - \frac{V_A + V_B}{2}\right)$$
$$= \tfrac{1}{2}G\theta^2 + P\theta(V_A - V_B)\left(V_C - \frac{V_A + V_B}{2}\right),$$

or

$$\theta = K(V_A - V_B)\left(V_C - \frac{V_A + V_B}{2}\right), \quad \text{. . . (4.4)}$$

where $K = 2P/G = $ constant.

The constant K, which involves the linear dimensions of the apparatus, cannot be accurately calculated and consequently the instrument is *not absolute* but requires calibration with sources of known potential. The two points whose potential difference is required are

connected to A and B respectively, and the paddle C is connected
either (1) to an independent potential of much greater magnitude than
either V_A or V_B, or (2) to A or B. The former or *heterostatic arrangement* is most frequently used for measuring steady potentials. The
steady potential difference is connected across A and B while the
paddle C is connected to a separate and much higher potential. Since
then $V_C \gg V_A$ or V_B, if small potentials are being measured,

$$\left(V_C - \frac{V_A + V_B}{2}\right) \simeq V_C = \text{constant};$$

so that equation (4.4) becomes

$$\theta = K'(V_A - V_B), \quad \ldots \ldots \quad (4.5)$$

where $K' = KV_C = \text{constant}$. The potential difference is therefore
directly proportional to the deflection.

If the potential to be measured across A and B is alternating, the
previous arrangement will show no deflection, for the paddle is alternately attracted and repelled by a given pair
of quadrants too rapidly for it to respond.
A unidirectional effect is produced by connecting the paddle to either A or B so that
$V_C = V_A$, say. Then equation (4.4) becomes

$$\theta = \frac{K}{2}(V_A - V_B)^2. \quad . \quad (4.6)$$

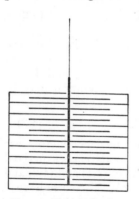

Fig. 3. — Multiple Quadrant
Electrometer

The deflection is now proportional to the
square of the potential difference and its
direction is therefore independent of the sign
of the potential. Physically, the quadrant
and leaves which are connected together
always acquire charge of the same sign
simultaneously and therefore always exert a
mutual repulsion.

By increasing the number of paddles and quadrant boxes, as shown
in fig. 3, the deflection may be proportionately magnified. A more
robust suspension then becomes possible without decrease of sensitivity and such instruments constitute **electrostatic voltmeters.**

3. Attracted Disk or Absolute Electrometer.

In fig. 4 is shown a diagram of the attracted disk electrometer. This
instrument requires careful manipulation and consequently is used
only for standard calibrations. It consists of two flat circular condenser plates P_1 and P_2 set horizontally. One plate is suspended by
inclined strings from a balance arm which can be suitably counter-

poised. The other plate is insulated and attached to a micrometer
screw M so that the distance between the two plates can be varied.
When a potential difference is applied between the plates, an attraction takes place between the equal and opposite charges acquired by
the plates, the force of attraction being

$$F = 2\pi\sigma^2 A,$$

according to equation (3.18).

This force is directly measured from the value of the counterpoise
on the opposite arm of the balance and hence

$$F = mg = 2\pi\sigma^2 A. \quad . \quad . \quad . \quad . \quad (4.7)$$

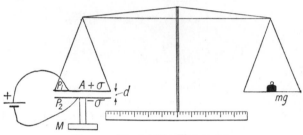

Fig. 4. — Attracted Disk Electrometer

Since m, g and A are known, σ can be calculated **absolutely** from
(4.7). Finally since the potential difference V between the two plates
is given by

$$V = 4\pi\sigma d,$$

equation (4.7) may be written

$$V = 4\pi d\sqrt{\frac{mg}{2\pi A}}. \quad . \quad . \quad . \quad . \quad . \quad (4.8)$$

It is much easier to achieve a balance by varying d than by varying
m, and consequently the final adjustment is made with the micrometer
screw.

Since the calculations apply to the attraction between two plates
when the lines of force *all* run perpendicular to the plates, a correction
is necessary for the curvature of the peripheral lines if the apparatus
is as in fig. 4. In practice, the use of a correction is avoided by using
annular metal guard rings (not shown) in the plane of the plates. The
gap between the plates and the rings is very small and the moving
plates behave essentially as the central portion of larger plates. The
lines of force are therefore all practically perpendicular to the moving
plates.

4. Measurement of Dielectric Constant.

As an example of the use of the quadrant electrometer we shall describe the determination of the dielectric constant of a slab of material. We require a parallel plate condenser which fits the slab; the capacity C_1 of this condenser is calculated from equation (3.10) when the area of the plates and the plate separation have been measured. It is first essential to determine the capacity C_E of the electrometer itself. The electrometer is initially charged with an unknown charge Q which gives a deflection θ_1. This charge is then shared with the condenser and the deflection falls to θ_2. Introducing a constant of proportionality P, we have

$$Q = C_E \,.\, P\theta_1 = (C_E + C_1)P\theta_2,$$

whence

$$C_E = C_1 \frac{\theta_2}{(\theta_1 - \theta_2)}. \qquad \cdots \cdots \cdots \quad (4.9)$$

The slab of dielectric is then inserted and the deflection falls still farther to θ_3 as the capacity of the condenser increases to C_2, where the dielectric constant k is defined by $k = C_2/C_1$. By analogy with our deduction of (4.9) we have

$$Q = C_E \,.\, P\theta_1 = (C_2 + C_E)P\theta_3,$$

whence

$$C_2 = C_E \frac{(\theta_1 - \theta_3)}{\theta_3}, \qquad \cdots \cdots \cdots \quad (4.10)$$

and from (4.9) and (4.10)

$$C_2 = \frac{C_1 \theta_2}{\theta_3} \frac{(\theta_1 - \theta_3)}{(\theta_1 - \theta_2)},$$

or

$$k = \frac{C_2}{C_1} = \frac{\theta_2}{\theta_3} \frac{(\theta_1 - \theta_3)}{(\theta_1 - \theta_2)}. \qquad \cdots \cdots \quad (4.11)$$

The dielectric constant of gases and conducting liquids is found by filling a container with the fluid and inserting it as a close fit in the condenser. The correction due to the container itself is found by a subsidiary experiment. The dielectric constant of a gas is directly proportional to the pressure over a wide range.

These values of the dielectric constant are for a steady electric field between the plates. If the field is varying (see Chap. XV) the dielectric constant is a function of the frequency of the electrical oscillations. This is because the electrical strain set up in the dielectric takes a finite time to change when the field variation takes place.

5. Electrostatic Units of Measurement.

We have already defined the *electrostatic unit charge* (p. 539); it remains to specify units of potential and capacity.

Unit electrostatic potential difference is said to exist between two points when one erg of work is done in transferring one electrostatic unit of charge from one point to the other.

The *unit of capacity in the electrostatic system* is the capacity of a condenser in which electrostatic unit charge is associated with electrostatic unit difference of potential; it has the dimensions of a length, and therefore may be said to be 1 cm.

When electromagnetic phenomena have been considered we shall find that a second system of units, the **electromagnetic system,** arises quite naturally from the phenomena considered. Owing to the physical connexion between electrostatic and electromagnetic phenomena these two systems of units are interrelated and it is frequently necessary to convert from one system to the other.

In practice, the potentials, charges, currents and other electrical quantities involved are often of a magnitude which is of a different order from the units defined in the electrostatic and electromagnetic systems. There is therefore a third or **practical system of units.** The subject is discussed more fully in Chap. VIII.

EXERCISES

1. Describe the quadrant electrometer and explain how it may be used to measure (*a*) alternating potential, (*b*) direct potential.

2. Compare and contrast the gold-leaf electroscope and the quadrant electrometer as potential measuring instruments.

3. Describe the operation of the attracted disk electrometer, deducing any formulæ required from first principles.

CHAPTER V

Electrostatic Machines

1. The Electrophorus.

The amount of electricity which can be obtained by friction with cat's fur on an ebonite rod is very limited, and consequently machines have been devised to supply larger quantities of electricity at higher potentials. The simplest of these devices is the electrophorus, a diagram of which is shown in fig. 1. It consists essentially of a flat ebonite disk D, the upper surface of which is electrified by friction with cat's fur in the usual fashion. A flat brass covering disk C fitted with an insulating handle rests on the excited ebonite disk and a charge is conveyed to C by induction. This, of course, necessitates earthing C

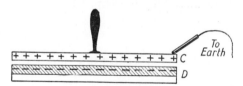

Fig. 1. — Electrophorus

while it is in close proximity to D, either by touching it with the finger or by the automatic device of a short brass rod passing vertically through the ebonite disk and connecting the top brass plate with another brass plate lying underneath the ebonite disk. When the covering plate has been charged by induction it is removed by the insulating handle and gives up its charge to a condenser. The disk C is then returned to the ebonite disk, which throughout the process has retained its original charge, and the whole operation is repeated. In this way, theoretically an infinite charge may be taken away on the brass disk. The electrical energy is derived from the mechanical energy required to separate the opposite induced and inducing charges. In practice, the charge which may be conveyed to a given condenser is limited by the rise in potential of that condenser as the charging process continues. A time arrives when the potential acquired by the charging disk C of the electrophorus is little more than that of the insulated plate of the charged condenser. Very little additional charge is then conveyed in each further operation as the charging disk is put in contact with the condenser.

It must be noted that the production of a charge on C is entirely due to induction from the ebonite disk D. That is, although C is laid on D, the latter is such a poor conductor that C acquires little charge by contact from D. If C and D are exceptionally smooth, C may carry away very little charge indeed, for the charge obtained by good contact with D may exactly neutralize the charge produced by induction. A high degree of planarity of D is therefore deliberately avoided, so that good contact with C is made at only a few unavoidable places when the latter is laid over the former.

2. The Wimshurst Influence Machine.

To avoid the labour of manipulation with the electrophorus and to provide still greater electrical energy, continuously operated machines were devised. These were originally friction machines in which charges were generated by rotating glass cylinders against rubbers which pressed in contact with the surface. Metal foils fixed to the surface of the cylinder served to collect the charges which were removed by wire brushes which were in light contact with the surface of the cylinder. Such friction machines were found to be very erratic and gave way to various influence machines, of which the Wimshurst is a typical example.

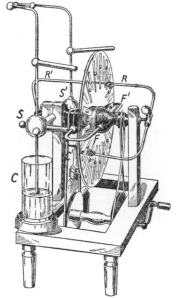

As shown in fig. 2, the Wimshurst machine consists of two flat glass disks mounted on a common axis and capable of rotation in opposite directions. The disks are coated with shellac to render them non-hygroscopic, and are rotated either by hand or by electric motor. A number of tin-foil sectors are fixed symmetrically to the disks and the latter revolve between two forks F, F' provided with sharp points which are situated close to the disks but which do not actually come in contact with them. The forks or *collectors* are connected by brass rods to two metal spheres S, S' on which the charges collect, and the spheres are usually fitted with condensers C, C', so that the charge, which is generated continuously, may be continuously stored. Two mutually

Fig. 2. — Wimshurst Machine

19

perpendicular brass induction rods R, R', terminated by fine wire brushes which pass over the surface of the metal sectors, remain stationary as the disks rotate.

The operation of the machine may be explained by reference to fig. 3, in which the two disks are for clarity drawn of unequal size, although in reality they are as identical as possible. The machine requires a small residual charge on the sector A before the generation of subsequent charge will take place. This initial charge is usually resident on the surface of the machine when it has once been used, but in damp weather it may be necessary to convey a charge to the surface by induction from an excited ebonite rod in the usual fashion. The positive charge on A induces a negative charge on the sector B, and since the latter is connected to the brass rod R, a corresponding

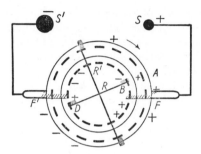

Fig. 3. — Action of Wimshurst Machine

induced positive charge develops on the conductor D which is at the remote end of R. Owing to the rotation of the two disks in opposite directions, the R-B and R-D contacts are broken while they are still under the influence of the charge on A. Consequently a positive and negative charge is left on the sectors D and B respectively. The charge on A has therefore now generated two additional charges on the system. These two charges repeat the inducing effect when they come opposite the ends of the second rod R'. In this way more charges are produced on the back plate containing the original sector A. This mutual induction process continues until large charges and consequently high potentials are produced on the sectors of both plates. It will be observed that the rotation of the two plates in opposite directions is such as to convey charges of one sign to one side of the apparatus and of the opposite sign to the other side. This has an important result on the collection process which thereby becomes unidirectional. The collectors on the fork F acquire a negative charge which is so high that the insulation resistance of the air gap breaks down. The negative electricity streams from the points and partially neutralizes the positively charged sectors. An equal and opposite positive charge therefore develops on the sphere S, so the effect is as if an equal positive charge were conveyed from sector to points. Meanwhile, at the other fork F', the negative charge streams from the sector to the points under the action of the intense electric field produced between the high negative charge on the sectors and the high positive charge which is induced on the points. The sphere S' therefore acquires a net negative charge. We emphasize that at both collectors it is the negative electricity which moves, in one case from sector to points, and in the other in the reverse direction from points to sector. Actually, when the insulation resistance breaks down, the air in the spark becomes ionized (see Chap. XVIII), and ions of both signs being present, there is a certain amount of electricity of both signs travelling across the gaps between sectors and points at both F and F' under the potential difference which exists.

Theoretically there is no limit to the electrical energy which may be obtained. In practice, frictional losses are inevitable in the moving system, but the real limit to the electrical energy available lies in electrical losses. The air in the whole neighbourhood of the machine becomes slightly conducting owing to the ionization at the collectors and unavoidable sparking at the brushes. Consequently losses occur through the air from various parts of the machine, the losses being proportionately greater where the surface density is largest, that is at angles and points. The losses there are usually so intense that a blue glow is observed in the neighbourhood; the process is commonly termed " brushing " and is said to be due to *corona discharge*. Again, the surface insulation between the sectors breaks down as the potential difference between different sectors becomes very large, and brushing to earth across various parts of the insulators is always taking place to a certain extent. In spite of these difficulties, several Wimshurst machines connected in parallel and suitably motor-driven will supply a current of several milliamperes at a hundred thousand volts.

3. The Van der Graaff Generator.

If potentials of millions of volts are required, a machine like the Van der Graaff generator must be used. This consists of a vertical tube of insulating material which may be several metres high and up to a metre in diameter. As shown in fig. 4, the tube is surmounted by a large metal sphere which is the system ultimately to be charged to the high potential. Inside the vertical tube runs a silk band which is connected electrically at the top to the inside of the metal sphere so that any charge on the band may be communicated to the inside, and hence automatically to the outside, of the sphere. The silk band is caused to rotate, and charge is sprayed on the band either by a battery of mechanically-driven Wimshurst machines situated at the base of the tube or from a high-voltage transformer (see Chap. XIII). In this way the charge on the sphere may be continuously increased until it is several million volts above earth potential. If one such system is

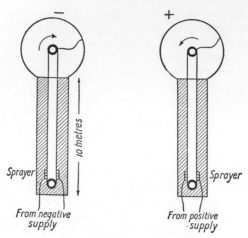

Fig. 4. — Van der Graaff Generator

charged with positive, and another with negative electricity a potential difference of ten million volts may be set up comparatively easily between the two spheres.

EXERCISES

1. Explain in detail the operation of an electrostatic induction machine.

2. Compare the advantages and disadvantages of a battery of Wimshurst machines and a transformer as sources of high potential.

CHAPTER VI

Elementary Magnetism

1. Introduction.

The fact that certain iron ore found in Magnesia in Asia Minor possessed the property of attracting small pieces of iron and steel was known to the ancients. This ore, which is termed **magnetite,** is said to exhibit magnetic properties or to possess **magnetism** just in the same way as rubbed amber is said to possess electrification.

2. Magnetic Substances.

All materials, if they are sufficiently light, show electrical attraction; but unless the apparatus is extremely sensitive, only a few substances exhibit any attraction under magnetic forces. These substances form the *ferro-magnetic group* and consist essentially of iron, nickel and cobalt and certain of their alloys. Again, while a closed conducting surface acts as a perfect *electrostatic screen* in that enormous charges outside or on the surface fail to produce any electrical forces within the conductor, magnetic forces readily penetrate conductors. For example, iron filings inside a brass vase respond as readily to magnetite placed outside the vase as when the separation is due to air only.

In the case of electric charge, mere contact between the electrified body and an initially uncharged conductor is sufficient to convey charge to the latter, especially if the electrified body is itself a conductor. On the other hand, mere contact between a magnet and a magnetic body is quite insufficient to produce any **permanent magnetism** of the latter. Magnetic substances readily become magnets, however, if stroked systematically by natural magnetite. This process may be repeated indefinitely without any appreciable diminution of the magnetic power of the magnets used. This again contrasts with the transference of electric charge, the latter being continually reduced in amount by sharing.

If a bar of iron which has been magnetized—that is a **bar magnet**— is plunged into a bed of iron filings the latter are found to adhere most strongly at the ends of the bar. These regions of intense magnetic force are termed the **poles** of the magnet. An imaginary line joining the two poles is termed the **magnetic axis,** and an imaginary line running round the centre of the magnet is termed the **magnetic equator.**

3. Directional Properties.

If a bar magnet is suspended by a torsionless fibre it is found that it sets with its axis pointing approximately geographically north and south, and if disturbed always returns to this position. This property—the knowledge of which, as of magnetic attraction, is of great antiquity,—constitutes the basis of the *magnetic compass*. The pole which points to the north, or the *north-seeking pole*, is termed the **north pole** and the other is termed the **south pole** of the magnet. There is therefore a formal correspondence with the N-pole and S-pole and positive and negative electricity. Experiment shows that this correspondence is much deeper, for just as like charges repel and unlike charges attract each other, **like poles repel and unlike poles attract each other.** Thus, if one bar magnet is freely suspended, and another is brought up to it, repulsion takes place if the two N-poles or two S-poles are presented to each other and attraction if a N-pole and a S-pole are so presented.

4. Magnetic Field and Unit Pole.

The region around a magnetic pole is termed its **magnetic field** and, just as in the electrical case, magnetic forces are imagined as due to myriads of **magnetic lines of force.** A magnetic line of force is therefore an *imaginary line showing the direction of the magnetic force at any point in the magnetic field.* Similarly, attractions and repulsions are

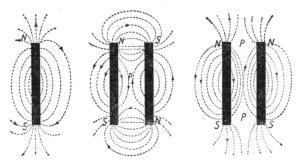

Fig. 1. — Magnetic Lines of Force

pictured mechanically as arising from the tension and repulsion of *magnetic tubes of force.*

In the same way that electrostatic lines of force are mapped out with crystals of oxalic acid, so magnetic lines of force may be mapped out with iron fillings. In fig. 1 is shown the distribution of the lines of force for various arrangements of one or more magnets. The centres P of the diamond-shaped regions which are free from magnetic force are termed *neutral points.*

Again, the definition of unit magnetic pole is absolutely analogous to that of unit charge. *A unit magnetic pole is that pole which exerts a force of 1 dyne on an equal pole at a distance of 1 cm., both poles being situated in a vacuum.*

Similarly, the *intensity of a magnetic field at any point is measured by the force which would be exerted on a unit pole placed at that point.* The unit of magnetic field strength is termed the *oersted* (originally *gauss*).

Experiment shows, however, one fundamental difference between magnetic poles and electric charges in that while it is easy and usual to obtain separate positive and negative charges, N-poles and S-poles always occur together, as in a bar magnet. If the bar magnet is broken diametrically in an effort to separate the N-pole from the S-pole, another N-pole and S-pole will be found to have been generated at the point of fracture. This process is repeated until the fragments are of molecular size. The concept of a unit pole is therefore a purely theoretical one, the experimental unit being a short bar magnet or *magnetic dipole.*

5. Molecular Theory of Magnetism.

The behaviour of magnetic substances is readily explained on the molecular theory of magnetism. This states that magnetic substances consist permanently of large numbers of molecular magnets. In an unmagnetized bar these molecular magnets are arranged completely

Fig. 2. — Unmagnetized Bar

at random as shown in fig. 2. The bar as a whole therefore exhibits no magnetism, neither attractive nor directive. The process of magnetization consists in the gradual adjustment of these molecular magnets as shown in fig. 3. Under the influence of the magnetic field of the stroking magnet, the small molecular magnets turn slightly into the

Fig. 3. — Process of Magnetisation

direction of the external magnetic field. The motion of the molecular magnets is opposed partly by friction and partly by their mutual magnetic interactions. Consequently the stroking process has to be repeated several times before appreciable magnetization is produced. When all the molecular magnets have become orientated in one direction, further magnetization is clearly impossible. This prediction of a limiting state by the molecular theory accords well with experimental observation. It is termed **magnetic saturation.**

Again, since mechanical fracture results in the separation of groups of molecules and not the fracture of any one molecule, the impossibility of separating a N-pole from a S-pole is easily explained. The development of fresh N-poles and S-poles on fracture is merely the separation of two adjacent layers of N-poles and S-poles already present. The large magnetic intensity at the poles of a magnet is clearly to be attributed to the large number of unbalanced N-poles and S-poles at the two ends respectively. Farther towards the centre of the magnet there is negligible external field, as the N-poles and S-poles are extremely close to each other and all the lines of force which arise from them run straight from one to the other.

It is to be expected that any process which tends to derange the molecules of a magnet would be likely to demagnetize it. This is found experimentally, percussion or heating being well-known methods of demagnetization.

6. Magnetic Induction.

If an unmagnetized iron bar is presented to a compass needle it attracts both ends. On the other hand, one end of a magnetized bar will repel one end of the compass needle when like poles are presented to each other. Consider now the experiment shown in fig. 4, where an

Fig. 4. — Magnetic Induction

unmagnetized bar is placed close to a compass needle and a bar magnet is brought up to the far end of the unmagnetized bar. It is found that the hitherto unmagnetized bar will repel one end of the compass needle, showing that under the influence of the neighbouring magnet it becomes temporarily magnetized. This process is termed **magnetic induction.** If the unmagnetized bar is of soft iron the effect will be large while the magnet is in the neighbourhood, but will completely disappear when the magnet is removed. Soft iron is therefore said to possess high magnetic **susceptibility** but poor **retentivity.** On the other hand, if the bar is of steel, the effect is small but persists slightly after the exciting magnet is removed. Steel therefore possesses low susceptibility but high retentivity.

The analogy with electrostatic induction is complete in that the attraction of unmagnetized bodies is due to induction. Under the inducing field, a pole of opposite sign is temporarily formed at the end closest to the magnet and a pole of the same sign is formed at the far end. Owing to the closer proximity of the unlike poles, a net attraction occurs between the magnetic substance and the magnet.

7. Terrestrial Magnetism.

The directional properties shown by a freely suspended bar magnet are due to the presence of a magnetic field associated with the earth. The precise cause of the earth's magnetic field is still uncertain, but its properties are conveniently summarized by noting that except for local irregularities it is the field which would be expected if a short bar magnet were situated at the earth's centre, and lay so that its S-pole pointed not quite N along the earth's geographical axis. This

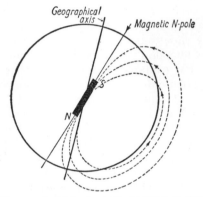

Fig. 5. — Approximation to Earth's Magnetic Field

implies a distribution of lines of force as shown in fig. 5. The points where the magnetic axis cuts the earth's surface are termed the magnetic poles.

It will be observed that the lines of force do not in general lie parallel to the earth's surface. If a magnet were freely suspended it would therefore be expected to set at an angle to the horizontal. This angle is termed the **angle of dip**, and is characteristic of the magnetic field at any place. As we travel from the magnetic equator to the magnetic pole, the angle of dip varies from 0° to 90°. In practice the angle of dip is measured with a dip circle, as described in the next chapter. The **isoclinal lines** are imaginary lines drawn over the earth's surface connecting points of equal dip. They lie parallel to the lines of latitude except for local variations. It is clear that the horizontal force exerted on a bar magnet as ordinarily suspended, or on a compass needle, is only the *horizontal component H* of a *total magnetic intensity I* which is directed along the angle of dip. It is often convenient to regard I as possessing both the horizontal component H and a vertical component V and to make use of the relations

$$I^2 = H^2 + V^2, \quad \ldots \ldots \quad (6.1)$$

and

$$\tan D = \frac{V}{H}, \quad \ldots \ldots \quad (6.2)$$

where D is the angle of dip.

The deviation of a compass needle from the geographical meridian at any point is termed the **angle of declination** at that point. The **isogonal lines** or lines of equal declination run roughly parallel to the geographical lines of longitude but large irregularities are common. For example, there is an **agonal line** of zero declination which forms a closed curve termed the *Siberian oval*. Such irregularities are usually associated with massive ore deposits of magnetic material. Lines connecting points of equal H are termed **isodynamic lines.**

Apart from the variations in terrestrial magnetic properties across the earth's surface, temporal variations occur of both a regular and an irregular nature. For example, records show that there is a cyclic variation in the magnetic declination with a complete period of about 1000 years. Its present value in London is about 14° W., its maximum of $24\frac{1}{2}$° W. was reached in 1820, and it is expected to reach zero in 2139. Superposed on this long-period variation are annual and daily variations. The annual variation, which is oppositely directed in the northern and southern hemispheres, is about $2\frac{1}{4}'$: the maximum westerly deviation occurring in the spring and the maximum easterly deviation in the autumn. Daily variations are more irregular, but are generally to be distinguished from *magnetic storms*. These give rise to large and irregular fluctuations in magnetic intensity and are usually quite unpredictable.

As sources of the earth's magnetism, the existence of permanent magnets in the interior of the earth, of magnetism arising from electric currents in the earth's interior, of effects due to the circulation of large electric currents in the upper atmosphere, and of magnetic influences from the sun and other celestial bodies have all been suggested. Little agreement has been reached among authorities except as to the inadequacy of the proposed suggestions.

EXERCISES

1. Compare and contrast electrification and magnetization. What is meant by the statement that the natural unit of magnetism is a dipole?

2. Define *unit magnetic pole* and *strength of a magnetic field*. Give a brief account of the molecular theory of magnetism.

3. Write a short essay on terrestrial magnetism.

CHAPTER VII

Magnetic Measurements

1. Magnetic Moment.

We have seen that experimentally it is impossible to separate completely a N-pole and a S-pole and that the natural magnetic element is the dipole rather than the unit pole. Similarly, on a larger scale the behaviour of a magnet is characterized by the distance between the poles as well as the pole strengths themselves. We shall now show that the characteristic quantity is the **magnetic moment** M, which is defined as the *product of the pole strength m and the distance between the poles 2l*, that is

$$M = 2ml. \quad \ldots \ldots \quad (7.1)$$

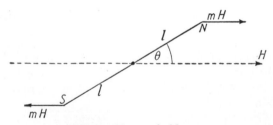

Fig. 1. — Moment of a Magnet

If a magnet is freely suspended so as to turn in a horizontal plane, it can be seen from fig. 1 that when the displacement from the magnetic meridian is θ, there is a *restoring couple or moment G* given by

$$G = 2Hml \sin \theta. \quad \ldots \ldots \quad (7.2)$$

If the field H is of unit strength and the magnetic axis is at right angles to the field so that $\theta = 90°$, equation (7.2) becomes

$$G = 2ml. \quad \ldots \ldots \quad (7.3)$$

The magnetic moment, or moment of the magnet, $2ml$, is thus connected with a mechanical turning couple or moment.

2. Magnetic Law of Force.

The law of force between two magnetic poles, just as for two electric charges, is that of the inverse square. We have seen how a very indirect proof is necessary in the electrostatic case, owing to the inevitable leakage of charge if a direct proof is attempted. In the magnetic case, since separate N- and S-poles cannot be obtained, a proof based upon the forces between two dipoles must be devised. It is, however, convenient to note here that since the same law is obeyed as in electrostatics, Gauss's theorem and all the other theorems there derived may be taken over directly and applied to the magnetic case.

For example, *magnetic potential at a point in a magnetic field is defined as the work done in bringing a unit pole from infinity up to that point.* Further, its value at a distance r from a point magnetic pole of strength m will be

$$V = \frac{m}{r}, \quad \ldots \ldots \quad (7.3)$$

by analogy with (2.7). The lines of force will be radial and the equipotential surfaces concentric spheres.

3. Force due to a Magnetic Dipole.

Since the dipole is the natural magnetic unit, we require an expression for the force due to a magnetic dipole of pole-strength m, separation $2l$, at a distance r from the centre of the dipole, the line joining the point to the centre of the dipole being inclined at θ to the magnetic axis. We shall assume that $r \gg 2l$, to simplify the calculation. The total magnetic potential at P in fig. 2 is then approximately, from equation (7.3),

$$V = \frac{m}{(r - l \cos\theta)} - \frac{m}{(r + l \cos\theta)}$$

$$= \frac{2ml \cos\theta}{(r^2 - l^2 \cos^2\theta)}$$

$$= \frac{M \cos\theta}{r^2}, \quad \ldots \ldots \ldots \quad (7.4)$$

since $r \gg l$.

Now by equation (2.8), the force in any direction is equal to the derivative of the potential in that direction, with sign changed. Hence the force at P directed along r is

$$F_r = -\frac{\partial V}{\partial r} = \frac{2M \cos\theta}{r^3}. \quad \ldots \ldots \quad (7.5)$$

In a direction perpendicular to r the force is

$$F_\theta = -\frac{1}{r} \cdot \frac{\partial V}{\partial \theta} = \frac{M \sin \theta}{r^3}, \quad \ldots \quad (7.6)$$

and hence the total force F_T at P may be obtained if required from

$$F_\mathrm{T}{}^2 = F_r{}^2 + F_\theta{}^2. \quad \ldots \ldots \quad (7.7)$$

At a point on the magnetic axis produced, $\theta = 0$, hence $F_\theta = 0$, the force is directed along the axis, and

$$F = \frac{2M}{r^3}; \quad \ldots \ldots \ldots \quad (7.8)$$

while for a point on the perpendicular bisector of the axis $\theta = 90°$, hence $F_\mathrm{R} = 0$, the force is directed parallel to the axis and

$$F = \frac{M}{r^3}. \quad \ldots \ldots \ldots \quad (7.9)$$

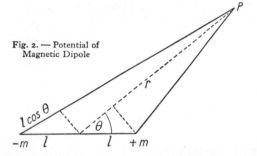

Fig. 2. — Potential of Magnetic Dipole

For an accurate test of the inverse square law we cannot neglect $l \cos \theta$ compared with r in the equation preceding (7.4). We shall, however, be concerned with only the two symmetrical positions, namely on the axis and on the perpendicular bisector of the axis. For these positions, which are known as the Gauss A and Gauss B positions respectively, we have $\theta = 0$ and $\theta = 90°$, so for the first position

$$F_1 = -\frac{\partial V}{\partial r} = -\frac{\partial}{\partial r}\left(\frac{M}{r^2 - l^2}\right) = \frac{2Mr}{(r^2 - l^2)^2}. \quad . \quad (7.10)$$

For the second position, which lies equidistant from the N- and S-poles, the potential is zero. Applying the inverse-square law, however, the force is easily calculated directly: thus

$$F_2 = 2 \cdot \frac{m}{(r^2 + l^2)} \cdot \frac{l}{(r^2 + l^2)^{1/2}}$$

$$= \frac{M}{(r^2 + l^2)^{3/2}}. \quad \ldots \ldots \ldots \quad (7.11)$$

4. The Deflection Magnetometer.

To test equations (7.8)–(7.11) the deflection magnetometer is used. As shown in fig. 3, this consists of a short bar magnet to which is attached a light aluminium pointer moving over a horizontal circular scale. In the most accurate instruments the pointer is replaced by a mirror and the system is usually suspended rather than pivoted from below. The case enclosing the needle is mounted accurately at the centre of a metre scale of some non-magnetic material such as wood, and a short bar magnet is placed on the arm of the magnetometer at a suitable distance from the suspended needle. Initially the bar magnet is removed

Fig. 3. — Deflection Magnetometer

and the needle comes to rest under the influence of the earth's horizontal component alone. If the Gauss A or *end-on* position is to be examined, the arms of the magnetometer are rotated until the suspended magnet lies at right angles to them. On putting the magnet in the end-on position, the needle swings through an angle θ which is then read. The conditions are as shown in fig. 4, that is,

$$F_1 = H \tan \theta_1 = \frac{2Mr}{(r^2 - l^2)^2} = \frac{2M}{r^3}, \text{ approx.} \quad (7.12)$$

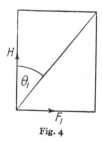

Fig. 4

Both ends of the pointer are read, the readings are repeated with the magnet reversed, and another set is taken with the magnet on the other side of the magnetometer. The final value of θ_1 is the average of the eight readings.

The arms of the magnetometer are then swung through 90° and the magnet placed in the *broadside* or Gauss B position and the new angle θ_2 observed. Hence from equation (7.9)

$$F_2 = H \tan \theta_2 = \frac{M}{r^3}, \quad \ldots \ldots \quad (7.13)$$

whence from (7.12) and (7.13)

$$\tan \theta_1 = 2 \tan \theta_2. \quad \ldots \ldots \quad (7.14)$$

This affords only an approximate test of the inverse square law as we have neglected l compared with r. More accurately, we may concentrate on a series of readings for different values of r in either the Gauss A or Gauss B positions. For the latter,

$$F_2 = H \tan \theta = \frac{M}{(r^2 + l^2)^{3/2}}, \quad \cdots \quad (7.15)$$

so that, since M and H are constant, a straight line should be obtained if $\cot \theta$ is plotted against $(r^2 + l^2)^{3/2}$. Now actually the poles of a magnet are not situated exactly at its geometrical ends; in fact $2l$ represents the *equivalent length* of an ideal magnet equal in strength to the actual magnet but with ideal point poles. As the quantity l is not known, the test of (7.15) is obtained by writing it in the form

$$(r^2 + l^2) = \left(\frac{M}{H} \cot \theta\right)^{2/3}. \quad \cdots \quad (7.16)$$

Plotting $(\cot \theta)^{2/3}$ against r^2 is found to give a straight line in accordance with the inverse square law on which the deduction of the formula is based. Further, the intercept on the r^2 axis when (7.16) is plotted gives the square of the equivalent length of the magnet.

5. Measurement of M and H.

Consideration of equations (7.12) and (7.13) shows that they are of such a form that even by taking several positions it is impossible to determine either M or H unless the other is known. Some other experiment is therefore required. This is obtained by suspending the short bar magnet, used on the arm of the deflection magnetometer, from a thread of unspun silk and allowing it to undergo torsional oscillations under the action of the earth's horizontal field. From fig. 1, the restoring couple for an angle of twist θ is

$$G = MH \sin \theta = MH\theta, \quad \cdots \quad (7.17)$$

if θ is small. Hence from the treatment in Part I, Chap. IV, section 5, the period of oscillation is

$$t = 2\pi\sqrt{\frac{I}{MH}}, \quad \cdots \cdots \quad (7.18)$$

where I is the moment of inertia of the magnet about the axis of suspension. In practice the magnet is suspended in a draught-free enclosure and oscillations are timed with a stop-clock. The moment of inertia is obtained from the mass and linear dimensions of the magnet. Application of (7.18) then gives the product MH and the ratio M/H is obtained from experiments in either the Gauss A or Gauss B positions. Hence the values of M and H are obtained absolutely.

6. The Oscillation or Vibration Magnetometer.

An oscillation or vibration magnetometer is a useful device for estimating the strengths of the horizontal components of magnetic fields. It consists simply of a very short magnet carrying a light aluminium pointer symmetrically at right angles and suspended inside a small cylindrical glass enclosure. For all positions of the magnetometer M and I remain constant, so that from (7.18)

$$H \propto \frac{1}{t^2} \propto n^2,$$

where n is the number of oscillations executed in a given time. If H varies rapidly from place to place, that is if the *field gradient* is steep, the magnet must be correspondingly small or the field will be different at the two ends of the magnet.

7. The Dip Circle.

The angle of dip which we have discussed in the previous chapter is measured with a dip circle, a diagram of which is shown in fig. 5. It consists of a compass needle which is initially unmagnetized and balanced about a horizontal axis. The needle is then magnetized and it is found that it dips at some angle to the horizontal. If the supporting axis is in any arbitrary position the dip observed will not in general

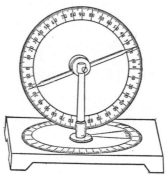

Fig. 5. — Dip Circle

be the true angle of dip. This is clear from fig. 6, for if the supporting axis is at an angle α to the magnetic meridian, the effective horizontal component acting on the *dip needle* is only $H \cos \alpha$. As the axis is rotated, therefore, the effective horizontal component varies from H, when the axis lies in the magnetic meridian, to zero, when the axis is perpendicular to this direction. In this last position the dip needle is under the influence of the earth's vertical component V only, and the dip needle therefore stands vertically. The horizontal axis is itself attached to a vertical axis, and the process of setting the dip needle is to locate the position when the dip needle stands vertical and then to rotate through 90° about the vertical axis. The horizontal axis then lies perpendicular to the magnetic meridian and the true angle of dip is registered.

In using the instrument, it is first levelled with a spirit-level and

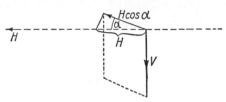

Fig. 6.— Forces on Dip Needle

then rotated so that the dip needle stands vertical on the circular scale which lies in a vertical plane. Rotation through 90° then brings the needle into the magnetic meridian and the readings of the two ends of the needle are taken. Further operations are:

(1) The horizontal axis is turned through 180° and a further pair of readings is taken. This is to eliminate error due to the zero line of the vertical scale not being horizontal (fig. 7a).

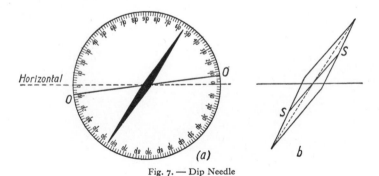

Fig. 7. — Dip Needle

(2) The needle is then turned over sideways and four further readings are taken. This allows for the magnetic axis of the needle not coinciding with the geometrical axis, as shown in fig. 7b.

(3) The needle is removed and remagnetized in the reverse direction and the preceding eight readings are repeated. This is to allow for the needle not being accurately supported through its C.G.

The average of the sixteen readings is taken as the angle of dip.

We consider magnetism further in later chapters after we have discussed the magnetic effect of an electric current.

EXERCISES

1. Define (a) the moment of a magnet, (b) the equivalent length of a magnet.

How may the equivalent length of a bar magnet be determined?

2. Upon what evidence may it be assumed that the force between two magnetic poles varies inversely as the square of their distance apart?

3. Define the term *magnetic potential* and calculate an expression for the magnetic potential at a point a distance r from the centre of a short magnet of moment M if the point lies on the magnetic axis produced. $[M/r^2.]$

4. Describe *two* experiments by which the moments of two magnets may be compared. Which method do you consider to be the better?

5. Describe carefully how the total intensity of the earth's magnetic field may be measured absolutely and accurately at any place.

6. Describe the use of the dip circle. If a dip needle which has been correctly set is then slightly displaced and allowed to oscillate it makes 3 vibrations per second at one place and 4 vibrations per second at another place. Compare the total intensity of the earth's magnetic field at the two places. [9 : 16.]

CHAPTER VIII

Elementary Properties of the Electric Current

1. Production of Electric Current.

An electric current consists of movement of electric charge. In solids generally, and in conductors in particular, motion is confined to the negative charges or electrons. We have seen in Chap. II that a charge moves, if it is free to do so, when a potential difference exists. For example, the charged disk of an electrophorus continues to convey charge to a conductor until the potential of disk and conductor is the same; that is, an electric current flows into the conductor until the potential is everywhere the same. Strictly speaking, the charge will only flow from the disk to the conductor if the former is negatively charged. If it is positively charged, electrons flow from the conductor to the disk until, as before, the potentials of the two are the same. Of course, the effect is the same as if positive charge had flowed from the disk to the conductor, and it is customary to use this description, as is quite permissible if it is borne in mind that in reality the flow is that of electrons in the reverse direction.

In electrostatics the flow of current is clearly very temporary, the potential being equalized in a very short space of time unless the bodies are very poor conductors indeed. The basic problem of current electricity is the continuous production of a potential difference so that a continuous current may be produced. This can be effected by some device such as the Wimshurst machine in which fresh charge is being continually generated. It suffers from the disadvantage, however, of producing too small a current for the majority of purposes, besides being cumbersome and requiring a source of mechanical power to drive the machine. Fortunately nature provides a great many ways in which a potential difference may be established. We tabulate some of these below. Only a few of them are of practical importance, but all are of interest in explaining electrical phenomena.

(1) *Percussion.*—This is closely allied to the production of electricity by friction between two bodies.

(2) *Vibration.*—This is simply internal friction in a body as opposed to external friction.

(3) *Disruption and Cleavage.*—These are further examples of violent friction.

(4) *Crystallization and Solidification.*

(5) *Combustion.*

(6) *Evaporation.*

(7) *Atmospheric Electricity.*—The analogy between electric sparks between two electrostatic charges at greatly differing potentials and lightning flashes is obvious. Franklin performed classical experiments to show that the two phenomena were identical. A kite flown in the clouds yielded abundant sparks between the string and the ground in thundery weather, especially if the string was rendered conducting by moisture. The function of pointed metal lightning conductors is to discharge clouds before they acquire sufficient potential to strike with

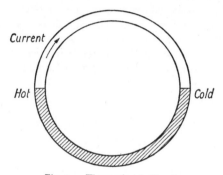

Fig. 1. — Thermoelectric Circuit

dangerous violence. As a source of electricity, atmospheric electricity is much too uncontrollable to be of practical importance.

(8) *Pressure.*—This is termed **piezo-electricity** and has important applications in the quartz oscillator which has been discussed in Part IV, Chap. IV.

(9) *Pyro-electricity.*—This is the development of differences of potential between different parts of certain crystals when they are heated. It is too small to be of use as a source of potential.

(10) *Thermo-electricity.*—If two dissimilar metals are joined together and one junction is at a higher temperature than the other, a steady potential difference is set up and hence a steady current flows around the wires which, when connected as in fig. 1, are said to constitute an **electric circuit.** The potential difference is small, but has important practical applications, and is discussed fully in Chap. XVII.

(11) *Contact of Dissimilar Metals.*—The ease with which electrons leave a given metal varies from metal to metal. Consequently, when two dissimilar metals are joined there is a temporary flow of electrons

from one metal to the other. This is said to be due to contact potential. It is not suitable as a source of electric current, but it must frequently be taken into account in interpreting electrical phenomena.

(12) *Chemical Action.*—If a zinc plate and a copper plate are placed side by side but not in contact in a dilute solution of sulphuric acid and the two plates are joined by a wire outside the solution, a steady current flows from one plate to the other. This source of potential difference is termed a **simple cell.** The process is accompanied by the formation of zinc sulphate and hydrogen, thus showing that chemical action is accompanying the electrical phenomena. This process is of great practical importance and forms the basis of **electric batteries.**

(13) *Magneto-electricity.*—Whenever a conductor moves so as to cut across the lines of force of a magnetic field, a potential difference is caused between the ends of the conductor. If the conductor forms a closed circuit a current will flow round the circuit. This process is the most important of all in the practical generation of electric current.

2. Passage of a Current through Solid Conductors.

The potential difference which exists between the zinc and copper plates, or **electrodes,** of the simple cell discussed above is not large enough to create an appreciable spark when the electrodes are joined by a wire. The presence of the current is shown most easily by two other distinct effects which it produces. These are the **heating effect** and the **magnetic effect.**

If the wire is short and thin it may actually be raised in temperature sufficiently to glow; otherwise the effect may be shown by winding the wire round a thermometer.

That a steady magnetic field is established in the neighbourhood of a current may be shown by the deflection of a compass needle placed in the vicinity of the wire.

A third distinct effect of an electric current is that it will produce chemical action when it passes through solutions, though not through solids. We discuss this further in Chap. XII.

The fact that an electric current produces a magnetic field was discovered by Oersted. It suggested the connexion between the hitherto unconnected phenomena of electricity and magnetism. The complete reciprocity of this connexion was established by Faraday's discovery that motion of a conductor in a magnetic field produces electricity. It should be noted that the magnetic field due to electric charge exists only while the charge is in motion; and conversely, electric current is generated only while the conductor and the field are in relative motion.

If the electrodes or **poles** of a simple cell are connected to one of the electrometers described in Chap. IV, the existence of a steady potential difference between the poles may be established. In particular, the copper pole is at a higher potential than the zinc pole. The former is therefore said to be positive and the latter negative. This distinction is only relative to the pair of metals concerned. For example, other cells may be constructed in which the zinc is positive with respect to the second electrode. Before the electronic nature of solid conduction was realized, it was always considered that the electric current flowed from regions of high potential to regions of low potential. Consequently in all literature up to 1900 the current is depicted as flowing from the copper to the zinc electrode, whereas in reality the electrons which constitute the current are proceeding in the reverse direction. Now unfortunately many rules had been established governing, for example, the direction of the magnetic field consequent upon a current flowing in a particular direction, and all these rules would need to be put the other way round if the direction of the current were reversed. It is therefore conventionally accepted that in circumstances where the electronic nature of the circuit need not be considered, the current shall be considered to flow from regions of high potential to regions of low potential. Such a distinction is only an academic one since, for example, in the highly practical case of radio valves, electronic considerations are paramount.

3. Unit of Current.

For the electrostatic (or E.S.) system, since a current consists of a flow of electrical charge, no further unit is necessary in fixing the unit of current. Unit current on the electrostatic system is that current which is present when unit quantity of electricity as defined on the E.S. system passes any point in the electric circuit per second. We wish, however, in practice to make use of the heating or the magnetic effects to define the unit of current. The heating effect is unsatisfactory since it increases with time and is not easily measured with accuracy. It also involves the heat capacity of the wire composing the circuit and introduces uncertain corrections due to heat lost by conduction along the wire itself. The magnetic effect, however, is stationary with time and is independent of the nature of the wire provided it is not of magnetic material.

Now we have to make use of a compass needle, or ideally a unit magnetic pole, in measuring the intensity of the magnetic field produced by the current. We have, however, already defined the unit magnetic pole from purely magnetic considerations. The unit of current which we shall now define is therefore dependent on the properties of the unit magnetic pole, and consequently no simple connexion might be expected to exist between the unit of current on the electromagnetic or E.M. system, and the unit of current on the E.S. system. Actually a very fundamental and simple relation does exist between the units on the two systems, but this was not realized at the time of the formulation of the two systems. It constituted a separate physical deduction of profound significance and led to the discovery of electromagnetic waves and to the electromagnetic theory of light as discussed in Chap. XVI.

The effect on a compass needle was found by Ampère to depend on (1) the shape of the conductor carrying the current, (2) the distance of the magnet or unit pole from the conductor. Eventually a symmetrical circuit was chosen, and the unit of current of the E.M. system is defined as follows: *Unit E.M. current is said to flow in a circular conductor of unit radius (1 cm.) if a force of 2π dynes acts on a unit pole placed at the centre of the circle.*

Whereas on the E.S. system the unit of charge is defined first and the E.S. unit of current derived from it by considering the charge in motion, the E.M. unit of charge is derived from the E.M. current as first defined above. *The unit of charge on the* E.M. *system is that charge which has flowed past a point in a conductor when unit* E.M. *current has been flowing for* 1 sec.

4. Electromagnetic Unit of Potential Difference.

Just as the E.S. unit of P.D. was defined as that P.D. which exists when one erg of work is performed in moving unit E.S. charge through that P.D., so unit P.D. will exist on the E.M. system when one erg of work is done in moving unit E.M. charge through that P.D. Actually it is more usual to speak of unit P.D. " maintaining unit E.M. current for 1 sec. between the two points ", but this is clearly the same as conveying unit E.M. charge.

5. Electrical Resistance.

Measurement with an electrometer shows that the potential difference between the copper and zinc plates of a simple cell is quite independent of the area of the plates, or their separation. If, however, the wire connecting the poles is long and thin, the current as estimated from its magnetic effect is much smaller than if the wire is short and thick. Similarly, a platinum wire will allow much less current to pass than a copper wire of the same dimensions. Materials are therefore said to offer a resistance to the passage of an electric current. The behaviour of this resistance is closely analogous to the resistance of a pipe to the flow of liquid through it. In fact the comparison between flow of liquid along a pipe and flow of current along a wire may be extended considerably if pressure difference in the former is identified with potential difference in the latter.

For example, we have seen in Part I, Chap. XII, that, provided the flow is streamline, the quantity of liquid flowing through a tube per second is directly proportional to the pressure difference. In exact analogy, for a given wire, the current is directly proportional to the potential difference across the wire. This important relation is termed **Ohm's law,** and is written mathematically

$$\frac{E}{I} = \text{constant} = R, \quad \ldots \ldots \quad (8.1)$$

where E and I are the potential difference and the current respectively, and the constant R is termed the **resistance** of the wire. Since the units of potential difference and current have already been fixed on both the E.S. and E.M. systems, the unit of resistance on both systems is fixed automatically from equation (8.1).

If one material only is considered, and wires of different cross-sections and lengths are inserted into a circuit operating at fixed potential, it will be found that the current is directly proportional to the area of cross-section and inversely proportional to the length of the wire. Since from (8.1) the resistance is inversely proportional to the current for a fixed potential,

$$R = \frac{sl}{A}, \quad \ldots \ldots \ldots \quad (8.2)$$

where l is the length, A is the area of cross-section assumed uniform, and s is a constant which depends on the nature of the material of the wire. The quantity s is defined by (8.2) and is termed the **specific resistance** of the material. If the conductor is in the form of a unit cube, that is, if $l = 1$, $A = 1$, then $s = R$, or the specific resistance may be defined as the *resistance of a unit cube of the material.* In practice it is found that the resistance varies considerably with the temperature of the wire, and indeed this property, when reversed, forms the basis of the *platinum resistance thermometer* which is mentioned in Part II, Chap. I, and the use of which is described more fully in Chap. XI.

We shall see in Chaps. XII and XVIII that liquids also obey Ohm's law, but that gases show deviations from the law. The existence of these deviations is responsible for many of the most important applications of gaseous conduction.

6. Practical Electrical Units.

The electrical units based on the E.S. and E.M. systems are either too large or too small for practical purposes. Since measurement of current is more frequently required than measurement of charge, the practical system is linked directly with the E.M. rather than with the E.S. system. The E.M. or **absolute** unit of current is too large for practical purposes, and the practical unit or **ampere** is defined as **one-tenth the E.M. unit of current.** The ampere is also defined from the amount of electrochemical action which occurs when the current traverses certain solutions, as discussed in Chap. XII.

On the other hand, the E.M. unit of potential difference is much too small for practical purposes and the practical unit or **volt** is defined as 10^8 **E.M. units of P.D.** Now by Ohm's law, if the units of current and P.D. are fixed, the unit of resistance is automatically fixed. The practical unit of resistance is termed the **ohm,** and from equation (8.1)

$$1 \text{ ohm} = \frac{10^8}{10^{-1}} = 10^9 \text{ E.M. units of resistance.}$$

It is also, of course, equal to 1 volt/1 amp. Since the resistance of a given conductor at a given temperature is fixed if the length and area of cross-section of the conductor are fixed, *standard ohms* are available consisting of conductors of given material and dimensions. The resistance of a solid depends to some extent on the drawing and annealing of the material as well as upon its nature. It is also very dependent on the presence of small quantities of impurities. The choice of material for standard ohms is therefore very restricted. Copper and silver might be used but are very good conductors and an inconvenient length would be required to construct a standard ohm. Platinum is more suitable but is again dependent on the previous treatment of the specimen. In practice, the liquid metal mercury has been chosen, although copies made of platinum and other solids are convenient to use if they can be repeatedly calibrated against a mercury standard. *The standard mercury ohm, sometimes termed the* **international ohm,** *is the resistance of a column of mercury of length* 106·300 *cm. and weight* 14·4521 *gm. at* 0° *C.* This corresponds to an area of cross-section of about 1 mm.[2], but owing to the difficulty of drawing a glass tube container of uniform bore, the standard is preferably specified by the weight of mercury present.

7. Magnetic Field due to a Straight Wire.

If a long straight wire is arranged to pass vertically through a board supporting a piece of drawing paper, the nature of the magnetic field due to the current in the wire may be explored with iron filings in the usual manner, or with a compass needle, as shown in fig. 2. If the current is high and the needle is kept close to the wire the effect of the earth's magnetic field may be neglected, and on tracing the lines of force they will be found to consist of **concentric circles** round the wire. The magnetic field F therefore acts in a direction perpendicular to the wire and perpendicular to a line joining the point under consideration to the wire itself. The direction in which the needle sets when it is at a considerable distance from the wire, and free to turn in a horizontal plane, is therefore the direction of the force R resulting from F and H as shown in fig. 3, H being the horizontal component of the earth's field.

The direction of the magnetic field due to the current alone, that is, the direction in which a free N-pole would be urged, is given by certain useful rules of which we select the **corkscrew rule**. This states that if the point of an ordinary right-handed corkscrew is directed along the current, a free N-pole would be urged in the direction of rotation of the handle of the corkscrew in its forward travel. Reversal of the direction of the current reverses the direction of its magnetic field but otherwise leaves it unchanged. If the direction of the current is upward, at some point due W of the wire a neutral point will occur when the fields due to the earth and the current are exactly equal and

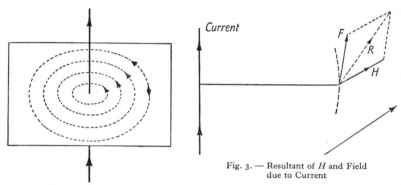

Fig. 3. — Resultant of H and Field
due to Current

Fig. 2. — Magnetic Field due to Current
in Straight Wire

opposite. Again, at points on a N-S line, the inclination θ to this line at which the needle sets will be given by

$$\tan \theta = \frac{F}{H}, \quad \cdot \quad \cdot \quad \cdot \quad \cdot \quad \cdot \quad \cdot \quad (8.3)$$

where F is the magnetic field due to the current in the wire, and H is the earth's horizontal component. Since the latter remains constant, $F \propto \tan \theta$, and hence the variation of F with distance from the wire is easily examined. It is found that the *force varies inversely as the distance from the wire*. As we are defining the strength of the current from the magnetic effect, the strength of the magnetic field is assumed to be directly proportional to the electric current. For a long straight wire, the complete relation is shown in Chap. X to be

$$F = \frac{2i}{r}, \quad \cdot \quad \cdot \quad \cdot \quad \cdot \quad \cdot \quad \cdot \quad (8.4)$$

where i is the current strength in E.M. units.

8. Magnetic Field due to a Circular Coil.

If the previous experiment is repeated using a circular coil in place of the long straight wire, the lines of force are found to be as in fig. 4. At the centre of the coil the lines of force run perpendicular to the plane of the coil. If, therefore, the latter is placed in the magnetic meridian, the force due to the current and the earth's horizontal component are again at right angles, and the tangent of the angle of deflection is again a measure of the force. If the number of turns in the coil is increased, the force is found to increase proportionally: *the force at the centre of the coil is directly proportional to the length of the*

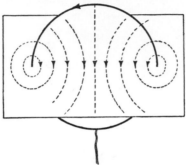

Fig. 4. — Magnetic Field due to Circular Coil

circuit present. Again, if coils of different radii are used, the *force varies inversely as the radius.* For a circular coil we therefore have

$$F \propto \frac{ni}{r} = \frac{kni}{r}, \qquad \ldots \ldots \ldots \quad (8.5)$$

where k is a constant. Now for $n = r = i = 1$, $F = 2\pi$ from the definition of unit current. Hence, for a circular coil,

$$F = \frac{2\pi ni}{r}. \qquad \ldots \ldots \ldots \quad (8.6)$$

For circuits of any shape we require a general theorem in an integral form expressing the force at any point distant r from a circuit element of length ds. This theorem may be conveniently derived from (8.6); for if the force varies inversely as r^x we have for a circular coil

$$\int_0^s \frac{i\, ds}{r^x} = \frac{2\pi ni}{r}. \qquad \ldots \ldots \ldots \quad (8.7)$$

Now $\int_0^s ds = 2\pi rn$ for the circular coil: hence from (8.7)

$$x = 2.$$

Finally, remembering that the force always acts perpendicular to the wire and in a direction at right angles to the perpendicular on to the wire, if the line joining the circuit element ds to the point is inclined at an angle θ to ds, the complete general expression is

$$F = \int \frac{i\,ds}{r^2} \sin\theta. \quad \ldots \ldots \quad (8.8)$$

9. Action of a Magnetic Field on a Conductor carrying a Current.

The fact so far observed that the magnetic needle moves while the conductor remains stationary is solely due to the light suspension of the magnet and the heavy or fixed nature of the conductor. The action and reaction between the two must be equal and opposite, and

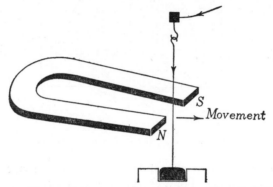

Fig. 5. — Force on Conductor carrying a Current in a Magnetic Field

if the conductor is light and free to move it will do so. In fig. 5 is shown a copper wire hanging between the poles of a powerful horseshoe magnet. The wire is lightly suspended at the top and dips into a pool of mercury at the bottom so as to complete the electrical circuit. On switching on the current the wire will move either way according to the direction of the current. If the permanent magnetic field and the current are situated perpendicular to each other, the wire will move in the remaining direction at right angles to the other two. Experiment shows that the force is given directly by

$$F = Hil,$$

where H is the strength of the permanent magnetic field, i is the current strength, and l is the length of the conductor in the uniform field. If the conductor lies at an angle θ to the field, the force is given generally by the equation

$$F = Hil \sin\theta, \quad \ldots \ldots \quad (8.9)$$

and in accordance with this relation the force is zero if the magnetic field and the conductor are parallel to each other. The direction of motion of the conductor is given by the *left-hand rule*, which states that if the *F*orefinger of the left hand points in the direction of the *F*ield, the m*I*ddle finger in the direction of the current *I*, then the thu*M*b gives the direction of *M*otion.

10. Electrical Energy Absorbed by Resistance.

In the passage of a viscous fluid down a tube under a given pressure difference, work is done by the viscous friction and is converted into heat. The work done is equal to the product of the pressure difference and the volume of liquid which has passed. In exact analogy, the electrical work done when a wire conveys a current is equal to the product of the potential difference (p. 587) and the electrical charge which has passed, and this electrical energy is converted into heat energy. Thus, if the potential difference and current respectively are e, i in E.M. units, and E, I in practical units, then

$$W = e(it) \text{ ergs} = E(It)10^7 \text{ ergs,}$$

where W is the electrical work done in t sec.; or, if the heat H is expressed in calories, since (Part II, Chap. VI) $W = JH$, where $J = 4\cdot2 \times 10^7$ ergs/cal.,

$$H = \frac{EIt}{4\cdot2}. \quad \ldots \ldots \quad (8.10)$$

This heating is referred to as the **Joule heating**. Again, since from Ohm's law $E = IR$, equation (8.10) may be written

$$H = \frac{E^2t}{4\cdot2R} = \frac{I^2Rt}{4\cdot2}. \quad \ldots \ldots \quad (8.11)$$

The heating effect is seen to be proportional to the square of the current and heat is therefore always *evolved*, independent of the direction of the current.

Additional Practical Units.—It has been found convenient to introduce further units on the practical system.

The practical unit of quantity of electricity is termed the **coulomb**, and is the quantity of electricity which flows past when 1 amp flows for 1 sec.

The practical unit of *electrical energy* is termed the **joule**, and

1 joule = 1 volt × 1 coulomb = 1 volt × 1 amp × 1 sec.
 = 10^7 ergs.

Electrical power or *rate of working* is the electrical energy expended per second; the power P is therefore given by

$$P = EI.$$

The unit of electrical power, 1 joule per second, is termed the **watt:**

$$1 \text{ watt} = 1 \text{ volt} \times 1 \text{ amp.};$$
$$1 \text{ horse-power} = 746 \text{ watts} = 0\cdot746 \text{ kilowatt.}$$

EXERCISES

1. Discuss the methods available for producing an electric current, indicating the practical value or otherwise of the methods described.

2. State three distinct physical effects accompanying the passage of an electric current. Which of these effects is considered to be best suited to the definition of unit current, and why?

3. Define unit current on the electromagnetic system. Hence define unit potential difference and unit resistance on the same system. In what way are these units related to (a) the practical system, (b) the electrostatic system, of units?

4. Upon what factors does the resistance of a solid conductor depend? Define the specific resistance of a material and indicate how far Ohm's law is obeyed by solids, liquids and gases.

5. Sketch the lines of force arising from a current flowing in (a) a straight wire, (b) a circular coil, (c) a solenoid. What arrangement will produce a uniform magnetic field over a volume of a few cubic centimetres?

6. State *one* rule governing the direction of the magnetic field arising from a current flowing in a conductor. State also one rule governing the direction of motion of a conductor carrying a current and situated in a magnetic field. What determines the magnitude of the force on a conductor carrying a current and situated in a magnetic field?

7. Define the ampere, volt, ohm, coulomb, joule and watt. State Ohm's law and compare the heat generated in two wires connected in parallel if the first has twice the resistance of the second. [1 : 2.]

CHAPTER IX

Galvanometers, Ammeters and Voltmeters

1. The Tangent Galvanometer.

To measure the strength of a current from its magnetic effect an instrument is required in which a magnetic needle is suspended at a definite distance from a circuit of symmetrical shape. Such instruments are termed galvanometers, and one of the simplest is the tangent galvanometer shown in fig. 1. It consists essentially of a small magnet carrying a light pointer at right angles (this part of the apparatus is identical with the deflection magnetometer described in Chap. VII), situated at the centre of a circular coil of wire which is supported rigidly in a vertical plane. The radius of the coil must be large

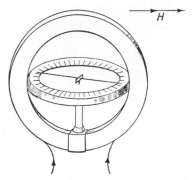

Fig. 1. — Tangent Galvanometer

compared with the dimensions of the suspended magnet, so that the latter may be considered to be subject to the magnetic field at the centre of the coil. Then from equations (8.6) and (8.3)

$$F = \frac{2\pi n i}{r} = H \tan \theta,$$

or expressing the current in amperes,

$$I = \left(\frac{10 H r}{2\pi n}\right) \tan \theta. \quad \ldots \ldots \quad (9.1)$$

The expression in brackets in (9.1), which is constant for a given instrument, is termed the *galvanometer constant* or *reduction factor*. The disadvantages of the instrument are:

(1) It requires setting with the plane of the coil in the magnetic meridian;

(2) It uses a tangent relation and therefore becomes inaccurate at angles greater than 70°;

(3) It is bulky, and the supported needle system is not robust.

2. The Astatic Galvanometer.

The first of these disadvantages is avoided in the astatic galvano-meter, a diagram of which is shown in fig. 2. It consists of two short, light magnetic needles joined rigidly together by a short light vertical rod attached to their centres, the whole being suspended by a torsion fibre of phosphor-bronze. The two needles are magnetically oppositely directed and each is supplied with a small surrounding coil, the two coils being connected in series. Since the needles are oppositely directed and are otherwise equal in all respects, the system will set in any position, and does not respond directively to the earth's field. There is no simple relation connecting the deflection with the current strength, and the instrument needs calibration against some absolute instru-ment such as the tangent galvanometer. The current is proportional to the angle of deflection for small deflections.

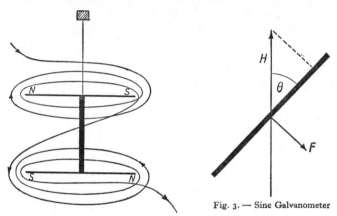

Fig. 2. — Astatic Galvanometer

Fig. 3. — Sine Galvanometer

3. Sine Galvanometer.

If the large coil of a tangent galvanometer is supported by a vertical axle so that it may be rotated in a vertical plane, it may be used as a sine galvanometer. The principle is to rotate the coil until it catches up the deflected needle and both needle and coil lie in one common plane. The forces acting are shown in fig. 3, whence $F = H \sin \theta$, and hence

$$I = \left(\frac{10Hr}{2\pi n}\right) \sin \theta. \quad \cdots \cdots \quad (9.2)$$

The instrument has the advantage that deflections up to 90° may be used, but the numerical value of the maximum current which may be read is clearly equal to the reduction factor of the galvanometer.

4. Moving-coil Galvanometer.

There is a rather low limit to the pole-strength which the suspended needle may have if it is not to suffer from self-demagnetization due to the proximity of its own poles. Consequently, since the force between the magnetic field of the current and the suspended magnet depends on the strength of the latter as well as the former, the sensitivity is too small when very small currents are to be measured, even if the pointer is replaced by a mirror, lamp and scale device. In sensitive current measuring instruments, therefore, the roles of magnet and conductor are reversed. The magnetic needle is replaced by a powerful permanent horse-shoe magnet as shown in fig. 4, and the conductor

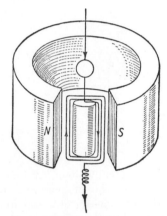

Fig. 4. — Moving-coil Galvanometer

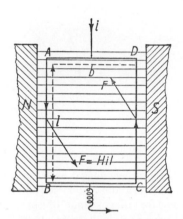

Fig. 5. — Moving-coil Galvanometer

carrying the current is in the shape of a circular or rectangular coil suspended between the poles of the permanent magnet.

For a **rectangular coil**, from the considerations of section 9 of the preceding chapter, we have by reference to fig. 5 a force $F = Hil$ on each vertical side of the rectangle, and zero force on the top and bottom sides since these are parallel to the field. The current traverses the sides AB and CD in opposite directions, so that the forces on these sides are oppositely directed, and a net couple

$$G = 2F \frac{b}{2} = Hilb = HAi \quad . \quad . \quad . \quad (9.3)$$

is produced, where A is the area of the rectangle, causing it to rotate until an equal and opposite couple $c\theta$ is brought into play owing to the twist in the suspension.

We must note, however, that as soon as the coil rotates from its

20

rest position, in which it lies with its area parallel to the field, the couple is reduced to $HAi \cos \theta$, so that

$$c\theta = HAi \cos \theta, \quad \ldots \ldots \quad (9.4)$$

where θ is the inclination of the plane of the coil to the field. The top and bottom of the rectangle are also now subject to forces since they are inclined to the direction of the field. These forces are, however, oppositely directed in a vertical plane and therefore produce no effect on the suspended system. If there are n turns of wire in the rectangle, the complete expression for the current becomes

$$i = \frac{c}{nAH} \cdot \frac{\theta}{\cos \theta}. \quad \ldots \ldots \quad (9.5)$$

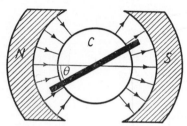

Fig. 6. — Radial Field

A scale which varied as $\theta / \cos \theta$ would be very inconvenient, and consequently a device is introduced which reduces the denominator to unity for all positions of the coil. This device consists of a soft-iron cylinder C, which together with the circular-shaped pole-pieces produces a **radial field**. The coil now lies along the lines of force for all values of θ and consequently, as shown in fig. 6, the couple maintains a uniform value of $nAiH$ for all orientations. Equation (9.5) then reduces to

$$i = \left(\frac{c}{nAH}\right) \theta, \quad \ldots \ldots \quad (9.6)$$

which gives a linear scale.

The ordinary **direct-current ammeter**, shown in fig. 7, is simply a moving-coil galvanometer of robust design. The phosphor-bronze suspension is replaced by a pivot and the coil is returned to zero by a hair-spring. Since an ammeter is introduced into a circuit in series in order to measure the current in that circuit, the resistance of the coil of the ammeter must be exceedingly small if its introduction is not to change the total resistance, and hence the current, in the circuit. This low resistance may be effected by using a few turns of good conducting wire for the coil. Alternatively, a low resistance shunt may be used.

5. The Hot-wire Ammeter.

In fig. 8 is shown a diagram of the hot-wire ammeter, the action of which depends on the thermal expansion of the wire W when it is heated by the passage of the electrical current. The slack which results from the expansion of the wire W is taken up by the spring S, the movement of which rotates the pointer over the scale of the ammeter. The instrument requires calibration with one of the absolute current measuring instruments. An important advantage of the hot-wire ammeter is that since the heat evolved is independent of the direction of the current, the instrument will measure alternating current as well as direct current. However, the scale of the instrument is not linear, since the heating effect is proportional to the square of the current.

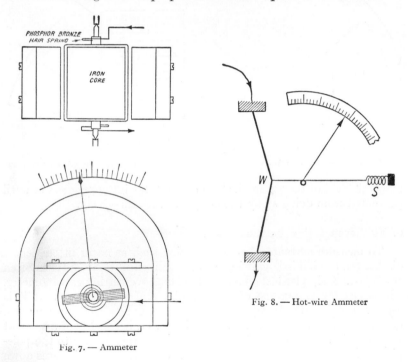

Fig. 7. — Ammeter

Fig. 8. — Hot-wire Ammeter

6. Soft Iron Ammeter.

This ammeter also is suitable for measuring A.C. or D.C. As shown in fig. 9, it consists of two soft iron rods lying inside and parallel to the axis of a long coil or **solenoid**. The current to be measured flows through the solenoid, and under the influence of the magnetic field produced, the soft iron rods become magnetized. One rod is fixed but the other is pivoted, and since the rods acquire the same polarity at neighbouring ends, the pivoted rod is repelled by the fixed rod. A suitable counterpoise or control spring limits the movement of the movable rod, and since the latter is attached to a pointer the current is read off directly. On reversal of the current in the solenoid the polarity of both rods reverses simultaneously, the repulsion is maintained, and the instrument is therefore suitable for A.C. measurement. As with the hot-wire ammeter, the deflection is proportional to the square of the current.

Another modification of the soft iron ammeter is shown in fig. 10, where an eccentrically mounted soft iron core is attracted by the

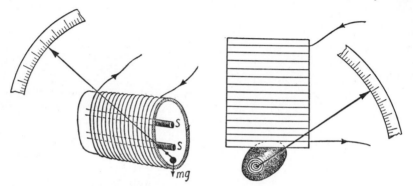

Fig. 9. — Soft Iron Ammeter   Fig. 10. — Soft iron Ammeter

magnetic field of the solenoid. The core rotates into the solenoid until prevented from doing so by the couple in the hair-spring.

6. Einthoven String Galvanometer.

To measure currents of short duration such as occur in condenser discharges, the ballistic galvanometer described in Chap. XIII is often employed. A simpler instrument is the Einthoven string galvanometer, which has the advantage of great rapidity of response so that it is especially suited to the measurement of discharges which occur with only short time intervals. As shown in fig. 11, it consists of a straight wire held in a state of tension and situated perpendicular to the pole-pieces of a powerful permanent magnet. When a discharge passes down the wire, the latter is urged mechanically at right angles to the field of the permanent magnet, but as soon as the discharge has passed the wire returns to its original position. The pole pieces of the magnet are bored so that a beam of light travels from one through the other and throws a shadow of the wire on a screen. When the discharge passes, the shadow flicks sideways temporarily, and if the shadow falls on sensitive photographic paper which is travelling parallel to the wire

or " string ", a succession of discharges gives a succession of " kicks "
on a straight base line as shown in fig. 12. The length of the duration

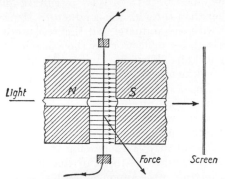

Fig. 11. — Einthoven String Galvanometer

of the kicks can be estimated if the speed of movement of the photographic paper is known. The relative magnitude of the discharges is
shown by the relative height of the kicks.

Fig. 12. — Einthoven Galvanometer Record

7. Moving-coil Voltmeter.

The electrometer described in Chap. IV may be used to measure
potential difference, but unless the voltage is greater than about 500
it is difficult to make an electrostatic voltmeter which is both sensitive
and robust. It is therefore usual to reserve such instruments for high
potentials, modified ammeters being used for ordinary voltages. The

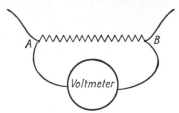

Fig. 13. — Moving-coil Voltmeter

ordinary moving-coil voltmeter simply consists of a moving-coil
ammeter with a high resistance fitted in series with the low resistance
moving-coil. If the potential difference across AB in fig. 13 were
required, the voltmeter would be connected across AB, that is, in

parallel with the conductor. Now it clearly would not do to connect a low resistance ammeter across AB in parallel with the conductor for the current would take the path of least resistance and pass through the ammeter rather than through the conductor. Hence a resistance is included in series with the ammeter and this resistance is as high as is consistent with a suitable deflection on the voltmeter scale. The use of a high resistance introduces the minimum disturbance into the circuit when the voltmeter is introduced, just as the use of a low resistance ammeter in series introduces the minimum disturbance when a current measurement is required.

An ammeter may therefore always be used as a voltmeter by the inclusion of a separate resistance in series with the moving coil. Some voltmeters are made directly with moving coils of large resistance, consisting of a large number of turns of fine wire to ensure a high sensitivity. Such instruments cannot be used as ammeters since their high resistance is a permanent feature of the voltmeter.

The hot-wire and soft iron ammeters are directly convertible to voltmeters by the insertion of resistance in series with the hot wire and the solenoid respectively. These instruments are then suitable for measuring either alternating or direct voltages.

The **sensitivity** of galvanometers generally is defined as the deflection in scale divisions per microamp. Alternatively, the *figure of merit* of a galvanometer is defined as the current required to produce a deflection of one-scale division.

EXERCISES

1. Describe and give the theory of the tangent galvanometer. In what way does it differ from the sine galvanometer?

2. Compare the moving magnet and moving-coil galvanometers. How are the latter modified to form ammeters?

3. Give the theory of the moving-coil galvanometer with a linear scale. What are the essentials of a ballistic-coil galvanometer?

4. Describe some form of ammeter suitable for measuring alternating current. Has the instrument a linear scale?

5. What is the essential difference between an ammeter and a voltmeter? Describe some instrument suitable for measuring a series of electrical discharges produced at short time intervals.

CHAPTER X

Magnetic Interactions of the Electric Current

* 1. Magnetic Shell.

We have already considered in Chaps. VIII and IX some elementary properties and applications of the magnetic field which accompanies an electric current. More complicated instances, such as the magnetic interactions of two or more coils carrying currents, require a more general approach to the problem such as is provided by the concept of the **magnetic shell**. By a series of experiments Ampère showed that the magnetic effect produced by a conductor carrying a current was the same as that produced by regarding the area enclosed by the conductor as a magnetic polar sheet or magnetic shell. The magnetic moment per unit area or **strength** of such a shell is commonly represented by σ, and the total magnetic moment of the shell in fig. 1

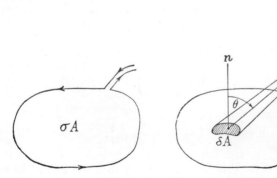

Fig. 1. — Magnetic Shell   Fig. 2. — Potential due to Magnetic Shell

is σA, where A is the area bounded by the conductor. By equation (7.4) the magnetic potential at the point **P** in fig. 2 due to a small element of area δA of the shell is

$$dV = \sigma \frac{\delta A \cos \theta}{r^2}, \quad \cdot \quad \cdot \quad \cdot \quad \cdot \quad \cdot \quad (10.1)$$

where θ is the angle between OP $(= r)$ and the normal ON to the shell at O.

Now if $d\omega$ is the solid angle subtended at P by the area δA, by definition $d\omega = \delta A \cos\theta / r^2$. Hence equation (10.1) becomes

$$dV = \sigma \, d\omega,$$

and the total magnetic potential at P becomes

$$V = \sigma\Omega, \quad \ldots \ldots \ldots \quad (10.2)$$

where Ω is the whole solid angle subtended by the conductor at P.

2. Helmholtz Coils.

We have derived from elementary considerations in Chap. VIII an expression for the force at the centre of a circular conductor. We now require a more general expression for the force at any point on the axis perpendicular to the plane of the circular coil. The solid angle subtended at the point P, at distance x from the centre of the coil, is A/r^2, where r is the radius of a sphere with centre P as shown in fig. 3, and A is the area of the cap DCB. Since the surface area of the cap is equal to that of a circumscribing cylinder of height h equal to that of the cap,

$$A = 2\pi r h = 2\pi r(r - x),$$

and

$$\Omega = 2\pi r(r - x)/r^2 = 2\pi \left(1 - \frac{x}{r}\right).$$

The magnetic potential at P is therefore, from (10.2),

$$V = 2\pi\sigma \left(1 - \frac{x}{r}\right). \quad \ldots \ldots \quad (10.3)$$

Now $r^2 = x^2 + a^2$: hence

$$V = 2\pi\sigma \left\{1 - \frac{x}{(x^2 + a^2)^{1/2}}\right\}. \quad \ldots \ldots \quad (10.4)$$

The magnetic force F at P is from symmetry directed along the axis and hence

$$F = -\frac{\partial V}{\partial x} = \frac{2\pi a^2 \sigma}{(x^2 + a^2)^{3/2}}. \quad \ldots \ldots \quad (10.5)$$

Equation (10.5) must reduce to (8.6) when $x = 0$, that is at the centre of the coil

$$F = \frac{2\pi\sigma}{a} = \frac{2\pi i}{a}, \quad \ldots \ldots \quad (10.6)$$

and hence $\sigma = i$, or *the strength of the shell is equal to the current in the conductor.*

Helmholtz's Arrangement.—Let two equal coils be mounted coaxially as in fig. 4, the currents being in such directions that the magnetic fields assist each other. The object of the arrangement is to obtain as uniform a field as possible near the point midway between the coils; this is achieved by proper choice of the distance $2b$ between them.

Now, by (10.5), the force F at distance x from the mid-point is

$$F = 2\pi a^2 i \left[\{a^2 + (b + x)^2\}^{-3/2} + \{a^2 + (b - x)^2\}^{-3/2} \right].$$

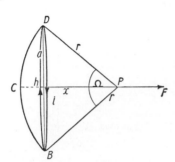

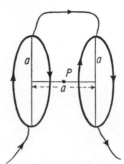

Fig. 3. — Magnetic Force on Axis of Circular Coil   Fig. 4. — Helmholtz Coils

The field gradient is $\partial F/\partial x$, and this changes very slowly if $\partial^2 F/\partial x^2 = 0$, when $x = 0$.

By carrying out the differentiations, it is easily found that $2b = a$, or the separation of the coils is equal to their radius, as shown in fig. 4.

3. Field of a Solenoid.

The magnetic field at any point on the axis of a solenoid may be calculated by considering the solenoid to consist of a series of plane circular coils and integrating the total effect of all the coils. Referring

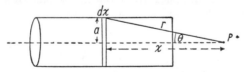

Fig. 5. — Field of a Solenoid

to fig. 5, the strength of the field at P due to the coil of elementary length dx, if i is the current per unit length, is

$$dF = \frac{2\pi a^2 i}{(x^2 + a^2)^{3/2}} \, dx. \quad \ldots \ldots (10.8)$$

Now $r\,d\theta = dx \cdot \sin\theta$, as shown in fig. 6. Hence

$$dF = \frac{2\pi a^2 i}{(x^2 + a^2)^{3/2}} \frac{r\,d\theta}{\sin\theta}. \quad \cdots \cdots \quad (10.9)$$

Since $(x^2 + a^2) = r^2$ and $a = r\sin\theta$, substituting in equation (10.9) we have

$$F = 2\pi i \int_{\theta_1}^{\theta_2} \sin\theta\,d\theta \quad \cdots \cdots \quad (10.10)$$

$$= 2\pi i \left[-\cos\theta \right]_{\theta_1}^{\theta_2}. \quad \cdots \cdots \quad (10.11)$$

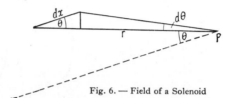

Fig. 6. — Field of a Solenoid

If the solenoid contains n turns per unit length,

$$F = 2\pi n i (\cos\theta_1 - \cos\theta_2). \quad \cdots \cdots \quad (10.12)$$

For an infinitely long solenoid $\theta_1 = 0$ and $\theta_2 = \pi$, and hence from (10.12)

$$F = 4\pi n i. \quad \cdots \cdots \quad (10.13)$$

* 4. Work done in taking a Unit Pole round a Current.

If we consider a point P_1 close to the surface of a magnetic shell, from equation (10.2) the magnetic potential at P_1 is given by $i\Omega$, where i is the current in the conductor to which the shell is equivalent, and Ω is the solid angle subtended by the conductor at P_1. Suppose now that the unit pole is taken once round any closed path encircling the current and brought back from the other side to a point P_2 infinitely close to P_1. Then the solid angle subtended by the equivalent magnetic shell at P_2 is $(\Omega - 4\pi)$ and the magnetic potential of this point is therefore $\sigma(\Omega - 4\pi) = i(\Omega - 4\pi)$. If we make P_2 coincide with P_1 in the limit, the change in magnetic potential which occurs in carrying a unit pole round a current is clearly

$$V = i\Omega - i(\Omega - 4\pi) = 4\pi i,$$

or the work done in taking a unit pole once round a current by any closed path is 4π times the current encircled. If the strength of the magnetic field at any point is H and the unit pole is taken an infinitesimally small distance ds, the work done in this short element of path is $H\,ds$. Hence the total work done, or **line integral of the magnetic field,** or the **magnetomotive force** involved in once encircling a current i, is

$$\text{M.M.F.} = \int H\,ds = V = 4\pi i. \quad \ldots \quad (10.14)$$

5. Applications of the Work Theorem.

(i) *Infinite Straight Wire.*

If the field is H at a point a distance r from the wire, the work done in once encircling the wire and returning to the initial position is

$$W = \text{force} \times \text{distance}$$
$$= H\,.\,2\pi r = 4\pi i$$

by equation (10.14).

Hence
$$H = \frac{2i}{r}. \quad \ldots \ldots \ldots \quad (10.15)$$

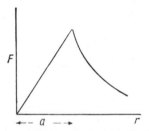

Fig. 7. — Field for Wire of Finite Thickness

We note that if the wire is replaced by a tube there is no field inside the tube, since no current is encircled by a closed curve entirely within the tube. Similarly if the conductor is a wire of finite thickness, the only contribution to the magnetic field at a point inside the wire is due to current flowing nearer to the axis than the point under consideration. If ρ represents the current density per unit area of the conductor of radius a, and the point is situated a distance r from the axis, the field is

$$F = \frac{2}{r}\,(\pi r^2 \rho) = 2\pi r \rho = \frac{2ri}{a^2}, \quad \ldots \quad (10.16)$$

since the whole current $i = \pi a^2 \rho$. From equation (10.16), therefore, the field increases proportionally to the distance from the axis reaching a maximum value of $2i/a$ at the surface of the conductor and then falling inversely as the distance for points external to the wire, as shown in fig. 7.

(ii) *Endless Solenoid or Anchor Ring.*

If the magnetic field is F in the endless solenoid or anchor ring shown in fig. 8, the work done in one complete revolution of a unit pole is

$$W = 2\pi r \,.\, F = 4\pi(2\pi rni)$$

by the work theorem, if n is the number of turns per unit length of the solenoid and r is the mean radius of the ring. Hence

$$F = 4\pi ni, \quad \text{. . . . . .} \quad (10.17)$$

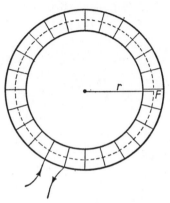

Fig. 8. — Field of an Endless Solenoid

which shows that the field is independent both of the radius and the thickness of the ring.

6. Force Between Currents.

(i) *Two Infinite Parallel Straight Conductors.*

The force on a unit pole (i.e. the magnetic field) at a distance r from an infinite straight wire carrying a current i is from equation (10.15) $F = 2i_1/r$, and this force is at right angles to the plane containing the wire and the pole. Hence, by Chap. VIII, section 9, the mechanical force on unit length of a second wire parallel to the first, at distance r from it, and carrying a current i_2, is

$$\frac{2i_1 i_2}{r}. \quad \text{. . . . . . .} \quad (10.18)$$

The force is perpendicular to both wires, and is an attraction if the currents are in the same direction.

(ii) *Two Coaxial Coils.*

By applying the principles which we have already considered, the force between two coaxial coils may be obtained. In general, the expressions obtained are complicated and only approximate. For the special case where $r_1 \ll r_2$, the force may be shown to be

$$F = \frac{6\pi^2 r_1^2 r_2^2 \cdot i_1 i_2}{(r_2^2 + x^2)^{5/2}} x, \quad \ldots \ldots \quad (10.19)$$

where i_1 and i_2 are the currents through the two coils of radii r_1 and r_2 respectively and x is the distance between them. The expression has a maximum when $x = r_2/2$.

7. Kelvin Current Balance.

In fig. 9 is shown the essential part of the Kelvin current balance, which is an instrument designed to operate from the magnetic force of interaction of coaxial coils. It consists of four fixed coils arranged at

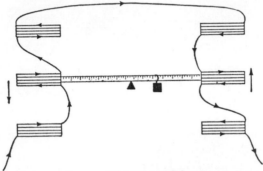

Fig. 9. — Kelvin Current Balance

the corners of a rectangle, with two similar coils attached to the arms of a centrally pivoted horizontal lever. The coils are arranged in series and the current circulates in such a direction that one coil is urged upwards and the other downwards. To restore the balance of the lever, a small rider is slid along the graduated lever arm. The expression for the forces between the coils cannot be calculated with sufficient accuracy, so the instrument has to be calibrated with some instrument such as the silver voltameter. If the rider has to be displaced a distance d to obtain equilibrium when the current changes by i, the couple is proportional to

$$kd = i^2, \quad \ldots \ldots \ldots \quad (10.20)$$

since the force between the coils is proportional to the current in both the fixed- and moving-coil systems. The lever is therefore graduated with a current scale obeying a square root law.

8. Kelvin Watt Balance.

The coils of the Kelvin current balance must all be of low resistance, since they are connected in series and in series with the circuit in which the current is to be measured. In the Kelvin watt balance, the outward appearance of the instrument is the same. The two moving coils, however, are now of high resistance, and only the four fixed coils have a low resistance. The current i_1 in the main circuit flows through the fixed low resistance coils as shown in fig. 10, but the current in the high resistance coils is obtained by connecting them in parallel with the system whose power absorption is required. The current i_2 in the high resistance coils is proportional to the potential difference E across

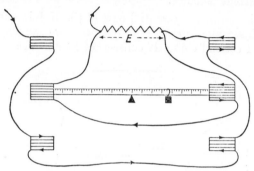

Fig. 10. — Kelvin Watt Balance

them, and hence the force F on the moving coils is a measure of the power W absorbed, for we have

$$W = Ei_1 = (i_2 R)i_1 = ki_1 i_2 = k'F = k''d,$$

where R is the resistance of the moving coils, and k, k' and k'' are constants. A linear scale is thus obtained between the displacement d of the rider and the power absorbed.

9. Siemens Electrodynamometer.

As shown in fig. 11, this instrument consists of two coils mounted in a vertical plane, one coil being fixed and the other free to move about a vertical axis which lies along a common diameter of the coils. In the zero position the coils are perpendicular to each other, but under the action of a common current i the movable coil tends to parallelism with the other until returned to the perpendicular position by twist applied to the torsion head. Then we have

$$\text{Couple} \propto \theta \propto i^2,$$

or
$$i = k\theta^{\frac{1}{2}}, \quad \ldots \ldots \ldots \quad (10.21)$$

so that the instrument acts as a current balance with a square-root torsion scale. The dynamometer may easily be modified for use as a wattmeter by inserting a high resistance in series with one of the coils and connecting this high resistance arrangement in parallel with the system whose power absorption is required. The other low resistance coil is, of course, placed in series with the system and takes its common current i. If i_1 is the current through the high resistance circuit, this

Fig. 11. — Siemens Electrodynamometer

is proportional to the potential difference E across it. Hence if W is the power absorbed,

$$W = Ei = ki_1i = k'\theta,$$

where k and k' are constants. The torsion head therefore gives a linear scale with respect to power absorbed (wattage).

EXERCISES

1. Explain the concept of the magnetic shell and use it to find the strength of the magnetic field at a point on the axis of a solenoid carrying a current.

2. Prove that the work done in conveying a unit pole once round a current is 4π times the current encircled. Apply this theorem to find the strength of the magnetic field inside an endless solenoid or anchor ring.

3. Describe the Kelvin current balance. In what essential features does it differ from the watt balance?

CHAPTER XI

Measurement of Resistance and Potential

1. Resistances in Series and in Parallel.

If resistances are connected in series, the total resistance is equal to the sum of the individual resistances. With reference to fig. 1 we have, if E represents the total fall in potential between A and D,

$$E = E_1 + E_2 + E_3 = IR, \qquad \cdots \quad (11.1)$$

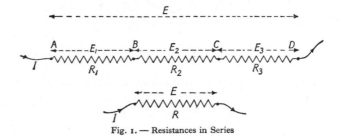

Fig. 1. — Resistances in Series

where R is the equivalent resistance. For the separate resistances, however, we have, by application of Ohm's law,

$$E_1 = IR_1,$$
$$E_2 = IR_2, \qquad \cdots \cdots \quad (11.2)$$
$$E_3 = IR_3.$$

Hence, adding,

$$E_1 + E_2 + E_3 = I(R_1 + R_2 + R_3), \qquad \cdots \quad (11.3)$$

and, equating (11.1) and (11.3),

$$R = R_1 + R_2 + R_3. \qquad \cdots \cdots \quad (11.4)$$

If the resistances are connected in parallel, the total resistance is such that its reciprocal is equal to the sum of the reciprocals of the individual resistances. From fig. 2 we have, on application of Ohm's law,

$$E = IR = I_1R_1 = I_2R_2 = I_3R_3. \qquad \cdots \quad (11.5)$$

Now $$I = I_1 + I_2 + I_3,$$

or, from (11.5),

$$\frac{E}{R} = \frac{E}{R_1} + \frac{E}{R_2} + \frac{E}{R_3},$$

or $$\frac{1}{R} = \frac{1}{R_1} + \frac{1}{R_2} + \frac{1}{R_3}. \quad \ldots \ldots \ldots \quad (11.6)$$

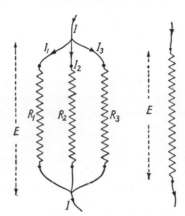

Fig. 2. — Resistances in Parallel

2. Currents in Divided Circuits.

We shall now calculate the currents in a circuit divided into two branches, as shown in fig. 3. Let the main current I divide into I_1 through R_1 and I_2 through R_2. Then, since the total current is unchanged,

$$I = I_1 + I_2. \quad \ldots \ldots \quad (11.7)$$

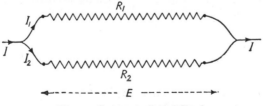

Fig. 3. — Currents in divided Circuit

Application of Ohm's law to first one resistance and then the other gives

$$E = I_1 R_1 = I_2 R_2. \quad \ldots \ldots \quad (11.8)$$

Hence, from (11.7) and (11.8),

$$I_1 = I \frac{R_2}{(R_1 + R_2)},$$

and

$$I_2 = I \frac{R_1}{(R_1 + R_2)}. \quad \cdots \cdots \quad (11.9)$$

In such a circuit, therefore, the current divides inversely as the sum of the resistances and directly as the other resistance.

3. Currents in any Network: Kirchhoff's Laws.

The magnitude of the current in any portion of a network, and the potential difference acting between any two parts of the network, are readily derived by the application of **Kirchhoff's laws**. The first law states that the *sum of the currents arriving at any point equals the sum of the currents leaving that point*; or, in algebraic form,

$$\Sigma I = 0. \quad \cdots \cdots \quad (11.10)$$

This law is a statement of the experimental fact that there is no accumulation of charge at any point in a complete electrical circuit. It corresponds exactly to the *equation of continuity* of a perfectly incompressible fluid, mentioned in Part I.

Kirchhoff's second law is simply Ohm's law applied to closed networks or closed portions of networks. It states that the *algebraic sum of the potential differences acting around separate portions of a closed network is equal to zero*, that is

$$\Sigma(E - IR) = 0, \quad \cdots \cdots \quad (11.11)$$

where E represents the potential difference arising from batteries present and IR that from the operation of Ohm's law. The combination of (11.10) and (11.11), which we have already used in a simple manner in deriving expressions in sections 1 and 2 of this chapter, is sufficient to solve completely any problem concerning the distribution of steady currents in networks.

4. Approximate Resistance Measurements.

Perhaps the simplest way of measuring the resistance of a wire is to connect it in series with an ammeter and a cell and place a voltmeter across the resistance as shown in fig. 4. Then application of Ohm's law gives $R = E/I$, where E is the reading on the voltmeter and I that on the ammeter. The result can only be approximately correct, because when the voltmeter is placed in parallel with the resistance alone as in fig. 4, the current I registered by the ammeter is only partially going through the resistance, part going through the voltmeter itself. Strictly Ohm's law would require $R = E/I_R$, where I_R is the current in the resistance. If, however, I_R is determined by placing the voltmeter across the ammeter and resistance together as in fig. 5, the

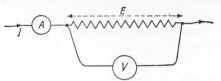

Fig. 4. — Approximate Measurement of Resistance

voltage E is now no longer that across the resistance alone but across ammeter and resistance together. However, the lower the resistance of the ammeter and the higher the resistance of the voltmeter, the more accurate the result, and if an electrostatic voltmeter is used, an accurate

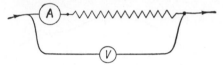

Fig. 5. — Approximate Measurement of Resistance

value for the resistance may be obtained, since the electrostatic voltmeter takes no current.

If a **resistance box** containing known resistances is available, the *method of substitution* affords a simple means of determining an unknown resistance. A tangent galvanometer, a cell and the resistance box are

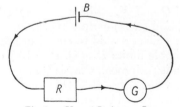

Fig. 6. — Use of Resistance Box

connected in series as in fig. 6, and a graph is obtained of R against $\cot \theta$. From the equation $I = k \tan \theta$ and by Ohm's law we have, if E is the voltage of the cell and r its **internal resistance** (see p. 624),

$$E = I(R + G + r), \quad \ldots \ldots \quad (11.12)$$

where G is the resistance of the galvanometer coil. Hence

$$R + G + r = \frac{E}{k \tan \theta} = k' \cot \theta, \quad \ldots \quad (11.13)$$

where $k' = E/k$ = constant. Since G and r remain constant a straight-line graph will be obtained, the intercept of which on the resistance axis gives the combined resistances of galvanometer and battery. To find the value of an unknown resistance, the latter is simply inserted in place of the resistance box and, when the deflection has been noted, reference to the already obtained $R \cot \theta$ graph gives the value of the unknown resistance.

5. Wheatstone Bridge.

Very accurate values of resistance may be obtained with a special arrangement of resistances termed the *Wheatstone bridge* or *net*. As shown in fig. 7, this consists of three known resistances P, Q and R and the unknown resistance X, connected to form the four sides of a quadrilateral. A battery is connected across the junction of P and R

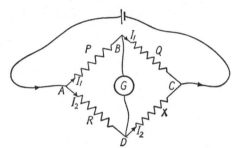

Fig. 7. — Wheatstone Bridge

and the junction of Q and X, while a galvanometer connected across the junctions $(P$-$Q)$ and $(R$-$X)$ completes the symmetry of the circuit. In general P and Q, which are said to constitute the *ratio arms*, may be varied within the simple limits $P = Q$, $P = 10Q$ or $P = 100Q$ respectively. The relation is reciprocal, that is Q may be made equal to $10P$ or $100P$; the basic value when $P = Q$ is usually 10 ohms. The resistance R is variable over a wide range usually from 1 ohm to several thousand ohms. Any sensitive galvanometer is suitable.

The action of the instrument depends on the adjustment of the value of R until there is no deflection in the galvanometer. This *null condition* is realized when no current flows in the galvanometer, that is, when the potential of B equals the potential of D. From fig. 7 we have

$$V_{AB} = I_1 P,$$

and $$V_{AD} = I_2 R. \qquad \cdots \cdots \quad (11.14)$$

Now the potential of A is common to both P and R, and if no current flows in the galvanometer, the potentials of B and D are equal. Hence

$$V_{AB} = V_{AD},$$

and therefore, from (11.14),

$$I_1 P = I_2 R. \quad . \quad . \quad . \quad . \quad . \quad .(11.15)$$

Similarly for the resistances Q and X,

$$V_{BC} = V_{DC},$$

and hence $\qquad I_1 Q = I_2 X. \quad . \quad , \quad . \quad . \quad . \quad (11.16)$

Hence, finally from (11.15) and (11.16) we have

$$\frac{Q}{P} = \frac{X}{R}, \quad . \quad . \quad . \quad . \quad . \quad (11.17)$$

from which X is easily determined if P, Q and R are known.

In using the bridge, the resistance R is changed until ideally the galvanometer shows no deflection. In practice, for values of R slightly greater than a certain amount the galvanometer will generally show a small deflection in one direction, while for values of R slightly less than the same amount, the galvanometer will be deflected in the reverse direction. In general, R can be varied by steps of one ohm or larger so that the value of X can be found only within a certain accuracy. If the ratio arms are equal, so that $P = Q$, from (11.17) $R = X$ for a balance to be obtained, so X will usually lie somewhere between two integral values of R differing by 1 ohm.

When an approximate value for X has been obtained as above, the ratio arms are changed so that $P = 10Q$. The value of R, which now gives a balance, is from (11.17) equal to $10X$. Hence the accuracy of determination of X is carried to one-tenth of an ohm. By further increasing the ratio to $P = 100Q$, the value of $R = 100X$, and X is determined to one-hundredth of an ohm. Of course, the value of X must be such that the resistances available for R in the given instrument are sufficient to cover the range $R = 100X$, or alternatively $R = X/100$ if the ratio arms are reversed. Theoretically by having greater ratio arms the accuracy could be extended indefinitely, but in practice the introduction of very large resistances reduces the current in the circuit to such an extent that the galvanometer sensitivity becomes insufficient to respond to small charges in R, and a natural limit is thereby set to the accuracy obtainable.

6. Post Office Box and Metre Bridge.

The Wheatstone bridge is available in many different forms, two of which are the *Post Office box* and the *metre bridge*. The former, which is shown diagrammatically in fig. 8, is fitted with two tapping keys which are situated in the battery and galvanometer circuits respectively. Incidentally, the bridge is symmetrical in that the battery and galvanometer may be interchanged without affecting the balance point. Owing to the existence of electromagnetic induction (see Chap. XIII), the battery circuit should be closed before the galvanometer circuit, so that steady current conditions are already established in the circuit. The resistances in the box are usually *non-inductively wound* so as to reduce induction effects to a minimum. In any case, it is the final steady deflection of the galvanometer which is observed and not any temporary kick which may occur when the keys are depressed. Since resistance varies with temperature, only small currents are permis-

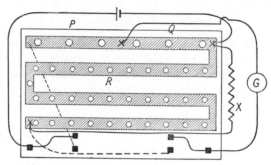

Fig. 8. — Post Office Box

sible and boxes are usually *rated* at a definite maximum current which can be carried with safety. This should on no account be exceeded or the resistances may be permanently damaged and acquire values differing from their nominal amounts.

The **metre bridge** or **slide-wire bridge** was devised to allow a continuous change in the value of the resistances instead of only integral values such as the Post Office box affords. As shown in fig. 9(a), it consists of a rectangular board to which is attached a metre rule, stretched beside which is a wire about a metre long. The wire is made of some resistance material, such as Eureka alloy, so that the whole wire has a resistance of about 1 ohm. The ends of the wire are soldered to terminals which are in turn connected to stout copper strips of negligible resistance. These strips are provided with two gaps in which are inserted a known resistance R and the unknown resistance X respectively. A third copper strip joins R and X, and a third terminal is attached to the centre of this strip. This terminal is joined by a wire to a galvanometer, the other lead of which goes to a metal slider or *jockey* which slides along the bare wire of the metre bridge. The battery is joined to the extremities of the bridge wire, and the whole constitutes the usual Wheatstone quadrilateral. A balance is obtained by sliding the jockey until no deflection is shown in the galvanometer. If the two resistances into which the bridge wire is then divided are R_1 and R_2, we have by (11.17)

$$\frac{R_1}{R_2} = \frac{R}{X}. \qquad \dotsb \qquad (11.18)$$

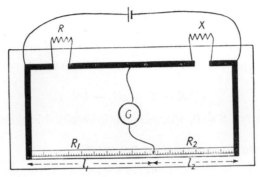

Fig. 9 (a). — Metre Bridge

The wire is assumed to be of uniform cross-section; hence the resistance of any portion of it is proportional to the length. Therefore $R_1 \propto l_1$ and $R_2 \propto l_2$, whence from (11.18)

$$X = R\frac{l_2}{l_1}. \qquad \dotsb \qquad (11.19)$$

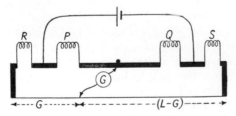

Fig. 9 (b).—Carey Foster Bridge

Since readings of l_1 and l_2 may be taken to a fraction of a millimetre, good accuracy is obtainable in the value of X if R is chosen to be nearly equal to X. If R is very different from X, l_2 is very different from l_1 and the ratio l_2/l_1 becomes very susceptible to error.

The *Carey Foster bridge*, a diagram of which is shown in fig. 9 (b), is a modification of the metre bridge to allow the accurate comparison of two nearly equal resistances R and S. From the diagram, if a balance occurs when the jockey is G from one end of the bridge of total length L and resistance per unit length ρ, we have

$$\frac{P}{Q} = \frac{R + \rho G}{S + \rho(L - G)}.$$

The resistances R and S are now interchanged, a new balance point is found at l_2, and as before we have

$$\frac{P}{Q} = \frac{S + \rho l_2}{R + \rho(L - l_2)}.$$

Hence, equating the two preceding expressions, adding unity to both sides of the equation and cancelling the numerators which then become identical, we have

$$R - S = \rho(l_2 - G).$$

To find ρ, we put $S = 0$, whereupon ρ is obtained in terms of R.

7. Approximate Measurement of Potential.

The electrostatic voltmeter is the ideal instrument, since it takes no current from the circuit and therefore leaves undisturbed the circuit to which it is applied. It is, however, insensitive for potentials less than about 500 volts. The ordinary moving-coil voltmeter is fairly satisfactory if its resistance is high, but clearly it will cause great disturbance if it is introduced across a circuit in which resistances of several thousand ohms are present. The *potentiometer* is a device which allows the measurement of potential without taking any current from the system.

8. The Potentiometer.

In construction, the potentiometer is identical with the metre bridge, which is often used as a potentiometer, except that the resistances R and X are omitted, these spaces being left unoccupied. The instrument therefore consists, in its simplest form, of a wire stretched beside a metre scale and connected to a *steady* supply battery such as an accumulator (see Chap. XII) as shown in fig. 10. The potentiometer will only *compare* voltages (potential differences, electromotive forces), that is, a standard voltage is first necessary to calibrate the potentiometer wire. Such a standard voltage is provided by the E.M.F. of a standard cell (see p. 638); we denote this by E_s. The positive pole of the standard cell is connected to that end of the potentiometer wire to which is attached the positive pole of the accumulator. The negative pole of the standard cell is connected through a sensitive galvanometer to a jockey sliding on the potentiometer wire.

Now at certain positions of the jockey it will be found that the galvanometer shows no deflection. This means that the drop in potential between the common point A and the point of contact C of the jockey, due to the current supplied from the accumulator to the bridge wire, is exactly equal to the potential E_s between the poles of the standard cell; the E.M.F. of a cell being by definition the potential between its poles when no current is flowing through the cell. Since the wire is uniform, the drop E in potential across any length l is known by simple ratio,

$$\frac{E}{E_s} = \frac{l}{l_s}, \quad \ldots \ldots \quad (11.20)$$

where l_s is the distance AC.

To determine any other potential, therefore, the source to be measured simply replaces the standard cell and the new balance point

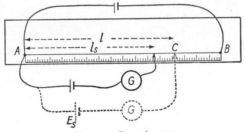

Fig. 10. — Potentiometer

is obtained. To avoid errors due to fluctuations in the voltage of the accumulator, it is usual to have a two-way switch included in the circuit so that readings of the balance points for E and E_s may be taken alternately at regular intervals and an average result obtained. The voltage to be measured must not exceed that of the accumulator; otherwise no balance point will be found anywhere along the wire. To overcome this difficulty it is not usually sufficient to increase the number of accumulators since a prohibitively large current may be produced in the slide wire. Conversely, very small potentials could not be measured accurately if the standard voltage drop had its ordinary value of 2 volts per 100 cm. of potentiometer wire. These difficulties are overcome by the use of *auxiliary resistances* in series with the slide wire of the potentiometer, and commercial potentiometers are available for measuring potentials over a very wide range.

If the potential to be measured is, say, between 99 and 100 volts, an auxiliary resistance B of some value such as 98 ohms is included in series with the wire as shown in fig. 11. The resistance of the bridge wire itself must have been accurately determined simply by inserting it in one arm of a Wheatstone bridge in the usual fashion. If we assume for simplicity that its resistance is 2 ohms, a steady applied voltage

E, which must be somewhat greater than 100 volts, would produce a current of $E/100$ amps and consequently a drop in potential of $E/50$ volts down the wire. The value of $E/50$ is easily determined by connecting a standard cell to the bridge wire but not across the auxiliary resistance; for

$$\frac{E_s}{E/50} = \frac{l_s}{100},$$

or

$$\frac{E}{50} = 100 \frac{E_s}{l_s}; \quad \ldots \ldots \quad (11.21)$$

The standard cell is now replaced by the unknown potential difference, which, however, is connected across the auxiliary resistance as well as

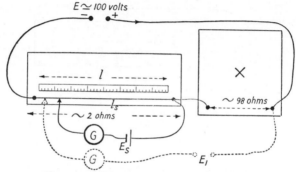

Fig. 11. — Potentiometer with Auxiliary Resistance

across the bridge wire. If the balance point occurs at some point l, we have, by reference to fig. 11,

$$E_1 = IR$$

$$= \frac{E}{100}\left(98 + \frac{l}{50}\right); \quad \ldots \ldots \quad (11.22)$$

whence, from (11.21) and (11.22),

$$E_1 = 50 \frac{E_s}{l_s}\left(98 + \frac{l}{50}\right). \quad \ldots \ldots \quad (11.23)$$

If the potential to be measured is of the order of millivolts or microvolts, as when thermoelectric potentials (see Chap. XVIII) are under consideration, the auxiliary resistance is raised to some suitable value, such that when a 2-volt accumulator is connected across auxiliary resistance and bridge wire the potential drop across the latter is of the order of several millivolts or microvolts. The actual method of procedure in this case is described in Chap. XVII.

9. Measurement of Current and Resistance with a Potentiometer.

A potentiometer will only compare potentials, but since, by Ohm's law, a current may be estimated by the potential which is required to drive it through a known resistance, the indirect measurement of current may be carried out with great accuracy with the potentiometer. Referring to fig. 12, a *small* known resistance R is inserted in the circuit carrying the current I whose value is required, and the ends of R are then connected to the potentiometer, in place of the normal standard cell. If the potentiometer wire has been calibrated with a standard cell we have

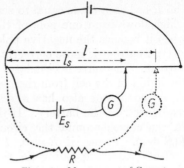

Fig. 12. — Measurement of Current

$$\frac{E_s}{l_s} = \frac{IR}{l},$$

whence
$$I = \frac{E_s}{R}\frac{l}{l_s}. \quad . \quad . \quad . \quad . \quad . \quad (11.24)$$

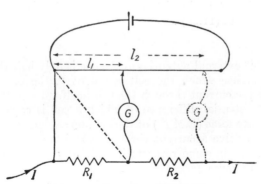

Fig. 13. — Comparison of Resistances

Two resistances R_1 and R_2 may be accurately compared by comparing the potentials E_1 and E_2 developed across them when they are carrying a common current, as in fig. 13. If balances are obtained for lengths l_1 and l_2 when the ends of first R_1 and then R_2 are connected to the potentiometer, then

$$\frac{E_1}{E_2} = \frac{IR_1}{IR_2} = \frac{l_1}{l_2}. \quad . \quad . \quad . \quad . \quad (11.25)$$

10. Measurement of the Internal Resistance of a Battery.

If the poles of a battery are joined by a short thick wire of negligible resistance, the current which results, although large, does not rise to infinity as it should according to Ohm's law, where $I = E/R$ and R has been made equal to zero. This is because the electric current which flows from one pole of the battery to the other does not stop when it reaches the negative pole. On the contrary, the passage of an electric current is more correctly described as the *circulation* of electric current. The current circulates right round the circuit back through the liquid in the cell from the negative to the positive plate. Now this liquid conductor also has a resistance, which is called the **internal resistance** r of the battery. If the external resistance of the circuit is R, the current round the circuit is, by Ohm's law, given by $E = I(R + r)$. Hence if $R = 0$, $I = E/r$, i.e. the current has a finite limiting value depending on the internal resistance of the battery. Further, the potential difference available for the external circuit varies with the external resistance or load. Thus, for an external resistance R, this potential difference V is by Ohm's law

$$V = IR = E\,\frac{R}{(R + r)}. \quad \cdot \quad \cdot \quad \cdot \quad \cdot \quad (11.26)$$

If, therefore, the external resistance and internal resistance were equal, that is $R = r$, from (11.26)

$$V = E/2,$$

or the available external potential difference is only half the maximum potential difference which the cell can deliver, the other half being used to drive the current through the cell itself.

The total potential difference of which a cell is capable is termed the **electromotive force** (E.M.F.) of the cell, on the analogy that a force is necessary to drive a current through a resistance. The term is in common use, but in some respects is unfortunate since it is actually simply the maximum potential difference available. It is therefore measured in energy or work done per unit charge conveyed, and not in force units as the name would imply.

11. Platinum Resistance Thermometer.

As an example of the practical application of the Wheatstone bridge circuit we shall now describe its use in conjunction with the platinum resistance thermometer for temperature measurement. This thermometer when used for the measurement of high temperatures consists of a spiral of platinum wire wound on a mica former and in-

serted in a silica tube, as shown in fig. 14. The leads from the thermometer are connected to one arm of the Wheatstone bridge which
incorporates a slide wire MO. The ratio arms are represented by
P and Q, and these are generally arranged to be equal. The balance
arm contains a suitable resistance R approximately equal to the resistance of the thermometer. Included in the balance arm are a pair of
dummy leads identical in size, position and resistance with the leads
which go to the platinum resistance thermometer. Let the resistance
of the thermometer be T and let the resistance of MN be X, where

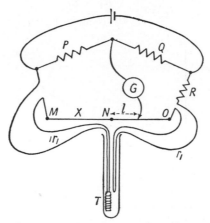

Fig. 14. — Platinum Resistance Thermometer

N is the mid-point of MO. Then if ρ is the resistance per centimetre
of MN and the resistance of the leads is r_1, since $P = Q$ we have

$$r_1 + R + (X - l\rho) = r_1 + T + (X + l\rho)$$

where a balance occurs l cm. from the centre of MO. Hence

$$T = R - 2l\rho.$$

Owing to the passage of current through T even in the balance
position, a certain rise in temperature occurs in the thermometer
quite apart from that due to the heat supply in which it is inserted.
To obtain the resistance for zero current an ammeter is inserted in the
battery circuit, and a curve is plotted of T against I. This curve may
be extrapolated to zero as shown in fig. 15 and hence the value of T
for zero current may be estimated.

To deduce the relation between the temperature as measured on
the resistance scale and that which would be found on the gas scale,
we may note that Callendar found on placing a platinum resistance
thermometer inside a gas thermometer that the resistance-tempera-

ture variation over a range of a few hundred degrees from 0° C. was given by

$$R_t = R_0(1 + at + \beta t^2), \quad \ldots \quad (11.27)$$

where t is measured on the gas thermometer and R_t and R_0 are the resistances at t and 0° C. respectively. The quantities a and β are constants depending on the nature of the metal.

Now from the definition of temperature on the Centigrade scale (see Part II), the temperature on the platinum resistance scale is

$$t_{\text{Pt}} = \frac{R_t - R_0}{1/100\,(R_{100} - R_0)}. \quad \ldots \quad (11.28)$$

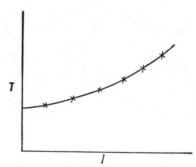

Fig. 15. — Extrapolation for Zero Current

Substituting for R_t from (11.27) in (11.28) we have

$$t_{\text{Pt}} = \frac{t(a + \beta t)}{(a + 100\beta)}. \quad \ldots \quad (11.29)$$

We express (11.29) in the form of a difference correction thus:

$$(t - t_{\text{Pt}}) = \frac{100\beta}{(a + 100\beta)}\,t\left(1 - \frac{t}{100}\right), \quad \ldots \quad (11.30)$$

whence

$$(t - t_{\text{Pt}}) = \frac{\Delta t}{100}\left(\frac{t}{100} - 1\right), \quad \ldots \quad (11.30)$$

where $\Delta = -10^4\beta/(a + 100\beta) = $ constant.

We note that if the variation of resistance with gas-scale temperature had been a linear one, that is $\beta = 0$, then $\Delta = 0$, and from (11.30) the platinum resistance scale and the gas scale would have been identical. Actually, for platinum $\Delta \simeq 1\cdot57$. Its value is usually found by calculating t_{Pt} from (11.28) for some fixed point such as the melting-point of sulphur, which is 444° C. on the gas scale, and substituting these values in equation (11.30). A slightly different value of Δ is required at higher temperatures, since α and β are not quite constant, the most suitable values for Δ being found by choosing suitable higher fixed points such as the melting-point of gold and other metals.

EXERCISES

1. Two wires of equal resistance are connected first in series and then in parallel. Show that the equivalent resistance of the former arrangement is four times that of the latter.

2. State and explain Kirchhoff's laws of the electric circuit. What modification if any is necessary to their formulation for a circuit containing varying currents?

3. Describe two distinct methods for finding the value of an unknown resistance suspected to be about 100 ohms.

4. Give the theory of the Wheatstone bridge circuit for steady currents. Give examples of the application of the Wheatstone bridge to physical problems.

5. Describe the use of the metre bridge in the comparison of two nearly equal resistances. How would you compare two resistances whose ratio is expected to be about 100 : 1?

6. How may a potentiometer be used (a) to compare E.M.F.s, (b) to measure a current and (c) to compare two resistances?

7. Owing to the resistance between wire and binding-post a potentiometer has a certain zero error. Calculate this error in the form of a length to be added to the observed balance length, given that one cell is balanced by a length of 50 cm., a second cell by a length of 40 cm., whereas when the two cells are used in series, the balance length is 93 cm. [3 cm.]

8. Describe an accurate method for finding the internal resistance of a battery. How does the internal resistance of a cell vary with temperature.

9. Explain fully how the temperature of a furnace is measured with the aid of a platinum resistance thermometer.

CHAPTER XII

Electrolysis

1. Qualitative Laws.

When an electric current is passed through a solution, in general chemical action occurs at the electrodes. For example, when an electric current is passed through a solution of copper sulphate in water it is found that metallic copper is deposited at the negative electrode or cathode. What occurs at the anode depends on the chemical nature of the electrodes. If these are of copper, the anode gradually dissolves, forming copper sulphate solution. Moreover, it dissolves at the same rate as copper is deposited at the cathode. The concentration of the solution therefore remains constant as a whole, although the distribution of the concentration, as shown by the intensity of the blue colour of the solution, is such that a decrease occurs in the neighbourhood of the cathode and a corresponding equal increase in the concentration near the anode. Although it is sometimes stated that the electrolysis of copper sulphate between copper electrodes consists in the transfer of copper from anode to cathode, it is clear from the above experimental considerations that the copper which dissolves from the anode does not proceed immediately to the cathode. The explanation of electrolysis lies in the *ionic hypothesis*, which we discuss in section 4.

If the copper electrodes are replaced by platinum electrodes, copper is still deposited at the cathode but no solution of the platinum occurs at the anode. Instead, oxygen gas is evolved. Briefly it may be stated that the products obtained by electrolysis depend on the

(i) Nature of the solute;

(ii) Nature of the solvent;

(iii) Nature of the electrodes;

(iv) Current density, that is the current divided by the area of the electrodes immersed.

These qualitative laws are illustrated by various examples which we shall consider throughout this chapter.

2. Quantitative Laws.

Faraday's laws of electrolysis are:

(1) *The amount of chemical action is the same at all points.*

This law is illustrated in fig. 1, showing several different solutions subjected simultaneously to a common current. Electrolysis takes place in all the solutions just as if the other solutions were not present.

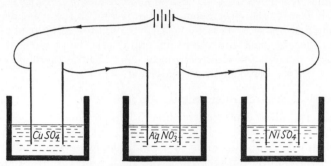

Fig. 1. — Simultaneous Electrolysis

(2) *The mass deposited or evolved is proportional to the current, the chemical equivalent of the solute and the time.*

If an ammeter is included in the circuit in which electrolysis of copper sulphate is taking place, then it is easily shown that the mass deposited is directly proportional to the time during which the current passes, and to the magnitude of the current.

Suppose now that a second electrolytic cell or **voltameter,** containing silver nitrate, is included in the circuit containing the copper voltameter. Then it is found on comparing the weights of copper and silver deposited that they are in the ratio of their chemical equivalents. The same law is obeyed if the substances are evolved as gases, as may be shown if the latter are collected, as in the *hydrogen and oxygen voltameter* shown in fig. 2, in which the liquid is dilute H_2SO_4.

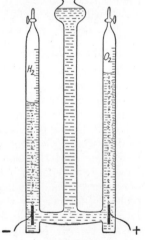

Fig. 2. — Hydrogen and Oxygen Voltameter

Faraday's laws may be expressed mathematically thus:

$$m = Izt, \quad \ldots \ldots \quad (12.1)$$

where m = mass deposited,
$\quad t$ = time of passage of current,
$\quad I$ = current,
$\quad z$ = electrochemical equivalent.

The **electrochemical equivalent** is simply the chemical equivalent

      (H 394)

multiplied by the necessary number (constant) to make equation (12.1) valid numerically. The product (I_o) is, of course, the **quantity** of electricity which has passed, measured in coulombs. Since in (12.1) $z = m$ if $It = 1$. the electrochemical equivalent is the mass deposited by 1 ampere in 1 sec. It is found that it requires 98,470 coulombs to deposit the chemical equivalent in grammes of any element. The numerical value of the electrochemical equivalent is therefore slightly larger than 10^{-5} of its chemical equivalent.

3. Electrochemical or International Ampere.

Since the mass deposited is directly proportional to the current, the ampere may be defined on an electrochemical basis. In practice, the amount deposited depends to a small extent on the concentration of the solution, the temperature, the nature of the electrodes, the current density and the nature of the other ions (see section 4) present. Consequently, precise details must be stipulated in the definition of the unit of current. Actually, silver nitrate solution is preferred, and the electrochemical or international ampere is defined as that current which will deposit 0·001118 gm. of silver per second from a specified solution under specified conditions.

4. Nature of Electrolysis.

The nature of electrolysis is intimately connected with the processes which occur when a solute forms a solution. On the molecular hypothesis it was originally thought that the process of solution consisted merely in the suspension of molecules of the solute between molecules of the solvent. Owing to their heat energy, the molecules of both solute and solvent were in continual random motion, as evidenced by Brownian movement, but the molecules still retained their molecular structure. Now on this hypothesis the production of copper during the electrolysis of copper sulphate would consist in the disruption of the copper sulphate molecule, followed by the transfer of the copper atom to the cathode. It is clearly difficult to understand why the copper atom should proceed to the cathode except under electrical forces, which implies that the copper atom has somehow acquired a positive charge. This might conceivably take place on disruption of the molecule by the electric force acting between anode and cathode, by analogy with electrification known to be produced by cleavage. In view of the now well established electrical theory of matter it would be a waste of time to pursue the above arguments further, but we may note one experimental fact that was strongly against the disruption hypothesis. If measurement is made of the potential E across, and the current I passing through, a solution undergoing electrolysis, the electrical energy consumed is given by EIt, where t is the time of passage of the current. Now, if the water equivalent of the electrolytic cell is known and a thermometer is inserted, it will be found that heat is evolved just as in the passage of the current through a solid conductor. Moreover, the heat generated is found to be exactly equal to the electrical energy consumed (but compare section 11). There is therefore *no energy available to disrupt the molecules of the solute.*

From this fact, and other considerations, Arrhenius argued that the process of solution consisted in far more than the distribution of molecules of solute between molecules of solvent. He suggested that **dissociation** of the solute molecule into **ions** takes place immediately the solute dissolves. A copper sulphate solution therefore consists of copper and sulphion (SO_4) ions in solution. Electrolysis then consists in the attraction of the copper ions, which are positively charged, to the cathode and of sulphions to the anode. The hypothesis was very revolutionary and met with the bitterest opposition, but that it represents the facts there is not now any question. Anomalies regarding the magnitude of osmotic pressure, variation of electrical conductivity with concentration, change in the boiling- and freezing-points of solutions, and many other phenomena, receive entirely satisfactory and natural explanation on the **ionic hypothesis.**

In a dilute solution, dissociation is complete. With concentrated solutions, dissociation is only partial and, of course, there is a balance between the number of ions which dissociate in any given time and the number which recombine. Incidentally, the analogy with gaseous conduction, which is also ionic, is complete (see Chapter XVIII). Further, the charge carried by a monovalent ion is exactly equal to the electronic charge, so the ionic hypothesis is in complete agreement with modern electron theory. Indeed, the latter received much initial support and encouragement from the ionic theory. Silver, being monovalent, carries one positive electronic charge, while the nitrate radical (NO_3) carries the corresponding negative charge. With copper sulphate, in which the binding is divalent, the copper ion carries a double positive electronic charge and the sulphion radical a double negative charge. The fact that the mass deposited is directly proportional to the chemical equivalent is therefore a natural result of the number of charges carried being numerically equal to the valency. That the charge carried is independent of the chemical nature of the substance suggests strongly what has been proved to be the case, namely that the same electronic charge is associated with all matter.

5. Further Examples.

We shall now discuss further examples of electrolysis in the light of the ionic hypothesis. Under the action of the electric field between anode and cathode, two streams of ions commence to move in opposite directions. The accelerations under the field are opposed by the viscous friction of the solute molecules, and a steady velocity is ultimately reached in agreement with Stokes's law (see Part I, p. 137). These ionic velocities will clearly be different since, while the charges of the two ions may be equal and opposite, their masses will in general be different. The velocity of an ion for unit field gradient is defined as the **mobility** of the ion; methods of measuring mobilities are described in section 6.

In the electrolysis of copper sulphate between platinum electrodes, oxygen is evolved from the anode because platinum is not susceptible to attack by the neutralized SO_4 ion. Instead, the SO_4 ions attack the solvent, water, liberating oxygen and forming sulphuric acid, which, of course, remains dissociated in solution. We express these results thus:

$$CuSO_4 \rightleftharpoons Cu^{++} + SO_4^{--},$$
$$SO_4 + H_2O \rightarrow H_2SO_4 + O, \quad \ldots \quad \text{(12.2)}$$
$$H_2SO_4 \rightleftharpoons H^+ + H^+ + SO_4^{--}.$$

This example illustrates how the products of electrolysis depend on the nature of the solvent and the electrodes.

The behaviour of water is instructive. Pure distilled water conducts very little. The explanation of this is that it consists almost entirely of undissociated molecules (actually they are often associated into higher groups of nH_2O, where n is integral). Consequently there are few ions to carry the current. If now a small quantity of sulphuric acid is added to the water, hydrogen and oxygen are evolved when the solution is electrolysed between platinum electrodes. The equations representing the reaction are

$$H_2SO_4 \rightleftharpoons H^+ + H^+ + SO_4^{--},$$
$$SO_4 + H_2O \rightarrow H_2SO_4 + O. \quad \cdots \quad \text{(12.3)}$$

Since the sulphuric acid is reformed in the process while water is removed, the solution grows continually more acid. In fact, the sulphuric acid is acting like a chemical catalyst, for it remains unchanged in amount throughout the process.

With sodium chloride in water, if platinum electrodes are used, hydrogen is evolved at the cathode and platinic chloride forms in the solution. Soon after the process has commenced, therefore, platinum may be deposited together with hydrogen at the cathode. The hydrogen is formed indirectly, owing to the chemical reaction between the sodium and the water. The equations are:

$$NaCl \rightleftharpoons Na^+ + Cl^-,$$
$$Na + H_2O \rightarrow NaOH + H,$$
$$4Cl + Pt \rightarrow PtCl_4, \qquad \cdots \quad \text{(12.4)}$$
$$PtCl_4 \rightleftharpoons Pt^{++++} + Cl^- + Cl^- + Cl^- + Cl^-.$$

The sodium hydroxide itself also undergoes electrolysis with the liberation of oxygen at the anode. If carbon electrodes are used, these are moderately resistant chemically to chlorine, and consequently the latter is evolved from the carbon anode instead of attacking it. For rapid evolution of chlorine, however, the current density should be high, for chlorine reacts slowly with water according to the equation

$$2Cl + H_2O \rightarrow 2HCl + O, \quad \ldots \quad (12.5)$$

so that some oxygen is also evolved at the anode.

Finally, if the current density is high, acidulated water gives some ozone as well as oxygen at platinum electrodes.

*6. Measurement of Ionic Velocities.

Simple but approximate methods of measuring ionic velocities are based upon chemical action between the travelling ions and the material through which they travel. In Lodge's method, two vessels

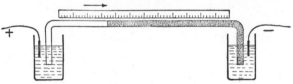

Fig. 3. — Measurement of Ionic Velocities

containing dilute sulphuric acid are joined by a horizontal tube containing sodium chloride suspended in gelatine, together with a trace of phenolphthalein as indicator, as shown in fig. 3. As electrolysis proceeds, the H^+ ions form HCl and decolorize the phenolphthalein. The velocity of the H^+ ions may therefore be determined directly from the rate of recession of the coloured edge along the tube. Alternative methods may be used based upon the change of refractive index along a tube containing the electrolyte.

More accurate methods depend on a determination of the change in concentration in the region of the anode and cathode, either by direct chemical sampling or by refractive index measurements. If u and v are the velocities of the positive and negative ions respectively, the total current and total deposition in unit time are proportional to $(u + v)$. If the current flows for such a time that $(u + v)$ gram-molecules of solute are removed from the solution, in the region near the cathode $(u + v)$ gram-atoms of positive ions have been removed, but u gram-atoms have been gained by migration, leaving a total loss of v gram-atoms of positive ions near this electrode. An equal loss of v gram-atoms of negative ions is lost by migration from the same neighbourhood. By a similar process u gram-atoms of solute are lost near the anode and hence we have

$$\frac{\text{Loss of concentration near the cathode}}{\text{Loss of concentration near the anode}} = \frac{v}{u}. \quad . \quad (12.6)$$

If the concentration of completely dissociated solute is w gram-equivalents per c.c., since 1 gram equivalent requires 1 Faraday, that is 96,470 coulombs for its deposition, the current density accompanying the electrolysis is given by

$$\rho = w(u + v) \, 96,470. \quad . \quad . \quad . \quad . \quad (12.7)$$

Since w may be measured, equations (12.6) and (12.7) are sufficient to determine v and u completely. It is usual to determine the conductivity σ of the electrolyte by some method such as that described in Chap. XIII, section 16 (iv). Then if the potential acting across the solution is V and the distance between the electrodes is l, the *field gradient* E is defined by $E = V/l$. Applying Ohm's law we have

$$\rho = \sigma E,$$

where ρ is measured in amperes per sq. cm., σ in ohm^{-1}/cm.$^{-1}$, and E in volts per cm., and hence equation (12.7) acquires its usual form

$$(u + v) = \frac{\sigma}{w} \frac{E}{96,470}. \quad . \quad . \quad . \quad . \quad (12.8)$$

7. Applications of Electrolysis.

The great variety of chemical products which may be obtained by suitable adjustment of the physical parameters makes electrolysis one of the most valuable processes in industry. We select the following typical applications of electrolysis.

(a) Production of Metals.

Aluminium is now rarely extracted by chemical smelting. The general process is to dissolve alumina, the oxide Al_2O_3, in fused cryolite, Na_3AlF_6, as solvent. Pure aluminium forms at the cathode and the process goes on as though it were simple electrolysis of the alumina, fresh supplies of which are added from time to time.

(b) Refining of Copper.

Crude copper obtained by smelting is used as the anode in a solution of copper sulphate, a pure copper rod being used as cathode. Arsenic and other impurities form at the anode and drop to the bottom of the vessel, where they form *anode sludge*.

(c) Electroplating.

Valuable metals such as gold and silver, or metals which resist atmospheric corrosion such as chromium, may be deposited on baser metals. In gold and silver plating, the articles are suspended to form the cathode in a solution of the double cyanides $KAu(CN)_2$ or $KAg(CN)_2$. To obtain a strongly adhesive coating the articles must be scrupulously clean and the current density must be very low. The latter consideration requires the plating process to occupy several weeks.

(d) Electrotyping.

If moulds of plaster or wax are coated with graphite to render them conducting, metal type may be built up by using suitable solutions and using the cast as cathode.

(e) Anodizing.

Aluminium and its alloys do not readily take up paint and dyes. By using the aluminium as the anode in an acidulated solution, a thin film of oxide is formed on the aluminium, after which it will readily take up the dye.

(f) Alloys.

By using certain concentrations of mixed solutions of metals together with suitable current densities, alloys may be formed directly by electrolysis. Examples are alloys of Cu-Zn, Cu-Sn and Zn-Cd.

Many of the processes are trade secrets, which depend on small changes in the conditions. For example, addition of certain colloids adds a lustrous finish to some electroplated articles, thus obviating subsequent polishing. Other applications are to the formation of seamless metal tubing, to the surfacing of machine tools with more durable materials, and to the building up of worn machine parts.

8. The Voltaic Cell.

The student will now realize that since electric current flows not only from the positive pole to the negative pole outside a cell but circulates right through the cell, the latter is undergoing continual electrolysis. The solution in a voltaic cell is dilute sulphuric acid, and the poles are of Zn and Cu. Reference to fig. 4 shows that the positive pole for the external circuit acts as the negative pole for the internal circuit. Consequently the copper electrode acts as the cathode and the hydrogen is given off at that electrode. At the zinc anode, the SO_4 attacks the electrode to form zinc sulphate. In practice such a cell is found to give a steady current only if the latter is very small or if the cell is in action only intermittently. The explanation of this effect, which is termed **polarization** (not to be confused with optical polarization, with which there is no connexion), is simply that some of the hydrogen bubbles adhere to the copper plate. This results in a twofold action. First, the gas is an excellent insulator and introduces an internal layer of very high resistance. Secondly, owing to the electric field present, a double layer of positive and negative ions forms on the surface of the hydrogen and the cell actually tries to send a current in the reverse direction or a **back E.M.F.** develops. Clearly the two opposing E.M.F.s eventually balance, and the current falls to zero.

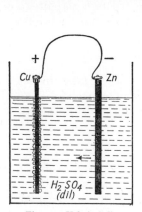

Fig. 4. — Voltaic Cell

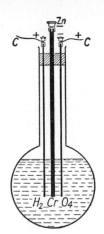

Fig. 5. — Bichromate Cell

9. Remedies for Polarization.

The remedies for polarization are of three distinct types:

(a) *Mechanical.*

If the copper plate is brushed the hydrogen may be removed. Such a process is clearly impracticable and suggested the construction of plates with pointed surfaces to burst the bubbles, but such methods have a very limited success.

(b) *Chemical.*

If a strong oxidizing agent is present, the hydrogen may be oxidized to water as fast as it is formed. Cells based on this process are fairly successful, but usually use highly corrosive liquids which require careful handling.

The **bichromate cell,** shown in fig. 5, consists of two carbon plates dipping in chromic acid, which is formed by dissolving potassium bichromate in concentrated sulphuric acid and then diluting somewhat with water. The negative pole is still zinc, but must be removed from the cell except when it is in operation or the zinc will dissolve.

(c) *Electrochemical.*

These cells are the most satisfactory, and the best of them is the Daniell cell. The general principle is to separate the two electrodes by a porous pot and to surround each electrode with a different solution. The porous pot prevents these solutions from mixing except by very slow diffusion but it allows free passage of ions under the influence of the electric field.

The **Daniell cell** consists of a copper vessel which forms the positive electrode. This vessel contains copper sulphate solution and a porous pot, as shown in fig. 6. The zinc electrode stands in a bath of dilute

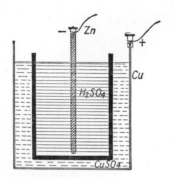

Fig. 6. — Daniell Cell

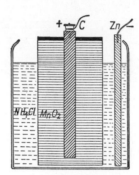

Fig. 7. — Leclanché Cell

sulphuric acid contained in the porous pot. Hydrogen ions which travel towards the copper electrode displace the copper ions in solution, and it is the latter which are deposited on the copper electrode. The chemical action therefore consists in the solution of zinc and the deposition of copper, and polarization is prevented.

Other cells are the **Bunsen cell,** using Zn and H_2SO_4 outside the porous pot, nitric acid as depolarizer and carbon as the positive electrode. **Grove's cell** uses the same materials as the Bunsen cell except that platinum is used in place of carbon.

A cell of great practical importance is the **Leclanché cell.** As shown in fig. 7, this consists of a zinc rod dipping in ammonium chloride solution outside the porous pot, inside which a carbon rod serves as anode, surrounded by solid powdered manganese dioxide as depolarizer. The equations expressing the reactions are:

$$2NH_4Cl + Zn \rightarrow ZnCl_2 + 2NH_3 + H_2,$$
$$H_2 + 2MnO_2 \rightarrow Mn_2O_3 + H_2O. \qquad \cdot \quad \cdot \quad (12.9)$$

The E.M.F. is about 1·4 volts. Owing to the fairly slow action of the solid depolarizer, the cell is only suitable for small or intermittent currents.

The common dry battery is a set of Leclanché cells constructed in portable form. The liquid ammonium chloride solution is in the form of a paste and the china porous pot is replaced by a linen bag.

10. Standard Cells.

The E.M.F. of the cells described so far varies somewhat with the conditions under which they are used. They are therefore quite unsuitable as standards. Two cells which suffer little variation of E.M.F. with temperature and which have been chosen as standards are the

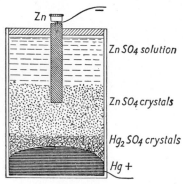

Fig. 8. — Latimer Clark Cell

Latimer Clark cell and the **Weston cadmium cell.** The former is shown diagrammatically in fig. 8. The electrodes are zinc-mercury amalgam and mercury, and zinc sulphate crystals are in contact with the zinc electrode, while zinc sulphate solution fills the main bulk of the cell. A layer of mercury sulphate crystals covers the positive mercury electrode. The E.M.F. of this cell is given by the equation

$$E = 1\cdot4328 - 0\cdot00119(t - 15° \text{ C.}) - 0\cdot000007(t - 15)^2 \text{ volts.} \quad (12.10)$$

In the Weston cell, the zinc-mercury amalgam is replaced by a cadmium-mercury amalgam, and the zinc sulphate by cadmium sulphate. The E.M.F.-temperature equation is

$$E = 1\cdot0184 - 0\cdot0000406(t - 20) - 0\cdot000000(t - 20)^2$$
$$+ 0\cdot00000001(t - 20)^3 \text{ volts.} \quad . \quad . \quad (12.11)$$

The Weston cell therefore has a much lower temperature coefficient than the Latimer Clark cell. A high resistance is always included in the circuit of a standard cell, for the E.M.F. is constant only for the passage of a very small current. The cells are therefore usually used in potentiometer and other null circuits.

11. Energetics of a Cell.

We shall now consider the source of energy in electric cells, selecting for the purpose the Daniell cell. When an equivalent weight of zinc dissolves to form zinc sulphate, a definite amount of chemical energy disappears and a corresponding amount of heat energy H_1 makes its appearance. A definite amount of heat energy H_2 likewise appears when an equivalent weight of copper dissolves to form copper sulphate. Now in the Daniell cell for every equivalent weight of zinc which passes into solution an equivalent weight of copper is deposited. Hence a net amount of energy $(H_1 - H_2)$ is available and this represents the source of electrical energy. Now the passage of 96,470 coulombs is required to deposit a gram-equivalent of any element. Hence, from the conservation of energy, we should have

$$E \frac{96,470}{4 \cdot 2} = (H_1 - H_2), \quad \ldots \ldots (12.12)$$

where E is the E.M.F. of the Daniell cell. Equation (12.12) therefore allows E to be calculated and the value obtained agrees well with the experimentally observed E.M.F. of the cell. It should be noted, however, that this agreement is due largely to the fact that the Daniell cell has a very small E.M.F.-temperature coefficient. Referring to the thermodynamical argument in Part II, Chap. XIII, p. 274, we have here $dE/d\theta = 0$, and therefore $E = H$. The constancy of the standard cells is to be attributed to the fact that they are strictly reversible and therefore have a constant E.M.F. if the temperature is kept constant, and a constant temperature coefficient if the temperature varies.

12. Secondary Cells.

The cells described so far have been **primary cells,** that is, cells in which the negative electrode is dissolved away irreversibly as time goes on. Such cells therefore require replacement of the negative electrode, of the acid solution and of the depolarizer. Secondary cells are, however, available, in which the electrodes may be reformed by electrolysis, so that effectively the cell gives current in one direction when in use, that is when *discharging*, and is then subjected to electrolysis by a current from an external supply passing in the opposite direction, until the electrodes and the original acid solution have been completely reformed. The best-known secondary cell is the **lead accumulator,** which consists of electrodes of lead and lead peroxide respectively, dipping in dilute sulphuric acid. Such a cell acts as a primary cell, the peroxide electrode being at a steady potential of about 2 volts above the lead electrode. The chemical process which occurs on discharge is shown by the following equations:

$$PbO_2 + H_2 \rightarrow PbO + H_2O,$$
$$PbO + H_2SO_4 \rightarrow PbSO_4 + H_2O, \quad \cdot \quad \cdot \quad (12.13)$$

and
$$Pb + SO_4 \rightarrow PbSO_4.$$

The discharging process therefore results in the formation of two electrodes each covered with lead sulphate, and therefore showing no difference in potential when the process is complete or the cell is " discharged ".

In the charging process, current is passed through the cell in such a direction that the original lead electrode is reconverted into lead according to the equation:

$$PbSO_4 + H_2 \rightarrow H_2SO_4 + Pb, \quad \cdot \quad \cdot \quad \cdot \quad (12.14)$$

while the lead peroxide is reformed according to the equation

$$PbSO_4 + SO_4 + 2H_2O \rightarrow PbO_2 + 2H_2SO_4. \quad \cdot \quad (12.15)$$

It is clear from equations (12.13) that in the discharging process water is formed, so that the specific gravity of the acid solution drops steadily. Conversely, in the charging process, equations (12.14) and (12.15) show that the acid concentration increases. Indeed, the state of charge of an accumulator is estimated from the density of the electrolyte, which varies from about 1.15 when completely discharged to 1.21 when fully charged. Throughout all these processes the E.M.F. remains approximately constant at 2.1 volts and is therefore useless as a sign of the degree of charge in the battery.

The lead peroxide plate is formed in two distinct ways. It may be formed over a long period by electrolysis, using a lead plate as an anode and allowing it to undergo oxidation. This process is lengthy and costly in the electrical energy assumed. Alternatively, red lead Pb_3O_4, which is easily obtained, is compressed into lead grids. On immersion in sulphuric acid peroxide is formed immediately according to the chemical reaction

$$Pb_3O_4 + 2H_2SO_4 \rightarrow 2PbSO_4 + PbO_2 + 2H_2O, \quad (12.16)$$

and the lead sulphate is readily converted to lead peroxide by charging over a moderate time.

13. Properties of a Good Cell.

The following properties should be possessed by the ideal cell:
(a) The E.M.F. should be high and constant;
(b) The internal resistance should be small;

(c) A constant current should be delivered and the cell should have a long life;

(d) It should be quite inactive chemically when on open circuit;

(e) The electrodes and electrolyte should consist of cheap and durable materials;

(f) It should be manageable and should not emit corrosive fumes.

All these properties are possessed by the lead accumulator, which suffers only from the disadvantage of its heavy weight. Other types of secondary cell have been attempted such as the *Drum battery*, which consists of nickel and zinc electrodes with a sodium hydroxide electrolyte. A lighter cell results, but the E.M.F. is little more than half that of the lead accumulator and the durability much less. How far the various primary cells obey the criteria (a) to (f) may be considered by the student. The low internal resistance of the lead accumulator is in part due to the method of construction in which plates of large area are situated a fraction of an inch apart. Great care must be taken not to short-circuit the accumulator, for owing to its low internal resistance the current will rise to a prohibitively high value. The internal heat developed may then be sufficient to buckle the plates, and even if this should not occur, the chemical action is so rapid that partial disintegration of the plates occurs and their life is considerably shortened. Likewise, in charging the accumulator, the current density must not be too high or fragmentation of the plates will occur.

14. Grouping of Cells.

The choice of connexion of cells in series or in parallel depends on the use to which they are to be put. For the best *economy* in electrical energy, as little as possible should be wasted as heat internally. This requires the internal resistance of the combination to be as small as possible compared with the external resistance, and the cells are therefore grouped in parallel. For the *quickest action*, such as may be required in a circuit of *high induction* (see Chap. XIII), for example an electromagnet, the total resistance of the circuit should be as high as possible. The cells are therefore connected in series.

To obtain the *maximum current* in a given external circuit the grouping of the cells varies according to the particular value of the external resistance. We shall now show that the cells must be grouped partly in series and partly in parallel, so that the resistance of the combination is as nearly as possible equal to the external resistance.

Suppose there are n files of m cells in series as shown in fig. 9, and that the internal resistance and E.M.F. of each cell are r and e respectively, the external resistance being R. The total number N of cells is then given by

$$N = mn, \qquad \dots \dots \quad (12.17),$$

while the total E.M.F. E is

$$E = me. \quad \cdots \quad \cdots \quad (12.18)$$

Applying Ohm's law, the current I is given by

$$I = \frac{me}{mr/n + R}, \quad \cdots \quad (12.19)$$

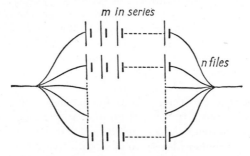

m in series

n files

Fig. 9. — Grouping of Cells for a maximum Current

since the total internal resistance of the cells as grouped is mr/n. Substituting for m in terms of n from (12.17) in (12.19) we have

$$I = \frac{Nne}{Nr + Rn^2}. \quad \cdots \quad (12.20)$$

For a maximum value of I, forming the expression $\dfrac{dI}{dn}$ and equating to zero, we find $Nr = Rn^2$, whence

$$\frac{mr}{n} = R, \quad \cdots \quad \cdots \quad (12.21)$$

or the external resistance is equal to the combined internal resistance of the group of cells.

EXERCISES

1. State the laws of electrolysis and discuss the factors which govern the ultimate products obtained by electrolytic processes.

2. Outline the application of the ionic theory to the explanation of electrolysis. What other phenomena are readily accounted for on the ionic theory?

3. Describe one method for the determination of the velocity of ions during electrolysis.

If a given solution shows a loss in concentration near the cathode and anode respectively in the ratio $2 : 1$, calculate the ionic velocities, given that the concentration of completely dissociated solute is 10^{-3} gm.-equivalents/c.c., the field gradient is 3 volts/cm., and the conductivity of the solution 0.289 ohm^{-1} cm.$^{-1}$. [3×10^{-3} cm./sec.; 6×10^{-3} cm./sec.]

4. Write a short essay on the applications of electrolysis to industry.

5. Give a brief account of the processes by which polarization in cells is overcome. What are the essential properties of a good cell?

6. From what source is the energy of a primary cell derived and in what respect are the energetics of a Daniell cell unique?

7. Describe in detail the construction and mode of action of some form of secondary cell.

CHAPTER XIII

Electromagnetism

1. Faraday's Experiments.

Faraday made the most important discovery that any change in the magnetic flux threading (or " linked with ") a conductor resulted in an E.M.F. acting along that conductor. Experiments to illustrate this fact are shown in figs. 1a and 1b. In fig. 1a a solenoid is connected in series with a galvanometer and a bar magnet is inserted into the solenoid. A deflection of the galvanometer takes place at the instant that the magnet is introduced, but falls to zero again as soon as movement ceases, even though magnetic flux is still threading the solenoid.

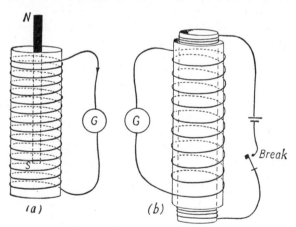

Fig. 1. — Electromagnetic Induction

If relative movement of magnetic field and conductor again occurs owing to removal of the magnet, a temporary deflection of the galvanometer in the reverse direction is observed. The permanent magnet may be replaced by a second solenoid carrying a current and thereby producing a magnetic field, with the same result as shown in fig. 1b. If the sign of the magnetic pole which is introduced is changed, the deflection is in the reverse direction. The magnitude of the deflection is found to depend on the speed of movement of the magnet. Faraday summed up these results in the following **Laws of Electromagnetic Induction**:

(1) *If the magnetic flux through a conductor is changed, an E.M.F. acts round the conductor.*

(2) *The magnitude of the E.M.F. is equal to the rate of change of the flux N, that is*

$$E = -\frac{dN}{dt}. \quad \ldots \ldots \quad (13.1)$$

If N is expressed in oersteds and t in seconds, E is obtained in *absolute electromagnetic units*. Hence to obtain the potential difference in volts (13.1) must be multiplied by 10^{-8}.

The negative sign in (13.1) indicates that the E.M.F. which is established produces a current which in turn produces a magnetic

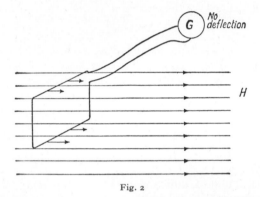

Fig. 2

field of such a sign as to prevent relative motion of the primary magnet and the conductor. This third law of electromagnetic induction, which is often termed **Lenz's law**, and which has important practical applications, may be expressed as follows:

The magnetic field produced by the excited current is always in such a direction as to oppose the change of flux being produced by the primary magnetic field.

Since a change in flux is all that is required to produce an **induced E.M.F.**, it is sufficient to leave the inner and outer solenoids in fig. 1*b* completely at rest and simply to vary the primary magnetic field by varying the current in the centre or *primary coil*. This may be achieved by starting and stopping the current in the primary, since this results in a changing primary magnetic flux. Many important practical applications, such as the induction coil, described in section 9, depend on this principle.

It will be noted that if a conductor moves *along* the lines of force of a magnetic field as shown in fig. 2, there is no change in the particular lines of force which cut the conductor. There is therefore no induced E.M.F. in this case.

2. Mutual Induction.

The magnitude of the magnetic flux threading the *secondary circuit* in fig. 1(b) depends on the number of turns of wire in the primary and secondary coils and the geometry of their disposition. Clearly, the galvanometer could be connected to either coil and the other coil used as the primary coil. This mutual effect of two or more circuits in close proximity is termed *mutual induction*. Its quantitative measure may be defined in the two following ways:

(i) If N is the total flux linked with the secondary circuit, and I is the current in the primary responsible for the flux, the **mutual inductance** M is defined by the equation

$$N = MI. \qquad \ldots \ldots \ldots \quad (13.2)$$

The mutual inductance may therefore be defined as the magnetic flux linked with the secondary when unit current flows in the primary.

(ii) Alternatively, combining (13.1) and (13.2) we have

$$E = - M \frac{dI}{dt}, \qquad \ldots \ldots \ldots \quad (13.3)$$

and hence the *mutual inductance is equal to the E.M.F. induced in the secondary when* $dI/dt = 1$, *that is, when the current is changing at unit rate in the primary.*

The practical unit of inductance is termed the **henry**. This is defined so that equation (13.3) still holds in practical units. Hence the inductance in henries is equal to the E.M.F. in volts induced in the secondary when the current in the primary charges at the rate of one ampere per second.

3. Self-induction.

If an ammeter is placed in a circuit containing a battery and a large electromagnet it will be found on completing the circuit that the ammeter creeps rather sluggishly to its final steady reading, which is that consistent with Ohm's law for the circuit. This effect is due to *self-induction*, which we may explain by reference to fig. 3. The current as it enters one turn after another gradually builds up a larger and larger field to thread the remaining turns. The remaining turns are therefore subject to a changing magnetic flux and consequently an E.M.F. is induced in them. By Lenz's law this E.M.F. acts in a back direction to oppose the increasing primary current, so that a finite time is required for the latter to become established.

By analogy with the definition of mutual inductance, the self-inductance L is defined by

$$N = LI, \qquad \ldots \ldots (13.4)$$

where N is the magnetic flux linked with the circuit due to the current I. Alternatively, combining (13.1) and (13.4),

$$E = -L\frac{dI}{dt}, \qquad \ldots \ldots (13.5)$$

which shows that the *self-inductance in henries is equal to the back E.M.F. in volts set up in the circuit when the current is growing at the rate of* 1 *amp./sec.*

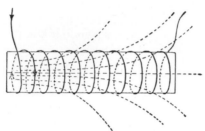

Fig. 3.— Self Induction

4. Calculation of Mutual and Self-inductance.

The value of self-inductances and mutual inductances is calculated with the aid of equations (13.5) and (13.3). For example, the self-inductance of a long solenoid is derived as follows. From equation (10.13), the field due to a steady current I in the solenoid is

$$F = 4\pi n I.$$

Hence if the area of cross-section of the solenoid is A, the magnetic flux through the area is

$$N = 4\pi n A I.$$

As I varies, the resultant change in flux threads the solenoid nl times, where l is the length of the solenoid, and nl therefore the total number of turns. Hence

$$E = -\frac{dN}{dt} = -nl\frac{d}{dt}(4\pi nAI) = -4\pi n^2 lA\frac{dI}{dt}. \quad (13.6)$$

Since by (13.5) L is defined by

$$E = -L\frac{dI}{dt},$$

from this equation and (13.6) we have

$$L = 4\pi n^2 lA. \qquad \ldots \ldots (13.7)$$

By a similar argument if a mutual inductance consists of a primary in the form of a long solenoid with n_1 turns per unit length, and n_2 turns of wire are wound round the centre of the primary to constitute the secondary, we have

$$E = - n_2 \frac{d}{dt} (4\pi n_1 AI) = - 4\pi n_1 n_2 A \frac{dI}{dt}$$

and, since $E = - M \frac{dI}{dt}$,

$$M = 4\pi n_1 n_2 A. \quad \ldots \ldots \quad (13.8)$$

* 5. Growth and Decay of Currents.

The student will now realize that the steady currents governed by Ohm's law represent a particular case. In general in any circuit such as that shown in fig. 4, there is present *resistance, inductance* and *capacity*. Although steady conditions governed by Ohm's law may be

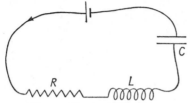

Fig. 4.— Circuit with Resistance,
Inductance and Capacity

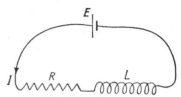

Fig. 5.— Circuit with Resistance
and Inductance

eventually set up, more general considerations are required during the starting and cessation of the current. Actually a most important condition arises for certain particular values of resistance, inductance and capacity, where no steady value of current is ever attained but *electrical oscillations* are produced, the current swinging between two equal extreme values, first in one direction and then in the other.

We concentrate first on the growth of current in a circuit containing only *resistance* and *inductance*, as shown in fig. 5. Initially, before the battery is connected, the current in the circuit is zero. Eventually, the current attains a steady value I_0 given by $I_0 = E/R$, where E is the E.M.F. of the battery and R is the resistance in the circuit. We require an expression for the current I at any time t after the circuit has been completed. If E' representes the back E.M.F. present at this instant, application of Ohm's law gives

$$IR = E - E'; \quad \ldots \ldots \quad (13.9)$$

and, substituting for E' from (13.5) and remembering that we have already allowed for the sign of E', we obtain

$$IR = E - L \frac{dI}{dt}. \quad \ldots \ldots \quad (13.10)$$

We therefore obtain a differential equation of the first order. Re-arranging (13.10), we have

$$\frac{L\,dI}{(E-IR)} = dt; \quad \ldots \ldots \quad (13.11)$$

whence, by integration, we obtain

$$-\frac{L}{R}\log_e(E-IR) = t + A, \quad \ldots \quad (13.12)$$

where A is a constant.

Now when $t = 0$, that is before the circuit is completed, $I = 0$, so substitution in (13.12) gives $A = -(L\log_e E)/R$. Hence

$$\log_e\frac{(E-IR)}{E} = -\frac{R}{L}t, \quad \ldots \ldots \quad (13.13)$$

or

$$E - IR = E\exp.\left(-\frac{R}{L}t\right), \quad \ldots \quad (13.14)$$

or

$$I = \frac{E}{R}\left(1 - \left(\exp. -\frac{R}{L}t\right)\right). \quad . \quad (13.15)$$

Now the final steady current $I_0 = E/R$, so that (13.15) becomes

$$I = I_0\left(1 - \exp. -\frac{R}{L}t\right). \quad \ldots \quad (13.16)$$

In fig. 6 the full curve is the graph of I against t. It shows that the final steady value I_0 is theoretically reached only when $t = \infty$. The important fact emerges that the speed with which the current rises to its final steady value is governed not by the magnitude of L alone but rather by the ratio L/R. This ratio is termed the **time constant** of the circuit.

By analogy with the preceding considerations, if the battery is cut out and the circuit immediately closed again, the current I at some subsequent time t will be given by

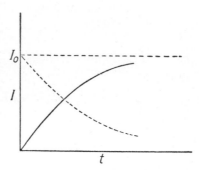

Fig. 6.—Growth and Decay of Current

$$IR = E', \quad . \quad (13.17)$$

where E' is the back E.M.F. at time t. This E.M.F. opposes the de-caying E.M.F. and tends to prolong the current. Its value is given by $E' = -L\,dI/dt$ as usual, and hence we have

$$\frac{dI}{I} = -\frac{R}{L}dt. \quad \ldots \ldots \quad (13.18)$$

By integration of (13.18) and substitution of the initial condition $I = I_0$ when $t = 0$, we obtain

$$I = I_0 \exp.\left(-\frac{R}{L}t\right). \quad . \quad . \quad . \quad . \quad (13.19)$$

This expression is shown graphically by the dotted curve in fig. 6. The growth and decay curves have the same time constant and are in every way complementary.

We discuss further cases in Chap. XV.

6. Coil rotating in a Magnetic Field.

We have seen that for a continual E.M.F. to be generated, relative movement must take place between the lines of force and the conductor. This is most easily achieved by rotating a coil in a uniform magnetic field, as shown in fig. 7, where the rectangular coil rotates about an axis (shown dotted) in the plane of the coil and perpendicular to the field. To calculate the E.M.F. acting round the coil at any instant when the inclination of the plane of the coil to the uniform magnetic field H is θ, we note that the flux N changes from HA to zero as the coil rotates from $\theta = \pi/2$ to $\theta = 0$, and that the effective flux at any intermediate value is

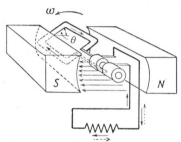

Fig. 7.—Coil rotating in Magnetic Field

$$N = nHA \sin\theta, \quad . \quad . \quad . \quad . \quad (13.20)$$

where n is the number of turns of wire in the coil. Hence from (13.20) and (13.1)

$$E = - nHA \cos\theta \frac{d\theta}{dt}. \quad . \quad . \quad . \quad (13.21)$$

Now the steady angular velocity ω of rotation of the coil equals $d\theta/dt$. Hence (13.21) becomes

$$E = - nHA\omega \cos\theta. \quad . \quad . \quad . \quad (13.22)$$

The change in flux and in E.M.F. during the rotation are shown in fig. 8. The flux is a maximum when $\theta = \pi/2$, that is when the coil is perpendicular to the field, but the E.M.F. is then zero. Conversely, when the plane of the coil and the field direction coincide and the flux is zero, the E.M.F. attains its maximum value $nAH\omega$. The explanation lies in the fact that the *rate of change* of flux is a maximum in the latter position.

If the coil circuit is completed by the **slip rings** (see fig. 7) being joined to some external circuit, the current in the latter will clearly be in one direction for one half-cycle of revolution and in the reverse

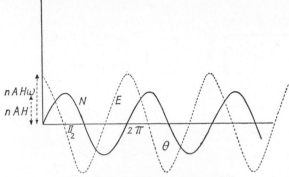

Fig. 8.—Flux and E.M.F. for Rotating Coil

direction for the second half-cycle.   Such an arrangement therefore acts as a source of **alternating current.**

By a mechanical split-ring device, known as a **commutator** and shown in fig. 9, the connexions to the external circuit are reversed each half-cycle of revolution.   In this way the current in the external circuit

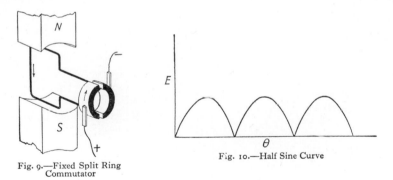

Fig. 9.—Fixed Split Ring Commutator

Fig. 10.—Half Sine Curve

becomes **direct current,** though, of course, it varies in magnitude according to the *half sine curve* shown in fig. 10.   The alternating current is said to have undergone mechanical **rectification** by the commutator.

The **earth-inductor** shown in fig. 11 simply consists of a coil which may be rotated in the earth's magnetic field.   It is mounted in gimbals so that it may be rotated in any orientation and is fitted with a commutator.   Clearly, if it is rotated with its axis horizontal and in the magnetic meridian, the coil effectively cuts the earth's vertical magnetic component V. Again, if it is rotated with its axis in a vertical plane, it is cutting the earth's horizontal component H. If the deflections on a tangent galvanometer connected to the inductor are θ_1 and θ_2 respectively, and the speed of rotation is the same in both experiments,

$$\frac{V}{H} = \frac{\tan\theta_1}{\tan\theta_2} = \tan D, \quad (13.23)$$

where D is the angle of dip.

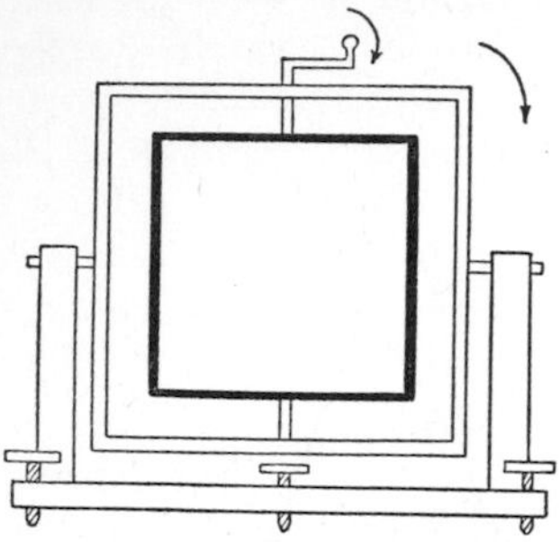

Finally, if the coil is rotated with its axle along the total intensity of the earth's field, no deflection will be produced in the galvanometer, as there is no effective change of flux. The angle of dip of the axle is then the magnetic angle of dip. Such an instrument is instructive but does not give such an accurate value of the angle of dip as the method described in Chap. VII.

Fig. 11.—Earth-Inductor

7. The Dynamo.

The rotating coil described in section 6 is a simple form of *dynamo*. In practice, each dynamo is designed for a specific purpose, but certain general rules are applicable. First, a more powerful magnetic field than that of the earth is required, and this is generally provided by an electromagnet or **field coils** excited by the current from the coil or **armature** itself. These field coils may either be connected *in series* or *in parallel* with the armature windings and, more commonly, part of the windings of the field coil may be in series and part in parallel with the armature. Such an instrument is said to be **compound wound,** and we shall now consider the advantage of a compound winding.

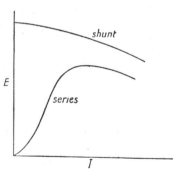

Fig. 12.—Characteristic Curves for Shunt and Series Windings

Consider first the curve obtained by plotting the E.M.F. available in an external circuit of the **series-wound** dynamo, against the current in the external circuit. As shown in the lower curve in fig. 12, this curve starts at the origin, rises rapidly to a fairly flat maximum and then falls slowly. The explanation of this *characteristic curve* is as follows. If the resistance of the external circuit is high, the current which is produced by revolution of the armature is necessarily low, since armature, field coils and external circuit are all in series. The electromagnetism which can be excited in the field coils is therefore small, and consequently the field cut by the armature is small. Hence only a small E.M.F. develops, and a small current accompanies the small E.M.F. As the external resistance is reduced, the current increases correspondingly, more excitation of the field coils takes place and a larger E.M.F. develops in the armature. Eventually, should the resistance of the external circuit fall below that of the armature and the field coils, the E.M.F. available for the external circuit becomes progressively less, and the E.M.F. at the terminals of the dynamo becomes correspondingly smaller.

In the **shunt-wound** dynamo, where the field coils and the external circuit are in parallel, a very different characteristic curve is obtained, as shown in the top curve in fig. 12. When the external resistance is high, almost all the current generated in the armature goes through the field coils. The latter are therefore highly excited, and the E.M.F. produced by the armature starts with its maximum value. As the resistance of the external circuit is gradually reduced, it allows more current to pass through it and less current is available for the field coils. The excitation of the latter therefore drops, and there is a corresponding fall in the E.M.F. generated by the armature. The characteristic curve of the shunt-wound dynamo therefore falls steadily as shown in fig. 12.

Now it is clearly undesirable that the voltage available at a main supply should vary with the external resistance, that is with the **load** taken by the external circuit. Since the characteristic curves of the series-wound and shunt-wound dynamos are oppositely directed over a considerable range, a compound winding may be constructed to give a reasonably constant voltage characteristic over a moderate range of load.

Quite apart from load variations, a single coil and commutator, as shown by the graph in fig. 10, will provide only a sinusoidal and not a steady E.M.F. The difficulty is overcome by using a number of conductors arranged around a central cylindrical axis or *drum* to constitute the *drum armature*. These conductors are connected partly in series and partly in parallel according to the precise design of the particular dynamo, but their essential function is that each contributes a certain amount to the total E.M.F. When one conductor moves to a fresh position its former place is occupied by a neighbouring conductor, so that the total E.M.F. remains constant except for a slight *ripple*, the elimination of which, if required, is obtained by some *smoothing device* such as the *choke coils and condensers* described on p. 688.

8. The Transformer.

The simple arrangement of the two solenoids described on p. 644 constitutes a form of *transformer*. If the secondary coil has a large number of turns compared with the primary coil it may be found that on completing the primary circuit with a battery of a few volts, the temporary E.M.F. set up in the secondary is of the order of several thousand volts. The low voltage in the primary has therefore been transformed into a much greater voltage by a step-up transformer. The process is entirely reciprocal and a large voltage applied to the secondary from some external source would result in a correspondingly small voltage being temporarily produced in the primary, the latter now acting as a low-voltage secondary. Such arrangements are known as **step-up** and **step-down transformers** respectively. To increase the magnetic flux between the primary and secondary circuits, the solenoids are usually wound concentrically on formers of magnetic materials. For such instruments no simple relation exists between the voltage and the number of turns in the coil, but for the less efficient case of an *air-core* transformer it is approximately true that

$$\frac{E_s}{E_p} = \frac{n_s}{n_p}, \quad \cdots \cdots \quad (13.24)$$

where E_s and E_p are the secondary and primary E.M.F.s and n_s and n_p the numbers of turns in the secondary and primary coils respectively.

In order to provide a continual difference of potential in the secondary, arrangements must be made to maintain a continual change in the magnetic flux. This may be achieved (1) by making and breaking the circuit repeatedly, (2) by using an alternating current in the primary.

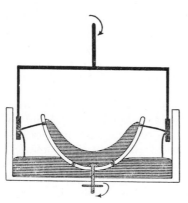

Fig. 13. — Rotary Mercury Make and Break

The latter method is generally the more convenient. With the former, either an electromagnetic trembler or a rotary mercury make and break may be used. The operation of the trembler is described as part of the induction coil in section 9. The rotary mercury make and break as shown in fig. 13 commonly consists of an electric motor attached to a centrifugal device which shoots a jet of mercury against revolving metal blades. The instrument runs in an atmosphere of coal gas to prevent oxidation at the spark.

The power output available from the secondary of a transformer cannot be greater than the power input in the primary. Consequently the high E.M.F. in the secondary of a step-up transformer is accompanied by a corresponding reduction in the secondary current, whereas for a step-down transformer a corresponding increase in current accompanies the reduction in E.M.F. With no losses, the ideal relation would be

$$E_p I_p = E_s I_s, \quad \ldots \ldots \quad (13.25)$$

where E_p, I_p are the E.M.F. and current at the primary and E_s, I_s the E.M.F. and current at the secondary.

While the introduction of ferromagnetic material increases the magnetic linkage between primary and secondary, it introduces other losses in the form of hysteresis and eddy currents.

9. The Induction Coil.

The induction coil is a particular form of transformer usually designed to give a potential of several thousand volts when a few volts and amps are applied to the primary. It is of great practical

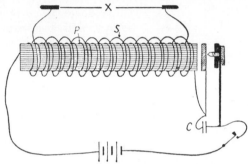

Fig. 14. — Induction Coil

importance in providing the spark for automobile ignition, and in providing a suitable source of power to operate X-ray and other discharge tubes. As shown in fig. 14, it consists of concentric solenoidal primary and secondary coils P and S wound on a bundle of iron wires which act as a core. Intermittent current is provided by the electromagnetic make and break across which a large condenser C is usually inserted. The practical function of the latter is to reduce the spark at the break by providing an alternative circuit for the battery which charges the condenser when it is no longer able to send a current through the primary. The condenser, of course, discharges through the primary at the make.

10. The Electric Motor.

As shown in fig. 15, the electric motor is in principle very similar in construction to the dynamo, and in fact operates by the reverse process. It consists of an armature and field coils and may be series wound, shunt wound or compound wound. In the series-wound motor, for example, rotation is produced by the interaction of the magnetic fields excited in the field coils and the armature when current is sent through the motor from an external supply. To produce continuous rotation a commutator is necessary to reverse the current so that portions of the armature which are attracted at any instant to the field coils are repelled at the appropriate instant later. The angular momentum of the armature is sufficient to carry it beyond the "dead" position and a continuous rotation results.

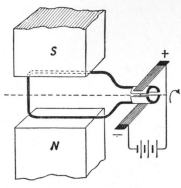

Fig. 15.—Simple Electric Motor

Now a motor when running constitutes a dynamo, and therefore generates an E.M.F. which by Lenz's law opposes the externally applied E.M.F. This back E.M.F. substantially reduces the current through the motor, when it is running steadily, below the value it has when the motor is first connected and no back E.M.F. has been generated. Motors are therefore fitted with variable resistances to avoid overheating of the machine by initial excess currents. These resistances are gradually cut out as the steady operating conditions are reached.

The **efficiency** of electric motors is usually considered from three aspects. The *electrical efficiency* is defined as

$$\frac{\text{Power obtained on rotation}}{\text{Electrical power supplied}}.$$

The *mechanical efficiency* is defined as

$$\frac{\text{Brake output (see Part I, p. 43)}}{\text{Electrical power spent in producing rotation}}.$$

The *commercial efficiency* is defined as

$$\frac{\text{Brake output}}{\text{Electrical power supplied}}.$$

We are particularly interested in the electrical efficiency F. If the back E.M.F. developed is E', and the current in the armature is I, the power obtained on rotation is $E'I$, while that supplied to the motor is EI, where E is the E.M.F. applied to the terminals. Hence

$$F = \frac{E'I}{EI} = \frac{E'}{E}. \quad \ldots \ldots \quad (13.26)$$

For maximum possible efficiency $F = 1$, and hence from (13.26) $E' = E$. Clearly such a state of affairs could never be reached, for no current would then flow through the motor. In practice when such a condition is almost reached, the motor rotates very rapidly but very little power is available for external work, as the following considerations show. If the power obtained is P,

$$P = E'I = I(E - IR), \quad \ldots \quad (13.27)$$

since $E' = E - IR$, where R is the resistance of the motor. The condition for maximum power is obtained by differentiating (13.27) thus:

$$\frac{dP}{dI} = 0 = E - 2IR$$

or $\qquad\qquad\qquad E' = \tfrac{1}{2}E. \quad \ldots \ldots \quad (13.28)$

Analogous considerations hold for the efficiencies of the dynamo, but, as with design, each machine requires special treatment and general considerations are of little value.

* 11. Ballistic Galvanometers.

The galvanometers described in Chap. IX were intended for use in measuring "steady" currents either in the form of direct current or of alternating current of constant amplitude. Ballistic galvanometers are designed to measure currents of short duration, such as result from the charging or discharging of a condenser, or that arise from the presence of self or mutual inductance in the circuit. Both suspended magnet and suspended coil instruments are available, but the formulæ deduced differ from steady current relations in that they involve the time of oscillation of the suspended system.

Considering first the *moving magnet type of tangent galvanometer* design, it is essential that the inertia of the moving system should be large enough to ensure that the discharge has passed before appreciable rotation has occurred. Suppose the current in the coil is i at any time t, that the magnetic field at the centre due to unit current in the galvanometer is G, and that the pole-strength of the suspended magnet is m. Then we have that the total impulse

$$P = \int_0^T Gim \, dt = Gm \int_0^T i \, dt = Gmq, \quad \ldots \quad (13.29)$$

where q is the total quantity of electricity discharged. If $2l$ is the equivalent length of the magnet, the moment of impulse about the axis is

$$2l \cdot Gmq = GMq, \quad \ldots \ldots \quad (13.30)$$

where M is the moment of the suspended magnet. This equals the product of the angular velocity of rotation ω of the magnet and its moment of inertia K. Hence

$$K\omega = GMq. \quad \ldots \ldots \quad (13.31)$$

If θ is the maximum angle of swing, the total kinetic energy imparted to the magnet eventually becomes potential energy in the earth's field. We therefore have

$$\tfrac{1}{2}K\omega^2 = MH\,(1 - \cos\theta), \quad \ldots \ldots \quad (13.32)$$

from fig. 16. Eliminating ω from (13.21) and (13.22), we obtain

$$q^2 = \frac{K}{MH} \cdot \frac{4H^2}{G^2} \cdot \sin^2\frac{\theta}{2}. \quad \ldots \ldots \quad (13.33)$$

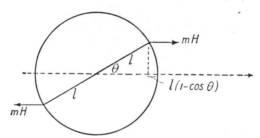

Fig. 16. — Potential Energy of Magnet

Now the time of oscillation T of the suspended magnet under the earth's field alone is given by

$$T = 2\pi \sqrt{\frac{K}{MH}}, \quad \ldots \ldots \quad (13.34)$$

so that, eliminating K and M from (13.33) and (13.34), we find

$$q = \frac{HT}{\pi G}\sin\frac{\theta}{2}. \quad \ldots \ldots \quad (13.35)$$

The quantity of electricity discharged is therefore proportional to the sine of half the angle of throw.

With the *suspended coil galvanometer*, if we consider initially for simplicity a rectangular coil of vertical side l and breadth b, the total impulse on one side is

$$P = \int_0^T Fil\,dt = Flq, \quad \ldots \ldots \quad (13.36)$$

where F is the force of the magnetic field in which the coil is situated. The moment of the impulse about the axis is therefore

$$Flqb = FqA = K\omega \quad \ldots \ldots \quad (13.37)$$

(the angular momentum), A being the area of cross-section of the coil. If the final angle of swing is θ, then the kinetic energy is ultimately all converted to potential energy in the suspension. Hence we have

$$\tfrac{1}{2}K\omega^2 = \tfrac{1}{2}c\theta^2, \quad \ldots \ldots \quad (13.38)$$

where c is the constant of the suspension. Eliminating ω from (13.37) and (13.38), and remembering that the time of free oscillation of the suspended coil under the torsion in the fibre is given by

$$T = 2\pi \sqrt{\frac{K}{c}}, \quad \ldots \ldots \quad (13.39)$$

we find
$$q = \frac{cT}{2\pi FA}\, \theta. \quad \ldots \ldots \quad (13.40)$$

The quantity of electricity discharged through the suspended coil galvanometer is therefore directly proportional to the maximum throw θ.

* 12. Damping.

The maximum throw which is observed is not as large as the throw to be expected theoretically, owing to two damping factors. The first of these is the air resistance to the motion of the coil. The second factor is the electromagnetic damping. As the coil swings in the permanent magnetic field F, by Lenz's law induced currents are set up in the coil which produce magnetic fields which interact with the primary field F so as to oppose the continual motion of the coil. If successive values of the maximum throws of the galvanometer as the energy dies away are given by θ_1, θ_2, θ_3, θ_4, &c., then it is found that

$$\frac{\theta_1}{\theta_2} = \frac{\theta_2}{\theta_3} = \frac{\theta_3}{\theta_4}, \text{ \&c.} = d = \text{constant.} \quad . \quad . \quad (13.41)$$

The constant ratio of successive throws is termed the **decrement,** and we introduce, for reasons which will be clear in a moment, the logarithmic decrement $\log_e d = \lambda$ or $d = \exp. \lambda$. From (13.41) we have for two successive throws on the same side

$$\frac{\theta_1}{\theta_3} = \exp. (2\lambda). \quad \ldots \ldots \quad (13.42)$$

Since for a whole swing the decrement is exp. (2λ) while for half a swing it is exp. λ, we infer that for a quarter swing such as constitutes the ordinary throw from zero to its maximum position,

$$\frac{\theta}{\theta_1} = \exp. \frac{\lambda}{2}, \quad \ldots \ldots \quad (13.43)$$

where θ is the theoretical value of the swing and θ_1 is the observed swing. Expanding the exponential and taking the first two terms as a sufficiently good approximation,

$$\theta = \theta_1 \exp.\frac{\lambda}{2} = \theta_1\left(1 + \frac{\lambda}{2}\right). \quad \cdots \quad (13.44)$$

It is important to note that T in (13.40) is the time of oscillation on open circuit.

Ballistic galvanometers are calibrated by the use of a small direct current. If the potential is E across the galvanometer, and the resistance of the circuit is R, then assuming it is a tangent instrument and the deflection is θ_1,

$$I = \frac{E}{R} = \frac{H}{G}\tan\theta_1 \quad \cdots \quad (13.45)$$

Hence, substituting for H/G in (13.35) from (13.45), for small angles of θ and θ_1 we have

$$q = \frac{ET}{2\pi R}\frac{\theta}{\theta_1}. \quad \cdots \quad (13.46)$$

For the suspended coil galvanometer, the steady deflection θ_1 due to a current $I = E/R$ is from (9.6) given by

$$\frac{E}{R} = \frac{c}{AF}\theta_1. \quad \cdots \quad (13.47)$$

Substituting $E/R\theta_1$ for c/AF in (13.40) we obtain

$$q = \frac{ET}{2\pi R}\frac{\theta}{\theta_1}, \quad \cdots \quad (13.48)$$

thus showing from the equivalence of (13.46) and (13.48) that the two galvanometers obey identical formulæ for small deflections.

* 13. Applications of Ballistic Galvanometers.

(i) *Comparison of Capacities.*

Much more convenient than the electrostatic methods described in Chap. IV, section 4, is the comparison of capacities with the ballistic galvanometer. A typical circuit for this purpose is shown in fig. 17, where a depression of the tapping key charges the condenser with a charge $q = EC$, where E is the potential supplied by the battery and C is the capacity of the condenser. On releasing the key, the condenser is discharged through the ballistic galvanometer, and a deflection proportional to the charge is obtained. If the applied potential is kept constant, the deflections given by the discharge of different condensers are directly proportional to their capacities.

The practical unit of capacity is the **farad** which is defined as one coulomb divided by one volt. Small capacities are expressed in microfarads.

(ii) *Measurement of Mutual Inductance.*

Suppose the current in the primary of a mutual inductance at any instant is I_1 and in the secondary I_2, and that the mutual inductance is M, while the self-inductance of the secondary is L_2. Then applying Ohm's law to the secondary after the fashion of section 4 of this chapter we have

$$L_2 \frac{dI_2}{dt} + M \frac{dI_1}{dt} + I_2 R_2 = 0, \quad \ldots \quad (13.49)$$

where R_2 is the resistance of the secondary circuit. Integrating (13.49) with respect to time from $t = 0$ to $t = \infty$ we get

$$\frac{L_2}{R_2} \int_0^\infty \frac{dI_2}{dt} \, dt + \frac{M}{R_2} \int_0^\infty \frac{dI_1}{dt} \, dt = - \int_0^\infty I_2 \, dt. \quad (13.50)$$

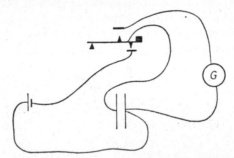

Fig. 17.— Ballistic Galvanometer and Capacities

The first term in (13.50) is zero at both limits, so we obtain

$$\frac{M}{R_2} \int_0^\infty dI_1 = - \int_0^\infty I_2 \, dt. \quad \ldots \quad (13.51)$$

Now the term on the R.H.S. represents (ignoring sign) the quantity of electricity q which has circulated round the secondary circuit, and

$$\int_0^\infty dI = \left| I_1 \right|_0^\infty = I_0.$$

Hence
$$q = \frac{M I_0}{R_2}. \quad \ldots \quad \ldots \quad (13.52)$$

If the current in the primary had been reversed from $+I_0$ to $-I_0$, the quantity circulating in the secondary would be double that given by (13.52). Since the quantity q can be easily measured with the ballistic

22

galvanometer, application of (13.52) allows the mutual inductance to
be calculated.

(iii) *Measurement of Magnetic Field Strength.*

The strength of a magnetic field which is uniform over a large volume
may be measured with the earth-inductor described in section 6. For
the powerful magnetic field between the poles of an electromagnet
where the homogeneity of the field is restricted to a very small volume,
the best method is to use the fluxmeter described in the next section.
The ballistic galvanometer, however, provides a method both convenient and accurate, as follows. A small flat circular coil termed a
search coil is connected in series with the ballistic galvanometer and is
initially situated between the poles of the electromagnet. It is then
rapidly flicked away and the throw of the ballistic galvanometer is a
direct measure of the magnetic field strength. Provided the induced
charge has circulated through the ballistic galvanometer before the
suspended coil of the latter has started to move, the magnitude of the
throw is independent of speed of removal of the coil. If R is the resistance of the galvanometer and search coil, and the magnetic flux is
N, then the current circulating through the coil at any time t during
the process of removal is, by equation (13.1),

$$I = -\frac{1}{R}\frac{dN}{dt}, \quad \ldots \ldots (13.53)$$

and since the quantity of electricity dq which flows through the circuit
in time dt is $I\,dt$, (13.53) may be written

$$q = -\int_0^N \frac{dN}{R}, \quad \ldots \ldots (13.54)$$

and hence the total charge q which circulates through the ballistic
galvanometer is

$$q = -\frac{N}{R}. \quad \ldots \ldots (13.55)$$

Now the flux $N = FAn$, where n is the number of turns in the search
coil of area A and F is the strength of the magnetic field. Hence we
have

$$F = -\frac{qR}{nA}. \quad \ldots \ldots (13.56)$$

(iv) *Hysteresis Curve.*

It frequently happens that it is inconvenient to use a specimen in
the form of a short rod when the hysteresis characteristics (see next
Chapter, section 6) are required. A dynamical method is available in
which the specimen is in the form of an anchor ring, thus forming a

closed magnetic circuit. A primary circuit P consists of an endless solenoid of n_1 turns per unit length wound on the ring: the secondary circuit S, which is connected to the ballistic galvanometer G, consists of a few turns n_2 of wire wound close together round the primary at one spot. Then, when the current is established in the primary, as shown in fig. 18, if the flux linked with the secondary circuit is N, by equation (13.55) the quantity of electricity which circulates through the secondary circuit is $q = N/R$, where the sign has been omitted as it only signifies the direction in which the charge circulates. Now

$$N = BAn_2, \quad . \quad . \quad . \quad . \quad . \quad (13.57)$$

where B is the magnetic induction in the ring and A is its area of cross-section, so we obtain

$$B = \frac{qR}{n_2A}. \quad . \quad . \quad . \quad . \quad (13.58)$$

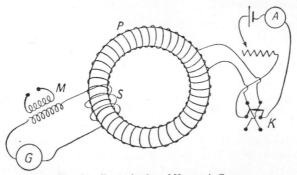

Fig. 18. — Determination of Hysteresis Curve

The magnetic field producing this flux is that due to an endless solenoid as given by equation (10.17). Hence, since $q \propto \theta$ where θ is the throw of the ballistic galvanometer, $B \propto \theta$; and H the magnetizing field is proportional to the primary current I, so that the curve obtained by plotting θ against I will give the B-H curve. This gives, of course, one half of the hysteresis loop if different values of I are used. The other half of the hysteresis loop is plotted from symmetry with the first half. In practice, the maximum saturation current is first used, and it is usual to reverse the current so as to obtain double the throw in the ballistic galvanometer. Indeed a reversing key K must always be included in the primary circuit to reduce the iron to a *cyclic state* by subjecting it to several reversals of current between each reading. To obtain B absolutely, the ballistic galvanometer must be calibrated by reversing a current through a known mutual inductance M, which must remain in the circuit throughout the hysteresis experiment, so that the resistance R of the secondary circuit remains constant throughout the experiment.

The standard mutual inductance is usually in the form of a long straight primary solenoid, round the centre of which are wound a few turns of wire to form a secondary circuit. The flux through the secondary consequent on reversing the current in the primary is, from equation (13.8),

$$N = 2 \times 4\pi n_1 n_2 A I, \quad \dots \dots \quad (13.59)$$

where n_1 is the number of turns per unit length of the primary, n_2 is the total number of turns of the secondary, A is the area of cross-section of the solenoid, and I is the maximum steady current in the primary in electromagnetic units. Such a standard magnetic flux is useful in calibrating the ballistic galvanometer when using it to measure the strength of a magnetic field as described in section (iii).

* 14. Grassot Fluxmeter.

The Grassot fluxmeter consists essentially of a moving-coil galvanometer in which the restoring torque in the suspension is negligibly small. The pointer attached to the coil therefore has no definite zero but remains normally at rest in any position on the scale. It is connected to a standard search coil and is initially calibrated by establishing a known magnetic flux through the coil. The point of particular interest about the instrument is that the deflection obtained on removing the coil from a given field whose value is required depends only on the initial and final value of the flux through the search coil and is quite independent of the speed of removal. To prove this, suppose that the current through the coil is I at any instant when the E.M.F. is E, and that the resistance of the fluxmeter circuit is R. Then $I = E/R$, and from the theory of the moving-coil galvanometer in Chap. IX, the couple on the moving coil is

$$G = nIAH = \frac{nEAH}{R}, \quad \dots \dots \quad (13.60)$$

where n is the number of turns in the galvanometer coil, H is the magnetic field in which it moves and A is its area of cross-section. This couple results in an angular acceleration such that

$$G = K \frac{d\omega}{dt} = \frac{nEAH}{R}, \quad \dots \dots \quad (13.61)$$

where K is the moment of inertia of the moving coil about its axis of suspension, and ω is its angular velocity of rotation. Now the E.M.F. is the difference between the E.M.F. dN/dt due to the search coil cutting the flux of the magnetic field, and the back E.M.F. due to the rotation of the galvanometer coil in its own magnetic field H. Hence

$$E = \left(\frac{dN}{dt} - AH\omega\right), \quad \ldots \quad (13.62)$$

since from equation (13.22) the back E.M.F. produced by the rotating coil is $AH\omega$ if θ is small. Substituting from (13.61) in (13.62) and integrating with respect to t, we obtain

$$\frac{nAH}{R}\int_0^t \left(\frac{dN}{dt} - AH\frac{d\theta}{dt}\right) dt = K\int_0^t \frac{d\omega}{dt}\, dt, \quad . \quad (13.63)$$

where $\omega = d\theta/dt$. The expression on the R.H.S. is zero at both limits since the galvanometer coil goes from rest to rest, that is $\omega = 0$. Hence (13.63) becomes

$$\Big[N\Big]_0^N = AH\Big[\theta\Big]_0^{\theta_0},$$

or $\qquad\qquad N = AH\theta_0, \quad \ldots \ldots \ldots \quad (13.64)$

where θ_0 is the change in reading of the pointer of the fluxmeter and N is the total change in the magnetic flux linked with the search coil.

* 15. Discharge through a Divided Circuit.

We have seen in Chap. XI that with steady currents the current divides in a two-branched circuit in inverse proportion to the resistances of the branches. We shall now obtain a corresponding result

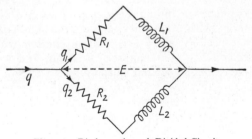

Fig. 19. — Discharge through Divided Circuit

when discharge of a system takes place through a two-branched circuit, such as that shown in fig. 19, where the inductance and resistance of one arm are L_1 and R_1 and of the other, L_2 and R_2. If the E.M.F. across each partial circuit is E at any time t, we have

$$L_1\frac{dI_1}{dt} + R_1 I_1 = E$$

for the first circuit, and

$$L_2 \frac{dI_2}{dt} + R_2 I_2 = E$$

for the second circuit. Hence

$$L_1 \int_0^t \frac{dI_1}{dt}\,dt + R_1 \int_0^t I_1\,dt = L_2 \int_0^{t'} \frac{dI_2}{dt}\,dt + R_2 \int_0^t I_2\,dt,$$

where we have integrated with respect to t. Now I_1 and I_2 are both zero at the beginning and end of the discharge. Hence the first terms on both the R.H.S. and L.H.S. of the preceding equation are zero. But $\int_0^t I_1\,dt = q_1$, and $\int_0^t I_2\,dt = q_2$, where q_1 and q_2 are the charges which pass through the two arms respectively. Hence

$$\frac{q_1}{q_2} = \frac{R_2}{R_1}, \quad \ldots \ldots \quad (13.65)$$

so that the distribution of charge depends only on the resistance and not upon the inductance of the circuit. A ballistic galvanometer may therefore be used with a shunt which has been fitted for steady current conditions.

* 16. Application of Bridge Methods to Varying Currents.

We have already seen in Chap. XI how the Wheatstone bridge affords a very valuable null method for the accurate measurement of resistance to steady currents. Exactly analogous methods have been devised to compare inductances, capacities and resistances, or even an inductance with a capacity, and so on. The number of such bridge circuits, especially when used in conjunction with oscillatory circuits described in the next chapter, is legion, and we shall select just a few simple examples for our purpose.

(i) *Comparison of Self-Inductances.*

The two self-inductances L_1 and L_2 are connected in the arms of the bridge, as shown in fig. 20, together with resistances P, Q, R and S, of which either P and Q, or R and S, must *both* be variable. A balance is first obtained for a steady current. We then have from the standard Wheatstone relation:

$$\frac{P}{R} = \frac{Q}{S}. \quad \ldots \ldots \quad (13.65a)$$

The additional condition which is now required is that no momentary discharge is registered by the ballistic galvanometer when the battery circuit is made or broken. We proceed to show that on this condition

$$\frac{L_1}{L_2} = \frac{P}{R} = \frac{Q}{S}. \quad \ldots \quad (13.66)$$

In general, the particular ratio of P/R chosen for a balance on steady currents will not satisfy equation (13.66) simultaneously, and the ratio P/R must be changed until this condition is satisfied. The operation of the bridge depends on rate of growth of potential at A and C remaining the same as the currents rise to their steady values in the two arms on completing the battery circuit. From our considerations of section 5 this equality of growth requires that the time constants shall be the same for the two arms. Hence

$$\frac{L_1}{P+Q} = \frac{L_2}{R+S},$$

and on combining this equation with (13.65a) we obtain equation (13.66).

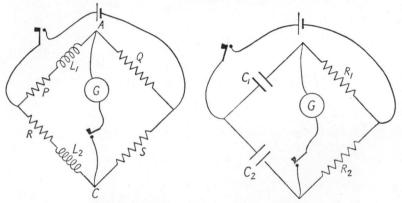

Fig. 20. — Bridge with Self-Inductances   Fig. 21. — Bridge with Capacities

(ii) *Comparison of Capacities.*

This bridge, due to de Sauty, is shown in fig. 21. In operation it is completely analogous to the inductance bridge described in the preceding section. There is, of course, no question of balancing the circuit for steady currents in this case. The condition for no throw in the ballistic galvanometer on completing the battery circuit is that the time constants of the two arms of the bridge shall be equal. From considerations analogous to those of section 5, the equality of the time constants of circuits containing capacity and resistance requires

$$C_1 R_1 = C_2 R_2;$$

and hence
$$\frac{C_1}{C_2} = \frac{R_2}{R_1}. \quad \cdots \cdots \quad (13.67)$$

(iii) *Comparison of Capacity and Mutual Inductance by Campbell's Bridge.*

As an example of the use of an alternating current bridge to compare capacity and mutual inductance, we use the circuit shown in fig. 22. With A.C. circuits the galvanometer could be either of the soft-iron or hot-wire type, but the sensitivity of such instruments is generally too low for accurate work. In practice the most common device is to replace the galvanometer by a telephone T, and to determine by the ear when no current is flowing through the telephone and the circuit is therefore balanced. The A.C. supply which replaces the battery used for steady current work must, of course, be of audio-frequency. With the current disposition shown in fig. 22, for no current through the telephone we have, considering circuit DEA,

$$L\frac{dI_1}{dt} - M\frac{dI}{dt} + R_2I_1 = 0,$$

or, since $I = I_1 + I_2$,

$$L\frac{dI_1}{dt} - M\frac{dI_1}{dt} + R_2I_1 = M\frac{dI_2}{dt}. \quad \cdots \quad (13.68)$$

For the circuit DBA, since A and D are always at the same potential,

$$RI_2 - R_1I_1 = \frac{q}{C},$$

where q is the charge on the condenser and equals $\int I_1 dt$. Hence

$$RI_2 - R_1I_1 = \frac{1}{C}\int I_1 dt,$$

or
$$R_1\frac{dI_1}{dt} + \frac{I_1}{C} = R\frac{dI_2}{dt}. \quad \cdots \cdots \quad (13.69)$$

Eliminating dI_2/dt from equations (13.68) and (13.69) we obtain

$$\left(L - M - \frac{MR_1}{R}\right)\frac{dI_1}{dt} + \left(R_2 - \frac{M}{RC}\right)I_1 = 0. \quad (13.70)$$

Now the first term in equation (13.70) is a function of the rate of change of the current while the second is not. Hence each term must vanish separately, so that

$$\left(L - M - M\frac{R_1}{R}\right) = 0 = \left(R_2 - \frac{M}{RC}\right)$$

or
$$\frac{L}{M} = \frac{R + R_1}{R} \text{ and } \frac{M}{C} = RR_2. \quad \cdots \quad (13.71)$$

The resistances are therefore adjusted until no sound is heard in the telephone, when application of equation (13.71) gives the comparison of the inductances and capacities.

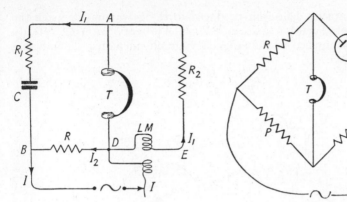

Fig. 22. — Campbell's Bridge   Fig. 23. — Conductivity of an Electrolyte

(iv) *Conductivity of an Electrolyte.*

The resistance or the conductivity of an electrolyte is required for various purposes, as for example when an estimate of the mobility of the ions is required as described in Chap. XII, section 6. Owing to the presence of polarization and the chemical action at the electrodes attendant upon electrolysis, the use of a direct current is inadmissible. By the use of an alternating current, the ordinary Wheatstone bridge methods may be applied directly to the solution, as shown in fig. 23. The resistances P and Q represent the ratio arms in the usual fashion, and R is adjusted until minimum sound is heard in the telephone T, which replaces the galvanometer normally used in D.C. work.

* 17. Absolute Determination of Resistance.

We have already described how the absolute unit of current is defined and measured by its magnetic or chemical effects. Of the remaining quantities, the unit of resistance or absolute ohm is determined independently, while the unit of E.M.F. is derived from the other two units by application of Ohm's law. The absolute ohm has been determined by methods based on: (i) the measurement of the deflection of a compass needle from the magnetic meridian due to the magnetic field of a rotating earth-inductor. The resultant deflection depends only on the area of the coil, its resistance and number of turns, and its angular velocity of rotation; (ii) the method of Lorenz which we describe below; (iii) the use of a suspended magnet ballistic galvanometer and a standard mutual inductance.

Combining equations (13.52) and (13.35) we have

$$\frac{MI_0}{R_2} = \frac{HT}{\pi G} \sin \frac{\theta}{2}. \quad \cdots \cdots \quad (13.72)$$

If θ_1 is the steady deflection produced in the galvanometer when the steady potential across a resistance R in the primary (carrying a steady current I_0) is applied to the secondary circuit, including the galvanometer, we have

$$\frac{I_0 R}{R_2} = \frac{H}{G} \tan \theta_1. \quad \cdots \cdots \quad (13.73)$$

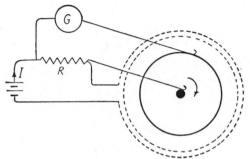

Fig. 24. — Resistance by Lorenz's Method

Hence from (13.72) and (13.73) we have

$$R = M \frac{\pi}{T} \frac{\tan \theta_1}{\sin \theta_2}, \quad \cdots \cdots \quad (13.74)$$

so that on measuring T and calculating M from the dimensions of the mutual inductance, R is obtained absolutely.

In Lorenz's method, a metal disk is rotated in the magnetic field produced by a current passing through a mutual inductance consisting of two coaxial circular coils. As shown in fig. 24, the E.M.F. generated between the centre and the circumference of the disk is balanced against the difference of potential between the ends of the resistance R, through which is passing the current which energises the coils of the mutual inductance. If the disk makes n revolutions per second we have

$$IR = nMI;$$

hence
$$R = nM,$$

and by calculating M from the dimensions of the mutual inductance, R is obtained absolutely. Special devices must be introduced to obtain an accurately known low resistance for R, and thermoelectric effects at the junctions of different parts of the circuit must be eliminated.

EXERCISES

1. State the laws of electromagnetic induction and give examples of their application.

2. Define the terms " mutual induction " and " self-induction " and calculate the self-induction of a solenoid of length l, cross-sectional area A, and having a total of N turns. $[4\pi N^2 A/l.]$

3. Show that for a circuit containing inductance and resistance, the growth and decay curves for the current are exponential and complementary.

4. Show that for a coil rotating uniformly in a magnetic field, the E.M.F. produced is sinusoidal and proportional to the angular velocity of rotation. How is the current rectified and smoothed?

5. Describe the use of the earth-inductor for finding the angle of magnetic dip.

6. Compare and contrast the operation of a dynamo and an electric motor, both of simple form.

7. What are the essentials of a good transformer, and how are certain phenomena, avoided in transformer construction, put to use in other instruments?

8. Describe the construction and mode of action of an induction coil and give examples of its application.

9. Obtain an expression for the throw of a ballistic coil galvanometer duly corrected for damping. How is such a galvanometer usually calibrated?

10. Describe how the strength of a magnetic field is determined with a search coil and a ballistic galvanometer.

11. How may a hysteresis curve be obtained by a dynamical method and what advantages does this method possess over the magnetometer method?

12. Give the theory of the Grassot fluxmeter, explaining clearly why the observed deflection is independent of the speed of removal of the search coil.

13. Obtain an expression for the distribution of discharge through a two-divided circuit, and hence show that a shunt fitted to a ballistic galvanometer under steady current conditions is still suitable when used for sudden discharges.

14. Describe two methods by which two capacities may be accurately compared.

15. Explain clearly how the conductivity of an electrolyte is determined.

16. Describe one method by which resistance may be measured absolutely.

CHAPTER XIV

Magnetic Properties of Materials

1. Introduction.

All substances show reaction to a magnetic field if the latter is sufficiently intense. This is consistent with the electron theory of matter (see Chap. XX), since the incessant motion of the electrons, on the dynamic model of the atom, is equivalent to electric currents, which are always associated with magnetic fields. Certain groupings of electrons, however, are far more effective in producing a resultant magnetic field than others, and the most effective of these constitutes the ferromagnetic group. We shall commence with a series of definitions based on the observed behaviour of materials in this strongly magnetic group.

2. Intensity of Magnetization.

As we have seen in Chap. VI, the effect produced by a magnet depends on the distance apart of the poles as well as on the pole strength, and consequently the magnetic moment is a better criterion of the " strength " of a magnet than the pole strength alone. Since a magnet is three-dimensional, a concept still more relevant to a real magnet is the *intensity of magnetization*, I, of a specimen, which is defined as the magnetic moment per unit volume, that is

$$I = \frac{M}{V}, \quad \cdots \cdots \quad (14.1)$$

where V is the volume of the specimen, and M its magnetic moment. If the magnet is rectangular as shown in fig. 1, and the area of cross-

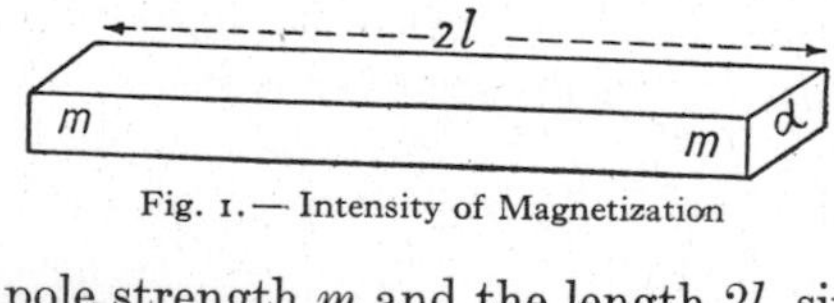

Fig. 1.— Intensity of Magnetization

section is a, the pole strength m and the length $2l$, since $M = 2ml$ and $V = 2la$, (14.1) may be written

$$I = \frac{2ml}{2la} = \frac{m}{a}, \quad \cdots \cdots \quad (14.2)$$

or the intensity of magnetization is equal to the *pole strength per unit area* or *polar density.* This last definition is useful but must be accepted with reserve, since (1) the magnetic pole is not in fact spread over the area of the end of the magnet in the same way as electric charge in the corresponding case of a charged conductor, (2) the length $2l$ used in defining the magnetic moment is the equivalent length of the magnet whereas in computing the volume it is the geometrical length.

3. Magnetic Susceptibility.

If a specimen acquires an intensity of magnetization I as a result of being in a magnetic field H, the *magnetic susceptibility* k is defined by

$$k = \frac{I}{H}. \quad \cdots \cdots \quad (14.3)$$

The quantitative definition is consistent with the qualitative concept of susceptibility as a measure of the ease of magnetization of a specimen.

4. Magnetic Intensity near Flat Poles.

By analogy with the electric intensity between two flat condenser plates, the magnetic intensity near two flat magnetic poles is obtained directly. The laws are exactly the same since they are based in both instances on the inverse square law. Referring to fig. 2, and assuming that the polar density is I, we have by analogy with (3.16), if F is the strength of the magnetic field between two (infinite) flat poles,

$$F = 4\pi I, \quad \cdots \quad (14.4)$$

while the effect due to a single pole is, from (3.17),

Fig. 2.— Field between two Flat Poles

$$F = 2\pi I. \quad \cdots \quad (14.5)$$

Finally, by analogy with (3.18), the mechanical force of attraction P between two flat poles of area A situated close together is

$$P = 2\pi I^2 A. \quad \cdots \cdots \quad (14.6)$$

Gauss's theorem is directly applicable to problems in magnetism just as in electrostatics.

5. Magnetic Induction and Permeability.

If a bar of ferro-magnetic material is placed with its longest axis parallel to a uniform magnetic field H as shown in fig. 3, the number of lines of force crossing unit area in the bar perpendicular to its axis is increased above H due to the original field, owing to the partial magnetization of the specimen. If the intensity of magnetization is I, then from the preceding section, the intensity of the field at P in fig. 3 due to the molecular orientation is $4\pi I$. Hence, the total magnetic intensity or the number of lines per unit area is given by

$$B = H + 4\pi I, \quad \ldots \ldots \ldots \quad (14.7)$$

where B is termed the **magnetic induction** in the specimen.

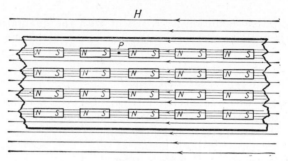

Fig. 3. — Magnetic Induction

The ratio of the magnetic induction to the inducing field is defined as the **permeability** μ of the specimen, that is,

$$\mu = \frac{B}{H}. \quad \ldots \ldots \ldots \quad (14.8)$$

Substituting from (14.3) and (14.8) in (14.7) we obtain

$$\mu = 1 + 4\pi k. \quad \ldots \ldots \ldots \quad (14.9)$$

Hence, if one of the magnetic constants μ or k is known, the other is easily calculated from (14.9). If the space between and around two theoretical unit poles is filled with material of permeability μ, there is a reduction in the force of attraction between the poles proportional to the permeability of the medium, and the law of force becomes

$$F = \frac{m_1 m_2}{\mu r^2}. \quad \ldots \ldots \ldots \quad (14.10)$$

6. Magnetic Constants and Magnetic Hysteresis.

To determine the magnetic susceptibility of a specimen of ferro-magnetic material the apparatus shown in fig. 4 may be used. It consists essentially of a deflection magnetometer similar to that described in Chap. VII, section 4. On one of the arms of the magneto-meter is a solenoid S to enclose the specimen, which is in the form of a thin rod. On the other arm is a compensating coil C, the purpose of which is to neutralize the effect of the magnetic field of the solenoid as distinct from the magnetic field produced by the magnetized specimen. Compensation is first obtained by removing the specimen, using a fairly high magnetizing current and adjusting the position of solenoid and compensating coil until no deflection is shown in the magneto-meter. The current is then cut off, the unmagnetized specimen in-

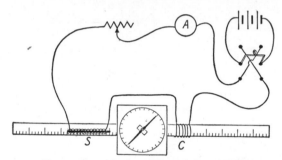

Fig. 4. — Determination of Magnetic Susceptibility

serted and a small current sent through the solenoid. The magnetic moment of the specimen is calculated from equation (7.12) for the standard end-on or Gauss A position. The intensity of magnetization is obtained by dividing the measured magnetic moment by the meas-ured volume of the rod. Finally, the intensity H of the magnetizing field of the solenoid is assumed to be that given in equation (10.13) for an infinite solenoid. Hence the magnetizing field is proportional to the current I, and the intensity of magnetization to $\tan \theta$, where θ is the magnetometer deflection. A graph of $\tan \theta$ against I is shown in fig. 5. The susceptibility k, defined from (14.3), is given by the slope of the tangent to the curve at any point. The susceptibility of ferro-magnetic substances therefore varies with the inducing field as shown in fig. 6. As the specimen acquires magnetic saturation the suscepti-bility approaches zero. The permeability is calculated from (14.9) when the susceptibility has been measured. Similarly the B-H curve is constructed from (14.7) after the I-H curve has been obtained.

It is very important in plotting fig. 5 that the current should be increased continually by small amounts, and that no temporary reduction of current is allowed to occur during the experiment. After saturation has been reached, if the current is reduced steadily by increments equal to those by which it was increased it is found that

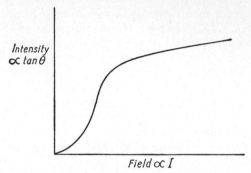

Fig. 5. — Intensity of Magnetization and Field

the specimen does not retrace its original path. The intensity of magnetization lags behind the reduced inducing field giving the curve BC shown in fig. 7. The ordinate OC is termed the **residual magnetism** of the specimen. To reduce the magnetization to zero, the current through the solenoid must be reversed in direction. If this is done and

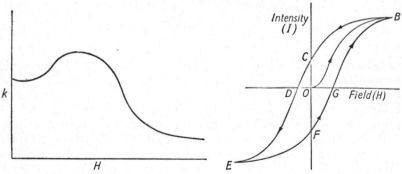

Fig. 6. — Susceptibility and Field   Fig. 7. — Hysteresis Cycle or Loop

the strength of the current continually increased, the magnetization is eventually destroyed. The abscissa DO is termed the **coercive force** of the specimen, as it represents the strength of field required to demagnetize the specimen. Further increase of the current in the reverse direction results in magnetic saturation in the reverse direction. Finally, if the current is reduced to zero and again increased to its maximum in the original direction, the path EFGB is traversed.

The path BCDEFGB is said to constitute a **hysteresis cycle** or **loop** and has many important properties. For example, it is shown in section 7 that the area enclosed by the loop represents electromagnetic energy which is converted, usually wastefully, into heat. Such a transformation occurs in the iron cores of transformers running on alternating current in the primary. Consideration of the hysteresis curves of various ferromagnetic materials makes it possible to choose a thin loop with minimum hysteresis loss. Soft iron has a thin loop while hard steel embraces a considerable area.

* **7. Energy Loss due to Hysteresis.**

We shall show that the area of the I-H hysteresis loop represents the loss of energy when the material is taken round the loop. From the molecular theory of magnetism, let M be the magnetic moment of any one of the molecular magnets, and suppose that at some stage the axis of this molecular magnet is inclined at θ to the field direction. Then the component of magnetic moment parallel to the field is $M \cos \theta$, and perpendicular to the field it is $M \sin \theta$. Hence for all the molecules in unit volume, remembering that the magnetic moment per unit volume is by definition the intensity of magnetization I,

$$\Sigma M \cos \theta = I,$$
$$\Sigma M \sin \theta = 0, \quad \cdots \cdots \quad (14.11)$$

since there is no resultant magnetism perpendicular to the magnetic axis.

Now the couple acting on any one of the molecular magnets when it is inclined at θ to the field is, from (7.2),

$$G = MH \sin \theta, \quad \cdots \cdots \quad (14.12)$$

and the work done in rotating the molecular magnets through further angles $(-d\theta)$, resulting in an increase in the intensity of magnetization dI of the specimen is

$$dW = \Sigma MH \sin \theta (-d\theta)$$
$$= -H . \Sigma M \sin \theta . d\theta. \quad \cdots \quad (14.13)$$

Differentiating the first of equations (14.11),

$$dI = -\Sigma M \sin \theta . d\theta, \quad \cdots \cdots \quad (14.14)$$

and substituting from (14.14) in (14.13) we have

$$dW = H . dI,$$

and hence the work done in a complete hysteresis cycle is

$$W = \int_{-I_{sat}}^{+I_{sat}} H \, dI = \text{area BCDEFGB}. \quad \cdots \quad (14.15)$$

Now if B is the magnetic induction,

$$B = H + 4\pi I,$$

or, by differentiating,

$$dB = dH + 4\pi \, dI. \quad \ldots \ldots \quad (14.16)$$

Substituting from (14.16) in (14.15) we obtain

$$W = \int_{-B_{sat}}^{+B_{sat}} \frac{H \, dB}{4\pi} - \int_{-H_{sat}}^{+H_{sat}} \frac{H \, dH}{4\pi}. \quad \ldots \quad (14.17)$$

The second term on the R.H.S. in (14.17) is zero, since $H \, dH = d(\frac{1}{2}H^2)$, and hence

$$W = \frac{1}{4\pi} \int_{-B_{sat}}^{+B_{sat}} H \, dB. \quad \ldots \ldots \quad (14.18)$$

The definite integral in (14.18) represents the area of the loop of the B-H curve, which can be drawn by means of (14.7), and is of similar shape to the I-H curve (fig. 7).

The following approximate expression was given by Steinmetz for the energy loss due to hysteresis:

$$\text{Work done per cycle} = \eta B_{max}^{1.68},$$

where η is a constant for a particular substance, usually lying between 10^{-2} and 10^{-3}, and B_{max} is the saturation value of the magnetic induction.

8. Paramagnetism, Diamagnetism and Ferromagnetism.

Careful examination of the behaviour of substances in a magnetic field shows that they may be classified in two distinct groups according to the behaviour of a rod or elongated portion of the material. If the substance moves so that the axis of the rod or the main bulk of the material moves from a weaker to the strongest portion of the field when the latter is established (say by switching on an electromagnet as shown in fig. 8) the substance is said to be **paramagnetic.** If a rod of the material sets transversely to the field, or if its main bulk moves from stronger to weaker portions of the field when the latter is established, the substance is said to be **diamagnetic.** The **ferromagnetic** group behaves essentially as a very powerful paramagnetic group. One standard apparatus for examining the magnetic behaviour of substances is the *Curie balance*. As shown in fig. 8, this consists of a powerful electromagnet with its axes inclined at an angle so as to form a magnetic field with a pronounced field gradient along the x-axis. It may be shown that the force along the x-axis at any point is

$$F_x = kH_x \frac{dH_x}{dx} \quad \ldots \ldots \quad (14.19)$$

per unit volume, where k is the susceptibility of the material. By suspending the material from the arm of a delicate torsion balance, the susceptibility of very feebly magnetic substances may be determined. The magnetic characteristics of gases are obtained by using

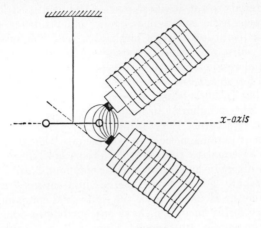

Fig. 8.—Curie Balance

a hollow suspended quartz sphere filled with the gas. The effect of the quartz is determined by a preliminary experiment with the sphere exhausted. A comparison of the properties of diamagnetic, paramagnetic and ferromagnetic substances is shown in the accompanying Table.

Property	Diamagnetic	Paramagnetic	Ferromagnetic
1. Nature.	Shown by solids, liquids and gases.		A few solids only.
2. k.	Negative.	Positive.	Positive.
3. μ.	< 1.	> 1.	$\gg 1$.
4. Variation of k with temperature.	Independent.	Inversely as absolute temperature.	Irregular, but decreases.
5. Variation of k with H.	Constant.	Constant.	Irregular, curve tending towards zero k at saturation.
6. Behaviour of compounds.	k additive	Irregular.	Irregular, e.g. Heusler alloys.

The fact that k is positive for paramagnetic and ferromagnetic substances implies that the polarity induced in these substances is opposite in sign to that of the inducing pole. On the other hand, with diamagnetic substances, induction results in poles of the same sign being formed in closest proximity, and hence the movement of dia-magnetic materials to the weakest part of the field is explained.

While diamagnetic substances show independence of suscepti-bility with temperature, **Curie's law** states that the susceptibility of paramagnetic substances varies inversely as the absolute temperature. There is a final residual negative susceptibility shown both by para-magnetic and ferromagnetic substances when the temperature is raised sufficiently, that is, all substances becomes diamagnetic at some tem-perature. Another peculiarity in magnetic properties is the dependence on crystalline structure. For example, grey tin is diamagnetic and crystalline tin is paramagnetic. In compounds, the total diamagnetic susceptibility is equal to the sum of the susceptibilities of the com-ponents. Paramagnetic and ferromagnetic compounds are quite irregular in their behaviour. For example, the gas iron carbonyl is very feebly magnetic, while the Heusler alloys, the individual component metals of which are very feebly magnetic, have susceptibilities comparable with those of ferromagnetic substances. Since k is independent of H for diamagnetic and paramagnetic substances, the I-H curve is a straight line. These substances therefore do not show magnetic hysteresis or residual magnetism like the ferromagnetic group. We discuss the explanation of magnetism on the electron theory in Chap. XX.

9. Magnetic Circuit.

If we consider the magnetic condition of a closed iron circuit of irregular cross-section as shown in fig. 9, we note that the number of lines of induction or the magnetic flux N is constant round the circuit. The magnetic induction B, therefore, de-fined as the number of lines of induc-tion per unit area of cross-section varies from place to place according to the relation

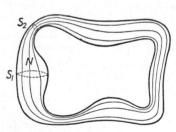

Fig. 9.—Magnetic Circuit

$$N = B_1 S_1 = B_2 S_2 = \&\text{c.,} \quad (14.20)$$

where B_1, B_2, &c., are the magnetic inductions at points where the areas of cross-section are S_1, S_2, &c. Now from section 4, Chap. X, the work done in taking a unit pole round a complete circuit of induc-tion is the magnetomotive force or M.M.F., that is

$$\text{M.M.F.} = \int H\,dl, \quad \cdots \cdots \quad (14.21)$$

where the integral extends over the length of the circuit, and H is the field strength at any point. Now from equation (14.8), $B = \mu H$ and hence, from (14.20) and (14.21), we have

$$\text{M.M.F.} = N \int \frac{dl}{\mu S},$$

or

$$N = \frac{\text{M.M.F.}}{\int dl/\mu S}. \qquad \cdots \cdots \quad (14.22)$$

Equation (14.22) is formally analogous to Ohm's law of the electric circuit, if we compare M.M.F. with E.M.F., and the magnetic flux N with the electric current I. The quantity $\int dl/\mu S$, which depends only on the length, area of cross-section and nature of the material comprising the circuit, is then clearly analogous to the electrical resistance and is termed the **magnetic resistance** or **reluctance.**

Equation (14.22) provides a useful general method of solving electromagnetic flux problems. As examples we shall consider first an anchor ring magnet with a small air gap, and then an electromagnet of the conventional design shown in fig. 10. The M.M.F. is given by the work theorem, that is, it is $4\pi \times$ current linked. Hence as at equation (10.17) we have for an *anchor ring*

$$\text{M.M.F.} = 4\pi(2\pi rni), \qquad \cdots \cdots \quad (14.23)$$

where r is the radius of the ring and n is the number of turns per unit length.

The total magnetic resistance is the sum of two resistances in series, that of the ring and that of the air gap. If the width of the gap is d, we have

$$\int \frac{dl}{\mu S} = \frac{d}{\mu_1 S} + \frac{(2\pi r - d)}{\mu S}, \qquad \cdots \cdots \quad (14.24)$$

where $\mu_1 = 1$ for the air gap, and the cross-section S is uniform.

Hence, substituting from (14.23) and (14.24) in (14.22) we have

$$N = 4\pi(2\pi rni) \frac{\mu S}{2\pi r + (\mu - 1)d}. \qquad \cdots \quad (14.25)$$

From (14.20)

$$B = \frac{N}{S} = \frac{4\pi(2\pi rni)\mu}{2\pi r + (\mu - 1)d}, \qquad \cdots \quad (14.26)$$

and the strength H of the field within the gap is obtained from

$$H = B/\mu_1 = B,$$

since $\mu_1 = 1$, and within the iron by

$$H = B/\mu = \frac{4\pi(2\pi r n i)}{2\pi r + (\mu - 1)d}. \quad \cdots \quad (14.27)$$

The field due to the *electromagnet* in fig. 10 is calculated in a precisely similar manner except that the total magnetic resistance becomes

$$\int \frac{dl}{\mu S} = \frac{l}{S_1} + \frac{2l_1}{\mu_1 S_1} + \frac{2l_2}{\mu_2 S_2} + \frac{l_3}{\mu_3 S_3},$$

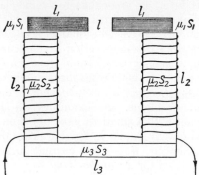

Fig. 10. — Reluctance of Electromagnet

where S_1, S_2 and S_3 are the areas of cross-section of the pole-pieces, the arms and the yoke respectively, and μ_1, μ_2, and μ_3 are the permeabilities of the materials of which the three portions are made.

EXERCISES

1. Define the terms *intensity of magnetization, magnetic susceptibility, magnetic permeability* and *magnetic induction*. How are these various quantities inter-related?

2. Show how and why the general expressions for the field strength between infinite plane magnetic poles and infinite plane condenser plates are formally similar. Are the formulæ derived for the magnetic or the electrical case likely to be in better agreement with practical observations?

3. Obtain an expression for the electromagnetic energy lost in a hysteresis cycle. Do paramagnetic bodies show hysteresis?

4. Write a short essay on diamagnetism, paramagnetism and ferromagnetism.

5. Explain the significance of the term *magnetic circuit* and use this concept to calculate an expression for the strength of the magnetic field inside a gap in the circumference of an electromagnet of anchor ring type.

CHAPTER XV

*Electrical Oscillations

1. Introduction.

The varying currents which we have so far encountered when considering the presence of inductance and resistance in a circuit (as in Chap. XIII), or the discharge which passes through a ballistic galvanometer when connected to a search coil which is being used to explore a magnetic field, have all been pulses of short duration. By suitable choice of circuit, however, it is possible to produce continuous electrical oscillations in which the current surges first in one direction and then in the other. These oscillations may be damped away gradually as in the condenser discharge considered in section 2, or they may be maintained indefinitely either from an alternating supply or with an oscillation generator such as a radio valve circuit.

2. Circuit containing Capacity and Inductance.

Consider the circuit shown in fig. 1, in which a condenser C is discharging through an inductance L. The resistance in the circuit is assumed to be negligible, to simplify the calculation, but we shall consider later the effect of introducing resistance into the circuit. Suppose at any time t the quantities of electricity on the plates of the condenser are $+Q$, $-Q$ respectively, and let I be the current through the inductance from $+Q$ to $-Q$, so that $I = -dQ/dt$.

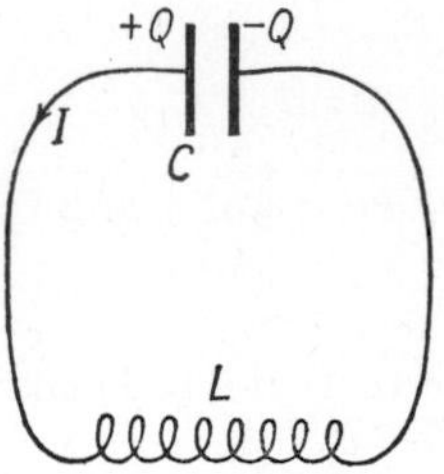

The E.M.F. acting round the wire is the difference of potential on the plates, i.e. Q/C. Hence (p. 647)

Fig. 1. — Oscillatory Circuit without Damping

$$L\frac{dI}{dt} = \frac{Q}{C}, \qquad \cdots \cdots \cdots (15.1)$$

or

$$L\frac{d^2Q}{dt^2} + \frac{Q}{C} = 0. \qquad \cdots \cdots \cdots (15.2)$$

This is the well-known Simple Harmonic Equation discussed in detail in Part I, Chap. III. section 9. Initially let the plates be insulated from each other, and carry charges $\pm Q_0$. At time $t = 0$, let them be short-circuited by the wire of inductance L. Then the solution of (15.2) is

$$Q = Q_0 \cos \frac{t}{\sqrt{LC}}, \quad \ldots \ldots \quad (15.3)$$

for this gives $Q = Q_0$ and $I = 0$, for $t = 0$. The discharge is therefore oscillatory, the period being given by

$$T = 2\pi\sqrt{LC}. \quad \ldots \ldots \quad (15.4)$$

The energy W at any time t consists of two parts, associated respectively with the capacity and the inductance. When the charge is Q, the

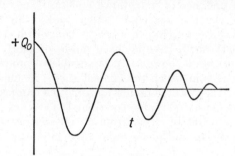

Fig. 2. — Decay of Oscillations

former part is $\frac{1}{2}Q^2/C$ (p. 554); the rate of increase of the latter part is

$$I \times \text{E.M.F.} = I \cdot L\,dI/dt = \frac{d}{dt}(\tfrac{1}{2}LI^2).$$

Hence $\qquad\qquad\qquad W = \tfrac{1}{2}Q^2/C + \tfrac{1}{2}LI^2, \quad \ldots \ldots \quad (15.5)$

no constant being required, since initially

$$W = \tfrac{1}{2}Q_0{}^2/C, \text{ and } I = 0.$$

Note that (15.1) may be obtained from (15.5) by using the fact that $dW/dt = 0$.

Since $I = -dQ/dt$, (15.3) gives

$$I = \frac{Q_0}{\sqrt{LC}} \sin \frac{t}{\sqrt{LC}}, \quad \ldots \ldots \quad (15.6)$$

the maximum value of which is

$$I_0 = Q_0/\sqrt{LC}.$$

In practice the oscillations gradually die away as shown in fig. 2. This is due to the presence of resistance which transforms some of the

electrical energy into heat energy at each oscillation. It may be shown
that, in the presence of resistance R, equation (15.2) transforms to

$$L\frac{d^2Q}{dt^2} + R\frac{dQ}{dt} + \frac{Q}{C} = 0, \quad \ldots \ldots \quad (15.7)$$

and (15.4) becomes

$$T = \frac{2\pi}{\sqrt{1/LC - R^2/4L^2}}, \quad \ldots \ldots \quad (15.8)$$

so the time of oscillation is increased in the presence of resistance.
It will be observed that the frequency of the oscillation depends on
the *product* LC and the *ratio* R/L and not on the individual values of
these three quantities.

3. Forced Oscillations.

A circuit containing inductance and capacity alone has a **natural
frequency** of oscillation given by $n = 1/(2\pi\sqrt{LC})$, according to the
considerations of the preceding paragraph. Consequently it corresponds exactly to any other vibrating system such as an organ pipe
or a stretched string. We have seen in Part IV, Chap. IV, how any
such system may be forced to oscillate if excited by some external
oscillating supply, but that the magnitude of the excited oscillations
is generally small except at resonance. Precisely similar relations are
found if an alternating E.M.F., such as is provided by a dynamo
without a commutator, is applied to a circuit containing inductance
and capacity. At any time t, let the applied E.M.F. be $E = E_0 \sin pt$,
where E_0 is the maximum amplitude of the E.M.F. and its period is $2\pi/p$.
The total E.M.F. is now $Q/C + E_0 \sin pt$, and equation (15.2) becomes

$$L\frac{d^2Q}{dt^2} + \frac{Q}{C} = -E_0 \sin pt. \quad \ldots \ldots \quad (15.9)$$

The forced oscillations which are set up will clearly be of the same
frequency as the forcing supply and of simple harmonic form. The
solution of (15.9) corresponding to the forced oscillations is therefore
of the form

$$Q = A \sin pt + B \cos pt, \quad \ldots \ldots \quad (15.10)$$

where A and B are constants.

Just as in our treatment of the S.H. equation in Part I, p. 23, to
determine A and B we differentiate (15.10) and substitute in (15.9).
Hence we obtain

$$\frac{dQ}{dt} = pA \cos pt - pB \sin pt$$

and

$$\frac{d^2Q}{dt^2} = -p^2(A \sin pt + B \cos pt). \quad \ldots \quad (15.11)$$

Substituting from (15.10) and (15.11) in (15.9) we obtain

$$-p^2L(A \sin pt + B \cos pt) + \frac{1}{C}(A \sin pt + B \cos pt)$$
$$= -E_0 \sin pt. \quad (15.12)$$

When $t = 0$, $\sin pt = 0$ and $\cos pt = 1$; hence, substituting this condition in (15.12), $(-p^2L + 1/C)B = 0$, and therefore $B = 0$ (if we assume that $-p^2L + 1/C$ is not zero). When $pt = \pi/2$, $\sin pt = 1$ and $\cos pt = 0$; substituting this condition in (15.12)

$$-p^2LA + \frac{A}{C} = -E_0,$$

or

$$A = -\frac{E_0}{(1/C - p^2L)} \quad \cdot \quad \cdot \quad \cdot \quad \cdot \quad (15.13)$$

and equation (15.10) becomes

$$Q = -\frac{E_0}{(1/C - p^2L)} \sin pt. \quad \cdot \quad \cdot \quad \cdot \quad (15.14)$$

The forced oscillation of Q is therefore in phase with the forcing oscillation, if p^2L is greater than $1/C$. If $Lp = 1/Cp$ or $p = 1/\sqrt{LC}$, that is, if the forced oscillations are of the same frequency as the natural period of the circuit, according to (15.14) the charge Q becomes infinite. With a circuit of zero resistance, if radiated energy is neglected (see Chap. XVI), this situation would occur. In practice, however, the resistance which is actually present acts as a damping factor and keeps the charge (and current) finite although large.

We next consider the case of a circuit containing inductance and resistance. The electromotive force equation becomes

$$L\frac{dI}{dt} + RI = E_0 \sin pt, \quad \cdot \quad \cdot \quad \cdot \quad (15.15)$$

and we solve this by precisely the same method as we have already used in this section. Assuming $I = A \sin pt + B \cos pt$, we find

$$A = \frac{RE_0}{L^2p^2 + R^2},$$
$$\quad \cdot \quad \cdot \quad \cdot \quad \cdot \quad (15.16)$$

and

$$B = \frac{-LpE_0}{L^2p^2 + R^2}.$$

Hence

$$I = \frac{E_0}{L^2p^2 + R^2}(R \sin pt - Lp \cos pt). \quad \cdot \quad (15.17)$$

If we construct a triangle as in fig. 3 with $\cos \theta = R/\sqrt{(L^2p^2 + R^2)}$,

$\sin \theta = Lp/\sqrt{(L^2p^2 + R^2)}$, and $\tan \theta = Lp/R$, we may write (15.17) in the form

$$I = \frac{E_0}{\sqrt{(L^2p^2 + R^2)}} \sin (pt - \theta). \qquad . \quad . \quad (15.18)$$

The current oscillations are therefore of amplitude $E_0/\sqrt{(L^2p^2 + R^2)}$, and they are no longer in phase with the applied E.M.F., but lag behind it by an amount θ. Of course, if there is no inductance present, that is if $L = 0$, then $\theta = 0$, and the current is given by $E_0 \sin pt/R$. The current is then in phase with the E.M.F. and is given by the ordinary ohmic relation. These considerations show that while capacity and resistance respond instantaneously to the applied E.M.F., *inductance behaves as inertia.*

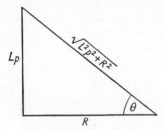

Fig. 3.—Phase of Current

When inductance, resistance and capacity are present simultaneously, the treatment is similar to that already given. As it is rather lengthy we simply quote the results here. The equation differs from (15.7) by having $-E_0 \sin pt$ on the right. The charge Q on the condenser at any time t is given by

$$Q = -\frac{E_0(1/Cp - Lp)}{p(1/Cp - Lp)^2 + pR^2} \sin pt$$

$$+ \frac{E_0R}{p(1/Cp - Lp)^2 + pR^2} \cos pt, \quad . \quad . \quad . \quad (15.19)$$

and constructing a triangle as before with

$$\tan \theta = \frac{1/Cp - Lp}{R}. \qquad . \quad . \quad . \quad (15.20)$$

we obtain (15.19) in the simpler form

$$I = \frac{E_0}{\sqrt{(1/Cp - Lp)^2 + R^2}} \sin(pt + \theta). \qquad . \quad (15.21)$$

The phase angle θ is positive or negative according as $1/Cp$ is greater or less than Lp.

Equation (15.21) bears a formal resemblance to Ohm's law for steady currents if we consider the simple resistance R in the denominator replaced by the quantity $\sqrt{(1/Cp - Lp)^2 + R^2}$. This quantity is termed the **impedance** of the oscillatory circuit. The difference of Lp and $1/Cp$ is called the **reactance**. If the circuit contains no capacity, the impedance reduces to $\sqrt{R^2 + L^2p^2}$. At very high frequencies $R^2 \ll L^2p^2$

and under these conditions the impedance consists of reactance only and has the value Lp.

4. Choke Coil.

If we require to reduce the current in a circuit conveying steady current, the procedure is to introduce additional resistance. This process is wasteful, as electrical energy is converted wastefully into heat in the added resistance. With varying currents a much more economical process is available. Suppose a coil of negligible resistance but appreciable inductance L is included in the circuit. Consideration of equation (15.18) then shows that $\theta = 90°$ or the current is $90°$ out of phase with the E.M.F. applied across the coil. The average energy absorbed per cycle by the coil is therefore

$$W = \frac{\int_0^{2\pi} E_0 \sin a \, I \, da}{\int_0^{2\pi} da}, \quad \cdots \quad (15.22)$$

where a is written for pt for convenience. Substituting for I from (15.21) in (15.22) and integrating, we obtain

$$W = \frac{E_0^2}{Lp} \frac{\int_0^{2\pi} \sin a \cos a \, da}{\int_0^{2\pi} da} = 0. \quad \cdots \quad (15.23)$$

Hence no energy is consumed by the coil although the current is reduced by the insertion of the choke coil by a factor $1/Lp$.

5. Measurement of Alternating Current and Voltage.

We have already stated that the hot-wire and soft-iron ammeters give a steady deflection when subjected to alternating current, but we have not yet considered what value of the alternating current amplitude this steady reading represents. It clearly depends upon the mean value of the *square* of the current, since the action of the ammeters considered depends on effects which are proportional to the square of the current. Representing the mean square current by $\overline{I^2}$, we have by its definition

$$\overline{I^2} = \frac{\int_0^{2\pi} I_0^2 \sin^2 a \, da}{\int_0^{2\pi} da} = \frac{I_0^2}{2}. \quad \cdots \quad (15.24)$$

The steady continuous current which would give the same reading on the ammeter as the alternating current is therefore $I = I_0/\sqrt{2}$; It is termed the *virtual current*. In the same way, the steady voltage which would give the same reading as the applied A.C. voltage is $E = E_0/\sqrt{2}$.

If we have a circuit containing inductance and resistance we can use an A.C. ammeter and voltmeter to determine its impedance just as we can use a D.C. ammeter and voltmeter to determine the resistance of a circuit to steady current. We may then apply the relation

$$\frac{I_0}{\sqrt{2}} = \frac{E_0}{\sqrt{2}} \frac{1}{\sqrt{L^2 p^2 + R^2}}; \quad \cdots \quad (15.25)$$

here $I_0/\sqrt{2}$ and $E_0/\sqrt{2}$ are measured, R is measured by application of a steady current and observation of ammeter and voltmeter readings, and p is calculated from the relation $p = 2\pi n$, where n is the frequency of the applied A.C.; thus L can be calculated from (15.25).

The nature of the electrical oscillations occurring in any circuit are best examined with the cathode ray oscillograph described on p. 724.

6. Foucault or Eddy Currents.

When an oscillatory circuit is in the neighbourhood of a mass of metal, since the latter constitutes a conductor in a varying magnetic field, currents are set up in the metal. The electrical energy of these Foucault or eddy currents is dissipated as heat in the metal, and the phenomenon constitutes a serious problem in the construction of the iron cores of such instruments as transformers. Transformer cores are therefore susceptible to two forms of electrical energy loss, hysteresis and eddy currents, the energy being transformed into heat in both instances. Hysteresis loss is reduced to a minimum by using material with a narrow hysteresis loop (see Chap. XIV). Eddy current loss is reduced to a minimum by making the core of as high an electrical resistance as possible. This is achieved by constructing it of thin laminations covered with oxide and bolted together. The energy loss due to an eddy current circulating round any part of the core is E^2/R, where E is the induced E.M.F. and R the resistance of the circuit. Hence by increasing R, the energy loss is reduced to a minimum. Eddy current action is put to a useful purpose in the *eddy current heater*. This consists essentially of a device for producing high-frequency oscillations of great intensity. When such an instrument is held close to any mass of metal the eddy currents are of considerable magnitude and are often sufficient to raise the metal to red or white heat. One of its most important applications is to the degassing of the metal parts of radio valves (see Chap. XIX), which could not be heated in situ conveniently in any other fashion.

7. Skin Effect.

With a steady current supply, the current is of uniform density across the section of a uniform wire. At high-frequency the current tends to be confined more to the outer surface of the wire. This is termed the *skin effect*; it results in an undesirable decrease of the effective cross-section, and therefore increase of the effective resistance of the conductor. The difficulty is in part overcome by using a stranded conductor of insulated wires, since these present a larger surface area for any cross-section than the corresponding single solid conductor. If a single conductor is used this is often made hollow to save material in the centre which would not be traversed by current. The reason for the skin effect may be explained with reference to fig. 4, where A and B represent two cross-sections of equal area, the former constituting the core of the conductor and the latter the outer cylindrical area. It may be shown that the self-inductance of a straight cylindrical conductor decreases if its radius increases. Hence the self-inductance of the core A is greater than that of the annulus B. The impedance of A is therefore greater than that of B, and a higher proportion of current will therefore flow through B.

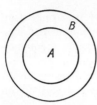

Fig. 4. — Skin Effect

EXERCISES

1. Obtain an expression for the time of oscillation of a circuit containing inductance and capacity.

Show that a circuit containing an inductance of 10^{-3} microhenries and a capacity of 1·9 microfarads will oscillate with a frequency corresponding to a wave-length in free space of about 26 m.

2. Distinguish between free and forced oscillations, and show that the forced oscillations set up in a circuit containing inductance and resistance lag behind the applied E.M.F. by an amount dependent on the value of the inductance, the resistance and the applied frequency.

3. Explain what is meant by the impedance of a circuit, and show how the magnitude of an alternating current may be reduced without loss of energy as heat.

4. Define the terms virtual current and virtual voltage as applied to A.C. circuits and describe how these quantities may be measured.

5. Explain the existence of eddy currents and the skin effect. To what practical purposes have eddy currents been applied?

CHAPTER XVI

Electromagnetic Waves

1. Hertz's Experiments.

We have seen in the preceding chapter how a circuit containing inductance, capacity and resistance may be the seat of electrical oscillations of a period depending upon the magnitudes of the three quantities involved. Hertz showed that these electrical oscillations were, in certain circumstances, not simply confined to the oscillating circuit, but that part of the electromagnetic energy could be radiated away completely from the oscillating system. The oscillatory system used for radiation and termed the **transmitter** is shown in fig. 1. It

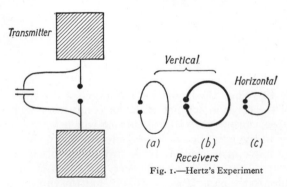

Fig. 1.—Hertz's Experiment

consisted of two square sheets of metal on each of which was fixed a short rod ending in a polished ball. The system is charged by connexion to an induction coil and then discharges across the ball-gap at regular intervals. If now a simple **receiver** is constructed from a circle of wire ending in two spheres with a short gap, a remarkable phenomenon may be observed. The receiver is placed so far from the transmitter that the direct induction effect of surges in the transmitter is negligible, and it is found that when the spheres are in the position (a) and (b) a spark jumps across, whereas when they are in the position (c) no effect is observed. The interpretation is that electromagnetic energy travels across the intervening space between transmitter and receiver, and the dependence on orientation of the receiver suggests that the radiation is in the form of a plane polarized electromagnetic wave (see Part III).

2. Tubes of Force and Electromagnetic Waves.

The fact that electrical oscillations might lead to the production of electromagnetic waves in free space had been deduced some years before Hertz's experiments by Maxwell, from consideration of electromagnetic theory (see Section 5). These considerations are too mathematical for this book, but we can arrive at a physical explanation of the production of electromagnetic waves using Faraday's concept of tubes of force, already mentioned in Chap. II. Referring to fig. 2(a), before the discharge across the gap commences, the distribution of (one half of) the tubes of force will be as shown, where we have considered a negative charge on the pole A and an equal positive charge

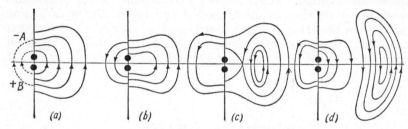

Fig. 2. — Electromagnetic Waves

on the pole B. When the insulation resistance of the gap breaks down, the ends of the tubes in contact with the conductors coalesce and the tubes collapse, causing the electric current which flows across the gap. Now owing to the existence of lateral pressure between the tubes, the outer tubes move in to the left to occupy the position originally held by the collapsed inner tubes and hence the tubes acquire a velocity perpendicular to the gap. If we postulate that the tubes possess inertia, the approaching ends of the tube will cross over at the gap while the body of the tube will pass through the gap and expand again on the other side as shown in fig. 2(b). In this way the polarity of A and B will have changed sign after the first oscillation, a situation which we know occurs in an oscillatory circuit from our considerations in Chap. XV, section 2. The process will clearly be repeated again as the tubes surge in the reverse direction, and would continue indefinitely were it not for the gradual loss of energy as heat in the charged rods and as heat, light and sound in the spark. Consider now the case shown in fig. 2(c). Here the ends of the tube have crossed at the gap before the main body of the tube has passed through the gap. A very short interval of time later the crossed portions coalesce and a completely closed tube of electromagnetic energy is left situated in free space and repelled away by the lateral pressure of neighbouring tubes. In this way electromagnetic energy is radiated away into space, and the result when several tubes are present simultaneously is shown in fig. 2(d). These tubes exert a mutual repulsion, so that the radiation spreads out until it becomes a plane surface with the electrical force directed parallel to the spark gap. Maxwell's theoretical calculations showed that the radiated energy took the form of electromagnetic waves travelling with a velocity equal to the square root of the ratio of the units of capacity on the electromagnetic and electrostatic systems respectively. On the C.G.S. system this quantity is found experimentally to be equal to the velocity of light, and consequently strong evidence was provided that light itself consisted of electromagnetic radiation. We have discussed the subject further from this point of view in Chap. IX, Part III. We therefore proceed here to give evidence that electromagnetic waves as generated by the **Hertzian oscillator** obey the laws of light.

3. Experiments with Electromagnetic Waves.

By using a parabolic metal reflector with the Hertzian oscillator at the focus, a parallel beam of electromagnetic radiation is produced. This may be received on a Hertzian receiver set at the focus of a receiving parabolic reflector. The existence of polarization, requiring definite orientation of the receiver to the transmitter, has already been mentioned. Using a large prism of paraffin wax, the laws of refraction are found to be obeyed for electromagnetic waves as for light.

To determine the wave-length of the radiation, the standard method of producing stationary waves by interference between incident waves and those reflected by a plane metal sheet is applicable, as in the corresponding experiment with sound waves described in Part IV, Chap. III. The receiver shows maximum response when situated at regular distances from the reflector, these distances clearly corresponding to half a wave-length. Further, all the general relations for wave motion derived in Part IV now become applicable. In particular, the well-known relation $V = \nu\lambda$, between velocity, frequency and wave-length may be examined, and if any two of these are known, the third may be calculated. For example, the frequency of the radiation will equal that of the oscillating source, which can be calculated according to the principles of section 2, Chap XV. The wave-length may be measured by a stationary wave method, and the product of frequency and wave-length then formed to show that the resulting velocity in free space is equal to that of light.

The source of oscillations now almost invariably used is the valve oscillator, the action of which is described briefly in Chap. XIX. Such an instrument allows of extremely sensitive control of frequency and radiated power.

23   (H 394)

4. Waves along Conductors.

If an oscillator such as the Hertzian oscillator is connected to two parallel conductors, then waves are set up in the conductors similar to the waves radiated into free space. The waves which pass down the wires are reflected either at the open end of the wires or at the end closed by a wire bridge, so that eventually stationary waves are formed just as with an open or closed organ pipe subjected to vibrations of a tuning fork held at the mouth. The presence of stationary nodes and antinodes spaced at intervals of half a wave-length along the wires is easily demonstrated with some device such as the neon lamp. This consists of two electrodes sealed in a glass envelope containing neon, and it has the property of glowing if the potential difference across the two electrodes exceeds a certain amount, although the current needed to produce the glow is very small. Consequently if such a lamp is

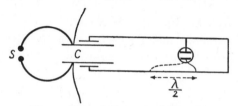

Fig. 3. — Dielectric Constant and Frequency

moved along the pair of **Lecher wires,** the distance between two points of maximum glow is the distance between two potential antinodes and is equal to half a wave-length. For an open-ended conductor, the free end is a potential maximum, whereas for a closed end the maximum occurs at $\lambda/4$ from the closed end, in complete analogy with the resonance tube. It may be shown that the current antinodes and nodes occur half-way between, and are completely out of phase with, the potential nodes and antinodes.

One important application of Lecher wires is the examination of the change of dielectric constant with frequency. In the circuit shown in fig. 3, the condenser C is first filled with dielectric and the wavelength of the oscillations is found on the associated Lecher wire system. The condenser is then emptied of dielectric, whereupon the wavelength will be found to have changed. Now since the velocity of the waves remains constant, the ratio of the two wave-lengths is inversely proportional to the ratios of the frequencies of the oscillations in the two circumstances. But the frequencies are given by $n = 1/2\pi\sqrt{LC}$, where n is the frequency, L the inductance and C the capacity of the oscillating circuit. Since L remains constant, $n/n' = \sqrt{C'/C} = \sqrt{k}$, where k is the dielectric constant by definition (Chap. III).

The dielectric constant is found by these experiments not to be constant at all but to vary with the frequency of the electrical oscillations to which it is submitted. The value normally taken for a dielectric constant is its electrostatic value, that is its asymptotic value for infinite wave-length and zero frequency. These experiments also show the existence of *electrical hysteresis* quite analogous to magnetic hysteresis. The response of the dielectric medium to the alternating electric field lags behind the change in the field, and electrical energy loss reappears as heat in the material.

5. Dimensional Relations between E.S. and E.M. Units.

Dimensional considerations similar to those developed in Part I, Chap. V, may be applied to electrical and magnetic quantities. As an illustration we shall consider the dimensional expressions for charge, potential and capacity in the two systems.

(i) *Electrostatic Units.*

The dimensions of electric charge on the E.S. system are obtained from the law of force between two equal charges q; thus

$$F = \frac{q^2}{k\,d^2}, \quad \cdots \cdots \quad (16.1)$$

where k is the dielectric constant of the surrounding medium and d is the distance between the charges. Hence, dimensionally,

$$q = k^{\frac{1}{2}}LF^{\frac{1}{2}}, \quad \cdots \cdots \quad (16.2)$$

since the dimensions of d are those of length. We may note that we have introduced k as a primary quantity along with mass, length and time. Now F has dimensions

$$F = \text{mass} \times \text{acceleration} = MLT^{-2}.$$

Hence (16.2) becomes

$$q = k^{\frac{1}{2}}L^{\frac{3}{2}}M^{\frac{1}{2}}T^{-1}. \quad \cdots \cdots \quad (16.3)$$

Next, the potential e is defined by

$$\text{Work done} = eq. \quad \cdots \cdots \quad (16.4)$$

Hence from (16.3) and (16.4)

$$e = \frac{\text{force} \times \text{distance}}{q}$$

$$= ML^2T^{-2} \cdot k^{-\frac{1}{2}}L^{-\frac{3}{2}}M^{-\frac{1}{2}}T$$

$$= M^{\frac{1}{2}}L^{\frac{1}{2}}T^{-1}k^{-\frac{1}{2}}. \quad \cdots \cdots \quad (16.5)$$

Finally, capacity is given by the quotient of (16.3) and (16.5), or

$$c = \frac{q}{e} = kL. \quad \ldots \ldots \quad (16.6)$$

(ii) *Electromagnetic Units.*

On the E.M. system charge is defined by

charge q = current × time,

so the dimensions of current must first be obtained. From the E.M. definition of unit current, if H is the magnetic field produced at the centre of a circular coil of radius a,

$$H = \frac{2\pi i}{a},$$

whence dimensionally

$$i = HL, \quad \ldots \ldots \quad (16.7)$$

since a has dimensions L and 2π is dimensionless. Now the strength of the magnetic field is the force exerted on unit magnetic pole m, hence

$$F = Hm,$$

or dimensionally,

$$H = \frac{F}{m} = ML\,T^{-2}\,m^{-1}. \quad \ldots \ldots \quad (16.8)$$

We can proceed further, expressing m dimensionally from the inverse square law of force, thus

$$F' = \frac{m^2}{\mu d^2},$$

where μ is the permeability of the medium in which the poles are situated a distance d apart. We therefore have dimensionally,

$$m = \mu^{\frac{1}{2}}LF'^{\frac{1}{2}}$$
$$= \mu^{\frac{1}{2}}M^{\frac{1}{2}}L^{\frac{3}{2}}T^{-1}. \quad \ldots \ldots \quad (16.9)$$

Substituting from (16.9) in (16.8) we obtain

$$H = \mu^{-\frac{1}{2}}M^{\frac{1}{2}}L^{-\frac{1}{2}}T^{-1}. \quad \ldots \ldots \quad (16.10)$$

Hence from (16.10) and (16.7) we have

$$i = \mu^{-\frac{1}{2}}M^{\frac{1}{2}}L^{\frac{1}{2}}T^{-1}. \quad \ldots \ldots \quad (16.11)$$

Finally

$$q = iT = \mu^{-\frac{1}{2}}M^{\frac{1}{2}}L^{\frac{1}{2}}. \quad \ldots \ldots \quad (16.12)$$

Again, the potential difference on the E.M. system will be given by

$$\text{rate of working} = ei,$$

and hence from (16.11)

$$e = \frac{\text{force} \times \text{distance}}{\text{time}} \frac{1}{i}$$
$$= ML^2T^{-3}\mu^{\frac{1}{2}}M^{-\frac{1}{2}}L^{-\frac{1}{2}}T$$
$$= \mu^{\frac{1}{2}}M^{\frac{1}{2}}L^{\frac{3}{2}}T^{-2}. \qquad \ldots \ldots \quad (16.13)$$

Finally, capacity is given by

$$c = \frac{q}{e} = \mu^{-1}L^{-1}T^2. \qquad \ldots \ldots \quad (16.14)$$

From (16.6) and (16.14) therefore we have

$$\frac{[c]\text{E.S.}}{[c]\text{E.M.}} = \frac{kL}{\mu^{-1}L^{-1}T^2} = \mu k \left(\frac{L}{T}\right)^2. \qquad \ldots \quad (16.15)$$

This expression indicates that if the capacity of a condenser is derived from its linear measurements according to the formulæ obtained in Chap. III, and then determined in the E.M. system, say by the use of a ballistic galvanometer and equation (13.40), the ratio of the two numerical values should represent a (velocity)^2. The actual value of the ratio obtained is $(3 \times 10^{10}$ cm./sec.$)^2$, that is it is exactly equal to the square of the velocity of light in vacuo. While this result alone does not "prove" that light is an electromagnetic wave, these dimensional considerations indicate strongly that light and electromagnetism are intimately connected.

6. M.K.S. Units.

On p. 49 mention has already been made of the M.K.S. units of force, energy and power as the *newton*, the *joule* and the *watt*. As stated on p. 593, the practical units of electrical energy and power are also the joule and the watt. It follows that the practical units of potential, resistance, charge, current, capacity and inductance are also the volt, ohm, coulomb, ampere, farad and henry on the M.K.S. system. Electric field strength will be expressed in volts metre^{-1}. From equation (13.1) on p. 645, the magnetic flux N, which is expressed in *maxwells* if the E.M.F. induced is in electromagnetic units of potential, is expressed in *volt-seconds* or *webers* on the M.K.S. system. The flux density B which is expressed in *gauss* in the E.M. system is in *webers metre^{-2}* on the M.K.S. system. The magnetomotive force, defined in equation (10.14) on p. 607 as $4\pi \times$ current encircled, is expressed on the M.K.S. system simply as the number of *ampere-turns* and is therefore $4\pi/10$ smaller than the magnetomotive force as measured on the electromagnetic system. It follows that the field strength H, expressed in *oersteds* in the E.M. system will be expressed as *ampere-turns metre*$^{-1}$ and is therefore smaller than the oersted by a factor $4\pi \times 10^{-3}$. It is clear that over a wide field of electromagnetic phenomena use of the M.K.S. system will eliminate the factor 4π and thus make the expressions more compact. In magnetostatics and electrostatics, however, such equations as (2.3) on p. 542 will require factors involving 4π and thus become more unwieldly. There are many arguments for and against the **general** adoption of one particular system of units but the present situation of several systems, although untidy, allows flexibility provided that care is always taken to state clearly the units used.

EXERCISES

1. Describe experiments illustrating the production of electromagnetic waves. How may the wave-length of such waves be determined?

2. Use the concept of tubes of force to explain the radiation of energy from an oscillatory circuit. What is the connexion between electromagnetic waves and light waves?

3. Write a short essay on " Electromagnetic wave propagation along conductors and its applications ".

4. Show by the method of dimensions that the ratio of the units of quantity of electricity in the electrostatic and electromagnetic systems is a function of a velocity. What is the significance of this result?

CHAPTER XVII

Thermoelectricity

1. Seebeck Effect.

It was discovered by Seebeck in 1821 that if the junctions of two dissimilar metals are at different temperatures, a current flows round the circuit. A list of metals was constructed such that the order of the metals indicated the direction in which the thermoelectric E.M.F.s acted when any pair of metals was chosen. Near opposite ends of the list occur antimony and bismuth, and a couple constructed of these metals gives one of the most sensitive couples available. However, as the melting-points of these metals are low they are unsuited for use over a large temperature range.

Experiment has shown that there are two laws of the thermo-electric effect which may be stated as follows:

(1) The total E.M.F. between two metals A and C is equal to the sum of the E.M.F.s of the couples AB + BC over the same temperature range.

(2) The total E.M.F. $E_{\theta_3\theta_1}$ when the junctions are at temperatures θ_3 and θ_1, is equal to the sum of the E.M.F.s $E_{\theta_3\theta_2} + E_{\theta_2\theta_1}$, where these are the E.M.F.s when the junctions are at (θ_3, θ_2) and (θ_2, θ_1) respectively.

These laws are sometimes known as the *Law of Intermediate Metals* and the *Law of Intermediate Temperatures*, respectively.

2. Peltier Effect.

In 1834, Peltier showed that the thermoelectric effect was reversible, that is heat is evolved at one junction and absorbed at the other if a current from some external source is sent round a circuit of two dissimilar metals as in fig. 1. The heating effect, which is confined entirely to the junctions, is quite distinct from the Joule heating, which takes place at all points of a conductor and arises from its resistance. Further, if the current is reversed in direction, the Peltier effect is reversed so that a junction which previously evolved heat now absorbs it and vice versa. This dependence on the direction or sign of the current implies that the Peltier heating depends on some odd power of the current, and experiment shows that it is directly proportional to it. The Peltier coefficient Π for two metals is defined by

$$H = \frac{\Pi I}{J}, \quad \ldots \ldots \quad (17.1)$$

where H is the heat evolved in calories/sec., I is the current in amperes and J is Joule's equivalent, equal to 4.2 joules/cal. Hence Π has the dimensions of an E.M.F. The Peltier coefficient is a function of the temperature, and the Peltier effect is connected directly with the Seebeck E.M.F. in that the latter is

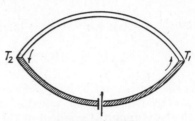

Fig. 1.— Peltier Effect

(approximately) equal to the difference in the two Peltier E.M.F.s which are present when the two junctions of a thermocouple are at different temperatures.

3. Thomson or Kelvin Effect.

From the complementary character of the Seebeck and Peltier effects it is clear that the thermoelectric effect behaves like a reversible heat engine. Application of thermodynamics according to the principles of Part II, Chap. XIII, then shows that there should be a straight line relation between Seebeck E.M.F. and absolute temperature. In practice the curves are parabolic as shown in fig. 2. Kelvin therefore suggested that a third thermoelectric effect exists such that an E.M.F. acts along a single metal if it is not at uniform temperature. Since both the metals in a couple are subject to a temperature gradient, two Kelvin E.M.F.s will be present, and the Seebeck E.M.F. is therefore the

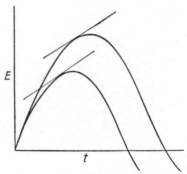

Fig. 2.— Seebeck E.M.F. and Absolute Temperature

result of the Peltier E.M.F.s and the Kelvin E.M.F.s acting together. The Kelvin E.M.F.s or coefficients are usually denoted by σ, where σ represents the E.M.F. acting under unit uniform temperature gradient. The complete expression connecting the Seebeck, Peltier and Kelvin E.M.F.s is therefore

$$E_{AB}(\theta_1 \theta_2) = \Pi_{AB}(\theta_1) - \Pi_{AB}(\theta_2) - \int_{\theta_1}^{\theta_2} (\sigma_A - \sigma_B) \, dT. \quad (17.2)$$

Regarding the thermoelectric couple as a reversible heat engine, we have shown in Part II, p. 277, that it follows that the Peltier coefficient is given by

$$\Pi = T\frac{dE}{dT}, \quad \ldots \ldots \quad (17.3)$$

and the difference in the Kelvin coefficients by

$$(\sigma_A - \sigma_B) = -T\frac{d^2E}{dT^2}. \quad \ldots \ldots \quad (17.4)$$

As the Peltier and Kelvin coefficients are difficult to measure directly, these relations are very valuable since they allow the coefficients to be calculated from the gradient of the Seebeck curve and the slope of the thermoelectric power diagram (see next section) respectively.

4. Thermoelectric Power Diagram.

It is very inconvenient mathematically to deal with sets of parabolic curves in estimating thermoelectric behaviour, and the usual procedure is as follows. The thermoelectric Seebeck curves are first plotted for a series of metals, the

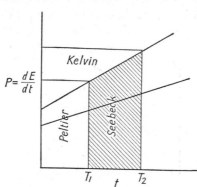

Fig. 3.—Thermoelectric Power Diagram

second metal of the junction being lead. The reason for this is that the Kelvin effect for lead is zero, so the Kelvin effect of the other metal can be obtained directly from the data. Tangents are then drawn to the Seebeck curves at a number of points, and a second graph as shown in fig. 3 is constructed of the slope of the tangents dE/dT against T. This diagram is termed the **thermo-electric power diagram** (the term is unfortunate since it is not measured in units of power but in volts per degree) and is a straight line. This follows from the parabolic nature of the Seebeck curve, for, representing this algebraically by

$$E = aT + bT^2, \quad \ldots \ldots \quad (17.5)$$

where a and b are constants, we have by differentiation with respect to T

$$\frac{dE}{dT} = P = a + 2bT, \quad \ldots \ldots \quad (17.6)$$

which is the equation of the thermoelectric power line. We note that the thermoelectric constants are given by the slope of the line and its intercept on the P axis respectively. From this diagram, the Seebeck, Peltier and Kelvin E.M.F.s are all calculable as areas. Thus the Seebeck E.M.F. is

$$\int_{T_1}^{T_2} P\,dT = \int_{T_1}^{T_2} \frac{dE}{dT}\,dT = \text{area of trapezium enclosed between ordinates at } T_1 \text{ and } T_2, \text{ the } T \text{ axis and the thermoelectric power line.}$$

The Peltier E.M.F. is, from (17.3),

$$T\frac{dE}{dT} = TP = \text{area of rectangle enclosed between the co-ordinate axes and perpendiculars dropped to them from the point on the thermoelectric power line.}$$

Finally, from equation (17.2), the Kelvin E.M.F. is given by

$$\int_{T_1}^{T_2} (\sigma_A - \sigma_B)\,dT = \Pi_{AB}(T_1) - \Pi_{AB}(T_2) - E_{AB}(T_1, T_2);$$

that is, it is represented by the difference between the areas of the two Peltier rectangles less the trapezoidal area which represents the Seebeck E.M.F. This area is clearly that of the trapezium enclosed between the abscissæ at T_1 and T_2, the P-axis and the thermoelectric power line.

5. Experimental Demonstration of the Peltier and Kelvin Effects.

To demonstrate the existence of the Peltier effect directly, an apparatus may be used as in fig. 4. Two bars of bismuth are connected

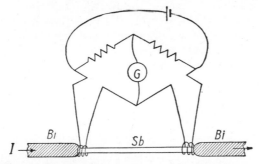

Fig. 4.—Experiment showing Peltier Effect

to a bar of antimony, and the junctions are wound with coils of insulated wire which are connected to the opposite arms of a Wheatstone bridge. The bridge is balanced and a current is then sent through the

bismuth-antimony junctions. Owing to the heat evolved at one junction and absorbed at the other, the resistances of the two coils are
changed, one being increased and the other decreased. Consequently
the balance of the bridge is disturbed, and if the heat capacity of the
junctions is known together with the current in the couple, application
of (17.1) allows a rough estimate of the Peltier coefficient to be made.
If the current is reversed, the Wheatstone bridge is thrown out of
balance in the reverse direction, thus demonstrating that the Peltier
effect depends on current direction.

To demonstrate the Kelvin effect, which is much smaller than the
Seebeck or Peltier effects, an apparatus as shown in fig. 5 may be used.
An iron rod several feet long is bent into the shape of a large hairpin
and heated to redness at the loop, the ends of the bar being cooled in

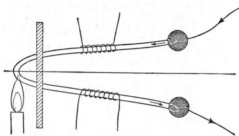

Fig. 5. — Experiment showing Kelvin Effect

pools of mercury. In this way a steep temperature gradient is created
between the loop and the ends of the bar. A current of several amperes
is then sent through the bar, and this current passes up the temperature gradient in one arm and down the temperature gradient in the
other. Owing to the existence of the Kelvin effect the current is therefore travelling against the Kelvin E.M.F. in one arm and with the
Kelvin E.M.F. in the other. Superimposed upon the Joule heating,
therefore, additional heat will be evolved in one arm and absorbed
in the other. The effect is shown as with the Peltier experiment, by
winding a coil of wire round each arm, connecting the coils to the
opposite arms of a Wheatstone bridge and establishing a balance when
no current flows through the bar. The balance is disturbed in opposite directions according to the direction of the current, thus showing
that, like the Peltier effect, the Kelvin effect is directly proportional to
the current.

6. Characteristics of the Thermoelectric Curves.

The parabolic nature of the thermoelectric curves implies that a
maximum E.M.F. occurs for a certain temperature difference between
the junctions, after which the E.M.F. decreases again to zero and then

increases again in the reverse direction. The temperature at which the
maximum occurs is termed the **neutral temperature,** and the temperature at which a reversal in direction of the E.M.F. takes place is termed
the **inversion temperature.**

Since the thermoelectric power lines are all plotted with respect
to lead, some metals will be positive with respect to lead at the hot
junction while others will be negative. The corresponding thermoelectric power lines will have slopes in the reverse direction. To estimate the Seebeck E.M.F. between any pair of metals, application of
the principles outlined in the preceding section shows that the Seebeck
E.M.F. is equal to the trapezoidal area enclosed between the two
thermoelectric power lines and the two ordinates corresponding to the
temperatures of the junctions.

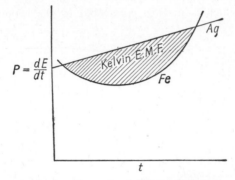

Fig. 6. — Thermoelectric Diagram for Iron

Certain cases are of particular interest. Thus the thermoelectric
power lines for platinum and a certain platinum-iridium alloy have
the same constant b and therefore the same slope. For a couple composed of these metals, therefore, the thermoelectric E.M.F. is proportional to the temperature difference, and thus a thermoelectric
temperature measuring instrument may be constructed which operates
on a linear scale. Again, the behaviour of iron is irregular, no definite
parabolic law being obeyed. Consequently the thermoelectric power
diagram for iron is non-linear and consists in fact of a loop as shown
in fig. 6. This loop crosses the thermoelectric power line for silver at
temperatures of 310° C. and 620° C. Now the Peltier coefficients for
both metals must be the same for both metals at these points of intersection, yet an E.M.F. acts round the couple equal in magnitude to
the area enclosed between the loop and the line. Hence we have an
example of a couple operating on the Kelvin coefficients only of the
two metals.

7. Measurement of Thermoelectric E.M.F.s.

The main practical use of the thermoelectric effect is in the measurement of temperature, and the apparatus used to measure the thermoelectric E.M.F. depends upon whether the temperature is steady or variable. If the temperature is varying, rapid reading is essential and the couple is connected directly to a microvoltmeter, which is simply a sensitive moving-coil milliammeter with a suitable resistance in series. Such an instrument will measure to about 1/50° C.

For steady temperatures a more accurate method is to use a potentiometer circuit as in fig. 7. The potentiometer wire AB is connected in series with two variable high resistances X and Y. One end of the thermocouple is connected to A, while the other end goes to a sensitive galvanometer which is in turn connected to the tapping point P of

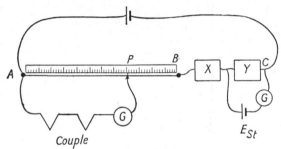

Fig. 7. — Measurement of Thermoelectric E.M.F.

the potentiometer wire. A standard cell is connected across Y as shown, with a second sensitive galvanometer in the standard cell circuit. The drop in potential across AC is about 2 volts, and since X and Y are each several thousand ohms while the resistance of AB is about 1 ohm, the drop in potential across AB is about a thousand microvolts. Consequently the balance point P occurs at a convenient distance along AB. Initially the procedure consists in varying the resistance Y but making corresponding alterations to the resistance X so as to keep the total resistance $(X + Y)$ constant. The resistance Y is varied until the standard cell is balanced. Then if I is the (unknown) current in the potentiometer, we have from Ohm's law

$$E_{\text{Th}} = l\rho I, \quad \cdots \cdots (17.7)$$

where E_{Th} is the E.M.F. of the thermocouple, l is the distance along AB corresponding to a balance, and ρ is the resistance per unit length of the potentiometer wire AB. (This must be determined by a separate experiment using AB as the unknown resistance in a post office box circuit.) Again,

$$E_{\text{st}} = IY, \quad \ldots \ldots \quad (17.8)$$

where E_{st} is the E.M.F. of the standard cell. Hence from (17.7) and (17.8), eliminating I we have

$$E_{\text{Th}} = \frac{l\rho}{Y} E_{\text{st}}. \quad \ldots \ldots \quad (17.9)$$

8. Applications of the Thermoelectric Effect.

The thermoelectric effect is far too small to serve as a practical source of electrical power, but it is invaluable as a means of measuring temperatures accurately and quickly and of measuring small quantities of heat. Its advantage over other heat-measuring appliances lies in

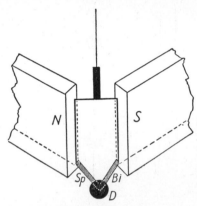

Fig. 8.—Boys' Radiomicrometer

its small bulk and in its small heat capacity, which results in the minimum mechanical and thermal disturbance of the system into which it is inserted. The application to thermometry is mentioned in Chap. II, Part II. As a typical instrument we shall describe first *Boys' radiomicrometer* for detecting very small intensity of heat radiation. As shown in fig. 8, it consists of a sensitive suspended coil galvanometer the coil of which has the circuit completed by an antimony-bismuth couple. The junction of the couple is covered with a small blackened disk D on to which the radiation is focused. This instrument is so sensitive that it will detect radiant heat equivalent to that from a candle at several miles. It is used to examine the heat radiation from stars.

The radiobalance shown in fig. 9 is an instrument used to detect the heat produced by elements undergoing radioactive decay (see

Chap. XX). It consists of two thermocouple units P and Q constructed of an array of iron and constantan wires joined together by a cup containing the radioactive element. The two cups are also at the junction of another iron-constantan couple which is connected to a galvanometer. The couple Q is a dummy arrangement to preserve symmetry: a variable current is passed through the couple Q, the magnitude of the current being registered on the ammeter A. Owing to the operation of the Peltier cooling, the heat emitted by the radioactive source is prevented from causing any rise in temperature and consequently the couple in the galvanometer circuit gives rise to no E.M.F. and no deflection in the galvanometer. Since some Joule heating inevitably

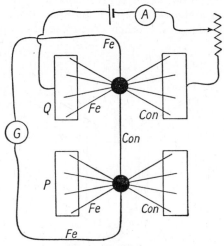

Fig. 9. — Radiobalance

arises due to the electrical resistance at the cup, a subsidiary experiment is made to allow for this. If I_0 is the current which produces no temperature rise in the junction when the radioactive element is absent, equating the Joule heating to the Peltier cooling we have

$$I_0{}^2 R = \Pi I_0. \quad \cdot \quad \cdot \quad \cdot \quad \cdot \quad \cdot \quad (17.10)$$

This current must be reduced to I when the radioactive substance is inserted if the junction is still to be free from rise in temperature. Hence if the radioactive heat generated per second is H, we have

$$H + I^2 R = \Pi I, \quad \cdot \quad \cdot \quad \cdot \quad \cdot \quad (17.11)$$

or, substituting from (17.10) in (17.11),

$$H = \frac{\Pi I (I_0 - I)}{I_0}. \quad \cdot \quad \cdot \quad \cdot \quad \cdot \quad (17.12)$$

EXERCISES

1. What are the three thermoelectric effects and how are they related?

2. How may the Seebeck E.M.F. be measured accurately? For what practical purposes has the existence of the Seebeck E.M.F. been used?

3. How may the Peltier and Kelvin effects be (a) demonstrated, (b) measured?

4. Define thermoelectric power and explain fully the significance of the areas on a thermoelectric power diagram.

5. What are the laws of intermediate temperatures and intermediate metals as applied to thermoelectric circuits? Is there any practical example of a current being produced entirely by the Kelvin effect?

CHAPTER XVIII

Electrical Discharge through Gases

1. Introduction.

We have seen in Chap. XII how liquids will conduct electricity only if there are carriers or ions present. The high insulation properties of gases in their normal state arises from the almost complete absence of ions. Now certain agents such as X-rays and the rays from radio-active substances are capable of ionizing gases, and a current will then flow if two electrodes at different potential are inserted in the

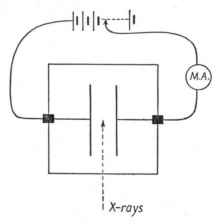

Fig. 1. — Ionization Chamber

gas. A suitable experimental arrangement, sometimes termed an *ionization chamber,* is shown in fig. 1, and the curve showing the variation of current with the applied potential difference is shown in fig. 2. Initially the curve approximates to a straight line passing through the origin, showing that Ohm's law is obeyed just as for conduction in solids and liquids. Soon, however, the curve starts to bend over parallel to the potential axis and ultimately *saturation conditions* are produced. This clearly occurs when the ions are removed as rapidly as they are

generated by the ionizing radiation. If the potential is raised sufficiently, the current suddenly rises to an enormous value corresponding
to a spark discharge between the electrodes.

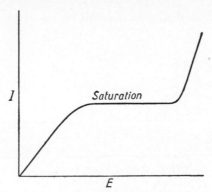

Fig. 2. — Current and Potential Difference

2. Effect of Gas Pressure on Conduction.

If a steady source of potential of several thousand volts is available,
the conductivity of gases may be examined without recourse to external
ionizing agents. If the vessel containing the gas is connected to a
pump it will be found that the potential required to produce a spark,
that is to effect conduction, is considerably reduced as the gas pressure

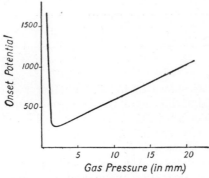

Fig. 3. — Onset Potential and Gas Pressure

is lowered. The onset potential-pressure curve is shown in fig. 3,
which indicates that a minimum effective potential occurs at about
1 mm. pressure for air. Above this pressure the necessary voltage
rises steadily and slowly while below this pressure it rises very steeply
indeed. Consequently the potential necessary to create a discharge
across a hard vacuum is very great.

In the region of minimum potential the discharge occurs even if the electrodes are situated a distance apart much larger than the sparking potential. This silent steady discharge is accompanied by a visible glow in the discharge tube, the general appearance being shown in fig. 4. The colour of the discharge depends on the nature of the gas, but

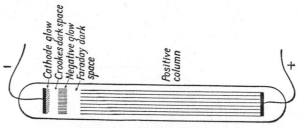

Fig. 4.— Silent Steady Discharge

certain general characteristics are in evidence. At moderately low pressures, proceeding from the cathode we note the *cathode glow*, after which comes the *Crookes dark space*. This is followed by another glowing region termed the *negative glow*, and this in turn by the *Faraday dark space*. Finally, we arrive at the glowing *positive column*, which stretches to the anode and may occupy most of the tube. As the pressure is reduced the positive column gradually splits up into a

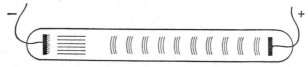

Fig. 5.— Striæ

number of *striæ*, as shown in fig. 5. Further reduction in pressure results in continual shrinkage of the positive column accompanied by a corresponding increase in the space occupied by the negative glow and the Crookes dark space. A degree of evacuation is eventually reached when the Crookes dark space occupies the entire tube and the glow is now confined to the walls of the containing vessel, being particularly intense near the anode and therefore opposite to the cathode.

3. Cathode Rays.

A number of simple experiments show that, when the discharge tube reaches the operating condition such that the Crookes dark space occupies the entire tube, the latter is filled with *cathode rays* proceeding from the cathode. These cathode rays are subject to rectilinear propagation, as is shown in fig 6, a sharp shadow of the obstacle being thrown on the glow at the end of the tube.

Another most important property of cathode rays is that they are

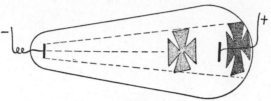

Fig. 6. — Cathode Rays

deflected by electric or magnetic fields. For example, if a bar magnet is presented to the rays as in fig. 7, the glow at the end of the tube is deflected up or down according to the sign of the pole presented. That

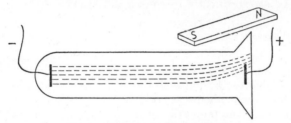

Fig. 7. — Deflection in Magnetic Field

magnetic deflection occurs implies that the cathode radiation consists of an *electric current*, the deflection process being analogous to the motion of a conductor carrying a current in a magnetic field and obeying the same rules.

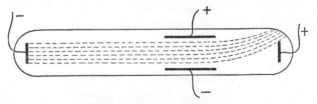

Fig. 8. — Deflection in Electric Field

Electrical deflection is less easily shown, but if the pressure is adjusted correctly, application of a difference of potential of a few thousand volts between the two flat condenser plates shown in fig. 8 results in deflection of the cathode ray beam in the electric field.

By using an apparatus as in fig. 9, the cathode radiation may be collected in a small brass cylinder (termed a *Faraday cylinder*) con-

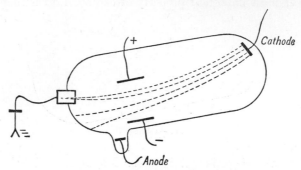

Fig. 9. — Collection in Faraday Cylinder

nected to an electroscope or electrometer. In this way the cathode rays may be shown directly to consist of negative electricity.

4. Positive Rays.

If a discharge tube is fitted with a perforated cathode, a glow will develop on the glass container immediately behind the cathode. This glow is due to the impact of *positive rays* proceeding along the discharge tube from anode to cathode and passing through the perforated cathode. The properties of the positive rays may be examined by experiments similar to those with cathode rays, and in this way it has been shown that they are positively charged and are deflected by electric and magnetic fields.

5. Electrons.

We have seen how electrolysis requires the assumption that each ion possesses a definite electric charge whose magnitude depends only on the valency and is quite independent of the nature of the solute. This fact implies that in conduction through liquids electricity is atomistic in nature, that is it occurs in definite quantities only, being either one ionic charge, two, or so on according to the valency. The possibility therefore arose that *all* electricity was atomistic and consisted of integral numbers of a small unit of charge termed the **electronic charge**. Thomson carried out experiments to show that a value for e/m, the ratio of the charge to the mass of an electron, could be obtained from the deflection of cathode rays in electric and magnetic fields, if the assumption was made that the cathode radiation consisted of a stream of negatively charged corpuscles or electrons. By means of the apparatus shown in fig. 10, electric and magnetic fields were simultaneously applied in directions mutually perpendicular to each other. Since the charged particles move in the direction of the applied electric field between the condenser plates C, the action of the electric field alone would cause the electron stream to move upwards, as shown by the deflection of a glowing spot at the end of the tube where the cathode rays impinge on a sensitive screen of zinc sulphide or willemite. The application of a magnetic field at right angles to the electric field may cause the spot to return to its original position, since the electron stream behaves as a conductor carrying a current and therefore obeys the left-hand rule.

If e is the charge of each of the electrons, all of which are assumed to be identical, and if the velocity with which they are moving is v,

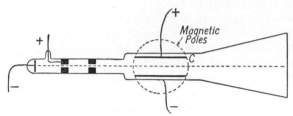

Fig. 10.— Simultaneous Electric and Magnetic Fields

the condition that no deflection shall occur is that the electric and magnetic forces shall be equal and opposite, that is:

$$Xe = Hev, \quad \ldots \ldots \quad (18.1)$$

or

$$v = \frac{X}{H}, \quad \ldots \ldots \ldots \quad (18.2)$$

where X and H are the strengths of the electric and magnetic fields respectively. If the electric field is now cut off, the spot shows a deflection of the cathode rays in the magnetic field alone. Since the electron stream and the magnetic field are mutually perpendicular, the deflection of the electrons is always in the direction at right angles to both, and it is therefore subject to a constant force perpendicular to its direction of motion. The path traversed by the electron stream is therefore circular according to Chap. III, Part I. If the mass of the electron is m, and the radius of curvature of its path is ρ, equating the magnetic force to the centrifugal force in the circular orbit we have

$$Hev = \frac{mv^2}{\rho}, \quad \ldots \ldots \quad (18.3)$$

or

$$\frac{e}{m} = \frac{v}{\rho H} = \frac{X}{\rho H^2}, \quad \ldots \ldots \quad (18.4)$$

from (18.2). Now the radius of curvature ρ can be calculated from the geometry of the apparatus if the deflection of the cathode spot is measured together with the distance from the magnetic field. Consequently the ratio of the charge to the mass of the electron may be derived. In this way Thomson showed that the ratio was independent of the nature of the gas in the discharge tube, thus indicating that electrons were a constituent of all gases. Subsequent experiment showed that electrons were constituents of all matter, and in this way arose the concept of the **electrical structure of matter.**

6. Positive Ray Analysis.

By deflection of the positive rays in electric and magnetic fields, the ratio of their charge to their mass, E/M, was likewise obtained, but no such generality as obtained for electrons was forthcoming. The values obtained depended greatly on the nature of the gas in the discharge tube, a decrease in E/M being observed for positive rays of the same velocity but increasing atomic weight.

For positive rays, Thomson introduced the use of *parallel* electric and magnetic fields. This results in the electric and magnetic forces acting at right angles to each other, and leads to the formation of a parabolic streak on a screen placed at right angles to the general direction of the positive ray beam. The equations governing the positive ray deflection are

$$x \propto \frac{1}{\rho} \propto \frac{EH}{MV}, \quad \cdots \cdots \quad (18.5)$$

according to (18.4), where x is the deflection due to the magnetic field, E and M are the charge and mass of the positive corpuscle, V is its velocity, and H is the magnetic field strength. Similarly, the deflection y in the electrostatic field is given by

$$y = \tfrac{1}{2}ft^2, \quad \cdots \cdots \quad (18.6)$$

where f is the acceleration under the electric force maintained for a time t. If the length of path in the electric field is l, $t = l/V$, and since $f = XE/M$, equation (18.6) becomes

$$y \propto X \frac{E}{M} \frac{l^2}{V^2}. \quad \cdots \cdots \quad (18.7)$$

Hence from (18.5) and (18.7), eliminating the velocity,

$$\frac{x^2}{y} \propto \frac{E}{M}. \quad \cdots \cdots \quad (18.8)$$

Equation (18.8) is the equation of a parabola and hence any stream of positive corpuscles, independently of their velocity, will lie on one parabola only if E/M is constant. By analysing the parabolas obtained by photographic recording, Thomson found that E/M, when hydrogen gas occupied the discharge tube, was about 1/1800 of e/m for electrons. Now the total charge Q required to deposit one chemical equivalent of an element is easily determined by electrolysis. Further, a rough estimate of Avogadro's number N, that is, the number of ions present in a chemical equivalent, had been afforded by measurements on Brownian movement (see Chap. XI, Part II). Hence the charge carried by one ion is

$$e = \frac{Q}{N},$$

and the value of this charge is exactly equal to that of the electron. Although these results had not been proved accurately at the time, Thomson suggested that very probably the charge E carried by the hydrogen ion in the discharge tube was equal to e, the electronic charge. Hence $m = M/1800$, and consequently the existence of a universal particle with a mass much less than that of the lightest atom had been demonstrated. Since electrons were found in the discharge tube quite independently of the nature of the gas present, very strong evidence was provided for assuming that electrons were a fundamental constituent of all matter.

EXERCISES

1. Describe the effect of pressure on gaseous conduction and explain the action of an internal ionizing agent in rendering a gas conducting.

2. Explain how a beam of cathode rays may be produced and how their nature has been elucidated.

3. How has the ratio e/m of the charge to the mass of an electron been determined? Why does the value obtained vary with the speed of the electrons?

4. Write a short essay on positive ray analysis.

CHAPTER XIX

Electronics

1. Electronic Charge and Mass.

Since the whole of electrical theory and modern ideas on the structure of matter depend largely on the properties and behaviour of electrons, we shall now devote considerable attention to what is, in fact, the essence of our subject. We shall see that not only is theory dependent on the electronic concept but that vitally important practical applications such as radio valves, X-ray tubes and photoelectric cells could never otherwise have been invented or understood.

We saw in the last chapter how a value of e/m could be obtained from the deflection of cathode rays in crossed electric and magnetic fields. We now have to consider the experimental determination of the individual values of the charge e and mass m respectively. There are very many methods available depending on various phenomena such as the photo-electric effect, X-radiation, spectral theory and so on, and even a brief comparison of the methods is beyond the scope of this book. We shall therefore describe only **Millikan's method,** which afforded the first accurate measurement of these fundamental quantities. The principle of the method was to charge a microscopic oil drop with a few electrons, and then to hold the drop balanced between the gravitational force downwards and the electric force upwards due to the drop being situated between two condenser plates. As shown in fig. 1, two circular horizontal condenser plates a few centimetres in diameter were separated by an ebonite ring about 1 cm. high fitted with three glass windows. Two of the windows were at opposite ends of a diameter of the ring, but the third was situated so that a radius to this window made an angle of about 20° with the diameter joining the other two windows. The purpose of the windows was the illumination and observation of the interior of the condenser. The condenser was placed at the bottom of a metal cylinder and drops of oil were squirted from an atomizer into the region above the condenser. Owing to the presence of a small hole in the top condenser plate, an occasional oil drop fell through the condenser. It was observed with a microscope by scattered light through one of the windows, illumination being provided by a powerful light beam via one of the other windows. In general, on applying an electric field to the region between the

718

condenser plates the drop either moved more rapidly, more slowly or even moved upwards owing to the electric field being greater than the gravitational field. For the very special case where a drop could be held completely stationary we have, by equating the electrical and gravitational forces,

$$X . ne = mg, \quad \ldots \ldots \quad (19.1)$$

where X is the strength of the electric field, e is the electronic charge, n is the number of electrons on the drop, m is the mass of the drop, and g the acceleration due to gravity. In this equation all the quantities except ne and m are known. The latter is determined by allowing

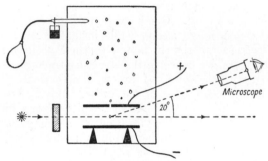

Fig. 1. — Millikan's Method for e

the drop to fall freely under gravity, and then, applying Stokes's law of Part I, Chap. XII, we have

$$mg = 6\pi\eta av = \tfrac{4}{3} \pi a^3 (\rho - \sigma)g, \quad \ldots \quad (19.2)$$

where a is the radius of the drop assumed spherical, η is the coefficient of viscosity of the gas surrounding the drop, v is the terminal velocity of the drop, and ρ and σ are the densities of the oil and the gas respectively. By using a special oil Millikan overcame difficulties associated with evaporation and oxidation, and thus obtained a series of values of ne. These were found all to be multiples of a certain definite value, which clearly corresponded to the electronic charge e when $n = 1$. In practice the method could be applied even when the electrical and gravitational fields did not exactly balance, from measurement of the velocities of the drop with and without an electric field present. The present accepted value for the electronic charge in terms of the unit electrostatic charge defined on p. 539 is $e = 4 \cdot 800 \times 10^{-10}$ e.s.u. By using the value of e/m obtained by deflection experiments or otherwise, the mass m of the electron is then found to be about 9×10^{-28} gm.

There are many other methods available for determining the electronic charge, but we shall discuss these when considering the various phenomena involved.

2. Conduction of Electricity through Solids.

Since the electric current must be essentially the same phenomenon whether it takes place through solids, liquids or gases, it follows that conduction through solids must consist in the passage of electrons through the conductor from the *negative* to the *positive* pole. Experiments on conduction through liquids and gases have shown that positive electricity is always accompanied by matter, that is by the positive ion. Since no transference of matter takes place in conduction through solids, the current is a one-way phenomenon, involving the passage of electrons only. Good conductors are substances through which the electrons move freely, while insulators are substances in which the electrons are tightly bound to their positive counterpart. In metals, therefore, we conceive the structure to consist of positively charged centres which are fixed except for thermal vibration and which contain the main mass of the atom. Moving freely amongst these positive residues are the electrons, which have a kinetic energy which is in equilibrium with the vibrational heat energy of the positive residues. Since the metal is uncharged in its normal state, the number of free electrons present must be equal to the number of positive residues. If now a difference in potential is applied between two parts of the metal, the electrons will be attracted to the positive and repelled by the negative pole. At first it would appear that a very large saturation current might be produced however small the applied potential, all the electrons present moving rapidly from the negative to the positive pole. Such behaviour does not occur and would, of course, be in disagreement with Ohm's law, which states that the number of electrons passing any point per second is proportional to the applied potential difference. It was first shown by Drude that a satisfactory qualitative and quantitative explanation of electron conduction in metals could be evolved if it were remembered that the electrons will collide with the atomic centres and that the effect will be that a resistance is provided to the free motion of the electrons. Further, as the temperature of the metal is raised, the amplitude of swing of the atomic centres is increased and consequently the area over which they become effective in stopping the passage of the electrons is also increased. Theory then agrees with experiment in indicating a rise of resistance with temperature. Drude's theory also allows a deduction of the **Wiedemann-Franz law,** which embodies the experimental observation that the ratio of the electrical to the thermal conductivities of good conductors is constant. Owing to the existence of the recently discovered wave-like properties of the electron (see section 8), Drude's theory has been much modified, but it still remains a useful concept in any initial approach to the explanation of conduction through solids.

Since the number of electrons per unit volume or **electron density** will vary from metal to metal, the existence of contact potentials between two dissimilar metals is easily explained. The two dissimilar metals will in general have a different electron pressure, and when they are placed in contact electrons will flow temporarily from one to the other until some equilibrium is attained. In the same way thermo-electric effects receive a ready explanation on electron theory. If the temperature of one junction differs from that of the other, the electrons at the hot junction will have greater energy than those at the cold junction. This fact, combined with the differing electron pressures of dissimilar metals, is sufficient to account for the Seebeck and Peltier effects. The Kelvin effect is similarly explained as due to a difference in electron pressure between different parts of the same metal if it is not at uniform temperature.

In recent years several *semi-conductors* such as *germanium* and *silicon* have been studied and their properties applied to form *transistors* which act as diodes and triodes of much smaller size than the vacuum diodes and triodes discussed in the next section. These semi-conductors behave oppositely to metallic conductors, giving decreased resistance with rise of temperature. This is explained in electron theory as due to the temperature increase in numbers of lightly-bound electrons released from atomic centres in the semi-conductor which more than compensates for the rise in resistance due to the increase in atomic vibration. Such materials give much larger Seebeck E.M.F.s than the metals discussed in Chap. XVII and are in use in space vehicles to supply electrical power from solar radiation.

3. Thermionics.

If the temperature of a metal is raised sufficiently, the kinetic energy of the electrons may become so great that they leave the metal completely. The analogy with evaporation is exceedingly close, and in

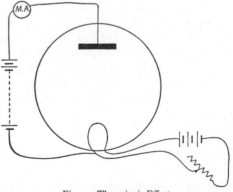

Fig. 2.—Thermionic Effect

fact thermodynamics may be applied directly to the phenomenon with excellent results. To demonstrate this **thermionic effect** experimentally a fine tungsten *filament* is sealed into a glass vessel together with another electrode as shown in fig. 2, and the vessel is exhausted as highly as possible. Such an arrangement is said to constitute a *diode*. When the filament or *cathode* is heated (usually electrically), if a positive potential is applied to the other electrode or *anode*, a milliammeter included in the circuit will show the presence of a current flowing from anode to cathode, corresponding to a stream of electrons from cathode to anode. By experiments similar to those described in Chap. XIX, it may be proved that these thermionic electrons are identical with the electrons in a cathode ray beam. Two *characteristic curves* may be obtained for a *diode*, one showing the variation of current with potential for a fixed temperature of the filament as shown in fig. 3, and the other showing the variation of the saturation current with temperature of the filament. The first curve shows that at first the current increases rapidly with the applied potential, but that ultimately a saturation current is reached. The explanation is that at first a reservoir of electrons is provided owing to the number evolved from the filament per second being greater than the number removed per second as electric current. Ultimately, however, when the potential is sufficiently great, the electrons are removed as rapidly as they are evolved from the filament, and further

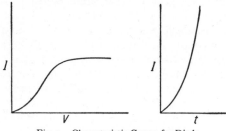

Fig. 3.—Characteristic Curves for Diode

increase in the applied potential produces no change in the current. The reason that the saturation current does not flow immediately a small positive potential is applied to the anode is due to the **space charge effect.** Thus, the region surrounding the filament consists of an atmosphere of electrons termed the space charge. Owing to the mutual repulsion which exists between charges of the same sign a fair proportion of the electrons which are emitted are repelled back to the cathode. When a small potential is applied the general behaviour of the electrons is still governed largely by their mutual repulsions, and consequently the space charge behaves as a reservoir of electrons. This behaviour holds until the potential is large enough to overcome the space charge control and then saturation rapidly sets in. The experimental law, which has a theoretical support, for the relation between anode current and anode potential for a fixed filament temperature, over the space charge controlled region of the curve, is

$$I = kV^{3/2}, \qquad \ldots \ldots \quad (19.3)$$

where k is a constant.

The second characteristic curve of a diode is that between saturation current and temperature. Experimentally, the equation de-

,duced theoretically by Richardson connecting these two quantities is $I = AT^2 \exp. \dfrac{-b}{T}$, where A and b are constants depending on the nature of the filament.

Now since electrons travel from cathode to anode when the latter is positive but not when it is negative (for then the electrons are repelled back to the cathode), the diode allows current to pass in *one direction only*. The general term **valve** is therefore applied to such contrivances, in analogy with a mechanical valve which has the same essentially one-way function. The practical applications of such an instrument are legion. For example, the diode will act as a *current limiter* in any circuit in which it is in series, for no matter how the

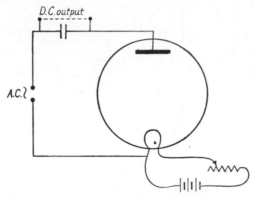

Fig. 4.—Valve Action of Diode

potential may rise, no current larger than the saturation current can flow and this current is uniquely determined by the filament temperature. Again, consider the circuit shown in fig. 4 where an alternating potential is applied between cathode and anode. The current in the associated *anode circuit* is unidirectional, for, owing to the valve action, current flows in this circuit only during the positive half-cycle of the alternating potential. The diode is then said to function as a **rectifier**.

4. The Triode.

In the triode valve, a third electrode is inserted in the form of a wire grid, the three electrodes usually having cylindrical symmetry represented by a central line filament surrounded by a concentric grid and finally a solid cylindrical anode. The presence of the third electrode or **grid** acts as an extremely sensitive control of the current flowing between the cathode and the anode. Owing to the open nature of the grid very few electrons travel to this electrode, but its potential profoundly affects the magnitude of the anode current. For example, if the grid is made strongly negative with respect to the filament, although a high positive potential may be applied to the anode, the anode current is almost entirely suppressed. As the negative grid potential is gradually raised to zero the anode current increases, while if the grid becomes positive, the anode current increases still further. When the grid potential is strongly positive, a small grid current is created consisting of a small proportion of electrons attracted from the anode current. If the anode is subjected to very vigorous electron bombardment, the anode itself may emit electrons. This phenomenon is termed *secondary emission*. The applications of the triode are very

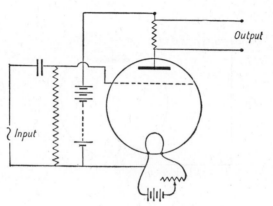

Fig. 5.— Triode as Amplifier

numerous, and form a considerable section in the science of radio-engineering. As an illustration of its properties we shall consider its use as an **amplifier**. Since small changes in the potential of the grid produce large changes in the anode current, if a large *anode resistance* is included in the anode circuit as shown in fig. 5, large fluctuations in potential are produced across the ends of this resistance. Consequently small fluctuations in potential in the grid circuit may be amplified and examined as large fluctuations in potential in the anode circuit. Moreover, if the large oscillations in potential in the anode circuit are fed into the primary of a mutual inductance, the secondary of which is in the grid circuit, the initial oscillations or fluctuations in potential in the grid circuit may be so augmented as to overcome entirely the natural decay of the oscillations due to ohmic losses. Consequently the valve itself becomes a permanent seat of oscillations and we obtain a **valve oscillator**.

Just as with the diode, characteristic curves are plotted for any

given triode. Owing to the presence of a third electrode two characteristic curves are obtained. The first shows the variation of anode
current with grid potential for a fixed anode voltage, and is shown in
fig. 6, where a family of curves is drawn each corresponding to a cer-

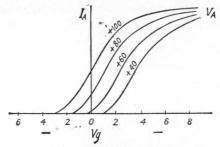

Fig. 6. — Anode Current and Grid Potential

tain anode voltage. The second type of characteristic shown in fig. 7
is obtained by plotting the anode current against anode voltage for
a fixed grid potential. Again a family of curves is obtained, this time
for different grid potentials.

Besides the triode, multiple-electrode valves containing up to ten

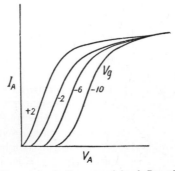

Fig. 7. — Anode Current and Anode Potential

electrodes are now available for a great variety of purposes. Additional electrodes up to the pentode are usually additional control
grids. When more electrodes than five are present the valve usually
functions as two or more valves in one envelope. Again, in modern
valves the cathode is usually heated indirectly by a small heating coil
close to it. In this way the whole of the cathode may be maintained
at a uniform potential, whereas if it carries a heating current there is
a potential drop along the filament.

5. Cathode Ray Oscillograph.

One of the most important applications of the cathode ray stream is to the cathode ray oscillograph, a diagram of which is shown in fig. 8. Many commercial variations are available, but it consists essentially of a hot cathode K emitting a canalized beam of electrons which

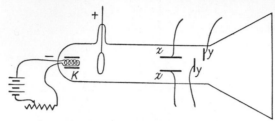

Fig. 8. — Cathode Ray Oscillograph

produce a glowing spot on a sensitive screen at the end of the tube. Two sets of plates (x, x) and (y, y) are placed on each side of the beam and to these are applied electric fields which deflect the spot. The (x, x) pair of plates is connected to a condenser which is charged at regular intervals to a known potential and then allowed to discharge through a high resistance. By a calculation similar to that of section 5, Chap. XIII, in which the inductance is replaced by the capacity of the condenser, the discharge may be shown to be exponential. Consequently the spot is first drawn to one side as the condenser receives its maximum potential and then returns to its original position as the condenser discharges. The time taken for the spot to traverse its path is easily calculated from the *time constant* of the condenser and resistance, and thus a *time base* is provided for the oscillograph. In practice the condenser charges and discharges many times per second, and owing to the persistence of vision the spot appears drawn out into a horizontal line. If now an alternating potential is applied to the (y, y) plates the spot will be subjected to two forces at right angles, and owing to the oscillating nature of the (y, y) potential will show the wave-form directly as in fig. 9. Since the horizontal time base is known for the instrument, the frequency and shape of the oscillating potential is obtained from direct measurement on the observed curve. Photographic fixing allows the trace to be

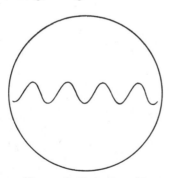

Fig. 9. — Oscillating Potential

studied at leisure, and in this way the instrument has many applications to the examination of electrical oscillations, or of sound oscillations (see Part IV) which have been converted to electrical oscillations.

6. Photoelectric Effect.

We have mentioned in Part III, Chap. IX, the experiments of Lenard which led to the theory of the photoelectric effect. On the electron theory of metals a free electron, if given sufficient energy, will leave the metal as in thermionic evaporation. This energy may be supplied by light or other radiation and then constitutes the photo-

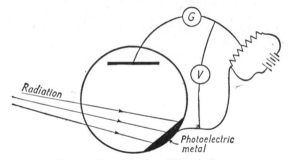

Fig. 10. — Determination of Planck's Constant

electric effect. Lenard's experiments are summed up in *Einstein's equation of the photoelectric effect* which states that

$$E = \tfrac{1}{2}mv^2 = h\nu - P, \quad \ldots \ldots \quad (19.4)$$

where E is the energy with which the electron escapes, h is Planck's constant of action, ν is the frequency of the radiation, and P represents the energy required just to liberate the electron from the metal with no appreciable velocity. In practice, examination is made of the photoelectric effect with an apparatus as in fig. 10. The energy of the electrons is estimated indirectly from the positive *retarding potential* V, which must be applied to the illuminated plate so that electrons are just unable to escape from the metal. Equation (19.4) then becomes

$$Ve = h\nu - P, \quad \ldots \ldots \quad (19.5)$$

where e is the charge on the electron. Hence if for a series of different frequencies V is plotted against ν, the slope of the line determines h/e, and since e is known from Millikan's experiment, h may be calculated. This method is one of the most accurate available for determining Planck's constant. The intercept of the straight line on the ν-axis gives the quantity P, which is sometimes termed the *work function* of the metal. Clearly for frequencies less than P/h, no electrons are emitted. There is therefore a **threshold frequency,** for which $\nu_0 = P/h$. The threshold frequency is in the red end of the visible spectrum for some metals like calcium and rubidium, and hence these are more suitable for use in photoelectric cells than other metals like copper, whose photoelectric threshold lies at higher frequencies. By the use of ultra-violet radiation, the photoelectric effect may be shown to exist in gases as well as in metals, and therefore to be characteristic of all matter subject to radiation.

The photoelectric effect described above in which the electrons actually leave the solid is sometimes termed the *outer photoelectric effect* to distinguish it from the *inner photoelectric effect* or *photoconductivity.* This is the lowering of resistance which occurs in semi-conducting materials like lead sulphide where conduction electrons are released by light inside the material and thus allow a current to flow. Since the current generated is directly proportional to the light intensity these photoconductors may be used as convenient and accurate photometers.

7. X-rays.

If a photographic plate wrapped in black paper is in the neighbourhood of a cathode ray tube running at high potential, the photographic plate is found to be affected. Likewise a photoelectric cell

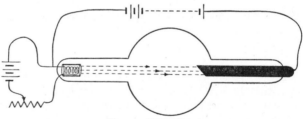

Fig. 11.—X-Ray Tube

which is screened from visible and ultra-violet radiation is shown to emit electrons when close to such a discharge tube. These and other experiments have shown that the impact of the cathode rays on the anode of the discharge tube produces an extremely penetrating radiation, termed X-radiation, which has all the properties of ultra-violet light except that it has greater penetrating power, penetrating layers of material normally regarded as opaque. A typical X-ray tube is shown in fig. 11, where the cathode rays are thermionic electrons: the anode is usually of tungsten, since the latter has a high melting-point and the anode becomes intensely hot if the cathode ray bombardment is continued for any length of time. By measurements on the photoelectric effect or otherwise, since P and h remain constant for a given metal, ν may be calculated for the X-radiation. In this way a definite frequency and wave-length may be ascribed to the X-rays. Since X-radiation as produced above contains a wide range of wave-lengths, some form of spectrometer is required if individual wave-lengths are to be separated. In light radiation the diffraction grating provides the standard instrument, but since X-radiation has wave-lengths several hundred times shorter than visible radiation,

application of the diffraction grating equation on p. 373, Part III, shows that the diffraction angle is so small as to render it impossible to distinguish the diffracted from the

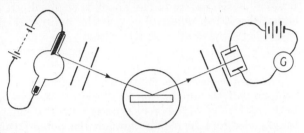

Fig. 12.—X-Ray Spectrometer

incident beam. Fortunately Nature has provided a three-dimensional diffraction grating in the form of crystals, which consists of layers of atoms arranged with a regular separation of the order of the wave-length of X-radiation. By a treatment similar to that used in Part III, p. 360, where the effect of reflected light from the top and bottom layers of a thin film is considered, it may be shown that if a wave-length λ is present in an X-ray beam, regular reflection occurs from a crystal surface at a **glancing angle** θ given by

$$2d \sin \theta = n\lambda, \quad . \quad . \quad . \quad . \quad . \quad (19.6)$$

where n is integral and d is the **grating constant,** that is the separation of the atomic layers constituting the crystal. Now d may be calculated

from the density of the crystal together with a knowledge of Avogadro's number, and θ may be measured by mounting the crystal on an **X-ray spectrometer.** This consists of a slit to define the X-ray beam and an ionization chamber, or photographic plate to detect the reflected beam as shown in fig. 12, the crystal being mounted on a rotating

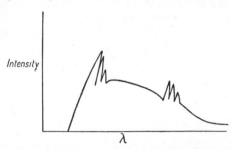

Fig. 13.—Intensity and Wave-length of X-radiation

table as in the ordinary optical spectrometer, and the slit and detector replacing the collimator and telescope of the optical spectrometer.

In fig. 13 a curve is plotted of the intensity of the X-radiation (measured from the degree of blackness of the photographic plate or the intensity of current in the ionization chamber) obtained from an X-ray tube, against the wave-length of the radiation. This shows that there is a definite lower limit of wave-length, below which no radiation occurs. A general or "white" background of radiation is present, superposed on which are sharp peaks at certain positions. These latter are termed the characteristic X-rays and change their position as the nature of the anode is changed. If V is the potential across the X-ray tube and $\nu_{\max}$ is the limiting (highest) frequency of the radiation present, it is found that

$$Ve = h\nu_{\max}, \quad \cdots \cdots \cdots \quad (19.7)$$

where e is the electronic charge and h is Planck's constant. The interpretation of the production of "white" X-rays is therefore that it is the reverse of the photoelectric effect. The kinetic energy acquired by the electrons in falling through the potential difference V in the X-ray tube is equal to the loss in potential energy Ve. This therefore represents the maximum energy which can be converted into radiation, and since the conversion is governed by Planck's radiation law, equation (19.7) represents the X-ray production process. In general, the efficiency of the tube is low, by far the greater part of the electronic energy being converted into heat at the anode. The other frequencies are therefore to be attributed to partial conversion only of the electron energy into radiant energy. We return to the consideration of the characteristic X-rays in the next chapter.

8. Electron Interference and Diffraction.

If a beam of electrons is reflected from the surface of a crystal, just as in the X-ray spectrometer it is found that for a particular glancing angle specular reflection is particularly pronounced. The analogy with the behaviour of X-radiation is complete, so that a definite wave-length λ may be said to be associated with the electrons, given as in equation (19.6) by

$$2d \sin \theta = n\lambda,$$

where d is the grating constant and θ is the glancing angle. Further, if the velocity of the electrons is v, the value of λ derived from the above equation is found to be

$$\lambda = \frac{h}{mv}, \quad \cdots \cdots \cdots \quad (19.8)$$

where h is Planck's constant. The electrons used in these experiments are of low velocity and hence the mass m may be taken as equal to the rest mass.

In a similar experiment, if electrons are sent normally through a thin foil, a photographic plate placed behind the foil shows in general a series of concentric diffraction rings very similar to those produced by the passage of a light wave through a circular aperture (see Part III, Chap. VII). Again, just as the wave-length of light may be estimated from measurements on its diffraction pattern, so the wave-length to be associated with the electron may be determined in the same way.

Although the nature of the wave motion associated with the electron is not well understood, and the wave is certainly not an ether wave, electron diffraction has already expanded into a separate science of *electron optics* with important applications in the *electron microscope*. We have seen in Part III that if structures to be examined are much finer than the wave-length of the light with which they are illuminated, the images of the structures will be very blurred and the structures will be said not to be resolved. Now substitution in (19.8) shows that for electrons which have fallen through a potential of a few hundred volts, λ is of the order of 10^{-8} cm. Hence a ray treatment is applicable to much finer structures in electron optics than with ordinary light.

EXERCISES

1. Describe Millikan's method of measuring the electronic charge. Of what significance is the fact that the electronic mass is much less than that of the hydrogen atom?

2. Outline Drude's theory of electronic conduction in solids. What other evidence is available that lightly bound electrons exist in good conductors?

3. Explain the phenomenon of the thermionic effect and describe how a diode may be used (a) as a rectifier of A.C. potential, (b) as a current limiter.

4. Describe the construction and mode of action of a simple triode and explain the shape of the characteristic curves obtained when anode current is plotted against grid potential at different anode potentials.

5. Give an account of the cathode ray oscillograph with special reference to its use in elucidating the wave form of electromagnetic oscillations.

6. Enumerate the main points associated with the photoelectric effect. In what sense may the production of X-rays be regarded as the inverse of the photoelectric effect?

7. Describe the construction of a typical X-ray tube and explain how the wave-length of X-radiation may be measured.

8. Describe experiments which indicate that cathode rays behave simultaneously as particles and as waves.

CHAPTER XX

Atomic and Nuclear Physics

1. Radioactivity.

It was discovered by Becquerel that uranium compounds, when placed close to a photographic plate covered with black paper, possessed the property of blackening the photographic plate. Similarly an electroscope could be discharged when in the neighbourhood of the uranium, and in fact all the general properties of X-rays were observed. In consequence it was established that uranium, and still more powerfully radium, emitted ionizing radiations *spontaneously* without any previous excitation by electrical discharge or any other means. The radiations from these **radioactive** substances were then examined by Rutherford and others with the following general results:

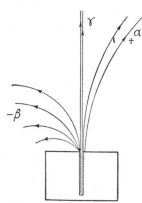

Fig. 1. — Separation of Rays by Magnetic Field

(i) The ionizing power of the radiations was much reduced by covering the radioactive substance with a thin layer of material, while the photographic action was little affected. Hence the radiations emitted are of at least two types. The easily absorbed but strongly ionizing component was termed α-**radiation.**

(ii) By subjecting the more penetrating radiations to magnetic and electric fields it was established that these were of two further types. One, termed β-**radiation,** was deflected by the fields and shown to consist simply of electrons moving with very great velocity, even approaching that of light. The other component, termed γ-**radiation**, which was more penetrating still, was unaffected by the fields and subsequently shown to be similar to X-rays but of shorter wave-length than this. The α-rays were deflected by the field in the reverse direction but less strongly than the β-rays, so that the application of a magnetic field effects a separation as shown in fig. 1.

(iii) In the process of emitting the radiations, the parent element is transformed into another element lower in the periodic table. The radioactive substance therefore decays, and the decay follows the simple law that the rate of decay is proportional to the mass of the radioactive element present. Expressing this mathematically, we have

$$\frac{dN}{dt} = -\lambda N, \quad \ldots \ldots \quad (20.1)$$

where N is the number of atoms of the radioactive material present at any time t, and λ is termed the **decay constant.** Integrating equation (20.1), we obtain

$$\frac{dN}{N} = -\int \lambda \, dt,$$

or
$$\log_e N = -\lambda t + A, \quad \ldots \ldots \quad (20.2)$$

where A is a constant. If $N = N_0$ at time $t = 0$, $A = \log_e N_0$, so (20.2) becomes

$$N = N_0 \exp.(-\lambda t), \quad \ldots \ldots \quad (20.3)$$

and an exponential decay law is obeyed.

In general, the new element which is formed is itself radioactive, and hence a radioactive chain is formed. This disintegration process continues down the periodic table until the element *lead* is reached, after which radioactive action ceases. Neither change in temperature nor electrical excitation nor any change in physical conditions affects the rate of decay of radioactive substances.

2. α-rays.

By deflection of α-rays in electric and magnetic fields according to the principles described in the preceding chapter, the ratio E/M was found to be half the value $(E/M)_H$ for the hydrogen ion in electrolysis. That α-rays consist of positively charged helium atoms may be shown directly by allowing them to accumulate in an exhausted tube and applying an electrical potential difference. Discharge gradually sets in, showing that a gas is forming, and examination of the glow with a spectrometer shows the characteristic lines of the spectrum of helium. We are therefore led to conclude that the charge on the α-particle is twice the electronic charge. The velocity of the α-particles emitted is calculated from the E/M experiment. It is the same for all α-rays from the same radioactive element, and is usually about 10^9 cm./sec., but varies from one element to another. The positive charge and velocity of the particles explain the easy absorption of the rays and their strong ionizing power.

In the disintegration of radium, α-rays are emitted in the first disintegration process. As may be seen from the periodic table on p. 734, the new element falls in the rare gas group and, in fact, constitutes the rare gas **radon.**

PERIODIC TABLE OF THE ELEMENTS

Period	Group I a	Group I b	Group II a	Group II b	Group III a	Group III b	Group IV a	Group IV b	Group V a	Group V b	Group VI a	Group VI b	Group VII a	Group VII b	Group VIII a	Group VIII b
I																2 He 4·003
II	3 Li 6·940		4 Be 9·013			5 B 10·82		6 C 12·011		7 N 14·008		8 O 16·0000		9 F 19·00		10 Ne 20·183
III	11 Na 22·991		12 Mg 24·32			13 Al 26·98		14 Si 28·09		15 P 30·975		16 S 32·066		17 Cl 35·457		18 A 39·944
IV	19 K 39·100	29 Cu 63·54	20 Ca 40·08	30 Zn 65·38	21 Sc 44·96	31 Ga 69·72	22 Ti 47·90	32 Ge 72·60	23 V 50·95	33 As 74·91	24 Cr 52·01	34 Se 78·96	25 Mn 54·94	35 Br 79·916	26 Fe 55·85 27 Co <——> 28 Ni 58·94 / 58·69	36 Kr 83·80
V	37 Rb 85·48	47 Ag 107·880	38 Sr 87·63	48 Cd 112·41	39 Y 88·92	49 In 114·76	40 Zr 91·22	50 Sn 118·70	41 Nb 92·91	51 Sb 121·76	42 Mo 95·95	52 Te 127·61	43 Tc 99	53 I <——> 126·92	44 Ru 101·1 45 Rh 102·91 46 Pd 106·7	54 Xe 131·3
VI	55 Cs 132·91	79 Au 197·0	56 Ba 137·36	80 Hg 200·61	57–71 RARE EARTHS	81 Tl 204·39	72 Hf 178·6	82 Pb 207·21	73 Ta 180·95	83 Bi 209·00	74 W 183·92	84 Po 209	75 Re 186·31	85 At 210	76 Os 190·2 77 Ir 192·2 78 Pt 195·23	86 Rn 222
VII	87 Fr 223		88 Ra 226·05		89 Ac 227		90 Th <——> 232·05		91 Pa 231	92 U 238·07	93 Np 237	94 Pu 239	95 Am 243	96 Cm 245	97 Bk 245 98 Cf 246 99 E 254 100 Fm 256 101 M 256	102 No 253

RARE EARTHS

VI 57–71															
57 La 138·92	58 Ce 140·13	59 Pr 140·92	60 Nd 144·27	61 Pm 145	62 Sm 150·43	63 Eu 152·0	64 Gd 156·9	65 Tb 158·93	66 Dy 162·46	67 Ho 164·94	68 Er 167·2	69 Tm 168·94	70 Yb 173·04	71 Lu 174·99

The numbers in front of the symbols of the elements denote the atomic numbers; the numbers underneath are the atomic weights. The double arrow <——> indicates the places where the order of atomic weights and that of atomic numbers do not agree. New elements are introduced by their symbols. Four of these fill gaps in older tables, namely, 43 Tc Technetium, 61 Pm Promethium, 85 At Astatine, 87 Fr Francium. The nine others are transuranic elements, 93 Np Neptunium, 94 Pu Plutonium, 95 Am Americium, 96 Cm Curium, 97 Bk Berkelium, 98 Cf Californium, 99 E Einsteinium, 100 Fm Fermium, 101 Mv Mendelevium, 102 No Nobelium.

3. β-rays.

By carrying out experiments similar to those devised to establish the nature of electrons, β-rays may be shown to be electrons moving with velocities which vary over an enormous range both with different elements and for any one element. While a value e/m exactly equal to that of electrons is obtained when the velocity of the β-rays is small, for large velocities the measured value becomes progressively less. This is due to the fact that these higher velocities approach that of light, and from our considerations in Part III, Chap. XII, we saw that ordinary mechanics has to be replaced by relativistic mechanics under such conditions. In particular, while the charge e is unaffected by the velocity, the mass m increases with the speed according to the simple relation

$$m = \frac{m_0}{\sqrt{1 - (v^2/c^2)}}, \quad \ldots \ldots \quad (20.4)$$

where m_0 is the rest mass, and m the mass when the velocity is v; c is the velocity of light. The deviation of the observed value of e/m for fast-moving electrons from its measured value for slow electrons affords one of the most direct and accurate tests of the relativistic mass equation (20.4).

4. γ-rays.

That γ-rays are similar to X-rays but of shorter wave-length is shown by a variety of experiments similar to those used for identifying the nature of X-rays. The less penetrating γ-rays may have their wave-length determined by the method of crystal reflection. By application of the photoelectric effect and using Einstein's equation, the frequency may be measured directly from the energy of the electrons ejected. Owing to the high retarding potentials which would be required to prevent photoelectric emission, it is impracticable to use exactly the same methods as for ultra-violet light. The energy of the electrons has therefore to be determined by magnetic deflection, and we may note that the relativistic expression

$$E_{kin} = m_0 c^2 \left[\frac{1}{\sqrt{1 - (v^2/c^2)}} - 1 \right], \quad \ldots \quad (20.5)$$

for kinetic energy must replace the Newtonian expression $E_{kin} = \frac{1}{2}mv^2$ at higher velocities.

5. Scattering of α-Particles by Matter.

Rutherford suggested that the energetic particles emitted by radioactive substances could be used as powerful probes to examine the structure of matter subject to the radiation. Experiments were carried out in which thin metal foils were bombarded by a stream of α-particles, and the number of α-particles scattered at various angles to the incident beam was observed. Now, Avogadro's number being known, the number of atoms present in a given layer of the scatterer could be calculated, and hence the chance of an α-particle being scattered through any given angle could also be calculated if the atoms were regarded as hard spheres of the diameter calculated from the kinetic theory of matter (see Part II, Chap. XI). The result showed that the observed scattering was in complete disagreement with that calculated on classical theory, but behaved instead as though the mass of the atom were concentrated in a region of about 10^{-13} cm. diameter instead of 10^{-8} cm. diameter as expected on classical theory. Rutherford was therefore led to suggest that the main mass of the atom was concentrated in a central **nucleus**. The scattering arose from the mutual repulsive electrostatic action between the positively charged nucleus and the positive α-particle. The electrons in the atom were assumed to be situated outside the nucleus and to play no part (owing to their small mass relative to that of the α-particle) in the scattering process.

*6. Bohr Theory of the Hydrogen Atom.

Guided by the α-particle scattering experiment and other considerations, Rutherford and Bohr suggested that an atom of matter consisted of a positively charged nucleus around which revolved one or more extra-nuclear electrons, the number of such electrons, multiplied by the electronic charge, being numerically equal to the positive charge on the nucleus, so as to render the matter electrically neutral in its normal state. The stability of such a system arises from the fact that the electrical force of attraction between the nucleus and the extra-nuclear electrons is just balanced by the centrifugal force of the latter, which are regarded as being in orbital motion about the central nucleus, in complete analogy with the planetary system revolving round the sun.

Bohr developed this theory mathematically to account for the properties of the hydrogen atom, which was chosen since it represented the simplest system, consisting of one electron revolving around a singly charged positive nucleus termed the **proton**. In particular, Bohr deduced the properties of the line spectrum of hydrogen (see Part III). From experimental measurement of the position of the hydrogen lines, Balmer had shown many years earlier that the frequency of any line was given by the simple empirical formula

$$\nu = R\left(\frac{1}{2^2} - \frac{1}{m^2}\right), \quad \cdots \cdots \quad (20.6)$$

where R is a constant termed the Rydberg constant, and m is integral and equal to 3, 4, 5, etc. We shall now deduce this relation from Bohr's theory. Equating the centrifugal force to the electrical force for the special case of an electron revolving in a circular orbit as shown in fig. 2, we have

$$\frac{mv^2}{a} = \frac{(Ze)e}{a^2}, \quad \cdots \cdots \quad (20.7)$$

where a is the radius of the orbit, v is the velocity of the electron of mass m and charge e, and (Ze) is the nuclear charge where $Z = 1$ for hydrogen. Bohr then made the assumption that the angular momentum of the electron about the nucleus could not have any arbitrary

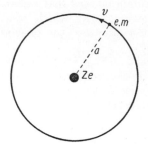

Fig. 2. — Electron in Circular Orbit

value (as in the gravitational case), but was " quantized " according to the relation

$$mva = \frac{nh}{2\pi}, \quad \cdots \cdots \quad (20.8)$$

where h is Planck's constant and n is integral. The reason for this suggestion, which at first seems quite arbitrary, will be explained later. For the present, eliminating a from (20.7) and (20.8), we have

$$v = \frac{2\pi Ze^2}{nh}, \quad \cdots \cdots \quad (20.9)$$

while eliminating v, we have

$$a = \frac{n^2h^2}{4\pi^2Zme^2}. \quad \cdots \cdots \quad (20.10)$$

The *total* energy of an electron in its orbit is partly kinetic and partly potential. The kinetic energy

$$E_{\text{kin}} = \tfrac{1}{2}mv^2, \quad \cdots \cdots \quad (20.11)$$

while the potential energy is

$$E_{\text{pot}} = -\frac{(Ze)e}{a} = -\frac{4\pi^2 Z^2 m e^4}{n^2 h^2} = -mv^2, \quad . \quad (20.12)$$

from equations (20.10) and (20.9).

Hence the total energy is

$$E = -\tfrac{1}{2}mv^2 = -\frac{2\pi^2 Z^2 m e^4}{n^2 h^2}. \quad . \quad . \quad . \quad (20.13)$$

Now from equation (20.10) it is clear that the radius of any orbit is uniquely determined by the value of the integer n. Hence Bohr's assumptions implied that the electron could not rotate in any circular orbit but only in certain allowed orbits or stationary states governed by (20.8). Bohr's final assumption was that radiation of the spectral line was due to the change in energy which resulted when an electron jumped from one orbit to another, the general quantum relation

$$E_2 - E_1 = h\nu \quad . \quad . \quad . \quad . \quad (20.14)$$

being obeyed, where ν is the frequency of the radiation emitted, and E_2 and E_1 are the energies of the initial and final orbit respectively. Hence, substituting in (20.14) from (20.13), we have

$$h\nu = \frac{2\pi^2 Z^2 m e^4}{h^2} \left(\frac{1}{n_1^2} - \frac{1}{n_2^2} \right),$$

or

$$\nu = \frac{2\pi^2 Z^2 m e^4}{h^3} \left(\frac{1}{n_1^2} - \frac{1}{n_2^2} \right). \quad . \quad . \quad . \quad (20.15)$$

Comparison of this result with Balmer's formula (20.6) shows that the two equations are identical if $n_1 = 2$ and $n_2 = m = 3, 4, 5$, &c. This general similarity is not surprising, since all Bohr's assumptions were made to lead to this result. The real test came from the fact that R, which is called the Rydberg constant, could be measured experimentally from spectroscopic data and (20.6), while (20.15) requires

$$R = \frac{2\pi^2 Z^2 m e^4}{h^3}. \quad . \quad . \quad . \quad . \quad (20.16)$$

Putting $Z = 1$, the Rydberg constant for hydrogen could therefore be calculated from the values of e, m and h derived from quite different experiments. The agreement between the observed and calculated values of R was complete, thus showing that Bohr's conception and assumptions about the nature of the hydrogen atom represented reality to a marked degree.

Owing to the fact that the electron behaves as a wave as well as a particle it has been found necessary to refine the original Bohr model of the atom. Unfortunately this refinement leads to great mathematical complication in which the simple dynamical picture of the atom is largely lost. It seems likely, however, that Bohr's original model, like that of the billiard ball atom in kinetic theory, will always serve as a useful tool in understanding at least a limited group of phenomena.

7. X-ray Spectra.

We have already described the type of spectrum obtained when the intensity of X-radiation from a discharge tube is plotted against the wave-length, and we have mentioned that certain peaks occur on the curve which are said to be the characteristic X-rays of the element composing the anode. These characteristic X-rays may be studied free from the " white " background by making use of the following phenomenon. If X-radiation of greater frequency than the characteristic X-rays is allowed to fall on an element, **secondary X-rays** are emitted from the element. On examination of these radiations with an X-ray spectrometer they are found to consist of the characteristic X-rays of the element. Moseley took a series of elements and excited their characteristic X-rays with high-frequency X-radiation. He demonstrated the remarkable facts: (1) that the **X-ray spectrum** of all elements consisted of a few lines only, in great contrast to the complicated visible spectrum; (2) that the appearance of the lines was similar for all elements, and that they occurred in groups termed the K-lines, L-lines, &c.; and (3) that the frequency of corresponding lines increased in a perfectly regular manner in the order of the elements in the periodic system.

From these facts it was deduced that some quantity associated with the atoms of the elements increased uniformly throughout the periodic system. In the light of this and further evidence it became clear that the quantity could only be the *atomic number Z* of the element, that is the number of the element in the periodic table. These results, together with Rutherford's experiments on the scattering of α-particles, led to the basic assumption of the modern electrical theory of matter, namely that the charge on the nucleus is simply equal to the electronic charge multiplied by the atomic number. To preserve neutrality of the element in its normal state it was inferred that the number of extra-nuclear electrons was equal to the atomic number. Now although $Z = 2$ for helium, since it is the second element in the periodic table, its mass is approximately 4 times that of hydrogen. It was therefore suggested that the helium nucleus consisted of four protons, but that since this would give $Z = 4$ it must also contain two electrons, thus giving a *net* positive charge $Z = 2$ to the nucleus. Incidentally the presence of the two negative electrons would explain the stability of the nucleus, for if it consisted of purely positive charges it would be expected to explode spontaneously owing to the mutual electrostatic repulsion of charges of one sign only. Very recent experiments have shown that the simple interpretation of a nucleus as consisting of protons and electrons is not tenable, and we discuss this further in section 14. For the moment, however, such a concept of nuclear constitution is satisfactory as giving an initial insight into nuclear structure.

Following his success with the theory of the hydrogen atom, Bohr suggested that for elements of higher atomic number all the electrons were arranged in orbits governed by quantum rules. To determine the arrangement of the electrons recourse was made to the periodic system. It was suggested that the regular behaviour of certain groups such as the rare gases, the alkali metals and so on, was due to the

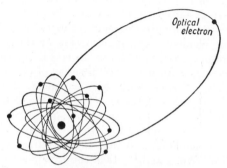

Fig. 3. — Electric Orbits in Sodium Atoms

similarity of the arrangement of the electron orbits for all elements in any one group. It was eventually shown that the first rare gas, helium, consisted of a doubly charged nucleus with $Z = 2$, surrounded by two electrons in equal orbits. The next element, lithium, has quite different chemical properties from helium, and it is therefore assumed that the third electron starts a new orbit outside the inner or **K-group.** As we proceed up the periodic system, additional electrons continue to occupy this second or **L-group** until eight more electrons have been added. We then arrive at the next rare gas neon with $Z = 10$, and since the properties of neon correspond to those of helium it is assumed that this second group is now complete. The next element, sodium, will then have the 11th electron commencing a fresh or **M-group,** and so on. Since this 11th electron is circulating in an orbit outside all the other electrons and the nucleus (as shown in fig. 3), the K- and L-groups and the nucleus constitute a sort of inner electric field in which the 11th electron moves. Now by Bohr's theory of the origin of spectra, in the case of hydrogen the spectrum originates when an electron switches from one possible allowed orbit to another which is vacant. It is clear that with sodium the only electron which can

" jump " freely from one orbit to another is the outermost electron, for the K- and L-orbits are all occupied. Hence we should expect the optical spectrum of sodium and all alkali metals to be similar to the hydrogen spectrum, a prediction which agrees well with experiment.

We are now in a position to interpret the characteristic X-rays of the elements. Ordinary photoelectric action is due simply to the removal of the outermost electron by the light quantum, for the electrostatic force of attraction between the nucleus and the electrons in the inner levels is too great for them to be affected even by ultra-violet light. The frequency of X-rays, however, is much greater, and hence the energy $h\nu$ of the X-ray quantum is often sufficient to remove electrons from any of the inner groups. Consider now what will occur if a K-electron is removed by such high energy photoelectric action. The vacant K-ring will now be filled by one of the outer electrons jumping down into the vacated orbit. But by Bohr's theory this will result in the emission of radiation of energy equal to the energy difference in the two orbits. The frequency of this radiation is very high, since the switch occurs to an orbit much closer to the nucleus than those of the outer or " optical electron ". In fact, the energy of the emitted radiation is that of the K-radiation of the characteristic X-rays. In general, the gap in the K-ring will be filled by an electron dropping from the L-ring, but it will sometimes happen that electrons from still higher orbits will take part in the transition. Hence the K-radiation consists of a group of lines of approximately the same frequency, the difference in frequency being equal to

$$\nu = (E_L - E_K)/h \quad \text{or} \quad (E_M - E_K)/h, \text{ &c.,}$$

according to the transition which occurs.

The gap created in the L-ring due to the switch to the vacant K-ring is in turn filled up by electron switches from still higher levels. These transitions give rise to the characteristic L-radiation, and so on. The great similarity in X-ray spectra of different elements shows conclusively that all elements are built up on the same structure, that is first a K-group, then an L-group, and so on.

Many physical properties and all the chemical properties of the elements are explicable in terms of the arrangement of the electrons in the extra-nuclear structure. For example, the inert chemical nature of the rare gases is due to the existence of the completed shell in these gases. Again, the alkali metals are monovalent because they have one less tightly bound electron operating outside the inner closed shell systems. The affinity of hydrogen for chlorine or sodium for chlorine lies in the tendency to form closed shells. Thus chlorine lacks one electron from its outermost shell to complete the number required for a rare gas grouping and therefore chemical inertness. This one electron is conspicuously present in hydrogen or the alkali metals, and hence chemical combination occurs with the additional electron entering the vacant space in the chlorine structure, giving the latter a structure like argon. Correspondingly the alkali metal by loss of an electron acquires an extra-nuclear structure like the rare gas which precedes it in the periodic table. Both elements are thereby chemically " satisfied ".

8. Magnetism on the Electron Theory.

On Bohr's model of the atom, each circulating extra-nuclear electron will produce a magnetic field just as if it consisted of an electric current traversing an elliptical conducting circuit. The total magnetic field possessed by the atom will be the vector sum of the magnetic fields of each electronic orbit. Now in the rare gas atoms, the electronic orbits are highly symmetrical and no resultant magnetic field exists external to the atom. If we consider the effect of establishing a magnetic field in the neighbourhood of such a gas, we know by Lenz's law that in a conducting circuit induced currents would be set up so as to produce an oppositely directed field to the inducing field. The electronic orbits are precisely similar to closed electrical circuits, and hence the effect of establishing the magnetic field is to cause the electrons to accelerate or decelerate (according to the sense of rotation of the electron) so as to produce an oppositely directed field to the inducing field. A repulsion is therefore set up between the opposing fields and the material moves away from the applied magnet, that is it behaves as a *diamagnetic* substance. In so far as the atoms of all elements contain these electronic orbits, so all matter is diamagnetic in its behaviour. If the material behaves like a paramagnetic or ferromagnetic body, this is due to some other mechanism which more than counterbalances the diamagnetic repulsion which is always present. The change in velocity of the electrons when a magnetic field is present results in a change in the frequency of the spectral lines which are normally emitted by the element. This behaviour is known as the **Zeeman effect**; a similar phenomenon in the presence of a strong electric field is termed the **Stark effect**.

If the magnetic moments of the individual orbits present in an atom show a resultant, the atom will behave as a magnetic dipole and will respond positively to a magnetic field. The diamagnetic opposition due to the operation of Lenz's law on each orbit will still be present, but will be feebler than the reaction of the resultant magnetic dipole. Materials which behave in this way constitute the *paramagnetic* group.

Finally, the most strongly magnetic or *ferromagnetic* group are generally assumed to consist of larger groupings of paramagnetic atoms, each group constituting the elementary " molecular " magnet of section 5, Chap. VI.

9. Isotopes.

At each α-ray change in a radioactive series a mass 4 (in terms of hydrogen as unity) is lost, whereas each β-ray change results in no appreciable alteration in mass. Hence between the beginning and the end of a radioactive series, the difference in atomic weight between the initial and final elements is $4n$, where n is the number of α-ray changes. Now radium and thorium, of atomic weights 226 and 232, undergo five and six α-ray changes respectively, both elements eventually being transformed into lead. But the atomic weight of the lead in the former case is $226 - 5 \times 4 = 206$, while in the latter it is $232 - 6 \times 4 = 208$. We are therefore led to conclude that the same element, that is, one with the same position in the periodic table, can exist with two different atomic weights. Ordinary lead and all elements which have fractional atomic weights are in fact mixtures of whole number components or **isotopes.** Thus chlorine with a chemical atomic weight about 35·5 may be shown to consist of a mixture of isotopes of masses 35 and 37.

The existence of isotopes of non-radioactive elements is shown by **positive ray analysis,** that is by examination of the positive ray parabolæ described in Chap. XVIII. If the discharge takes place in chlorine, two parabolæ are formed, one corresponding to each isotope of mass 35 and 37.

10. Origin of α-, β- and γ-rays.

Since the whole of the mass of the atom resides in the nucleus, α-rays must originate from the nucleus of the atom. At first it appears possible for the β-particles to originate either in the extra-nuclear structure or to consist of nuclear electrons. Now the radioactive element which results from a β-ray transition in radioactive decay is found to occupy a position in the periodic table with Z one unit higher than the parent element. Hence the β-ray must have originated from the nucleus so as to increase the effective positive charge of the latter by one unit.

Finally, γ-radiation has an energy greater than that of any X-ray due to a transition of extra-nuclear electrons to the lowermost or K-ring, and hence these radiations also are of nuclear origin. The inability of change in physical condition to affect radioactive decay is therefore easily explained as due to the fact that external physical changes are of insignificant energy compared with that involved in the strong electric fields within the nucleus.

11. Artificial Disintegration.

By using the α-particles which have an energy comparable with that of the nuclear electric fields, the nuclei of stable elements like

nitrogen may be disintegrated. If energetic α-particles are sent through
nitrogen gas, hydrogen (which is made up of protons) is produced and,
since the nitrogen has disintegrated, a new element is formed. The
equation governing the reaction is

$$_{14}^{7}N + _{4}^{2}He \rightarrow _{1}^{1}H + _{17}^{8}O, \quad . \quad . \quad . \quad . \quad (20.17)$$

where the top suffix gives the atomic number and the lower suffix the
atomic weight of the element involved. We note that the α-particle
amalgamates with the disintegrated nitrogen nucleus to give an
element with $Z = 8$, which is therefore oxygen. The mass of this
oxygen is, however, 17 instead of the customary 16 as found by a

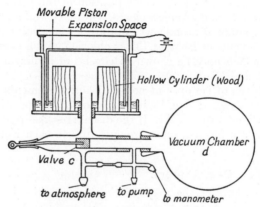

Fig. 4. — Wilson Cloud Chamber Diagram

The movable piston is suddenly lowered by opening the
valve c and so connecting the vacuum chamber d with the
part of the apparatus beneath the piston.

chemical determination of atomic weights. This $_{17}^{8}O$ is a rare isotope
of oxygen which has subsequently been shown to exist in a very small
proportion in ordinary oxygen.

Such nuclear reactions are shown in a pictorial manner by the
Wilson cloud chamber which is illustrated in fig. 4. This instrument
consists essentially of a glass vessel filled with saturated vapour.
Now electrical charges, like dust particles (see Part II, p. 234), have
the property of causing condensation of saturated vapour. Consequently if an ionizing particle such as an α-particle traverses the
vapour-laden atmosphere, it leaves in its wake a trail of ionization,
that is a trail of positive and negative charges on which the vapour
condenses as a line of drops. If this line of drops is strongly illuminated
and photographed, a permanent record of **α-ray tracks** is obtained.
Now should the vapour be present in nitrogen, about one track in a

million shows the curious appearance as shown in fig. 5. This shows the disintegration of the nitrogen nucleus. An α-particle has entered from below and pierced a nitrogen nucleus. The latter has then disintegrated into the long proton (hydrogen) track, the short recoil track being the relatively heavy nucleus of $_{17}^{8}O$. The whole process is subject to the same laws as the collision of billiard balls, momentum and energy being conserved in the process. Of course, in a disinte-

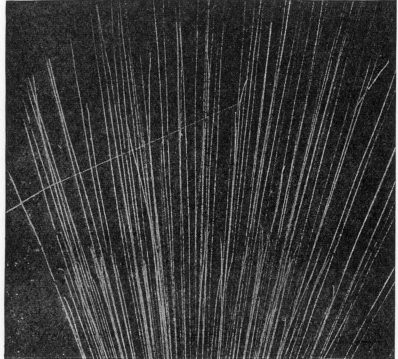

Fig. 5. — Cloud-track photograph showing the transmutation of a nitrogen nucleus by the capture of an α-particle and emission of a proton (after Blackett)

gration *kinetic energy* is not conserved, as the potential energy of the various nuclei involved has to be considered.

Nuclear transmutations may be achieved by any atomic particles of sufficiently high energy, and besides α-particles modern technique uses positive ions as the bombarding particles. Various ingenious devices such as the *cyclotron* have been made to produce bombarding particles of the requisite energy. In this way all elements in the periodic table have been disintegrated, and a vast chemistry of nuclear transformations governed by equations of the type of (20.17) is now in existence. Apart from the instantaneous disintegrations such as

occur when α-particles disintegrate nitrogen, "delayed action" disintegrations occur. In fact, a whole range of new radioactive elements
such as radioactive chlorine, radioactive arsenic, &c., may be manu-
factured.

12. The Neutron.

If lithium is bombarded by high energy α-particles, radiation is
emitted with a penetrating power millions of times that of the most
penetrating γ-radiation known. By ingenious experiments these rays
have been shown to owe their high penetrating power *not* to their
enormous energy as was first thought, but to the fact that they interact
little with matter and therefore do not readily lose their energy to
anything else. It has been shown that these radiations are *particles* of
mass equal to that of the proton but possessing no electric charge at
all. They are termed **neutrons** and have been shown by disintegration
experiments to be constituents of all nuclei.

13. Positive Electrons.

If the radiations emitted by *artificially prepared radioactive substances* are examined it is found that some elements emit β-particles
with a positive charge instead of a negative charge. These positive
electrons have values of *e* and *m* identical with those of ordinary
electrons. They are, however, very short-lived, as they easily undergo
annihilation by combination with the negative extra-nuclear electrons
present in all matter. The mass and energy of the two electrons are
not destroyed, for the process of annihilation results in the creation
of γ-radiation of such energy that energy is conserved.

Positive electrons were first discovered by examination of **cosmic
radiation.** The latter consists of a very penetrating ionizing radiation
which originates in outer space and is continually bombarding this
planet. By the application of the technique used for identifying and
examining radioactive radiations, these cosmic radiations have been
shown to consist very largely of extremely high energy positive and
negative electrons present in about equal quantity.

14. Nuclear Structure.

Since matter can be made to emit both neutrons and positive electrons as a result of bombardment by high-speed particles, the model
of the atom as composed entirely of protons and electrons is clearly
inadequate. The model of the atom at present accepted is as follows.
The extra-nuclear structure consists entirely of negative electrons as
on the original Rutherford-Bohr model. All chemical and many
physical changes are due to interactions of the extra-nuclear electrons,
and the nucleus is not involved except in so far as it provides a central

electric field in which the extra-nuclear electrons carry out their transitions.

The nucleus is now considered to consist of Z protons together with $(A - Z)$ neutrons, where Z is the atomic number and A is the atomic weight. No electrons are considered to be present in the nucleus, but the positive or negative β-particles emitted in the corresponding radioactive changes are considered to be created by the spontaneous transition of a proton into a neutron or a neutron into a proton, thus:

$$p \to n + e^+,$$
$$n \to p + e^-.$$

We are finally left with the problem as to why the nucleus holds together if no electron " cement " is present to counterbalance the mutual repulsion of the positively charged protons. It has become essential to assume that the neutrons and protons attract each other, and since the former are neutral the introduction of non-electric forces in the nucleus would seem inevitable. In this way the electrical theory of matter has by its very successes taken us so far that we now require a new theory of matter, in which non-electric as well as electric forces seem destined to play a part.

EXERCISES

1. By what simple experiment may it be shown that the radiations emitted by radioactive substances are of three distinct types? Give a fuller account of *one* of these radiations.

2. What do you understand by the transformation theory of radioactive decay? Given that the rate of decay is proportional to the quantity of radioactive material present, show that the decay follows an exponential law.

3. State briefly how the nature of α-radiation was determined, and give some account of what you consider to be the most important experiment ever performed with these rays as the main agent.

4. What are the properties of β- and γ-rays? Give reasons for believing that these radiations arise from the nucleus and not from the extra-nuclear structure.

5. Give Bohr's theory of the origin of the spectrum of atomic hydrogen. What effect is produced by the fact that the nucleus is not absolutely fixed but that, actually, nucleus and extra-nuclear electron both revolve about the common centre of gravity of the system?

6. Distinguish between continuous X-radiation and characteristic X-rays. Explain the origin of the latter on the Rutherford-Bohr atomic model.

7. How is magnetism explained on the electron theory, and by what means may diamagnetic susceptibilities be measured experimentally?

8. Write a short essay on isotopes.

9. How may one element be transmuted into another? What elements are formed when nitrogen is bombarded with high energy α-particles?

10. Write short notes on the following: neutrons, positive electrons, cosmic radiation. What is your conception of the atomic nucleus, and how do you account for its stability?

EXAMPLES

1. A bar magnet of equivalent length 10 cm. is lying in the magnetic meridian with its N pole pointing N. If the horizontal component of the earth's magnetic field is 0·18 gauss and is just balanced at a point on the perpendicular bisector of the axis of the magnet, find the magnetic moment of the magnet, given that the distance of the neutral point from the centre of the magnet is 12 cm.

2. Two magnets are lying in equilibrium in the same straight line, the distance between their centres being 100 cm. Find the force between them if they have equivalent lengths 20 cm. and 10 cm. and pole strengths 50 units and 25 units respectively.

3. A ball-ended magnet of mass 100 gm. is suspended vertically about a horizontal axis passing through its N pole. A second long ball-ended magnet is then slowly brought up horizontally with its S pole pointing towards the lower end of the suspended magnet until the S pole of the second magnet is vertically below the axis of suspension of the first magnet and 20 cm. from it. If the S poles are in the same horizontal line and the pole strength of each magnet is 200 units, find the maximum angle at which the suspended magnet is inclined to the vertical when in equilibrium.

4. A flat strip of wood capable of being rotated in a horizontal plane about a vertical axis carries a bar magnet in the broadside position. A compass needle is placed immediately over the vertical axis. Show that the needle points along the wooden strip when the latter is inclined to the magnetic meridian at an angle θ given by $\sin \theta = M/HL^3$, where M is the magnetic moment of the bar magnet, L the distance of either pole of the magnet from the vertical axis, and H the strength of the horizontal component of the earth's magnetic field.

5. In Ques. 4, the bar magnet is placed in the end-on position with its centre 100 cm. from the vertical axis. It is then found that there are two positions of the wooden strip in which the needle is perpendicular to the axis of the magnet, the angle between these two positions being 60°. Find the moment of the magnet, given that the earth's horizontal magnetic component is 0·18 gauss.

6. A vibration magnetometer when placed at a point on the

axis of a bar magnet lying in the magnetic meridian has a time of oscillation t_1, and when placed an equal distance along the axis on the opposite side of the magnet has a time of oscillation t_2. Prove that the time of oscillation t_3 in the earth's field alone is given by $t_3{}^2(t_1{}^2 - t_2{}^2) = 2t_1{}^2t_2{}^2$.

7. A dip circle lying initially in the magnetic meridian is rotated through an angle a in a horizontal plane. Show that the tangent of the angle of dip is increased in the ratio $\sec a : 1$.

8. A bar magnet is brought up in the end-on position to a point due E of a vibrating magnetometer which is thereby deflected through an angle θ. Show that the time of oscillation of the magnetometer is changed in the ratio $(\cos\theta)^{\frac{1}{2}} : 1$.

9. Regarding the earth's magnetic field as equivalent to that produced by a small magnet of moment μ situated at the centre of the earth, show that if λ is the magnetic latitude at any point, the angle of dip D is given by $\tan D = 2\tan\lambda$ and that the horizontal component H is given by $H = \cos\lambda/R^3$, where R is the radius of the earth.

10. Two small magnets of moments M and M' are so placed that their axes make angles θ and θ' with the line joining their centres. Show that the potential energy of one magnet in the field of the other is

$$W = MM' \left(\sin\theta\sin\theta' - 2\cos\theta\cos\theta'\right)/d^3,$$

where d is the distance between the centres of the magnets.

11. In Ques. 10, show that the translational force between the magnets along the line of centres is

$$F = 3MM' \left(\sin\theta\sin\theta' - 2\cos\theta\cos\theta'\right)/d^4.$$

12. In Ques. 10, show that the transverse force acting on either magnet in a direction perpendicular to the line of centres is

$$T = -3MM' \sin(\theta + \theta')/d^4.$$

13. In Ques. 10, show that the rotational couple acting on the second magnet is given by

$$G = MM'(2\cos\theta\cos\theta' - \sin\theta\sin\theta')/d^3.$$

14. A rectangular bar magnet of weight 200 gm., equivalent length 20 cm., and breadth 4 cm., gives a deflection of $45°$ in the end-on position when the centre of the magnet is 50 cm. from the needle of a deflection magnetometer. When the magnet is freely suspended and allowed to oscillate in the earth's field, it makes 10 oscillations in 100 sec. Find the strength of the earth's horizontal field and the moment of the magnet, neglecting the difference between actual and equivalent length of the magnet.

15. Two spherical pith-balls, each of diameter 0·5 cm. and weight 0·1 gm., are suspended from the same point by strings 13 cm. long. When charged with equal charges of electricity, the balls repel each other to a distance of 10 cm. Find the charge and potential of each ball.

16. Find the position of the neutral points in the neighbourhood of two equal small spheres carrying charges $+10$ units and -5 units and situated a distance 50 cm. apart, before and after the spheres have been connected by a wire.

17. Point charges $+q$ are placed at the corners of an equilateral triangle of side 3 cm. Find what charge will hold the three charges in equilibrium and where it must be placed.

18. If the three charges of Ques. 17 are held rigidly at the corners of the triangle, find the work done in taking the fourth charge from the centroid of the triangle to the mid-point of one of the sides.

19. Find the ratio of the electrostatic unit of charge on the lb. ft. sec. and C.G.S. systems respectively.

20. Two spherical condensers A and B carry charges of $+10$ and $+15$ units respectively. If the internal radii of A and B are 25 cm. and 35 cm. and their external radii are 30 cm. and 40 cm. respectively, find the loss in energy of the system when the condensers are joined by a wire. Find also the final charges on A and B.

21. The capacities of the systems formed by connecting a condenser (with a capacity equivalent to that of an insulated sphere of radius a) and an air-filled parallel plate condenser of plate separation d, in parallel and series respectively, are in the ratio $(a + d)^2 : ad$. Show that there are two possible values for the area of the parallel plate condenser and that these are in the ratio d^2/a^2.

22. Find the maximum value of the surface density of electrification of a conductor in air if the latter breaks down under a tension of more than 700 dynes/sq. cm.

23. Referring to Ques. 22, determine approximately the rise in level of the water of a lake immediately below a thunder-cloud just before the lightning strikes.

24. A piece of metal foil 1 sq. cm. in area and of weight 10^{-4} gm. lies on a flat metal plate of area 10^4 sq. cm. Find approximately the charge which must be communicated to the metal plate so as to lift the piece of foil.

25. Three thin flat parallel metal plates A, B and C form a double condenser, the inner plate B having a surface density of charge σ and the two outer plates A and C being earthed. Find the potential of B if A and C are at distances a and b respectively from B.

26. Two parallel metal plates A and B are situated a distance d apart; A is insulated and B is earthed. Show that the capacity per unit area of the system changes by an amount $t/4\pi d(d-t)$ if an insulated metal plate of thickness t is placed in between and parallel to A and B.

27. A hollow metal sphere of mass 2 gm. and radius 5 cm. rests on an insulating stand and is cut in half in a horizontal plane. It is then given an electric charge of 1000 e.s.u. Determine whether the top hemisphere will be lifted from the lower hemisphere.

28. In Ques. 27, show, in a general case, that if the two hemispheres (of radius a) are earthed, and a charge q is placed at the centre, forces $q^2/8a^2$ are required to separate them.

29. Three concentric spherical conductors of radii a, b and c having $c > b > a$ are given charges q_1, q_2 and q_3. If the innermost sphere is earthed, show that the loss in potential energy of the system is $a(q_1/a + q_2/b + q_3/c)^2/2$.

30. A conductor is charged by repeated contact with the brass disk of an electrophorus which supplies a constant amount of electricity Q to the brass disk. If the conductor acquires a charge q after the first contact, show that the limiting amount of charge which may be communicated to the conductor in this way is $Qq/(Q-q)$.

31. A gold-leaf electroscope is charged with electricity and reads 20 scale divisions. It is then connected to a parallel plate condenser of area 30 sq. cm. and plate separation 0·5 cm., whereupon the electroscope reading falls to 12 scale divisions. Find the capacity of the electroscope.

32. A small particle has an electric charge of $4\cdot800 \times 10^{-10}$ e.s.u. Find the mass of the particle if it is suspended in equilibrium between two flat condenser plates 2 cm. apart, charged to a potential difference of 3000 volts.

33. Find the additional weight required to balance an absolute electrometer if the area of the moving plate is 30 sq. cm. and its distance from the lower plate is 0·2 cm., the difference of potential between the two plates being 1000 volts.

34. If the electrometer of Ques. 33 is immersed in oil of dielectric constant 3·5, find the change in balance weight required.

35. The lower half of a spherical condenser is filled with a nonconductor of dielectric constant k. Show that the new capacity of the condenser is the same as if the whole space were filled with material of dielectric constant $(1+k)/2$.

36. A charged parallel plate condenser containing a slab of material of thickness a and dielectric constant k is connected to an electro-

scope whose capacity may be neglected. On removing the slab it is found necessary to move the plates of the condenser closer together by an amount b if the deflection of the electroscope is to remain unaltered. Show that $k = a/(a - b)$.

37. Find the capacity per unit length of a submarine cable from the following data: radius of core = 0·5 cm., outer radius = 1·0 cm., specific inductive capacity of insulating layer = 3·2.

38. A quadrant electrometer reads a deflection of 20 scale divisions when the paddle has been raised to a potential of 1000 volts, the pairs of quadrants having potentials of 10 and zero volts respectively. Find the mean potential of an A.C. supply which registers a deflection of 100 scale divisions when connected idiostatically to the electrometer.

39. What is the least horse-power required to drive a Wimshurst machine which is to deliver one milliampere at a pressure of 5000 volts?

40. Two flat condenser plates are at a potential difference of 3000 volts and are situated in a vacuum. If a small particle (an electron) of mass 9×10^{-28} gm. and carrying a charge of $4 \cdot 800 \times 10^{-10}$ e.s.u. starts out with negligible velocity from the negative plate, find the velocity with which it will strike the other plate.

41. The insulated plate of a parallel plate condenser of area A has a surface density of charge σ. Calculate the work done if the plates move together a distance d owing to the mutual force of attraction.

42. In Ques. 41, if the insulated plate is connected to a battery which supplies a constant potential V, given that the initial plate separation is t, find the energy supplied by the battery.

43. In Ques. 42, find the external work done during the movement.

44. Show that if any two condensers of capacities C_1 and C_2 and carrying charges q_1 and q_2 are connected in parallel by a wire, the system experiences a loss in energy given by

$$(C_2 q_1 - C_1 q_2)^2 / 2 C_1 C_2 (C_1 + C_2).$$

45. Find the horse-power required to run a 100 candle-power lamp of 2 c.p. per watt, and the current in the circuit when on a 220-volt circuit.

46. For a given resistance box the heating effect must not exceed 10^{-3} watts per ohm. Find the maximum voltages that may be applied across the box when resistances of 10^4 ohms and 1 ohm are being used respectively.

47. A circuit is to be supplied with a direct current of 200 amp. at a potential difference of 200 volts. Calculate the E.M.F. at the terminals of the dynamo if the leads to the circuit are half a mile long, 1 sq. in. in cross-section, and of copper of specific resistance

1·6 × 10⁻⁶ ohm . cm. Find also the percentage of power wasted in the leads.

48. Current is supplied to 100 filament lamps arranged in parallel, the resistance of each lamp being 250 ohms. When 50 more lamps are switched into the circuit, the voltage across the lamp terminals drops from 224 to 218. Neglecting the resistance of the leads, find the internal resistance of the supply batteries.

49. In finding the position of a fault in a transmission line AB 100 miles long, when A is maintained at a potential of 200 volts and B is insulated, the latter is found to be at a potential of 50 volts. Conversely, when A is insulated, A is found to be at a potential of 50 volts when B is maintained at a potential of 230 volts. Determine the position of the fault.

50. Show that the maximum current is obtained in an external circuit when its resistance is equal to that of the total effective internal resistance of the supply batteries.

51. Two batteries of E.M.F.s 2 volts and 1·5 volt and of internal resistance 2 ohms and 1 ohm respectively are found to give the same current when connected by a certain wire. Find the resistance of the wire and the current flowing.

52. The potential difference between the poles of a given battery is 1·2 volt when the poles are joined by a wire of resistance 2 ohms, and 1·0 volt when the wire has resistance 1 ohm. Find the internal resistance of the battery and its E.M.F. on open circuit.

53. ABCD is a quadrilateral of which the arms have resistance AB = 1 ohm, BC = 2 ohms, CD = 3 ohms, and DA = 4 ohms. A galvanometer of resistance 5 ohms is placed across BD. If the current of 1 amp. is passed in at A and leaves at C, calculate the current in the galvanometer.

54. The positive poles of two cells are joined by a uniform wire of resistance 6 ohms, and the negative poles by a uniform wire of resistance 10 ohms. The middle of the 10-ohm wire is earthed: the potential of the centre of the 6-ohm wire is then found to be 16/9 volts. If the E.M.F. of one cell is 3/2 volts and its internal resistance is 2 ohms, find the internal resistance of the other cell, given that its E.M.F. is 2 volts.

55. An equilateral triangle ABC has a 2-volt cell joined to the points A and B. The wire of which the triangle is constructed is of different cross-sections, so that these are in the ratio 1 : 2 : 3 for the sides, AB, BC and CA. The internal resistance of the cell which is equal to that of the side of least resistance is required. The current in AB is given to be 5/17 amp.

56. The insulation resistance of a cable between two points P and R is 20,000 ohms. If the insulation resistance between R and an intermediate point Q is 30,000 ohms, find the insulation resistance between P and Q.

57. A uniform circular wire is joined across a diameter by another wire of the same material and cross-section. Show that the equivalent resistance of the combination for a current which enters the circuit at one of the junctions of diameter and circumference and leaves at a point on the circumference midway between the ends of the diameter is given by $\pi R(6 + \pi)/4(4 + \pi)$, where R is the resistance of a length of the wire equal to a radius of the circle.

58. A regular hexagon is formed by six wires each of resistance r, and the corners are joined to the centre by wires of the same resistance. If the current enters at one corner and leaves at the opposite corner, find the equivalent resistance of the combination.

59. In Ques. 58, find the equivalent resistance if the current leaves at a corner adjacent to that at which it enters.

60. Find the equivalent resistance of a cube composed of 12 equal wires of resistance r for a current which enters at one corner and leaves at the opposite corner.

61. In Ques. 60, find the equivalent resistance if the current enters and leaves at the ends of one edge.

62. A circuit is composed of two uniform wires of resistances πr and $2r$, joined together in the form of a semicircle and its diameter. A similar third wire of resistance $2r$ is joined to one point of contact of diameter and semicircle, while the other end may make a sliding contact at any point between the far end of the diameter and halfway round the semicircle. If a current enters at the common junction of the three wires and leaves at the point of contact with the semicircle, show that the maximum resistance of the network is $2r(\pi + 2)/(\pi + 10)$.

63. In Ques. 62, find the minimum resistance.

64. Determine the value of the resistance of a shunt which must be placed in parallel with an ammeter whose coil has a resistance of 80 ohms, if the ammeter, which is to read up to 5 amp., shows a full-scale deflection under a potential difference of 100 millivolts.

65. When a given cell has a resistance of 10 ohms placed across its terminals, it is found that its E.M.F. is balanced by 120 cm. of a given potentiometer wire, whereas on open circuit the balance length is 150 cm. Find the internal resistance of the cell.

66. A vibration magnetometer makes 10 vibrations in 25 sec. when placed at a point 10 cm. due E of a long vertical wire carrying

a current, and 20 vibrations in 60 sec. when placed the same distance due W of the wire. Find the position of a neutral point in the magnetic field.

67. A small magnet is freely suspended at the centre of a metal ring of diameter 20 cm., the axis of the ring being in the magnetic meridian. If the magnet makes 10 vibrations in 30 sec. when under the influence of the earth's horizontal magnetic field alone, find the current in the ring when 20 vibrations are executed in 30 sec., the magnet still pointing in the same direction. $H = 0 \cdot 18$ gauss.

68. Given the same data for the times of oscillation as in Ques. 67, find the current in the ring if the plane of the ring is vertical but inclined at 30° to the magnetic meridian.

69. In Ques. 67, find the current in the ring for the same data but with the magnet situated at a point on the axis of the ring 10 cm. from the centre.

70. Two equal circular coils of radius a are mounted coaxially a distance x apart. Given that for any separation of the coils the magnetic field gradient due to a common similarly directed current in the two coils is least at a point on the axis midway between the two coils, find the separation x for which the magnetic field gradient is least.

71. If two equal circular coils of 10 turns and radius 20 cm. are arranged as in Ques. 70, find the strength of the common current necessary to neutralize the horizontal component of the earth's magnetic field of $0 \cdot 18$ gauss at a point on the axis midway between the two coils.

72. A cell of internal resistance 1 ohm, when used in conjunction with a given tangent galvanometer, may be connected either to a single turn of resistance 1 ohm or to a coil of the same radius but having 50 turns and of resistance 99 ohms. With which coil will the greater deflection be obtained?

73. The deflections produced when (a) one cell, (b) two such cells in parallel, (c) two such cells in series are connected to a given tangent galvanometer are θ_1, θ_2 and θ_3. Show that $2 \tan \theta_1 (\tan \theta_3 + \tan \theta_2) = 3 \tan \theta_2 \tan \theta_3$.

74. Find the maximum current which may be measured with a sine galvanometer which has a coil of 50 turns of radius 10 cm. at a place where the earth's magnetic field is $0 \cdot 18$ gauss.

75. Determine the strength of the current which must flow through a narrow solenoid of 1000 turns and of length 1 m., lying in the magnetic meridian, if the earth's magnetic field of $0 \cdot 18$ gauss is to be neutralized at the centre.

76. Find the strength of the current flowing in a solenoid of 10

turns per cm., length 10 cm. and radius 1 cm., if a compass needle is deflected through 45° when the solenoid is placed in the end-on position due E of the needle and with its centre 6 cm. from the needle. The earth's horizontal component may be taken as 0·18 gauss.

77. Calculate the reading which would be shown by a moving-coil galvanometer having a permanent radial magnetic field of 200 gauss, when a current of 1 milliamp. flows in the square suspended coil of 25 turns and of side 2 cm. The instrument has a sensitivity of one division per dyne-cm. of couple.

78. Find the deflection shown by a tangent galvanometer of 50 turns and radius 10 cm., at a point where the earth's horizontal magnetic component is 0·18 gauss, if the galvanometer is placed in a circuit containing also a copper voltameter in which the current deposits 1 dgm. of copper in 30 min. The atomic weight of silver is 107·9, that of copper is 63·6, and the electrochemical equivalent of silver is 0·001118 gm./coulomb.

79. With a given hydrogen voltameter, 214 c.c. of hydrogen are collected in 1 hour at a temperature of 15° C. and a total pressure of 783 mm. of mercury. Find the current flowing, given that the electrochemical equivalent of hydrogen is $1·04 \times 10^{-5}$ gm./coulomb, and that its density at N.T.P. is 0·09 gm./litre.

80. If 3800 calories are liberated when 1 gm. of water is formed by the combustion of hydrogen and oxygen, and $9·4 \times 10^{-5}$ gm. of water is decomposed during the passage of 1 coulomb through acidulated water, show that the minimum E.M.F. required for the electrolysis of water is about 1·5 volt.

81. Assuming that the increase of resistance with temperature is linear and of amount 5×10^{-3} ohms per °C. for tungsten, find the temperature of the incandescent filament of a tungsten lamp from the following data: resistance of lamp at 0° C. as found by a Wheatstone's bridge is 40 ohms; potential difference between terminals of lamp when incandescent is 200 volts, the current flowing being 0·5 amp.

82. A vertical silica tube of internal area of cross-section 1 sq. cm. contains a 25 per cent solution of sodium chloride in water, the length of the column of fluid at 15° C. being 100·00 cm. One electrode is let into the bottom of the tube and the other electrode floats on the surface of the liquid. Find the resistance of the liquid column at 65° C., given that the coefficient of thermal expansion of the liquid is $4·36 \times 10^{-4}$ per °C., the conductivity of the solution at 15° C. is 0·1642 ohm^{-1}. cm.$^{-1}$, and the temperature coefficient of conductivity is $3·5 \times 10^{-3}$ per °C.

83. Two straight cables carrying current to and from a circuit lie one on top of the other. If the radius of the cables is 5 cm. and their

25

weight is 10 Kgm. per metre, find the strength of the current for which one cable will just be lifted from the other.

84. If a couple of 10^5 dyne-cm. is required to hold a circular coil of 20 turns and diameter 20 cm. with its plane parallel to that of a magnetic field of strength 50 gauss, find the current in the coil.

85. Find the strength of the magnetic field in a small gap in an iron ring magnet whose intensity of magnetization is 80 C.G.S. units.

86. A short soft iron bar of susceptibility 80 lies horizontally in the direction of the earth's horizontal magnetic component of strength 0·18 gauss. Find the volume of the bar, given that a vibration magnetometer placed at a point on the perpendicular bisector of the axis of the bar and 30 cm. due E of it executes 10 vibrations a minute when the bar is present and 20 vibrations a minute when it is absent.

87. The soft iron bar of Ques. 86 is cut into two equal parts in a direction perpendicular to the axis of the bar. Find the stress now required to separate the two halves of the bar.

88. A ring electromagnet has a mean radius of 25 cm. and is to be excited by a current of 10 amp. to produce a magnetic field of 2500 gauss in a gap in the ring 0·5 cm. wide. If the permeability of the material of the ring is 800, what must be the number of turns of wire on the ring?

89. An electromagnet consists of a semicircular ring of iron of permeability 1000, wound with 600 turns of wire. The radius of the ring is 20 cm. On the ends of the semicircular ring slide two horizontal bars of the same area of cross-section as the ring but of magnetic permeability 800. If the two poles are slid towards each other until they are 0·5 cm. apart, determine the strength of the magnetic field in the gap when the exciting current is 10 amp.

90. A straight wire of length 80 cm. is lying horizontally E and W. Taking $H = 0·18$ gauss, find the E.M.F. acting down the wire if it is dropped (a) after falling 50 m., (b) after it has been falling for 10 sec.

91. Calculate the potential difference between the hub and the rim of the wheel of a locomotive which is running in a direction due magnetic E. The diameter of the wheel is 4 ft., $H = 0·18$ gauss, and the speed of the train is 60 m.p.h.

92. In Ques. 91, if the angle of dip is 65°, what is the potential difference acting between the ends of the axle of the wheels? Length of axle is 4 ft. 6 in.

93. A disk of radius 8 cm. is rotated inside a long solenoid of 50 turns per cm., the axis of rotation of the disk coinciding with the axis of the solenoid. If the disk makes 600 rev./min. and the current in the

solenoid is 1 amp., find the potential difference between the centre and the circumference of the disk.

94. An armature conductor of length 1 m. is mounted 1 m. from the axis of a shaft rotating at a speed of 1000 rev./min. Find the E.M.F. in the armature when it passes through the maximum field of 5000 gauss.

95. A solenoid of area of cross-section 2 sq. cm. has 50 windings per cm. and carries a current of 2 amp. Find the E.M.F. induced in 10 turns of wire wound round the centre of the solenoid if the current in the latter is cut off and falls to zero in 10^{-3} sec.

96. The windings of an electromagnet have a resistance of 5 ohms, and the self-inductance associated with the magnet is 4 henries. After how long will the current in the circuit rise to one-half its final steady value when the circuit is completed?

97. A long thin ball-ended magnet of very low susceptibility and of pole strength 60 units is balanced on a knife-edge. One pole is inserted into a small gap between the flat pole pieces of an electromagnet having an intensity of magnetization of 900 units. What weight must be added to the other pole of the balanced magnet if it is to remain horizontal after the magnet has been switched on?

98. Prove that for a series-wound electric motor the speed for maximum output of energy is about one-half that at which the back E.M.F. would equal the applied E.M.F.

99. A flat circular coil fitted with a commutator is rotated at a speed of 10 rev. per sec. in the horizontal component of the earth's magnetic field, and then at a speed of 5 rev. per sec. in the vertical component of the field. Determine the angle of dip if the steady deflections registered by a tangent galvanometer connected to the coil are 30° and 38° respectively.

100. Assuming that the E.M.F. of a thermo-couple is given by the relation $E(\text{micro-volts}) = a + bt + ct^2$, where t is the temperature difference in °C. between the junctions and a, b and c are constants, show from the data given below that a platinum-rhodium platinum-iridium couple has a nearly linear change of E.M.F. with temperature, and calculate the value of this E.M.F. when the temperature difference between the junctions is 50° C.

For a Pt, Pt-Rh couple $a = -307$, $b = 8\cdot1$, $c = 0\cdot0017$.

For a Pt, Pt-Ir couple $a = -550$, $b = 14\cdot8$, $c = 0\cdot0016$.

ANSWERS AND HINTS FOR SOLUTION

1. Resultant force due to magnet is $M/(d^2 + l^2)^{3/2}$, where M is moment of magnet, l is half equivalent length, and d is distance of neutral point from centre of magnet. Hence $M = 0 \cdot 18(144 + 25)^{3/2} = 395 \cdot 5$ gauss . cm.^{3}.

2. $1 \cdot 571 \times 10^{-2}$ dynes.

3. Taking moments about the axis $F \times 20 = 100 \times g \times d/2$: also $F = (200/d)^2$; if $g = 981$ cm./sec.^{2}, $d = 2 \cdot 54$ cm.; $7° 14'$.

4. Equating forces perpendicular to the strip $F = H \sin \theta$: also for the broadside position $F = M/D^3$.

5. If θ is the angle between the magnetic meridian and the axis of the magnet in one of the positions, since there is to be no force parallel to the axis, $F = H \cos \theta = H \cos(60° - \theta)$. Hence $\theta = 30°$; also $F = \dfrac{2M}{100^3}$, $4 \cdot 5 \sqrt{3} \times 10^4$ gauss cm.^{3}.

6. Apply $t = 2\pi \left(\dfrac{I}{MH} \right)^{\frac{1}{2}}$, making H equal to $H \pm F$ in the first two cases.

7. Angle of dip D is given by $\tan D = V/H$, where V and H are vertical and horizontal components of earth's field. If dip-circle is at a to magnetic meridian, effective H is $H \cos a$.

8. Field due to magnet is $H \tan \theta$; total field is $H \sec \theta$; apply

$$t = 2\pi \left(\frac{I}{MH} \right)^{\frac{1}{2}}.$$

9. Defining magnetic potential as the work done in bringing a unit magnetic pole from an infinite distance up to the required point, the magnetic potential at a point a distance r from the centre of a magnet, if θ is the angle between the line r and the axis of the magnet (fig. 1), is the integral of force $\times$ distance,

$$= W = \int_{\infty}^{r} \left\{ \frac{m \cos a}{(r - l \cos \theta)^2} - \frac{m \cos \beta}{(r + l \cos \theta)^2} \right\} (-dr)$$

$$= -\int_{\infty}^{r} \frac{2\mu \cos \theta}{r^3} \, dr = \frac{\mu \cos \theta}{r^2},$$

where $\cos a = \cos \beta = 1$ approx., m is the pole strength of the magnet, and l is very small compared with r. Referring to the earth's field,

$\theta = (90 - \lambda)$, the vertical component V is given by $V = -\dfrac{\delta W}{\delta r} = \dfrac{2\mu \cos \theta}{r^3}$, the horizontal component H by $H = -\dfrac{1}{r} \dfrac{\delta W}{\delta \theta} = \dfrac{\mu \sin \theta}{r^3}$. Hence $\tan D = V/H = 2 \tan \lambda$ and $H = \dfrac{\mu \cos \lambda}{R^3}$.

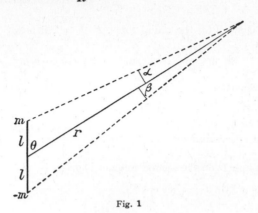

Fig. 1

10. Referring to fig. 2 and using the result of Ques. 9, $W = \dfrac{\mu \cos \theta}{r^2}$, the potential of the upper pole (strength m') of magnet 2 is $\dfrac{Mm'}{a^2} \cdot \cos (\theta - a)$, and that of the lower pole is $\dfrac{Mm'}{b^2} \cos (\theta + a')$. Hence the total magnetic potential of 2 in the field of 1 is

$$\frac{Mm' \cos (\theta - a)}{(d + l' \cos \theta')^2} - \frac{Mm' \cos (\theta + a')}{(d - l' \cos \theta')^2}$$

$$= \frac{Mm'}{d^4} \{ (\cos \theta + a \sin \theta)(d - l' \cos \theta')^2 \\ - (\cos \theta - a' \sin \theta)(d + l' \cos \theta')^2 \},$$

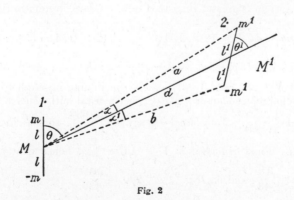

Fig. 2

where $l' \cos \theta' \ll d$. Put $a = a' = \dfrac{l' \sin \theta'}{d}$ approx., then

$$W = \frac{2Mm'l'}{d^3}\left\{\sin\theta \sin\theta' - 2\cos\theta\cos\theta'\right\}$$
$$= \frac{MM'}{d^3}(\sin\theta\sin\theta' - 2\cos\theta\cos\theta').$$

11. As in Ques. 9 for the radial force, $F = \dfrac{\delta W}{\delta r}$, hence

$$F = \frac{3MM'}{d^4}(\sin\theta\sin\theta' - 2\cos\theta\cos\theta').$$

12. The transverse force is

$$T = -\frac{1}{r}\left(\frac{\delta W}{\delta\theta} + \frac{\delta W}{\delta\theta'}\right) = -\frac{1}{d}\frac{MM'}{d^3}(\cos\theta\sin\theta' + 2\sin\theta\cos\theta'$$
$$+ \sin\theta\cos\theta' + 2\cos\theta\sin\theta') = \frac{-3MM'}{d^4}\sin(\theta+\theta').$$

13. The couple G on the second magnet is given by $G = -\dfrac{\delta W}{\delta\theta'}$. Hence
$G = \dfrac{MM'}{d^3}(2\cos\theta\sin\theta' - \sin\theta\cos\theta')$.

14. Apply $t = 2\pi\sqrt{\dfrac{I}{MH}}$ and $\dfrac{2Md}{(d^2-l^2)^2} = H\tan\theta$; $0\cdot218$ gauss; 12,560 gauss cm.³.

15. Considering the forces in equilibrium for one ball and taking moments about the point of suspension, $12F = 0\cdot1 \times 981 \times 5$ dynes; also $F = q^2/10^2$; $V = q/0\cdot25$; 64 e.s.u., 256 e.s.u. of potential.

16. $\dfrac{10}{(50+x)^2} = \dfrac{5}{x^2}$; $120\cdot7$ cm.; at mid-point between spheres.

17. $-q/\sqrt{3}$ at the centroid.

18. Work done on unit charge is difference in potential. Potential difference is $\dfrac{q}{1\cdot5} + \dfrac{q}{1\cdot5} + \dfrac{q}{3}\dfrac{2}{\sqrt{3}} - \dfrac{3q}{\sqrt{3}} = \dfrac{q}{9}(12 - 7\sqrt{3})$; $\dfrac{q^2}{9}(4\sqrt{3} - 7)$.

19. Unit of charge defined from $q^2/d^2 = F$; hence the unit on the lb.-ft. sec. system is greater than that on the C.G.S. system in the ratio

$$Q/q = d\sqrt{F} = 12 \times 2\cdot54\sqrt{\frac{1000}{2\cdot2}} \times 12 \times 2\cdot54 = 3588 : 1.$$

20. Capacity of spherical condenser $\dfrac{ab}{b-a}$; hence capacity of $A = 150$ cm. and of $B = 280$ cm. Total capacity on joining in parallel is 430 cm. Energy of charged condenser is $\frac{1}{2}Q^2/C$; hence total initial energy of system is $\dfrac{1}{2}\cdot\dfrac{100}{150} + \dfrac{1}{2}\cdot\dfrac{225}{280}$. Total final energy is $\dfrac{1}{2}\cdot\dfrac{625}{430}$, so loss in energy is $\dfrac{121}{14448}$ ergs. Final potential is $V = Q/C = \dfrac{25}{430}$, hence charge on A is $\dfrac{25}{430} \times 150 = \dfrac{375}{43}$, and on B is $\dfrac{25}{430} \times 280 = \dfrac{700}{43}$.

21. Let C_1 and C_2 be the capacities of the two condensers, where $C_1 = a$ and $C_2 = A/4\pi d$. Capacity in parallel is $C_1 + C_2$, in series is $C_1 C_2/(C_1 + C_2)$; hence ratio is $(C_1 + C_2)^2/C_1 C_2 = (a + d)^2/ad$. Solving, $C_2 = d$ or a^2/d.

22. Consider unit area of conductor with surface density of charge σ; air is charged by contact. Since air is very close to surface, latter behaves as an infinite plane, and force of repulsion of air will be $F = 2\pi\sigma . \sigma$ per unit area : $(350/\pi)^{\frac{1}{2}}$ e.s.u.

23. Let water rise d cm. above the general level; then electrostatic force of attraction equals hydrostatic pull downwards; $2\pi . 350/\pi = d . 981$; $700/981$ cm.

24. Force of repulsion is $2\pi\sigma^2 = mg$; 1249 e.s.u.

25. Capacity of whole system per unit area is $1/4\pi a + 1/4\pi b$; if surface density of charge is σ, potential is therefore $4\pi\sigma ab/(a + b)$.

26. Initial capacity per unit area is $1/4\pi d$; final capacity is $1/4\pi(d - t)$.

27. Consider any sphere of radius r, carrying a charge q. To find the force on any part of the sphere due to the charge on the remainder, describe a concentric sphere of radius R around the first sphere. By Gauss's theorem, total electrical force on second sphere is $4\pi q$. Let R approach r; when R nearly equals r, the force on any point of the second sphere may be considered as arising partly from the charged area immediately below the point and partly from the remainder of the charged sphere. For points sufficiently close to the surface, the area immediately below behaves as an infinite plane which exerts an electric force $2\pi\sigma$, hence the remainder of the sphere exerts a force $2\pi\sigma$, where $\sigma = q/4\pi r^2$. Letting the second sphere coincide with the first, the mechanical force on unit area due to the charge on the remainder is $2\pi\sigma . \sigma = 2\pi\sigma^2$. For every unit area of the sphere in question there is therefore an outward radial force per unit area of $2\pi\sigma^2$; hence total force on top hemisphere, resolving along a direction perpendicular to the horizontal bisecting plane, is

$$2\pi\sigma^2 . \pi r^2 = 2\pi^2\sigma^2 r^2 = q^2/8r^2 = 10^6/8 \times 25 = 5000 \text{ dynes,}$$

which is greater than 981 dynes due to the weight of the hemisphere.

28. Let induced surface density be σ; then $\sigma = q/4\pi a^2$; radial force of attraction per unit area of the hemisphere is $q\sigma/a^2$; hence total effective attractive force in direction perpendicular to horizontal dividing plane is $(q\sigma/a^2)\pi a^2 = q^2/4a^2$. Repulsion due to charge on sphere itself is, from Ques. 27, $q^2/8a^2$; hence net attractive force on each hemisphere is $q^2/8a^2$.

29. Let V_1, V_2 and V_3 be initial potentials of A, B and C. Then $V_1 = (q_1/a + q_2/b + q_3/c)$, $V_2 = (q_1/b + q_2/b + q_3/c)$, and $V_3 = (q_1/c + q_2/c + q_3/c)$. After inner sphere is earthed, it acquires an induced charge Q given by $Q/a + q_2/b + q_3/c = 0$, or $Q = -a(q_2/b + q_3/c)$. Hence final potentials of B and C are $V_2' = q_2/b + q_3/c - a(q_2/b + q_3/c)/b$ and $V_3' = q_2/c + q_3/c - a(q_2/b + q_3/c)/c$. Hence changes in potentials of the spheres are $\Delta V_1 = q_1/a + q_2/b + q_3/c$, $\Delta V_2 = q_1/b + aq_2/b^2 + aq_3/bc$, and $\Delta V_3 = q_1/c + aq_2/bc + aq_3/c^2$. Hence total change in energy is $\frac{1}{2}(q_1 . \Delta V_1 + q_2 . \Delta V_2 + q_3 . \Delta V_3)$.

30. Ratio of capacities of conductor and whole system is q/Q; after second contact, total charge on conductor and disk is $Q + q$, and charge now acquired by conductor is $q(Q + q)/Q = q(1 + q/Q)$; similarly after third charging, charge acquired by conductor is $q(1 + q/Q + q^2/Q^2)$. This is a geometrical progression with constant ratio q/Q, and the sum to infinity is $qQ/(Q - q)$.

31. Capacity of parallel plate condenser is $A/4\pi d = 4 \cdot 77$ cm. If C is capacity of electroscope and $q =$ charge on electroscope, since scale readings are proportional to potential,
$$q/C : q/(C + 4 \cdot 77) = 20 : 12; \quad 7 \cdot 16 \text{ cm.}$$

32. Electric field strength is $3000/2 \times 300 = 5$ e.s.u.; hence
$$5 \times 4 \cdot 8 \times 10^{-10} = m \times 981; \quad 2 \cdot 45 \times 10^{-12} \text{ gm.}$$

33. If surface density is σ, $4\pi\sigma \times 0 \cdot 2 = \dfrac{1000}{300}$. Force required is $m \times 981 = 2\pi\sigma^2 A$; $0 \cdot 34$ gm.

34. Capacity of system is increased, so if potential difference is maintained at 1000 volts, surface density is increased in the ratio $3 \cdot 5 : 1$; now force is decreased to $2\pi\sigma^2/3 \cdot 5$; hence total result is to increase force in ratio $3 \cdot 5 : 1$; $1 \cdot 19$ gm.

35. If initial capacity of condenser is C, capacity of lower half becomes $kC/2$, that of top half remaining $C/2$; hence total capacity becomes $C(1 + k)/2$.

36. Let initial separation of plates be d; the capacity of condenser with slab present is equal to $A/4\pi\{(d - a) + a/k\}$. On removing slab and moving plates closer, capacity regains its original value when plate separation is reduced to $(d - b)$; hence capacity is also given by $A/4\pi(d - b)$. Comparing the two expressions, $k = a/(a - b)$.

37. Capacity of two concentric cylinders per unit length $= k/(2 \log_e b/a)$, where b is external radius and a is radius of central core; $2 \cdot 31$ cm.

38. Deflection θ of quadrant electrometer is given by
$$\theta = k(V_A - V_B)\left(V_C - \frac{V_A + V_B}{2}\right),$$
where k is a constant and V_A, V_B and V_C are the potentials of the pairs of quadrants and the paddle respectively. First finding k, we have
$$20 = k(10)(1000 - 5) \quad \text{or} \quad k = 2/995.$$
On connecting idiostatically to the A.C. supply, $\theta = k(V_A - V_B)^2/2$ since $V_C = V_A$ or $V_A - V_B = 315 \cdot 4$ volts.

39. Wattage developed is $5 \times 10^3 \times 10^{-3} = 5$ watts; assuming no frictional losses, since 1 h.p. $= 746$ watts, h.p. required is $5/746$.

40. Gain in kinetic energy $=$ loss in potential energy. If velocity acquired is v, $\frac{1}{2}mv^2 = Ve$; $\frac{1}{2} \cdot 9 \times 10^{-28} \times v^2 = 3000 \times 4 \cdot 8 \times 10^{-10}/300$; $3 \cdot 27 \times 10^9$ cm./sec.

41. Force of attraction between plates is $2\pi\sigma^2 A$; hence work done in moving distance d is $2\pi\sigma^2 Ad$.

42. Initial charge on condenser is $AV/4\pi t$; final charge on condenser is $AV/4\pi(t-d)$; hence energy supplied by battery is $\dfrac{AV}{4\pi}\left\{\dfrac{1}{(t-d)} - \dfrac{1}{t}\right\} . V$.

43. Initial capacity is $A/4\pi t$ and initial energy is $\frac{1}{2}CV^2 = \frac{1}{2}AV^2/4\pi t$. Final capacity is $A/4\pi(t-d)$, hence final energy is $\frac{1}{2}AV^2/4\pi(t-d)$. Hence increase in energy of condenser is $AV^2 d/8\pi t(t-d)$. Hence from Ques. 42, external work done = energy supplied by battery less energy gained by condenser $= AV^2 d/8\pi t(t-d)$.

44. Total capacity becomes $C_1 + C_2$; total charge becomes $q_1 + q_2$; final energy is therefore $\frac{1}{2}(q_1 + q_2)^2/(C_1 + C_2)$. Initial energy was $\frac{1}{2}(q_1^2/C_1 + q_2^2/C_2)$.

45. Wattage required = 50. Hence h.p. required is 50/746; 5/22 amp.

46. Wattage $= EI = E^2/R$; $100 \times 10^{\frac{1}{2}}$; $1/10 \times 10^{\frac{1}{2}}$ volts.

47. Resistance of leads is $1 \cdot 6 \times 10^{-6} \times 5280 \times 12 \times 2 \cdot 54/2 \cdot 54^2 = 0 \cdot 04$ ohm nearly; 208 volts; percentage wasted, $8 \times 200/208 \times 200 = 3 \cdot 9$ per cent.

48. Initial effective resistance of lamps = 5/2 ohms; final resistance is 5/3 ohms. Let E.M.F. and internal resistance of supply battery be E and r. Then $\dfrac{E \cdot (5/2)}{r + 5/2} = 224$ and $\dfrac{E \cdot (5/3)}{r + 5/3} = 218$; 15/103 ohms.

49. Since B is insulated, there is no fall of potential between B and fault; hence potential at fault is 50 volts. Similarly in the second case, potential of fault is potential of A = 50 volts. Hence same current must flow through fault and therefore down cable in both cases. Hence $(200 - 50)/l = (230 - 50)/(100 - l)$, where l is distance of fault from A; $45\frac{5}{11}$ miles.

50. Let there be N supply cells which are grouped so that there are n files of m cells in series, that is, $N = mn$. Let R be external resistance and let r be internal resistance of one cell; then effective resistance of battery is mr/n. If E.M.F. of one cell is E, current flowing is

$$I = mE/(R + mr/n) \quad \text{or} \quad I - NnE/(n^2R + Nr),$$

and condition for maximum current is $dI/dn = 0$, hence $R = mr/n$ as required.

51. If resistance of wire is R and current is I, $2 = I(R + 2)$ and $1 \cdot 5 = I(R + 1)$; 2 ohms, $\frac{1}{2}$ amp.

52. $1 \cdot 2 = E \cdot 2/(2 + r)$, $1 \cdot 0 = E \cdot 1/(1 + r)$; $\frac{1}{2}$ ohm, $1 \cdot 5$ volt.

53. Let current along $AB = I_1$ and down $BD = I_2$; current in $AD = 1 - I_1$, in $BC = I_1 - I_2$, and in $DC = 1 - I_1 + I_2$. In circuit ABD, considering points A and D, the drop in potential between these points is the same whether we proceed along AD or via AB, BD. Applying Ohm's law, $4(1 - I_1) = I_1 + 5I_2$ or $5I_1 + 5I_2 = 4$. In circuit BCD, $2(I_1 - I_2) = 5I_2 + 3(1 - I_1 + I_2)$ or $5I_1 - 10I_2 = 3$; 1/15 amp.

25*

54. Current in circuit is

$$(2 - 3/2)/(18 + r) = 1/2(18 + r),$$

where r is internal resistance of second cell. Apply Ohm's law to find potential of centre point of 6-ohm wire, commencing at the centre point of 10-ohm wire and proceeding via 3/2 volt cell. We have $16/9 = (5 + 2 + 3)/2(18 + r) + 3/2$; zero.

55. Let resistance of side AB $= r$; that of BC is then $r/2$, and of AC is $r/3$. Equivalent resistance of AC + CB $= 5r/6$, and with AB in parallel

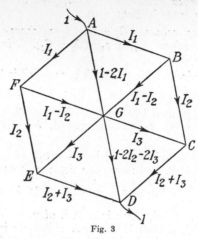

Fig. 3

with this, total external resistance is $5r/11$. Hence total current is $2/(5r/11 + r/3) = 33/13r$; therefore $r = 51/13$; $17/13$ ohms.

56. Insulation resistances between P and Q and between Q and R are effectively in parallel; hence if insulation resistance of PQ is r, $1/20,000 - 1/r = 1/30,000$; $60,000\,\omega$.

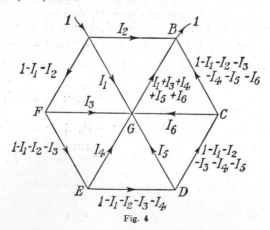

Fig. 4

57. Equivalent resistance of diam. and semicircle is $2\pi R/(\pi + 2)$; adding $\pi R/2$, we finally require equivalent resistance of $\pi R/2$ and $\pi R(6 + \pi)/2(2 + \pi)$ in parallel.

58. The circuit is symmetrical; taking the current entering as unity and putting in currents I_1, I_2 and I_3 as in fig. 3, and considering circuits

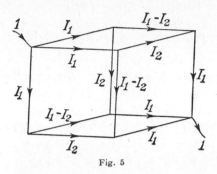

Fig. 5

ABG, BCG and CDG, $1 = 4I_1 - I_2$, $2I_2 = I_1 + I_3$, and $1 = 3I_2 + 4I_3$; $I_1 = 3/10$, $I_2 = 1/5$, $I_3 = 1/10$. Equivalent resistance is $(I_1 + 2I_2 + I_3)r = 4r/5$.

59. Taking the circuits AFG, GFE, GED, GCD, BCG and ABG (fig. 4), six equations are obtained. Find the value of I_2; $11r/20$.

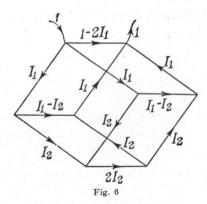

Fig. 6

60. The circuit is symmetrical (fig. 5); $5r/6$.

61. From partial symmetry currents will divide as in fig. 6; $7r/12$.

62. Let max. resistance occur when point of contact is at point on circumference distance x from far end of diam. The equivalent resistance of network is given by $1/R = 1/2r + 1/(2r + x) + 1/(\pi r - x)$. Differentiating and equating to zero, $x = r(\pi - 2)/2$; hence

$$R = 2r(\pi + 2)/(\pi + 10).$$

63. For wires connected in parallel, combined resistance is always less than the least single resistance present. This will occur when $x = r\pi/2$, that is, point of contact is as close to the point of entrance of the current as the conditions of the question will allow; $2\pi r(4 + \pi)/(\pi^2 + 12\pi + 16)$.

64. Max. current to be allowed in coil is $1/800$ amp.; $80/3999$ ohm.

65. $(E - e)/e = 120/(150 - 120) = IR/Ir = 10/r$; $2 \cdot 5$ ohms.

66. $t_1 = 2\pi\{I/(F + H)\}^{\frac{1}{2}}$, $t_2 = 2\pi\{I/(F - H)\}^{\frac{1}{2}}$, $F = 2I/10^2$. At neutral point $H = F' = 2I/10R$; $55 \cdot 6$ cm. due W.

67. $27/\pi$ amp.

68. Resultant field is given by $H'^2 = H^2 + F^2 + 2FH \cdot \cos 60°$; also $t_1 = 2\pi(I/MH)^{\frac{1}{2}}$ and $t_2 = 2\pi(I/MH')^{\frac{1}{2}}$; $30 \cdot 6/\pi$ amp.

69. As in Ques. 67, $F = 0 \cdot 54$ gauss; also since for point on axis at distance x from centre of coil $F = 2\pi n I r^2/10(r^2 + x^2)^{3/2}$, $I = 54\sqrt{2}/\pi$ amp.

70. Force due to both coils at point $x/2$ will be

$$F = 2 \cdot 2\pi n I a^2/10(a^2 + x^2/4)^{3/2}.$$

For field gradient to be a minimum $d^2F/dx^2 = 0$; $x = a$.

71. $1 \cdot 26/\pi$ amp.

72. $\tan\theta_1 \propto n_1 I_1 \propto n_1 E/R_1 \propto 1 \times E/2 \propto E/2$; similarly for $\tan\theta_2$; same deflection.

73. Apply $I = 10(Hr/2\pi n)\tan\theta$.

74. $F = H\sin\theta$; hence max. value of $F = H$; $0 \cdot 18/\pi$ amp.

75. $H = 4\pi n I/10$; $0 \cdot 18/4\pi$ amp.

76. Field at point on axis of solenoid is $F = 2\pi n i(\cos\theta_1 - \cos\theta_2)$, where θ_1 and θ_2 are semi-angles subtended at point by extremities of solenoid, and n is number of turns per unit length. Hence $F = H\tan\theta = H$ and $F = 2\pi \times 10 \times i(11/\sqrt{122} - 1/\sqrt{2})$; $1/10$ amp. nearly.

77. Couple $G = nAIH/10 = 2$ dynes-cm.; 2 divisions.

78. Mass $= I \times$ electrochemical equivalent $\times$ time; $71°$ approx.

79. $0 \cdot 5$ amp.

80. Equivalence in calories when 1 coulomb passed is $9 \cdot 4 \times 10^{-5} \times 3800 = 0 \cdot 357$ cal. Voltage required is therefore $4 \cdot 18 \times 0 \cdot 357 = 1 \cdot 5$ approx.

81. $R_t = R_0(1 + at)$; $400 = 40(1 + 5 \times 10^{-3}t)$; $1800°$ C.

82. $l_t = 102 \cdot 18$ cm., $\sigma_t = 0 \cdot 1642 \times 1 \cdot 175$ ohm^{-1} cm.$^{-1}$; $529 \cdot 7$ ohms.

83. Force of repulsion is $2I^2/100 \times 10$ dynes per unit length; 7000 amp. approx.

84. $G = nAIH/10$; $10/\pi$ amp.

85. Intensity of magnetization $=$ pole density per unit area; $F = 4\pi\sigma$; 320π gauss.

86. Intensity of magnetization $kH = 14\cdot4$; hence $M = 14\cdot4$ V; $t_1 = 2\pi(I/H)^{\frac{1}{2}}$, $t_2 = 2\pi\{I/(H - F)\}^{\frac{1}{2}}$; hence $F = 0\cdot135$ gauss, also $F = M/d^3$; 253 c.c.

87. $F = 2\pi I^2$ per unit area; $414\cdot8\pi$ dynes per sq. cm.

88. Magneto-motive force is M.M.F. $= 4\pi n I/10 = 4\pi n$; also M.M.F. $=$ flux(N) × magnetic resistance $\left(\int dl/\mu S\right)$ or $4\pi n = \dfrac{N}{S}\left\{\dfrac{(2\pi r - d)}{\mu} + d\right\}$. Now $N =$ induction(B) × area(S); hence $B = N/S$, and in gap $B = H$ since $\mu = 1$; 138 turns.

89. Magnetic resistance is $\pi r/\mu_1 S + (2r - d)/\mu_2 S + d/S$; M.M.F. $= 2400\pi$; hence flux $N = 2400\pi S/\{\pi r/\mu_1 + (2r - d)/\mu_2 + d\}$; now $B = N/S$, and in gap $\mu = 1$ and therefore $B = H$; 12,310 gauss.

90. $v^2 = 2fs$, $v = 100\sqrt{981}$ cm./sec. $E = dN/dt = 100\sqrt{981} \times 80 \times 0\cdot18/10^8$; $4\cdot51 \times 10^{-4}$ volts; $v = ft = 9810$ cm./sec.; $1\cdot41 \times 10^{-3}$ volts.

91. If wheel makes n rev./sec., $2\pi rn = v$; hence area swept per sec. due to rotation is $\pi r^2 n = rv/2$. Hence E.M.F. between hub and rim will be $rvH/2 = 1\cdot47 \times 10^{-4}$ volts. Superposed on this is an E.M.F. acting vertically upwards due to the translational movement of the wheel, its maximum value being $rvH = 2\cdot94 \times 10^{-4}$ volts. Hence E.M.F. between hub and circumference will depend on point of circumference considered, being $4\cdot41 \times 10^{-4}$ volts for a point vertically above the hub acting from hub to rim, and $1\cdot47 \times 10^{-4}$ volts for a point vertically below the hub acting from rim to hub.

92. $V/H = \tan D$, hence $V = 0\cdot18 \times 2\cdot1445$; $E = lvV/10^8 = 1\cdot42 \times 10^{-3}$ volts.

93. $E = \pi \times 64 \times 600 \times 4\pi \times 50 \times 1/10 \times 60 \times 10^8 = 1\cdot26 \times 10^{-3}$ volts.

94. Linear velocity of conductor is $2\pi \times 100 \times (1000/60)$ cm./sec.; hence $E = 100 \times 2\pi \times 100 \times 1000 \times 5000/(60 \times 10^{-8}) = 50\pi/3$ volts.

95. Total flux $N = 4\pi \times 50 \times 2 \times 2/10 = 80\pi$; hence

$$E = -dN/dt \cdot n/t = 2\cdot51 \times 10^{-2} \text{ volts.}$$

96. Current I at any time t after circuit is completed is given by $I = I_0(1 - exp^{-rt/l})$, where I_0 is final steady current, r is resistance, and l is inductance of circuit. $t = 4 \log_e 2/5 = 0\cdot55$ sec.

97. $4\pi\sigma m' = wg$; 692 gm.

98. Let applied E.M.F. $= E$ and back E.M.F. $= E'$; also let total resistance be R. Then current flowing is $I = (E - E')/R$ and energy wasted as heat is $(E - E')I$; hence since energy supplied is EI, electrical energy transformed into rotation is $E'I$. Efficiency of machine is therefore $E'I/EI = E'/E$, and this has its maximum value of unity when $E' = E$ or the back E.M.F. is equal to the applied E.M.F. In practice the most *efficient* running must occur at a speed just less than this, since if $E' = E$, no current would flow through the motor. Now rotational energy is given

by $P = E'I$ or $P = E'(E - E')/R$; hence for P to be a max. $dP/dE' = 0$, hence $E' = E/2$.

99. $E_1 \propto n_1 H$, $E_2 \propto n_2 V$; $V/H = \tan D$; 70° nearly.

100. Since E.M.F.s are additive with metals,

$$E = (a_1 - a_2) + (b_1 - b_2)t + (c_1 - c_2)t^2;$$

hence $E = -243 + 6 \cdot 7t - 0 \cdot 0001t^2$, in which the coefficient of t^2 is very small and E is approximately linear with temperature; 92 microvolts.

INDEX

choke coil, 688.
chords, 515.
chromatism, 350.
circle of least confusion, 340.
— motion in, 20.
circuit containing capacity and inductance, 683.
— divided, 613, 665.
— growth and decay of currents, 648.
— magnetic, 680.
— natural frequency of, 685.
— time-constant of, 649.
Clausius, 246, 250.
Clement and Désormes' experiment, 220, 262–4.
clinical thermometer, 160–1.
closed tube, 488.
coaxial magnetic coils, 605.
coefficient of linear expansion, 165, 169–170.
— of resistance, temperature increase, 624.
— of restitution, 27, 28.
— of surface expansion, 166.
— of volume expansion, 166, 171–2.
coercive force, 676.
coils, calculation of mutual inductance of, 647.
— choke, 688.
— circular, 591.
— force between, 609.
— Helmholtz, 604.
— induction, 655.
— rotating in magnetic field, 650.
— solenoidal, 605.
Colladon and Sturm, 481.
collimator, 348, 423.
collision of α-particles with matter, 735, 743.
colloids, 129.
colour, 407–9.
— and refractive index, 347.
— of pigments, 408, 409.
colours, three primary, 409.
columns of gas, 488.
coma, 343.
comparison of capacities, 562, 660, 667.
— of capacity and inductance, 668.
— of units, 695.
component harmonic waves, 511.
components of vectors, 7, 9, 15.
composition of S.H.M.'s, 512.
compound winding, 655.
compressibility of liquids, 100.
compression wave, 474.

concord, 515.
condensers, 548.
conduction, 189, 194–203; see also conductivity.
— along bar, 196–8.
— applications of, 195.
— in gases, 710.
— in liquids, 628.
— in solids, 585, 720.
conductivity, 195; see also conduction.
— electrical and thermal, 720.
— Forbes's method, 199–201.
— of an electrolyte, 669.
— of bad conductors, 202–3.
— of gases, 195, 203, 252–3.
— of good conductors, 199–201.
— Searle's method, 199.
conductors, 535.
conjugate points, 313.
conservation of heat, 180.
constant decay of radioactive substances, 733.
— dielectric, 542, 562, 694.
— pressure thermometer, 216–7.
— time, 649, 667.
— volume thermometer, 161, 214–6.
contact potential, 585.
continuity, equation of, 139.
— of state, 238–9.
continuous flow method, 186, 208, 220.
contraction with rise in temperature, 171.
convection, 189–93.
— forced, 189.
— in gases, 189–90.
— in liquids, 190–1.
— natural, 189.
cooling curve, 182, 222, 223.
— method of, 183–5.
— Newton's law of, 191–3.
corkscrew rule, 590.
cosmic radiation, 746.
Coulomb, 593.
— law of, 540.
couple, 32, 43.
critical angle, 318, 319.
— isothermal, 239.
— pressure, 239.
— temperature, 238, 239.
— velocity, 136.
— volume, 239.
Crookes, 712.
crystalloids, 129.
crystals, biaxial, 389.
— uniaxial, 379–82.